POULTRY
Science and Practice

THIRD EDITION

POULTRY
Science and Practice

By

A. R. WINTER

Professor of Poultry Husbandry
The Ohio State University

and

E. M. FUNK

Professor of Poultry Husbandry
University of Missouri

Edited by R. W. GREGORY

J. B. LIPPINCOTT COMPANY
Chicago · Philadelphia · New York

Preface

Poultry science is one of the newest of the agricultural sciences, although poultry keeping has been practiced for centuries. It is of interest to a great many people because poultry is produced on more than 85 per cent of all farms in the United States and is surpassed only by meat animals and dairy products as a source of farm income.

A great mass of poultry information has been published in recent years. As may be expected in any new science, some of it is based on sound experimental data, some is conflicting, and some is purely hypothetical.

The purpose of this book is to give what appears to be at the present time the practical factual information on general poultry production. It includes breeding, incubation, brooding, housing, feeding, disease, marketing, and poultry farm management.

The subject matter has been prepared as a general college poultry course and also as a reference book for students of vocational agriculture, for poultrymen, and for general farmers.

References, mostly recent ones, have been listed at the end of each chapter. They are typical of the references used as sources of information in the textbook and may be used for additional information.

A number of review questions are listed at the end of each chapter. It is hoped that these questions may stimulate thought and be helpful in studying the poultry industry.

Special credit is due James Hamilton for the preparation of the chapter on game bird production.

The authors greatly appreciate the courtesies extended by various organizations and individuals in permitting the use of illustrations and tables. Credit has been given in all such cases.

A. R. WINTER
E. M. FUNK

Contents

▼

vii

POULTRY

Science and Practice

CHAPTER 1 ||||||||||||||||||||||||||||||||||||||||||||||||||||||

The Poultry Industry

▼

Introduction

Definition of poultry. The term "poultry" is used to designate those species of birds which render man an economic service and reproduce freely under his care. It includes chickens, turkeys, ducks, geese, swans, guineas, pigeons, peafowl, pheasants, and ostriches, and refers to them whether alive or dressed.

Relation of poultry to other animals. There are about 600,000 species of animals in the world, including 10,000 species of birds. They are classified according to structure.

The most highly developed animals (Fig. 1) are mammals, which include man and farm animals, and aves or birds. Mammals are distinguished by the presence of hair and mammary glands. Birds are distinguished by the covering of feathers.

Poultry science. Poultry science is the study of principles and practices involved in the production and marketing of poultry and poultry products. It includes breeding, incubation, brooding, housing, feeding, disease, marketing, and poultry-farm management.

The study of the great numbers of birds not classed as poultry is *ornithology*. The science of all animal life is *zoology*.

Importance of the Poultry Industry

Source of farm income. Probably more persons are directly interested in poultry production than in any other single agricultural enterprise. More than 83 per cent of all farms in the United States reported poultry in 1945.

Poultry ranked fourth in cash income among agricultural commodities in the United States during the period 1942–1946 (Fig. 2).

Source of food supply. Poultry eggs and meat are used chiefly as human food.

Eggs are exceeded only by milk in food value (Table 1). They are a good source of proteins, minerals, and vitamins. Eggs are palatable, easily digested, and can be used in a great variety of appetizing ways (Fig. 3). They serve as binders and leavening agents in baking and furnish "richness" in icings,

3

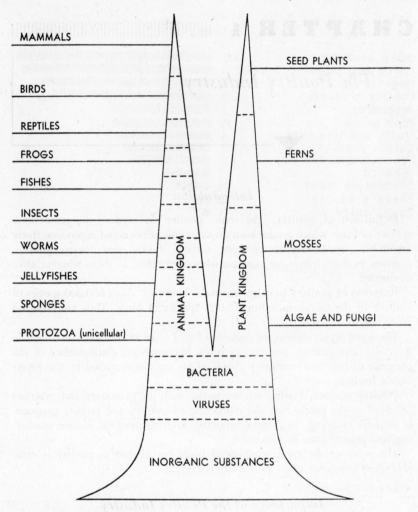

MAMMALS

SEED PLANTS

BIRDS

REPTILES

FROGS   FERNS

FISHES

INSECTS

WORMS   MOSSES

JELLYFISHES

SPONGES

PROTOZOA (unicellular)   ALGAE AND FUNGI

ANIMAL KINGDOM   PLANT KINGDOM

BACTERIA

VIRUSES

INORGANIC SUBSTANCES

Fig. 1. A diagram illustrating the probable relationships of living things.

sauces, candies, custards, ice cream, etc. The annual per capita consumption of eggs in the United States in 1949 was 374.

Poultry meat is supplied chiefly by chickens, turkeys, ducks, geese, and guinea fowls. The percentage of edible meat obtained from poultry compares favorably with that obtained from other kinds of livestock (Table 2). Poultry meat is probably the most palatable of all the meats and is easily digested. It is served in a great variety of ways such as fried, roasted, or stewed, and in combination with other foodstuffs as in salads, sandwiches, sauces, soups, etc. (Fig. 4). The annual per capita consumption of poultry meat in the United States in 1949 was about 29 pounds.

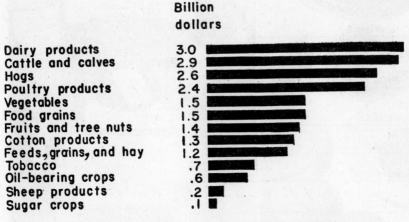

Billion dollars

Dairy products	3.0
Cattle and calves	2.9
Hogs	2.6
Poultry products	2.4
Vegetables	1.5
Food grains	1.5
Fruits and tree nuts	1.4
Cotton products	1.3
Feeds, grains, and hay	1.2
Tobacco	.7
Oil-bearing crops	.6
Sheep products	.2
Sugar crops	.1

Fig. 2. Cash value of leading agricultural products (Average annual value during the years 1942–1946)

Table 1

THE NUTRITIVE VALUE OF AN EGG AND A GLASS OF MILK

Nutrients	Two-Ounce Egg	One-Half Pint of Milk
Fuel value (calories)	74.00	169.0
Fat (grams)	5.21	9.8
Carbohydrate (grams)	....	11.88
Protein (grams)	6.66	8.16
Ash (grams)	.50	1.76
Calcium (grams)	.03	.294
Phosphorus (grams)	.08	.228
Iron (milligrams)	1.5	.49
Vitamin A (International units)	357	289
Thiamin (milligrams)	.075	.147
Vitamin D (International units)	7.5	4.9
Riboflavin (milligrams)	.137	.367

Table 2

THE PER CENT OF EDIBLE MEAT OBTAINED FROM DIFFERENT CLASSES OF LIVESTOCK AS PURCHASED [1]

Meat Animal	Dressing Shrinkage	Inedible Material	Edible Material
Hogs	20.50	3.75	75.75
Poultry	28.24	9.52	62.24
Cattle	29.60	10.30	60.01
Sheep	30.30	15.90	53.80

[1] Vernon, 1924.

Fig. 3. Some uses of eggs as food.

Industrial uses of poultry products. Poultry products are used extensively in industries (Table 3).

Eggs are used in the preparation of culture media for the growth of some species of bacteria.

Fig. 4. Poultry meat may now be purchased by the piece, cooked, and in salads, soups, etc.

Fertile eggs are used in the preparation of vaccines (Fig. 5).

Inedible eggs are used in the preparation of animal foods and fertilizers.

Egg whites are used in the manufacture of pharmaceuticals, paints, varnishes, adhesives, and printer's ink. They are also used in photography, bookbinding, wine clarification, tanning leather, and in textile dyeing.

Egg yolks are used in the manufacture of soap, paints, and shampoos. They are also used in finishing leather and in bookbinding.

Eggshells are used in mineral mixtures and for fertilizers.

Feathers are used in the making of millinery goods, pillows, cushions, mattresses, and dusters.

Endocrine glands are used in the preparation of biological products.

Use in research work. Chickens are being used extensively in biological research work because they are cheap and readily available, reproduce freely, have a sensitive metabolism, and are good laboratory animals (Fig. 6). Many of the findings made with chickens in the interest of pure science may be applied in a practical way for improving poultry production.

Development of the Poultry Industry

Early development. The poultry industry was brought to America from Europe by the earliest settlers. Small home flocks were started at the time of the establishment of the first permanent homes at Jamestown in 1607. They consisted of a few chickens which were kept to supply the home needs for

Table 3

USES FOR EGGS IN THE UNITED STATES. ESTIMATES FOR 1946[2]

USES	SHELL EGGS — FRESH AND STORAGE (82.1)	INEDIBLE AND WASTE (5.0)	FROZEN EGG PRODUCTS (6.4) — MIXED OR WHOLE	WHITES	PLAIN YOLK	SALT YOLK	SUGAR YOLK	GLYCERINE YOLK	DRIED EGG PRODUCTS (6.2) — MIXED OR WHOLE	ALBUMEN OR WHITES	YOLK
HUMAN FOOD USES											
DINING TABLE: HOME AND PUBLIC EATING PLACES	■		△	△	○		□		△		
BAKERY PRODUCTS	○		■	■	●		■	■	■	▲	●
CANDIES, CONFECTIONS, MARSHMALLOWS	△			▲						■	△
MAYONNAISE					●	■	▲	□	○		○
SALAD DRESSING			○		▲	●	○	○			
NOODLES, MACARONI			○		▲				○		□
ICE CREAM, FROZEN CUSTARDS, ICES	△		○	○	○		▲		○		
FOOD BEVERAGES AND FOOD BEVERAGE POWDERS	△		△	△	△		△		○		○
PREPARED MERINGUE AND WHIPPING POWDERS										▲	
PREPARED PUDDINGS									○		○
PREPARED FLOURS									▲	○	▲
BAKING POWDER										△	
SAUSAGE MANUFACTURING			△								
ANIMAL FOOD USES											
DOG FOOD									○		△
BIRD FOOD									○		△
FISH FOOD									△		
FOX FOOD		△							△		
HOG FOOD		△									
COMMERCIAL FEEDS									△		
TECHNICAL USES											
LEATHER AND FUR TRADE		□							○		△
LITHOGRAPHING	△								○		
PHOTO-ENGRAVING	△								△		
CEMENTING CORK TO JAR AND BOTTLE CAPS									○		
PHARMACEUTICALS					△	△			○		
TEXTILE PRINTING									□		
PAINTS FOR ARTISTIC WORK									△		
PRINTING INK										△	
PHOTOGRAPHY										△	
GILDING BOOKS, LEATHER, CLOTH, AND FABRIKOID									△		
EGG SHAMPOO	△								△		
LOSS OR WASTE											
ROTS, BROKEN, ETC., NOT RECOVERED		■									
FLOCK REPRODUCTION (FRESH EGGS)											
COMMERCIAL HATCHING	○										
FARM HATCHING	○										

■ 50% or more   ▲ 10% to 24.9%   ○ 1% to 4.9%
● 25% to 49.9%   □ 5% to 9.9%   △ Under 1%

eggs and meat. The Indians bought or stole birds from the early settlers, and poultry-keeping became common among them during Colonial days.

As villages and towns were established, the nearby home flocks were increased in size. The surplus eggs and meat were sold or exchanged for groceries in the nearby towns. Grain production and the development of transportation facilities encouraged the production of poultry west of the Allegheny Mountains in the early part of the nineteenth century. The de-

[2] U. S. D. A. Agricultural Statistics. 1947.

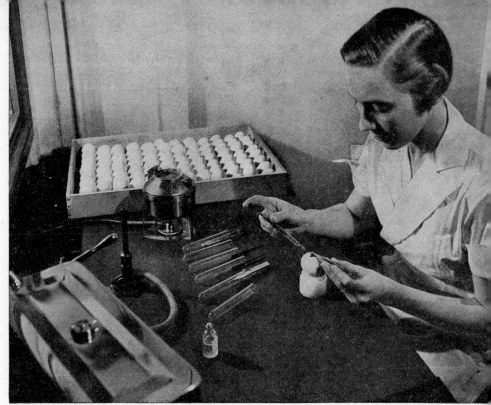

Fig. 5. Eggs being used for the production of vaccine.

velopment of refrigeration facilities and artificial methods of incubation and brooding were further stimuli for poultry production in the latter part of the century.

Development in recent years. Farms on which the chief source of income is from poultry began to appear early in the present century. The discovery of vitamins and their use in poultry feeding about 1925 revolutionized the poultry industry. Their use has made it possible to raise birds in confinement and at all seasons of the year. Recently, specialized poultry farms have been developed. These include egg, breeding, broiler, pullet rearing, turkey, and duck farms.

Growth of the poultry industry has been more rapid than the increase in population or the production of the larger farm animals (Fig. 7). These changes are typical of those that have taken place in older civilized countries. As population increases, more cereals and small fruits and vegetables are produced and smaller animals, including poultry, replace many of the larger farm animals. Egg production per capita has more than doubled during the last fifty years in spite of the fact that the population has increased two and one-half times during the same period. Most of the increased egg production has been consumed in our own country. A better appreciation of the nutritional value of eggs, better market facilities, and better quality of eggs have created a greater demand for eggs.

Fig. 6. A biological laboratory in which chickens are used for testing feeds.

The Present Poultry Industry

World distribution. The United States has about one-third of all the chickens and turkeys in the world (Table 4) and only about 6 per cent of the people.

Distribution in the United States. The country is usually divided into five geographical regions for statistical reports (Table 5 and Fig. 9).

The North Central states have about 48 per cent of the poultry and 30 per cent of the people according to 1946 estimates of population and chickens on farms January 1. General farm flocks predominate in the territory. There is a surplus of poultry products in most of the states in the territory.

The North Atlantic states have about 14 per cent of the poultry and 27 per cent of the people. There is a large shortage of poultry products in the territory. It provides a good market for nearby poultry and for the surplus products from the North Central states. Many large specialized poultry farms are found in North Atlantic states.

The South Atlantic states have about 10 per cent of the farm chickens and 13 per cent of the population. This is a deficit area for eggs. Small farm flocks are common in the South Atlantic states.

The South Central states have about 20 per cent of the poultry and 17 per cent of the population. Part of the states in the territory have a surplus of poultry products while others do not have enough to meet local needs. Small farm flocks are common in the South Central states.

The Western states have about 8 per cent of the poultry and 13 per cent

Table 4

WORLD CHICKEN AND EGG PRODUCTION [3]

Countries	Chickens in Countries		Eggs Produced	
	Av. 1935–38	1949 *	Av. 1934–38	1949 [2]
North America	Millions	Millions	Billions	Billions
Canada	44.1	37.2	2.6	3.6
Guatemala	.7			
Mexico	36.4			
Newfound. and Lab.	.4	.4		
Panama	.2	1.5		.05
United States	408.2	448.7	35.5	56.4
Cuba		9.0	.3	.3
Dom. Republic	2.4	1.9		.06
Europe				
Albania	2.1		.1	
Austria	8.9	5.6	.7	.4
Belgium	16.5	16.1	1.7	1.5
Bulgaria	11.8		.7	
Czechoslovakia	31.9	15.0	2.0	1.4
Denmark	27.6	28.0	2.0	1.9
Ireland	16.0	18.5	1.1	1.0
Finland	2.9		.3	.2
France	145.0	145.5	6.2	6.8
Germany	51.2	29.0	3.7	2.8
Greece	11.7	9.7	.6	.4
Hungary	17.9	16.0	1.1	.1
Italy	76.0	50.1	5.6	4.6
Luxembourg	.5	.4	.04	.04
Netherlands	29.6	9.9	2.0	1.0
Norway	5.7	5.5	.4	.3
Poland and Danzig	50.0	39.0	3.5	2.3
Portugal	5.7	5.7	.3	
Rumania	31.9	15.0	1.5	.5
Spain	29.0	33.5	1.7	1.8
Sweden	11.0	15.0	.9	1.5
Switzerland	5.5	6.1	.4	.5
United Kingdom	73.4	88.7	5.1	5.0
U.S.S.R. (Russia)	?	?	?	?
Yugoslavia	18.0		1.0	
Asia				
Lebanon		1.5		.04
Palestine	1.9		.1	.2
Syria	1.5	2.2	.09	.1
Turkey	16.8	17.3	1.0	.9
U.S.S.R. (Russia)	?	?	?	?
China	265.8	204.1		
Japan	51.1	19.0	3.6	.9
India		146.1		1.0
Pakistan		44.7		
Phil. Islands	25.4	25.0		.3
South America				
Argentina	43.0		1.1	
Brazil	59.0	60.0		2.2
Chile	1.0	3.6		.4
Paraguay		2.0		.1
Uraguay	4.8	3.8	.3	.3
Africa				
Egypt	26.9		.8	
French Morocco	50.0		1.0	
U. South Africa	14.0	16.0		1.2
Oceania				
Australia	15.5	15.0	.7	1.4
New Zealand	3.5		.4	.4

* For 1949 or the nearest year for which data were available.

[3] **Foreign Crops and Markets** 60: 12: Mar. 20, 1950.

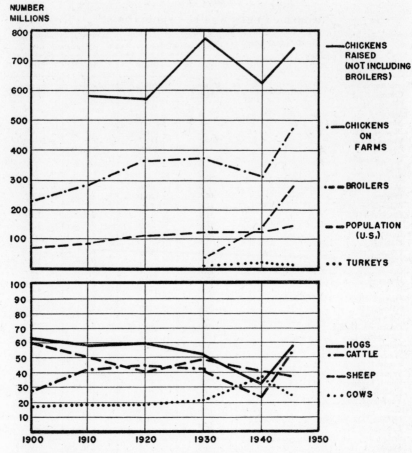

NUMBER
MILLIONS

Fig. 7. Comparative growth of poultry, other kinds of livestock, and human population, 1900–1945. (Data from U. S. Census and Agricultural Statistics, 1947.)

of the people. There is a shortage of poultry products in the territory. The West Coast states have turned from surplus egg-producing states before World War II to an egg shortage area since the war. The poultry population is small in the Rocky Mountain states. There are many large specialized poultry farms in the West Coast states.

The leading poultry states from the standpoint of the number of eggs produced in 1949 (Table 5) were Iowa, Minnesota, Pennsylvania, California and Texas. When compared on the basis of the value of the eggs produced in 1947, the states were Iowa, Pennsylvania, Minnesota, California, and New York.

Imports and exports. The United States is normally neither a large exporter nor importer of poultry products (Table 6). Some dried eggs were imported from China before World War II. During the war period there was

Table 5

POULTRY PRODUCTS PRODUCED

STATE	EGGS PRODUCED Number (Millions) in 1949 *	EGGS PRODUCED Value (Millions Dollars) 1947 †	CHICKENS RAISED ON FARMS Number (Millions) in 1950 *	CHICKENS RAISED ON FARMS Value (Millions Dollars) in 1947 †	TURKEYS RAISED IN 1949 * Number (Thousands)	COMMERCIAL BROILERS RAISED 1947 † Number (Millions)	HATCHERY CHICKS PRODUCED IN 1949 * Number (Millions)
Maine.	425	20.1	5.4	6.9	48	0.8	13.1
N. H.	387	19.5	5.0	6.4	69	2.2	32.6
Vt.	166	8.3	1.6	2.6	121	0.3	1.7
Mass.	829	47.4	8.5	12.3	335	4.1	32.0
R. I.	89	5.0	1.0	1.3	34	0.4	2.2
Conn.	511	28.1	5.6	7.6	206	5.9	33.6
N. Y.	2,324	101.9	22.5	31.7	786	5.4	27.6
N. J.	1,638	71.0	14.9	18.4	410	3.6	36.5
Pa.	3,097	135.5	35.7	47.2	1,378	6.1	63.0
N. Atlantic	9,466	436.7	100.1	134.4	3,387	29.0	127.1
Ohio.	2,578	98.4	27.4	35.8	1,237	3.2	63.6
Ind.	2,239	74.0	30.0	35.3	1,241	7.0	100.1
Ill.	2,800	89.4	30.0	38.6	1,118	7.1	95.0
Mich.	1,563	61.7	20.7	23.3	975	1.1	28.1
Wis.	2,474	89.8	22.0	21.5	606	3.7	24.8
E. N. Central	11,654	413.4	130.0	154.6	5,177	22.2	311.7
Minn.	3,858	129.0	33.7	33.8	3,752	1.2	59.8
Iowa.	4,398	136.5	43.6	54.6	2,659	2.6	81.0
Mo.	2,811	87.4	32.2	35.2	1,572	2.2	93.8
N. Dak.	528	17.0	6.5	7.4	825		5.5
S. Dak.	1,060	32.9	13.0	14.0	288		15.6
Nebr.	1,733	58.2	23.4	23.0	931		28.5
Kan.	1,918	64.3	22.8	21.3	742	0.8	38.3
W. N. Central	16,306	525.4	175.1	189.3	10,769	6.9	322.5
Del.	141	5.4	2.0	2.7	70	52.5	49.6
Md.	526	20.3	6.3	8.6	417	31.7	78.8
Va.	1,206	48.0	11.9	13.6	1,526	23.6	51.7
W. Va.	498	19.5	5.3	5.9	682	8.4	8.8
N. C.	1,009	39.2	17.5	19.3	486	16.2	44.5
S. C.	342	13.8	7.8	9.5	714	3.3	8.7
Ga.	648	26.3	13.2	13.0	299	28.7	68.6
Fla.	249	10.4	4.1	5.4	125	5.7	16.0
S. Atlantic	4,619	182.9	68.2	78.2	4,319	170.3	326.8
Ky.	1,248	41.8	16.8	18.3	216	1.1	13.4
Tenn.	1,047	36.3	15.6	15.5	182	1.8	13.5
Ala.	608	23.8	12.6	11.9	146	4.8	15.2
Miss.	542	19.7	13.4	12.2	95	2.3	11.5
Ark.	590	21.2	12.1	11.0	190	15.6	26.7
La.	331	11.7	9.0	10.8	58	1.2	6.0
Okla.	1,211	42.9	16.8	14.4	456	0.7	20.9
Tex.	2,826	97.5	35.9	28.5	4.225	10.6	61.2
S. Central	8,403	295.0	132.3	122.7	5,568	38.2	114.8
Mont.	227	8.2	3.3	3.9	130		2.3
Idaho.	272	12.4	3.7	3.8	268		3.3
Wyo.	102	3.7	1.2	1.3	124		0.4
Col.	417	13.7	5.5	5.9	759		7.8
N. Mex.	121	5.1	1.9	1.6	103		1.2
Ariz.	75	4.0	1.1	1.1	60	0.4	1.2
Utah.	442	18.0	4.5	3.8	1,710		2.7
Nev.	40	1.8	0.4	0.4	32		0.1
Wash.	788	33.8	9.0	9.2	1,118	1.8	20.0
Ore.	465	21.5	5.2	5.6	1,593	1.0	12.2
Calif.	2,985	106.5	28.5	25.6	6,353	13.2	81.7
Western	5,934	228.9	64.4	62.2	12,250	16.4	113.9
Total U. S.	56,382	2,082.2	670.3	741.4	41,470	283.1	1,504.9

* U. S. D. A. Bur. Agr. Economics Preliminary Estimate.
† Agricultural Statistics 1948.

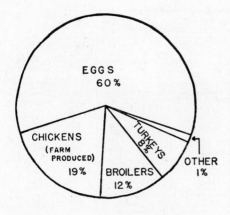

Fig. 8. Farm value of poultry products produced in 1949. (U. S. D. A. Poultry and Egg Situation, April, 1950.)

considerable expansion of the dried egg business in the United States. In recent years, the United States has exported egg products to European countries, Mexico, Cuba, and South America. Small amounts of poultry and eggs have been imported from Canada.

Relative importance of different species of poultry. Chickens constitute more than 90 per cent of all poultry raised (Table 7 and Fig. 8). The income from chicken eggs is more than that from all types of poultry meat production. The production of broilers and turkeys has increased rapidly during the last fifteen years.

Table 6

EXPORTS AND IMPORTS OF POULTRY PRODUCTS

YEAR	Eggs (Shell Egg Equivalent)		Poultry (Dressed Weight Equivalent)	
	Exports	Imports	Exports	Imports
	Million Dozen	*Million Dozen*	*Million Pounds*	*Million Pounds*
1910..........	5.7	3.3		
1920..........	26.8	50.1		
1930..........	18.7	40.7	3.3	2.8
1940..........	4.7	6.7	1.8	2.0
1948..........	132.6	2.4	9.5	42.5

The Poultry and Egg Situation, March, 1949. U. S. D. A.

Table 7

PRODUCTION OF PRINCIPAL SPECIES OF POULTRY IN THE UNITED STATES

YEAR	Species of Poultry			
	Chickens	Turkeys	Ducks	Geese
	Millions	*Millions*	*Millions*	*Millions*
1909...................				
1919...................	473			
1929...................	751	18.5	11.3	4.0
1939...................	803	33.6	12.1	1.2
1947...................	1028	34.8		

U. S. Census of Agriculture, Agricultural Statistics and the Poultry and Egg Situation, February, 1949.

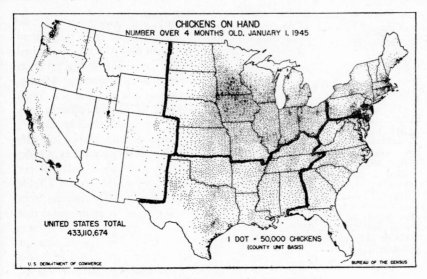

Fig. 9. Distribution of chickens in the United States.

The Future of the Poultry Industry

The poultry industry, as it is known today, is one of the newer branches of agriculture. It has grown rapidly during the last thirty years. As a result of these factors, many of the present-day poultry practices are not based on tested scientific facts. Some of them will undoubtedly be changed when science has had a chance to check the methods in use. The industry is not greatly influenced by foreign markets because there is a national balance between production and consumption.

The future of the poultry industry will depend largely on how economically poultry meat and eggs are produced.

Consumption problems. The consumption of poultry products is far from the saturation point (Table 8). The average annual per capita consumption of eggs in the United States in 1934 was 287, and in 1949 it was 374. The estimated yearly per capita consumption of eggs in rural communities is probably about double what it is in cities. Dieticians recommend an egg a day in liberal diets.

Consumption of poultry products has been hindered by a lack of education regarding their food value, very little advertising, difficulty of securing good products in cities, and the relatively high price of poultry meat and eggs. The economic status of people has a marked influence on the consumption of poultry products. Urban people, who can afford to spend enough money for an adequate diet, eat more than twice as much poultry products as those who have very little money to spend for food.

Egg-production possibilities. The average annual production per bird has been doubled during the past fifty years. This has been accomplished

Table 8

THE AMOUNT AND COST OF THE FOOD WE EAT [1]
(Based on Annual Purchase per Family of Three)

| FOOD PRODUCTS | AVERAGE YEARLY AMOUNT 1935-1939 | RETAIL PRICE | | | | FARMER'S SHARE OF RETAIL PRICE (PER CENT) | |
| | | 1935-1939 | | 1945 | | | |
		Cost Dollars	Per Cent of Total	Cost Dollars	Per Cent of Total	1935-9	1945
Market basket All foods......		340		459		40	54
Meat products Total.........	343 lb.	88	26	100	22	53	76
Pork and lard..............	176 lb.						
Beef......................	126 lb.						
Lamb.....................	17 lb.						
Other.....................	24 lb.						
Dairy products Total........		· 67	20	89	19	50	59
Fluid milk.................	254 qt.						
Condensed and evap. milk...	46 cans						
Butter....................	39 lb.						
Cheese....................	12 lb.						
Other.....................	80 lb.						
Fresh fruits and vegetables Total..................		58	17	105	23	35	47
Potatoes..................	281 lb.						
Apples....................	109 lb.						
Oranges...................	21 doz.						
Cabbage..................	65 lb.						
Lettuce...................	29 heads						
All others, including melons ..	492 lb.						
Bakery products..............		37	11	39	8	15	25
Bread, white...............	153 lb.						
Other.....................	139						
Poultry and eggs		26	8	43	9	66	73
Eggs.....................	47 doz.						
Chickens..................	32 lb.						
Other.....................	10 lb.						
Cereal products Other than bakery..................		18	5	25	5	32	41
Flour, white...............	237 lb.						
Corn meal.................	34 lb.						
Other.....................	82 lb.						
Canned fruits and vegetables...		14	4	17	4	14	26
Tomatoes..................	14 cans						
Peas......................	11 cans						
Corn......................	10 cans						
Other.....................	14 cans						
Other.....................	76 lb.						
Miscellaneous products........		26	8	32	7	18	30
Sugar.....................	55 lb.						
Vegetable shortening........	22 lb.						
Margarine.................	5 lb.						
Other.....................	68 lb.						

[1] U. S. D. A. Leaflet, 123.

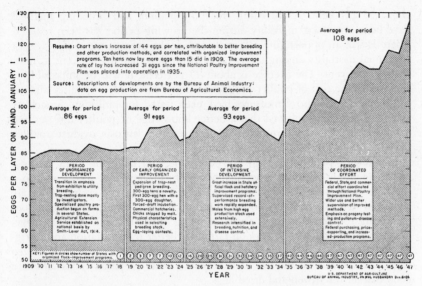

Fig. 10. Trend of average egg production in the United States as related to the development of the poultry industry.

through better breeding, feeding, and management (Fig. 10). Even now, the average annual egg production is only about 110 eggs. Well-fed and well-managed flocks average about 150 eggs per bird per year. If the flocks are also well-bred, they average 200 eggs or more per bird. Some birds produce more than 300 eggs per year. Better knowledge of breeding, feeding, and management will result in still better egg production and lower the cost of poultry production.

Hatchability problems. The estimated hatchability of all eggs set is about 68 per cent. In other words, about 32 eggs out of every 100 set are lost as a result of infertility or embryo mortality. Some hatches are obtained with 90 per cent or better hatchability. Better knowledge of breeding, management of breeders, and incubation will undoubtedly reduce hatching losses.

The problem of feed cost in poultry production. A hundred Leghorn hens require about nineteen pounds of feed per day for maintenance. For every ten eggs they lay, approximately one extra pound of feed is required. Therefore, the higher the production obtained, the less feed required per dozen of eggs.

A pound of poultry meat can be produced with every three to four pounds of feed fed, if rapid growth is obtained. The slower the rate of growth, the greater the amount of feed required per pound of gain.

Better knowledge of poultry physiology, nutrition, and management practice will result in better rations, better growth and production, lower feed costs, and cheaper poultry.

Mortality problems. The mortality of chickens during the growing period ranges from less than 5 per cent to more than 50 per cent. The average is about 25 per cent. As breeding stock, incubation, and brooding methods have been improved, mortality during the growing period has been reduced. There is still an opportunity to greatly reduce the average mortality.

Annual mortality among layers ranges from less than 10 per cent to more than 50 per cent. The average is about 25 per cent. It will be impossible to keep down the cost of poultry production unless losses due to poultry diseases can be checked. Control measures have been found for pullorum, bronchitis, and fowl pox. It is believed that a better knowledge of poultry diseases and management factors will result in fewer losses from leucosis, oviduct troubles, parasites, and other troublesome diseases.

Marketing problems. Eggs are perishable, and many of them are produced hundreds of miles from the point of consumption. There is also a shortage of eggs produced in the fall and a surplus in the spring. They are produced in small numbers on many farms. These factors present numerous marketing problems. Some of them are being solved through better management of flocks and care of eggs on farms, by better transportation and refrigeration facilities, and by new marketing methods, such as providing frozen eggs. The increase in the use of bakery and other prepared foods affords a good market for frozen and dried eggs.

Methods of marketing poultry meat are changing. Commercial broiler production and the sale of sexed chicks are resulting in a smaller surplus of cockerels in the summer. The sale of refrigerated dressed poultry is being replaced by drawn, fast-frozen poultry that is ready for the oven.

Many birds are culled from flocks and sold because of the effects of disease. This practice lowers the quality of market poultry. More of the poultry needs to be processed under more sanitary conditions, inspected for wholesomeness, and graded for quality in order to secure greater consumption.

A knowledge of economics and changing farm and marketing practices is needed in order to predict the course that should be followed in future poultry production.

REVIEW QUESTIONS

1. Why is general information regarding the poultry industry discussed before starting with specific phases of poultry production, such as breeds or breeding?
2. What are the chief distinguishing characteristics which separate poultry from other farm animals and from other birds?
3. How does poultry raising compare with other branches of agriculture as a source of farm income?
4. List the ways in which eggs may be used as a food.
5. In what ways are eggs used in industries?
6. Why are chickens increasing in popularity as laboratory animals?
7. List the principal factors responsible for the development of the poultry industry to its present position in the United States.
8. Describe the world distribution of poultry.
9. Are poultry population and human population similarly distributed in the United States?

Fig. 11. The Seventh World's Poultry Congress, held in Cleveland, Ohio, in 1939, with an attendance of more than 800,000. Top left, part of the exhibit buildings. Top right, viewing one of the nutrition exhibits. Center, the Japan exhibit. Bottom, part of the U. S. D. A. exhibit.

10. List two reasons why the northeastern states provide the best market for poultry products.
11. Compare the exports and imports of poultry products.
12. Why do this and other general poultry textbooks devote more space to the study of chickens than to all the other species of poultry combined?
13. Which has shown the greatest relative increase in relation to population: chickens on farms, dairy cows, or meat animals?
14. Have the production and consumption of poultry products about reached the saturation point in the United States? Give reasons for your answer.
15. List the major problems facing the poultry industry of the future.

REFERENCES

AGRICULTURAL STATISTICS. U. S. D. A. 1948.

BIRD, H. R.: THE NUTRITIVE VALUE OF EGGS AND POULTRY MEAT. Poultry and Egg National Board, Nutrition Research Bulletin No. 5. 1943.

CHRISTENSEN, R. P.: EFFICIENT USE OF FOOD RESOURCES IN THE UNITED STATES. U. S. Dept. Agr. Tech. Bul. 963. 1948.

CONSUMPTION OF FOOD IN THE UNITED STATES, 1909–1948. U. S. Dept. Agr. Misc. Pub. 691. 1949.

FOREIGN CROPS AND MARKETS. U. S. Department of Agriculture, 58, 60:12, Mar. 1950.

HENNEFRUND, H. E.: BIBLIOGRAPHY OF THE POULTRY INDUSTRY IN COUN-TRIES OTHER THAN CANADA AND THE UNITED STATES. U. S. D. A. Lib. List 12. 1944.

POTTS, R. C.: THE AMERICAN POULTRY INDUSTRY. Proc. Seventh World's Poultry Cong., pp. 305–308. 1939.

POULTRY AND EGG SITUATION. Published monthly or bimonthly. U. S. D. A. Bur. Agr. Economics. 1950.

STATISTICAL ABSTRACT OF THE UNITED STATES. U. S. D. A. 1948.

VERNON, W. M.: LOSSES SUSTAINED IN PREPARING POULTRY FOR THE TABLE. Poultry Sci., 3: 187–193. 1924.

WALLACE, H. A.: THE CONTRIBUTION OF THE POULTRY INDUSTRY TO WORLD-WIDE ABUNDANCE. Proc. Seventh World's Poultry Cong., pp. 1–4. 1939.

WORLD EGG PRODUCTION IN 1949; CURRENT CHICKEN NUMBERS. World's Poultry Science 6:106–111. 1950.

CHAPTER 2 ‖‖‖‖‖‖‖‖‖‖‖‖‖‖‖‖‖‖‖‖‖‖‖‖‖‖‖‖‖‖‖‖‖‖‖

Classes, Breeds, and Varieties of Chickens

▼

The Origin of the Chicken

The exact ancestry of the chicken is obscured by the antiquity of its origin. For more than 5,000 years the domesticated fowl has been one of man's benefactors. It is improbable that all the present-day varieties sprang from a common origin. The habits of the varieties in the Asiatic class indicate an ancestry which roosted on the ground and nested on a mound of earth. Such breeds as the Leghorns probably had tree-roosting ancestors. Authorities agree quite generally that the red jungle fowl, *Gallus bankiva* (Fig. 12), was one of the ancestors. Wild chickens of the *Gallus* genus are still found in the jungles of southeastern Asia. More recent investigations suggest that at least four species of the jungle fowl may have contributed to the development of the domestic fowl. These four species are the *Gallus bankiva* (red), *sonnerati* (gray), *lafayetti* (red and yellow), and *varius* (green). These may be accepted as the ancestors of the varieties which belong in the classes other than the Asiatic class. The ancestor of the Brahmas, Cochins, and Langshans was likely the Aseel or Malay fowl, which was domesticated in Asia more than 3,000 years ago.

Development of the Modern Breeds and Varieties of Chickens

There is a great biological difference between the two-pound jungle hen which laid only a few eggs and the modern hen which lays 300 eggs or a present-day thirteen-pound Jersey Giant. How has such progress been made? Heredity has been the force which nature and man have used to direct the development of the domesticated fowl. Fortunately there has been much variation so that man and nature could make selection. Natural selection both before and after domestication developed a more vigorous bird.

Cockfighting. Early references to cockfighting suggest that this was once one of the principal uses of the male of the species. This sport (Fig. 13) accelerated the law of the survival of the fittest and did much to develop the vigor and vitality of the species. It also served the very useful purpose of

21

Fig. 12. Gallus bankiva, one of the probable ancestors of the domestic fowl. The male weighs about two and one-half pounds.

giving wider distribution to the domestic fowl as cockfighting spread throughout the world.

Meat production. If the meat of the chicken had not possessed such delicious edible qualities, it is not likely that the so-called meat and general-purpose breeds would have been developed. However, man soon learned the value of the chicken as a source of food and he selected the larger and better-fleshed birds so that his meat supply might be increased. This type of selection increased the size of certain breeds. Many people are of the opinion that the meat qualities of the domestic fowl have been neglected in the twentieth century since egg production has been so much emphasized.

Exhibition qualities. The "Golden Era" of the fancier was from 1870 to 1920 when he reigned almost supreme. The trap nest had not yet caused the worship of egg records; fancy feathers and body form remained the goal of every true breeder. These breeders, by breeding for uniform type and definite color patterns, did much to establish the Standard breeds and varieties. Many beautiful color patterns were developed and excellent type birds were established. While in some cases vitality may have been lowered at the expense of

Fig. 13. A cockfight.

exhibition quality, the exhibition breeders made very definite and important contributions to the development of the chicken.

Egg production. The invention of the trap nest and the discovery of the laws of inheritance, together with their application to poultry breeding, were major contributions to the development of high-producing strains of poultry. The trap nest was a practical device for determining the number of eggs the individual bird would lay; and those eggs could be identified, and such characteristics as size, shape, color, and interior quality could be determined. Poultry breeders are today applying the laws of heredity to their breeding problems and using the trap nest to identify their breeding stock.

The American Poultry Association

The American Poultry Association, organized at Buffalo, New York, in 1873, has for its objective the protection and promotion of the Standard-bred poultry industry. The association issues the American Standard of Perfection, which describes the respective varieties, breeds, and classes of poultry which are recognized as Standard-bred (Chart 1, Appendix).

The association has the responsibility of recognizing new breeds and varieties of poultry. Breeds or varieties which the association considers obsolete are dropped from the list of Standard-bred poultry. The association issues licenses to judges who pass the examinations as given by the Committee on Licensing Judges and Flock Inspectors. These examinations consist of a written examination on the Standard of Perfection and practical judging work under the observation of a licensed judge. Those who pass the examination are authorized to officiate as judges in poultry shows.

Standard Classification

Breeds and varieties admitted to the Standard must possess distinctive type and color patterns (p. 626) and be sponsored by at least five members of the association who are active breeders of the variety.

The term *class* is used generally to designate groups of Standard breeds which have been developed in certain regions; thus, the class names—American, English, Asiatic, etc. The distinctive *breed* differences are primarily those of body shape and size. The color pattern (Fig. 14) and shape of comb (Fig. 15) distinguish the different *varieties*. Varieties in the same breed may have an entirely different ancestry. For example, the Barred Plymouth Rocks originated from the crossing of a hawk-colored cock (probably a Dominique) with Black Cochin hens, with possibly some Spanish and Dorking blood added later, while the Buff Plymouth Rocks were selected in 1889 from red fowls in the vicinity of Westport, Massachusetts.

American Class

The breeds and varieties in this class were developed by American breeders to serve the general purpose of supplying both meat and eggs. All varieties in this class possess certain common characteristics; for example, they have yellow skin, nonfeathered shanks, and red earlobes, and all lay brown-shelled eggs except the Lamonas, which lay white-shelled eggs. The chart on page 626 lists the varieties and breeds in this class and gives their more important characteristics. These breeds and varieties have proved their value, and today they are widely distributed in other countries as well as the United States and Canada.

Plymouth Rocks. The oldest and, until recent years, the most popular variety of this breed was the Barred Plymouth Rock, which originated in Connecticut from a Dominique-Black Cochin cross made in 1865. It created quite a sensation when exhibited in 1869 and became thereafter a very popular variety. It was admitted to the first Standard published in 1874. Other varieties of this breed and the order of their admittance to the Standard are White (1888), Buff (1892), Silver-Penciled (1894), Partridge (1909), Columbian (1910), and Blue (1920). The Barred and White varieties are the two most popular varieties of this breed. In recent years there has been an increasing demand for White Plymouth Rock chicks for broiler production. The sex-linked inheritance of barring, resulting in lighter males than females, has complicated the breeding of the Barred variety to a single standard for males and females.

Wyandottes. The oldest variety of this breed is the Silver-Laced (Fig. 17),

Fig. 14. Feather patterns of the domestic fowl. The above feathers are from the following varieties: 1, Buff-Laced Polish; 2, White-Laced Red Cornish; 3, Silver-Laced Wyandotte; 4, Columbian varieties; 5, Golden-Laced Wyandotte; 6, Blue varieties; 7, Golden Sebright Bantam; 8, Dark Cornish; 9, Partridge varieties; 10, Silver-Penciled varieties; 11, Ancona or Mottled Houdan; 12, Speckled Sussex; 13, Silver-Spangled Hamburg; 14, Golden-Spangled Hamburg; 15, Dark-Barred Plymouth Rock; 16, Buttercup; 17, Silver Campine, 18, Dominique; 19, Golden-Penciled Hamburg; 20, Silver-Penciled Hamburg; 21, Light-Barred Plymouth Rock.

U. S. D. A.

Fig. 15. Male heads showing different types of combs. 1, Single; 2, Pea; 3, Pea; 4, Rose; 5, Single; 6, Single; 7, V-shaped; 8, Rose; 9, Strawberry.

which was admitted to the Standard in 1883. There is some uncertainty as to the origin of this variety, but in 1870 John P. Ray of Hemlock, New York, crossed Silver Seabrights (large laced fowls) with the Asiatic Chittagongs. It is also reported that some strains of Silver-Laced Wyandottes originated by crossing Dark Brahmas with Hamburgs and White Cochins. The other varieties of this breed and the order of their admittance to the Standard are Golden-Laced (1888), Buff (1893), Black (1893), Partridge (1901), Silver-Penciled (1902), White (1903), and Columbian (1905).

The Wyandottes have had waves of popularity in America. Today the White variety is the most popular Wyandotte. While it has been handicapped by small-egg size and relatively poor hatching results, this variety is now

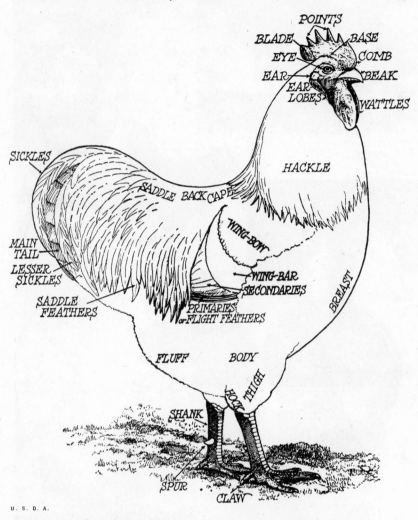

U. S. D. A.

Fig. 16. Nomenclature chart of the male chicken.

being bred by breeders who are correcting these defects; and excellent White Wyandottes are available for poultry raisers who prefer this variety.

Rhode Island Reds. The Rhode Island Reds were not developed by the fancier but were developed by the farmers of the Little Compton district of Rhode Island. The original crosses were red Malay Games and reddish-colored Shanghais, followed by the introduction of the blood of many other breeds, such as the Brown Leghorn, Cornish, and Wyandotte. The Single-Comb Reds were admitted to the Standard in 1904 and the Rose-Comb variety in 1905. The early development of this breed was for utility purposes. Later it became a fancier's fowl as well. Too much emphasis on color, in some cases, has been

Fig. 17. Some breeds of the American Class. Top left, Silver-Laced Wyandottes. Top right, Single-Comb Rhode Island Reds. Center, White Plymouth Rocks. Bottom, New Hampshires.

at the expense of utilitarian qualities. Some of the production breeders of Rhode Island Reds have neglected color in their breeding stock so that state inspectors supervising breeding work under the National Poultry Improvement Plan are confronted with either rejecting flocks of this breeding or classifying them as of some other breed. The goal of Rhode Island Red breeders should be high-producing birds which have definitely the type and color which distinguish this breed.

Rhode Island Whites. The Rhode Island Whites were developed from a mating of White Wyandotte cockerels and Partridge Cochin hens. The offspring were crossed with Partridge Cochin males and the pullets from this cross were mated to a Rose-Comb White Leghorn male. The progeny were then interbred, and selection was made for the Rhode Island White characters. The Rose-Comb Rhode Island Whites were admitted to the Standard in 1922. They established some remarkable egg records in egg-laying contests and became a popular variety. Their popularity has waned, and today relatively few poultry raisers keep this breed.

Single-Comb Rhode Island Whites are also raised by some poultrymen but they have failed to gain Standard recognition because of their close resemblance to the White Plymouth Rock.

New Hampshires. This breed developed from the Rhode Island Red stock which was introduced into New Hampshire from Rhode Island and Massachusetts. For more than twenty-five years the poultrymen of New Hampshire selected their Reds for such production qualities as early maturity, early feathering, large-egg size, and good meat type, apparently omitting color of plumage from consideration. There resulted fowls possessing distinctive characteristics. Their color pattern was lighter than that of exhibition Rhode Island Reds but not unlike some strains of Reds in which the breeders have emphasized egg production and let color "take care of itself." At present much interest is being manifested in New Hampshires because of their vitality, early maturing, rapid growth, early feathering, and large eggs. The continued popularity of this breed will depend on its ability to compete with other American breeds for the favor of the American farmer.

Two or more strains of New Hampshires have been developed: a broiler or meat strain; an egg strain; and a combination of the two to give a general purpose New Hampshire possessing both broiler requirements and high egg production.

Other breeds. The other breeds and varieties in the American class have not been generally adopted by the public, and therefore few flocks of these varieties are found on farms in the United States. These breeds are the Dominiques, Javas (Black and Mottled), Chantecler (White and Partridge), Jersey Black Giants, Jersey White Giants, and Lamonas.

Poultry breeders contribute more to the poultry industry by improving the productive qualities of existing breeds than by developing new breeds. Too many inferior breeds are recognized as pure breeds.

Mediterranean Class

This class contains those breeds which had their origin near the Mediterranean Sea—namely, Leghorns (Italy), Minorcas (Minorca Island), Spanish (Spain), Blue Andalusians (Andalusia, Spain), Anconas (Italy), and Buttercups (Sicily). The breeds in this class are characterized by white earlobes, relatively large combs, nonbroodiness, early maturity, nervous disposition, and production of white-shelled eggs. A list of all the breeds and varieties in this class is given in Chart 1, Appendix.

Leghorns. This breed (Fig. 18) is popular in America. The popularity of this breed rests upon its reputation as an egg producer. While there are thirteen Standard varieties of Leghorns, those which have gained public favor are the White, Brown, and Buff.

Minorcas. Five varieties of Minorcas are found in the United States—namely, Black (Single- and Rose-Comb), White (Single- and Rose-Comb), and the Single-Comb Buff.

Anconas. Since the Standard description of the type of this breed does not differ from that of the Leghorn, it appears that the Anconas might very well have been called mottled Leghorns. The breeders of Anconas have not been active in developing their ability as producers of eggs, and as a result the White Leghorn breeders have supplied the demand for high-producing birds which lay large eggs, and the Anconas have gradually decreased in popularity.

Other breeds. The other breeds in this class are the White-Faced Black Spanish, Blue Andalusians, and Buttercups. These breeds have not gained the favor of the American farmers or poultrymen because other breeds possessing similar characteristics and producing white-shelled eggs have been more efficient producers of eggs which satisfy American market requirements.

English Class

The breeds of English origin include the Orpingtons, Cornish, Australorps, Dorkings, Sussex, and Redcaps. They all have white skin except the Cornish, which has yellow skin. The breeds in this class have red earlobes and all except the Dorkings and Redcaps lay brown-shelled eggs. They possess good meat quality but some markets prefer poultry with yellow skin and therefore discriminate against these white-skinned breeds. The Cornish are poor layers, but they possess excellent meat type, having particularly well-developed breasts.

Orpingtons. The Orpington name came from the town of Orpington in Kent County, England, the home of William Cook, who developed Black Orpingtons. Of the four varieties—Buff, White, Blue, and Black—the Buff Orpington (Fig. 19) is the only variety which has widespread distribution in the United States, but its popularity has declined in recent years. The Buff Orpingtons were very likely developed from the Lincolnshire Buffs, which were produced by crossing Dorkings and Buff Cochins. Some flocks of White Orpingtons are found in the United States, but the Black Orpington and the Blue Orpington are rarely found in this country. The Orpingtons resemble the Plymouth Rocks in type but are slightly larger.

Cornish. The American Standard describes three varieties of Cornish: Dark, White, and White-Laced Red. The Cornish, formerly called the Cornish

Fig. 18. Some breeds of the Mediterranean Class. Top, Single-Comb Anconas. Center, Single-Comb Black Minorcas. Bottom, Single-Comb White Leghorns.

Indian Game, are very closely feathered and have unusually compact bodies. The Dark Cornish are raised in the United States, but they have not held the esteem of the American poultryman or farmer. The popularity of this variety appears to be waning, and unless there should be a definite revival of interest in their meat quality, fewer Dark Cornish will likely be raised in the United States in the future. They may find a place in crossbreeding to improve meat quality.

Dorking. The Standard recognizes three varieties: Silver-Gray, White, and Colored. Columella, a Roman agricultural writer of the first century A.D., no doubt referred to the ancestor of the Dorking fowl when he stated: "Those are believed to be the best breed that have five toes." The Silver-Gray Dorking is the only variety of this breed which has found even a limited number of admirers in America. The Dorkings have red earlobes but lay white-shelled eggs.

Sussex. Of the three Standard varieties—Speckled, Red, and Light—only the Speckled Sussex has met with favor in the United States, and of this variety there are only a few breeders. The Sussex are splendid meat birds and have been prized as market poultry in England for the past two hundred years. The Light Sussex is the most popular variety of this breed in Canada and England.

Australorps. This breed, as its name indicates, is an Australian Orpington. The Black Orpingtons which were taken to Australia were there bred into a very productive fowl and established at one time the world's annual egg record in an egg-laying contest. Some very high-producing Australorps were imported into the United States and good flocks of this breed were established here. Black Australorp cockerels are in demand for crossing with White Leghorns to produce White Australorps.

Redcaps. This breed is seldom found in the United States. It apparently has only a limited following in England. The Redcaps produce eggs with white shells.

Asiatic Class

The breeds of Asiatic origin have made valuable contributions to the blood lines of breeds in the American and English classes. Apparently the descendants of the jungle fowl and the Malay fowl were not interbred until they reached England and America in the nineteenth century. The large breeds imported into these countries from China and India evidently possessed plenty of size, stamina, and egg-laying ability. This stock made valuable contributions in the development of the American breeds and in this manner rendered the poultry industry of America a distinct service. However, their popularity as pure breeds has gradually decreased. At the World's Poultry Congress held in Cleveland, Ohio, in 1939, several specimens of this class were displayed. The beautiful type and color patterns which these specimens showed impressed observers with the beauty of a real fancier's fowl.

Brahmas. This breed (Fig. 20) came originally from the Brahmaputra district of India. The Gray Chittagongs still found in this part of India are quite similar to the modern Brahma. The first specimens imported to America in 1846 and England in 1853 were light in color. The varieties Light and Dark were developed in America and England and were admitted to the first

Fig. 19. Some breeds of the English Class. Upper left, Silver-Gray Dorkings. Upper right, Buff Orpingtons. Lower left, Speckled Sussex. Lower right, Dark Cornish.

American Standard published in 1874. The Buff Brahma was recognized as a Standard variety in 1924. The decline in popularity of the Brahmas was likely due to the fancier's overemphasis on feather development and neglect of production qualities.

Cochins. When first imported to America about 1847, the fowls which later came to be known as Cochins were called Shanghais. Their popularity was greatly enhanced in England by the interest manifested by Queen Victoria in exhibiting them at the Royal Dublin Society Show in April, 1846. They are reported to have created the "hen fever" and started the chicken fancy in America. The original importations were various shades of buff color and were said to be the first buff-colored fowls seen in England and America. The other Standard varieties—Partridge, White, and Black—are reported to have arisen by the selection and breeding of "off-colored" specimens which came from the early Cochin matings. It is more logical to assume that some outside blood was introduced to produce these varieties.

The popularity of the Cochins waned when the public discovered that they were poor producers and very broody. This is an example of what improper breeding can do to destroy a breed. If the breeders had bred for non-broodiness and egg production instead of concentrating effort on profuse and loose feathering, this breed, which had an auspicious beginning, might have remained one of the popular breeds of America.

Langshans. The Black Langshan was taken to England from China in 1872 and was imported to the United States from England. This breed was found in the Langshan district of northern China north of the Yangtsze Kiang River. The White Langshans probably arose as a sport from the Blacks. Though excellent flocks of Langshans were found a few years ago, their popularity has also declined. Artificial standards for the long-legged type injured their economic quality and contributed to their present unpopularity.

Other Standard Classes

The American Standard of Perfection describes several classes of chickens which have but little economic importance in the United States. Many of the breeds in these classes are of interest to fanciers only, while others are popular breeds in their homelands.

Polish class. The "Paduan" fowl which was described in Italy as early as 1600 possessed characteristics quite similar to the Polish breed. The Polish (Fig. 21) are crested and have an unusual skull structure. This peculiar skull formation suggests a crested jungle fowl ancestry. The Polish in the United States are a fancier's fowl.

Hamburg class. The Hamburgs originated in Holland. When first introduced into England and America they were popular with the fanciers, and at one of the early Boston shows three hundred specimens of this breed were exhibited. They remain a fancier's fowl and therefore are of little economic importance to the poultry industry of the United States.

French class. The French breeds and varieties described in the American Standard are Houdans (Mottled and White), Crevecoeurs (Black), LaFleche (Black), and the Faverolles (Salmon). These breeds are noted for the quality of their meat. The Houdans are sometimes found in the show room in the

Fig. 20. Breeds of the Asiatic Class. Top, Black Langshans. Center, Buff Cochins. Bottom, Light Brahmas.

United States but the other breeds are rarely seen even in these poultry exhibitions.

Continental class. The American Poultry Association recognizes only the Campines (Silver and Golden) and the Lakenvelders. These fowls have been bred in Belgium and Germany for several centuries. The modern Campine is reported to be half Campine and half Braekel. Though similar to the Leghorn in many respects, this breed has not been popular in America.

Game and Game Bantam class. The modern Game fowl is an exhibition bird and is raised for ornamental purposes. Though cockfighting is outlawed in the United States, the sport remains one of the gambler's devices for stimulating betting; and it is said that outside the law the sport flourishes in some communities. The English Pit Game is used for this purpose.

Oriental class. As the class name and the names of these breeds (Sumatra and Malay) indicate, they come from southeastern Asia. The Cubalaya was developed in Cuba.

Ornamental Bantams. The Bantams are excellent pets for children and ideal for the true fancier who desires to try his hand at shaping the type and arranging the color designs of his chosen variety.

Non-Standard Breeds and Varieties

While there are a great many varieties of chickens which have not been admitted to the American Standard, only those which have attracted the public because of some peculiar character or their economic possibilities will be discussed here.

Jersey White Giants. This variety is at present in the process of formation. These birds are similar in size and shape to the Jersey Black Giants. Their greenish shanks have caused market difficulties because the green pigment sometimes appears on the edible portions of the bird. This condition confuses the public as well as the market men, who discriminate against such birds because they believe this condition is evidence of bruising and subsequent decomposition.

White Australorp. This breed is similar to the Standard Black Australorp except for color.

Delaware (Indian River). This breed was developed from sports or "off-colored" chicks that occurred in the crossing of Barred Rock cockerels with New Hampshire hens. The sports selected had white bodies with barred hackle primary and secondary wing feathers and tail feathers. They were progeny tested for homozygosity and were selected for yellow legs, light undercolor, rapid growth, and good feathering.

The pure cockerel of this breed may be mated with a New Hampshire or a Rhode Island Red female, and the offspring will all be marked with white body feathers and barred black tail, wing tips, and hackles. The cock weighs 8.5 pounds and the hen 6.5 pounds. This breed is frequently used for broiler production because of its rapid growth, white body feathers, and yellow skin.

Yokohama. This long-tailed Japanese breed is of interest because of the unusual tail development. The sickle feathers sometimes attain a length of from fifteen to twenty feet.

Araucana. This breed, first reported in 1914 from South America, is often rumpless, has a peculiar muff development, and lays eggs with blue shells (but often containing some brown or red pigment).

Fig. 21. Some breeds of the Continental European classes. Upper left, Silver Campines. Upper right, Silver-Spangled Hamburgs. Lower left, Mottled Houdans. Lower right, White-Crested Black Polish.

Naked-necked fowl. This breed, erroneously referred to as the "Turken," has a bare neck. It should be noted that to date (1950) all fertile eggs produced by crossing chickens and turkeys at experiment stations have failed to hatch.

Crossbred poultry. In recent years the crossing of purebred breeds of chickens has received considerable attention by both poultrymen and farmers. (Chapters 5 and 6). Some of the more common crosses used are Barred Plymouth Rocks with Rhode Island Reds, White Plymouth Rocks with White Leghorns, and Black Australorps with White Leghorns.

Choosing a Variety to Raise

That there is a great diversity of opinion as to the best variety of poultry to raise is evidenced by the 167 varieties which the American Poultry Association recognized in its 1945 Standard. Each variety has its advocates. The Bantams surely have a place as pets, the Games and Game Bantams are the fanciers' creation, the breeds in the Mediterranean class are preferred because of their heavy production of large white-shelled eggs, and the breeds of the English class and the American class are good producers of eggs and meat. Each color pattern has its champions. The beginner will do well to observe the successful poultryman or breeder and start with some of the same stock. Many beginners have permitted some minor and probably fancy point to influence their selection of a variety which later caused the failure of their poultry enterprise.

Poultry producers have in recent years become more discriminating in their selection of varieties of poultry to raise. They are paying more attention to the productivity of the stock they purchase and placing less emphasis on color of feathers and other minor characters. This trend is shown in Table 9.

Results in official egg-laying contests. The reports from the official egg-laying contests should be of help to persons selecting a variety to raise. Table 10 presents a summary of the egg production for varieties having 100 or more entries in the official egg-laying contests of the United States in 1947–48.

Table 9

BREED DISTRIBUTION IN HATCHERY SUPPLY FLOCKS IN THE NATIONAL
POULTRY IMPROVEMENT PLAN [1]

Observation	Year	
	1941–42	1947–48
Number of states cooperating	33	41
Number of birds under supervision	10,712,027	24,789,976
New Hampshire	17.1 *per cent*	25.7 *per cent*
White Leghorn	26.3	24.2
White Rock	18.6	15.7
Barred Rock	15.8	10.4
Rhode Island Red	8.9	6.8
White Wyandotte	2.8	1.7
Cross Mated	5.0	12.4
Other	5.5	3.1

[1] U. S. D. A. Bur. An. Ind., A. H. D. 69. 1949.

Table 10

PRODUCTION SUMMARY OF ALL ENTRIES IN U. S. OFFICIAL EGG-LAYING
TESTS FOR 1947–48
(100 or more entries)

Variety	Birds Entered	Points Per Bird	Eggs Per Bird	Per Cent Mortality	Egg Weight (Ounces Per Dozen)
Rhode Island Reds.......	2,652	231.8	221.9	12.1	24.88
Inbred-hybrids..........	325	220.7	215.6	13.8	24.46
S. C. White Leghorns.....	5,642	217.9	211.8	16.2	24.56
Barred Plymouth Rocks...	985	213.0	207.3	14.5	24.54
New Hampshires.........	1,846	209.5	200.9	9.2	24.84
White Plymouth Rocks...	1,094	189.7	183.6	13.4	24.66
White Wyandottes.......	208	178.6	174.3	17.3	24.48
Australorps.............	130	174.5	174.1	15.4	24.04

It is evident from these results that only a few varieties remain popular and most productive.

U. S. Record of Performance summaries. The United States Department of Agriculture has in recent years issued an annual summary giving the results of records made on the breeders premises under U.S.R.O.P. supervision. This information should also be quite helpful to the beginner looking for a variety of chickens to raise. Table 11 gives the results reported for 1947–48 and indicates wide differences in egg production of the more common varieties.

The poultry raiser should select the most productive strains for his poultry

Table 11

ANNUAL U.S.R.O.P. SUMMARY FOR THE YEAR 1947–48

Breed and Variety	Flocks in Summary	Birds Entered in USROP	Birds Qualifying as USROP		Avg. Egg Production of All Birds Entered
	(Number)	(Number)	(Number)		(Number)
Single-Comb White Leghorn....	143	92,467	46,221	50.0	195
New Hampshire..............	94	41,576	15,830	38.1	172
White Plymouth Rock.........	52	20,495	7,426	36.2	166
Single-Comb Rhode Island Red..	51	25,337	11,955	47.2	185
Barred Plymouth Rock.........	43	14,902	6,968	46.8	187
Black Australorp..............	8	1,226	378	30.8	163
White Wyandotte.............	4	931	369	39.6	169
Buff Orpington...............	3	231	31	13.4	98
Buff Minorca.................	2	86	...	...	86
Black Langshan...............	1	45	...	...	43
Columbian Plymouth Rock.....	1	67	9	13.4	155
Jersey White Giant...........	1	134	...	...	65
Total.....................	403	197,497	89,187	45.2	185

enterprise. The broiler grower needs a bird that is efficient in producing poultry meat at an early age, whereas the general farmer very likely wants a general-purpose breed that lays well. Those who specialize in egg production prefer the high egg-producing strains.

Exhibition Judging of Poultry

The judging of poultry for exhibition quality, though not emphasized as much as it was twenty-five years ago, is important and should be understood by students interested in poultry. Although the emphasis has been shifted to utility and the demand for fancy feathers has decreased, breed type and the more fundamental exhibition qualities should be preserved in the so-called production strains.

Score card. The score card, once essential to every poultry show, today is seldom seen in the showroom. Score-card judging has given way to judging by comparison. Formerly, every bird entered in the show was "scored" and the winners determined by the birds' respective scores. The score card remains basic in the decisions of the experienced and conscientious judge.

SCALE OF POINTS USED IN JUDGING VARIETIES FOUND IN THE AMERICAN, MEDITERRANEAN, ENGLISH, AND ASIATIC CLASSES

	White		Solid Color Other Than White		Parti-Colored	
	Shape	Color	Shape	Color	Shape	Color
1. Symmetry	4	...	4	...	4	...
2. Weight or size	4	...	4	...	4	...
3. Condition and vigor	10	...	10	...	10	...
4. Comb	5	...	5	...	5	...
5. Beak	2	1	2	1	2	1
6. Head	3	1	3	1	3	1
7. Eyes	2	2	2	2	2	2
8. Wattles	2		2		2	
9. Ear lobes	2	2	2	2	2	2
10. Neck	3	3	2	4	1	5
11. Wings	5	3	4	4	3	5
12. Back	8	4	7	5	6	6
13. Tail	5	3	4	4	4	4
14. Breast	7	3	5	5	5	5
15. Body and fluff	5	3	5	3	4	4
16. Legs and toes	5	3	5	3	5	3
	72	28	66	34	62	38

Exhibiting Poultry

Because of the shift in emphasis from the exhibition ideal to the utility goal, the exhibition of poultry has almost become a lost art. While the competition which existed in the exhibition poultry shows encouraged faking, it also developed the art of training and conditioning birds for the showroom. It is hoped that the art of exhibiting poultry without its abuses may be retained by the industry.

Birds sent to shows should be placed in large coops where they have plenty of feed. Unless water can be placed in containers in the coops so that there is little danger of the bird or coop becoming soiled by it, some succulent feeds should be placed in the coop instead of water. If convenient, the owner of the birds should attend the show and carefully groom the birds before they are judged and be present to show them to interested spectators and prospective customers.

Many breeders have abandoned the exhibition poultry shows because of the danger of introducing disease in their flocks. The shows should bar all diseased birds and take all practical sanitary measures to prevent any outbreaks of disease during the show. All birds returned to the breeders' premises should be kept away from the flock for two weeks. Some breeders make it a policy to sell all birds exhibited and never return them to their flocks.

The tendency in poultry exhibitions is to show not only the live birds but to exhibit their products, such as eggs, chicks, and dressed birds. Because the hazards of disease would be eliminated, poultry shows may ultimately become exhibits of poultry products.

Selection and Preparation of Fowls for Exhibition

Fowls which are to be exhibited at poultry shows should be carefully selected and properly fitted before they are exhibited. The selection should be made by examining the birds in the flock which show good body type and general color. These birds should be compared with the Standard for their breed, and examined in detail as to surface color, undercolor, legs, toes, and disqualifications or defects. Any disqualification bars a fowl from being considered for a prize in the showroom. The birds selected should be placed in an exhibition coop for a portion of each day for a week or longer before they are entered in competition. The plumage should be examined so that the fowl will become accustomed to such movements when being handled by the judge. Varieties which show soiled plumage should be washed; and the head, feet, and shanks of all varieties should be carefully cleaned before they are exhibited. The only equipment needed for washing birds is a warm room, individual exhibition coops, clean litter, three wash tubs, soft water, and a good grade of soap. The room should be warmed to 90° F. and kept at about that temperature until the birds dry. The first tub should be filled about two-thirds full of warm water which is not too hot to be comfortable. In this tub should be dissolved one-half pound of soap. The birds should be held securely when placed in the water and all parts of the plumage should be thoroughly soaked before rubbing the feathers. The plumage should be lathered but care should be taken to avoid rubbing against the "grain" of the feather. After the birds have been thoroughly washed they should be passed through two tubs of rinsing water, the first tub containing water of about body temperature and the third tub containing cool water. All soap should be rinsed from the plumage to prevent the feathers from matting together. Much water may be removed from the plumage by wrapping the birds in a heavy towel.

The shanks and feet should be thoroughly scrubbed and all dirt removed from under the scales of the feet. By rubbing some thin oil on the shanks, beak, comb, face, wattles, and earlobes, the appearance of the bird can be greatly improved. Many valuable birds have been placed below less desirable specimens because their owners failed to train and prepare them for showroom competition. Exhibiting poultry is an art which was mastered by the early breeders and fanciers.

IMPORTANT GENERAL DISQUALIFICATIONS

Weight. Leghorn and Ancona males more than one and one-half pounds and females more than one pound below Standard weight. All other specimens except Bantams more than two pounds underweight.

Shape. Deformed back or beak. Split or slipped wing. Wry or squirrel tail (Fig. 22). Crooked breastbone in turkeys. Twisted feather in wing or tail. Single combs lopped, split, or having a side sprig (Fig. 23). Rose combs obstructing sight or without a spike. Combs foreign to the breed. Feathers on shanks or feet of any variety required to have unfeathered shanks. Decided bowlegs or knock-knees.

Color. Positive enamel white in the earlobes of the American, Asiatic, and English varieties except Dorkings, Redcaps, and Lamonas. Positive enamel white in the face of all Mediterranean cockerels and pullets except the White-Faced Black Spanish. Shanks or feet of color foreign to the breed. Red or yellow in the plumage of any black variety. Foreign color in any white variety except slight gray ticking.

The American Standard of Perfection, published by the American Poultry Association, Davenport, Iowa, should be consulted for the detailed description of all Standard varieties and for a complete list of all defects and disqualifications.

Poultry-Judging Contests

The judging of poultry by students of poultry husbandry has been encouraged during recent years by judging contests for 4-H Club members, vocational agricultural students, and college students.

State vocational agriculture contests. Many states hold poultry-judging contests for students enrolled in high school vocational agriculture classes. The Missouri contest held in 1949 consisted of the following: Judging three classes on egg production, breed type, market qualities and value as breeders; selection of ten birds for U. S. Approved flocks; classifying twenty eggs according to U. S. Standards; grading ten live birds according to U. S. Standards on grades of live market birds; and a written examination. These contests serve as a stimulus for instruction in poultry husbandry. Attractive

U. S. D. A.

Fig. 22. Males with defective tail carriage: 1, squirrel; 2, wry.

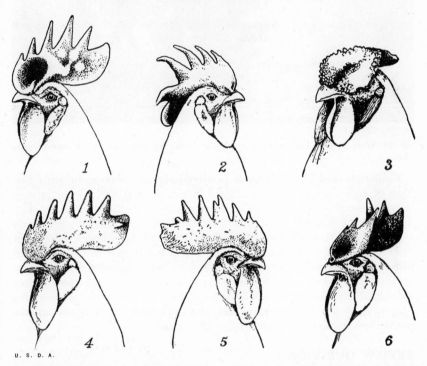

U. S. D. A.

Fig. 23. Male heads showing defective combs: 1, thumb mark; 2, lopped (single); 3, hollow center; 4, side-spring; 5, uneven serrations; 6, twisted.

premiums are provided for the winners. A National Contest for the state winners is held each fall at the American Royal Livestock Show, Kansas City, Missouri.

Four-H Club contests. Many states have annual 4-H Club poultry-judging contests. A national 4-H Club poultry-judging contest is held each year at the time of the International Livestock Show at Chicago.

COURTESY TEXAS A & M COLLEGE

Fig. 24. Texas A & M College Poultry Judging Team. Winning team in Chicago Contest, 1949.

Collegiate and intercollegiate poultry-judging contests. In many colleges of agriculture, students interested in poultry judging compete in contests sponsored by poultry clubs and departments of poultry husbandry (Fig. 24). Regional contests (East, South, and Midwest) are generally held each year. The Eastern Contest was started in 1915 and the Midwest Contest in 1921. The latter has become more of a national contest with more than fifteen teams generally entered. In 1948 this contest included for each contestant the following: placing five classes for egg production; three classes for exhibition; selecting twenty birds for R. O. P. qualifications; grading fifty eggs by U. S. Standards; grading forty dressed birds by U. S. Standards and placing two classes of live birds for market qualities.

REVIEW QUESTIONS

1. Was Darwin correct in his assumption that all chickens descended from the same common ancestor?
2. What fundamental biological condition made improvement possible in poultry?
3. Why did the interest in fancy poultry wane?
4. What is the American Standard of Perfection?
5. Who may become A.P.A. judges?
6. Will the number of popular varieties of poultry likely increase or decrease in the future? Why?

7. List the characteristics of the American breeds.
8. Name the varieties of Plymouth Rocks.
9. Why are the White Leghorns one of the most popular varieties of chickens in America?
10. Name the Mediterranean breeds.
11. What were the contributions of the Asiatic breeds to the American poultry industry?
12. What is a "Turken"?
13. What factors should guide the selection of a variety of poultry to raise?
14. Name ten general standard disqualifications.
15. What variety of chickens would you select for commercial poultry farming? Why?
16. If you were a general farmer, what variety of chickens would you raise? Explain.
17. What caused the exhibition poultry shows in America to lose their popularity?
18. What values are derived from poultry-judging contests for students?

REFERENCES

AMERICAN STANDARD OF PERFECTION. Amer. Poultry Assoc., Inc., Davenport, Iowa. 1945.

ANNUAL R. O. P. SUMMARY. 1947–48. U. S. D. A. Bur. An. Ind., A. H. D. 125. 1949.

BROWN, E.: Races of Domestic Poultry, 1st ed. Edward Arnold & Co., London. 1906.

CHICKENS IN THE NATIONAL POULTRY IMPROVEMENT PLAN HATCHERY SUPPLY FLOCKS AND THEIR DISTRIBUTION BY STATES AND VARIETIES 1941–42, 1944–45 AND 1947–48. U. S. D. A. Bur. An. Ind., A. H. D. 69. 1949.

JULL, M. A.: THE RACES OF DOMESTIC POULTRY. Natl. Geog. Mag., 51: 379–452. 1927.

PAYNE, L. F., AND AVERY, T. B.: INTERNATIONAL POULTRY GUIDE FOR FLOCK SELECTION. Int. Baby Chick Assoc., Kansas City, Mo. 1950.

PLATT, D. S.: LAYING TEST COUNCIL RECORDS. Special Rpt. No. 10. Council of American Official Egg-Laying Tests. 1948.

PLATT, F. L.: ALL BREEDS OF POULTRY. Amer. Poultry Jour., Chicago, Ill. 1925.

STANDARD BREEDS AND VARIETIES OF CHICKENS. I. AMERICAN, ASIATIC, ENGLISH, AND MEDITERRANEAN CLASSES. U. S. D. A. Farmers' Bul. 1506.

STANDARD BREEDS AND VARIETIES OF CHICKENS. II. CONTINENTAL EUROPEAN, ORIENTAL, GAME, ORNAMENTAL, AND MISCELLANEOUS CLASSES. U. S. D. A. Farmers' Bul. 1507.

THOMPSON, W. C.: A MANUAL FOR THE IDENTIFICATION OF THE BREEDS AND VARITIES OF DOMESTIC FOWLS. N. J. Sta. Bul. 642. 1938.

WARREN, D. C., AND SMITH, H.: THE ORIGIN OF BREEDS OF CHICKENS. Jour. Agr. Res., 78: 397–403. 1949.

CHAPTER 3 ||||||||||||||||||||||||||||||||||||||||||||||||||||||||||

The Anatomy and Physiology of the Chicken

▼

The chicken may be considered as a delicate, sensitive, and highly-geared machine. A knowledge of its structures, their functions and operation, is necessary in order to understand the bird's needs and care.

Structural peculiarities. Birds are just above the reptiles in the scale of animal development. They are warm-blooded and covered with feathers, while reptiles are cold-blooded and usually covered with scales or horny plates. The scales on the shanks and toes of birds are evidence of their reptilian ancestors. Birds have compact bodies, light skeletons, and well-developed wings and legs, adapted for flying or running.

Intensity of life. Birds are active, nervous, and alert in comparison with their slow-moving relatives, the reptiles. The nervous system is highly developed and the senses of sight and hearing are keen. Food is carefully selected and quickly and thoroughly digested. Oxidation takes place quickly, and a normal temperature of 105° to 109.5° F. is maintained.

Body systems. The body of the chicken is composed of groups of tissues and organs which carry on the body processes (Fig. 25).

The Body Covering or Exoskeleton

The body covering consists of the skin and its derivatives—the comb, wattles, earlobes, feathers, beak, toenails, and scales.

The skin. The skin of birds is relatively thin when compared with that of mammals. It has no sweat or sebaceous glands, except the uropygial or preen gland at the base of the tail.

The skin is a protective body covering. It consists of an outer layer, the epidermis, and an inner layer, the dermis. The feathers, beak, toenails, and scales develop from the epidermis. The comb, wattles, and earlobes develop from the dermis.

The uropygial gland produces an oily substance which the bird works into the plumage with its beak. The substance serves for weatherproofing the feathers.

A network of delicate nerves, muscles, and blood vessels courses the skin and extends to the feather roots. The skin of a fowl is very sensitive when a bird is molting.

46

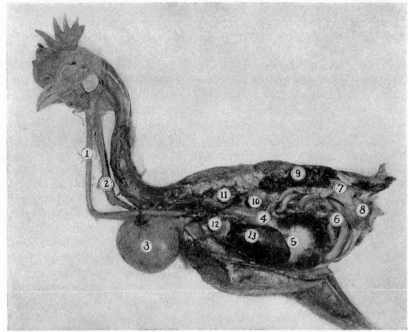

Fig. 25. Sectional view of the chicken, showing: 1, windpipe or trachea; 2, esophagus or gullet; 3, enlargement of gullet or crop; 4, glandular stomach or proventriculus; 5, gizzard; 6, duodenal loop of small intestine; 7, large intestine; 8, rectum; 9, kidneys; 10, ovary; 11, lungs; 12, heart; 13, liver.

The color of the skin, beak, and shanks is determined by the presence of skin pigments. For instance, yellow shanks are due to the presence of lipochrome pigment in the epidermis, with the absence of melanin pigment. Black and its variations depend upon the presence of melanin pigment. When a bird is in production, the yellow bleaches out of the skin, eye rings, earlobes, beak, and shanks. The practical use of pigmentation for estimating the past laying performance of hens is discussed in Chapter Five.

When a bird is growing or in production, the skin is soft and waxy. When a bird is out of production or in poor health, the skin is hard and dry.

Feathers. A bird is known by its plumage. This familiar statement is true because feathers are confined to birds and because different species of birds have different kinds of plumage. Feather patterns and colors are made use of in identifying breeds and varieties of chickens.

Feathers help protect the body from physical injury and aid in keeping it warm. Wing feathers are essential for flight. In most species of birds, including the fowl, the feathers are arranged in rows in definite areas or feather tracts. The ten major feather tracts of the chicken, listed in the usual order of feather development, are shoulder, thigh, rump, breast, neck, abdomen, leg, back, wing, and head.

There are three principal kinds of feathers, based on structure: contour, plumule, and filoplume. *Contour feathers* cover the body. They vary greatly in size and shape, depending on the sex of the chicken and location of the feathers on the body. Contour feathers so completely cover the body that they conceal possible body defects. It is therefore essential to handle the birds in order to determine their true body shapes. *Plumules* or small downy feathers cover chicks and are found on adult birds beneath the contour feathers. They possess a soft shaft and a vane without barbs. They retain body heat well. *Filoplumes* are hairlike degenerated feathers, remaining after a bird has been plucked. They are particularly abundant in the region of the head and neck.

A typical feather consists of eight parts: the quill, shaft, accessory plume, fluff or undercolor, web or surface colors, barbs, barbules, and barbicels (Fig. 26). The *quill* is cylindrical and hollow and makes up the base of the feather. Nutritive material for feather growth enters through the quill, giving it a pink to black appearance. In mature feathers the quill is filled with a gray pulp. The *shaft* or rachis is the continuation of the quill or stem up through the center of the feather. The *accessory plume* is a small rudimentary feather or down growing on the under side of the feather at the base of the shaft. It appears only on mature feathers and hence serves a useful purpose in distinguishing old feathers from the new. The *fluff* or undercolor is the downy portion of the feather, not visible when feathers are in normal position. The *web* or surface color is the flat visible portion of the feather. The *barbs* are projections extending from both sides of the shaft. The *barbules* are small processes projecting from either side of the barbs. The barbules from one side of a barb fit into notches of the barbules projecting from the adjacent side of the next barb. The *barbicels* or cilia are outgrowths from the sides of the barbules. Some of them bear microscopic hooklets which are linked to the barbules next in front. The barbules and barbicels hold the barbs together and add strength to the feather.

In the newly formed bird, the first indication of feathers is the formation of tiny papillae or buds on the delicate skin of the embryo (about the sixth day in the chick). The skin immediately around the papilla sinks downward, so that later the papilla is enclosed in a follicle of the skin.

The outer layer of the epidermis forms for the developing feather a protective sheath, which is cast off as the feather is formed. The elements of the tip and border of the feather are first laid down and then the shaft and the quill.

A second generation of feathers (at time of molt) is formed from the persisting follicles. A feather bud starts to grow at the base of the old feather, causing it to loosen and finally fall out. In the general body plumage a feather is not often regenerated more than three times. The precise pattern of the feather is usually reproduced each time.

Coloration of plumage is produced by pigments, by physical structure, or by combinations of them. Physical or structural coloration is illustrated by color changes with changing light and position of the eye. The pigments are chiefly lipochromes and melanins.

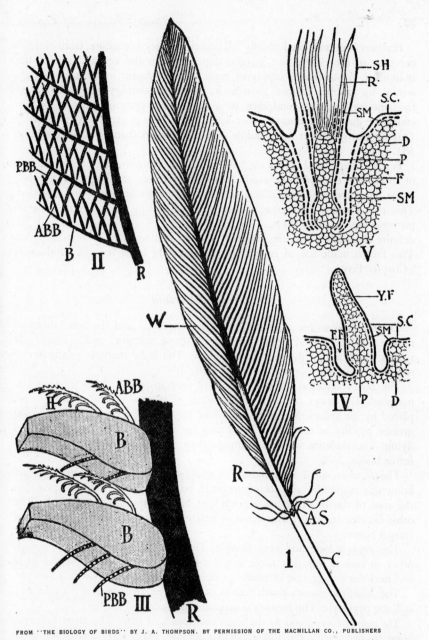

Fig. 26. Structure and development of the feather (diagrammatic). I. A typical feather: C, calamus or quill; A.S., after-shaft; R, rachis; W, web vane and barbs. II. An enlarged part of vane: R, rachis; B, barb; A.BB, anterior barbule; P.BB, posterior barbule. III. Two barbs enlarged. IV. An early stage in feather development: Y.F, young feather; P, the internal pulp or dermis; F.F, the feather follicle; D, the dermis. V. A later stage in feather development: R, barbs; SH, sheath; D, dermis; P, pulp; and F, follicle.

Feathers are composed chiefly of proteins. They constitute from 4 to 9 per cent of the empty live weight, depending on the age and sex of the individual. An adequate supply of good quality protein in the ration is essential for normal feather growth. Fairly high humidity and a moderate temperature are also conducive to good feather growth. Activity of the endocrine glands influences feather development. For example, castrated males (capons) grow longer neck, saddle, and tail feathers than do cockerels (Fig. 38).

Feather shapes and colors are helpful in the determination of sex and age of birds. For example, the saddle feathers of males are long and pointed, while the corresponding cushion feathers of females are short and rounded. This characteristic difference is helpful in separating the sexes of general-purpose breeds of broilers. The large feathers of the wings and tail are definite in number and are generally molted and replaced in regular order. This fact is made use of in culling and selecting birds for egg production (Chapter Five).

The Skeletal System

The skeleton serves as a framework for the body and the attachment of muscles, protects vital organs, holds the bone marrow, and contains air spaces which aid in flight and respiration. The bone marrow produces the red blood cells and part of the white cells.

The bird's skeleton (Fig. 27) differs very materially from that of the mammal. The bones are light and in some of them the bone marrow is replaced by air spaces. Many of the bones are fused together, thereby giving greater rigidity to the body. The limbs are adapted for both walking and flying. The skeleton is more compact than that of mammals and contains fewer bones.

The *head* is small in comparison with other body parts. The jaws are known as mandibles and form the bird's beak. The nasal cavities open into the roof of the mouth from a point just back of the upper mandible. The orbit cavities are large. The brain is well encased in the rounded and fused cranial bones.

The *neck* is long and very flexible. The cervical vertebrae fit upon each other in such a way that there is great freedom of movement of the head and neck for eating, care of plumage, defense, and other purposes.

The *backbone* shows much fusion of vertebrae. It ends in a rudimentary tail, the pygostyle. The pygostyle supports the main tail feathers.

The *wings* correspond to the arms and hands of man. The large humerus bone connects with the interclavicular air sac (Fig. 30). There are three fingers but only one of them is well developed. The wing is carried folded on the back.

The *hind limbs* are adapted for walking and perching. The thigh is concealed beneath the feathers. The tibia or "drumstick" is the largest bone of the limb. Most breeds of chickens have four toes, three extending forward and one backward, although Dorkings and Houdans have five toes. The

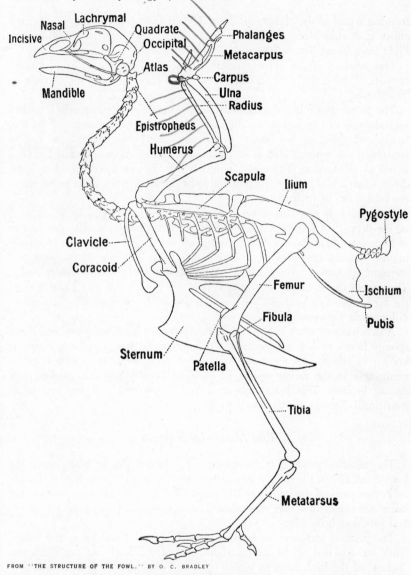

FROM "THE STRUCTURE OF THE FOWL," BY O. C. BRADLEY

Fig. 27. The skeleton of a fowl.

toes end in claws, which aid in scratching and perching. The spur, above the toes, is more developed in males than females and is used for defense. The older the bird the greater the spur development.

The *ribs* are attached above to the spinal column and below to the sternum. They are braced to each other by additional bones to give a firmer framework.

The *sternum* or breastbone is very large and projects back beyond the ribs, forming a part of the abdominal floor. The sternum protects the vital organs above it. A thin blade, the keel, projects downward from the sternum. The flight muscles are attached to it.

The *pectoral girdle,* corresponding to the shoulder girdle in mammals, consists of the scapulae or shoulder blades, the coracoids, and the clavicle or "wishbone."

The *pelvic girdle* is not a closed system of bones as in mammals. It makes reproduction or egg laying less difficult. The pelvic girdle consists of the ilia, ischia, and pubes or "lay bones" in the hen. The pubes have a tendency to straighten out when a bird is in production and to curve in when the bird is out of production. There is a tendency for the rear of the keel to drop down when a bird is in production and to be drawn up toward the pubes when the bird is out of production.

Bone tissue is first laid down as cartilage. This is followed by ossification or the deposit of inorganic salts, chiefly calcium phosphate. The dry matter of bone consists of about 75 per cent organic matter and 25 per cent inorganic matter. During the growth of long bones, such as those of the legs and sternum, unossified growth zones are left near the ends. They finally ossify. The rear of the sternum, for instance, does not harden and may be bent until the bird is nearly a year old. An examination of the sternum may be used to differentiate between pullets and hens.

A deficiency of vitamin D or minerals results in poor calcification and weak spongy bones of low ash content. This nutritional disease of the bones is known as rickets. An excessive amount of phosphorus or a deficiency of manganese in the ration results in enlarged hock joints and crooked legs among broilers. This bone disease is known as perosis. These and other nutritional diseases are discussed in Chapter Eleven.

The Muscular System

The muscles produce body movements, generate body heat, cover the bones, and fill out the body contour. The muscles of the wings, legs, abdomen, and other parts of the body work in pairs. While one of the pair contracts to cause movement the other one relaxes. Muscle work requires food for energy and produces body heat.

The *pectoral* muscles, the largest in the body, raise and lower the wings. They are attached to the sternum and keel of the fowl and constitute the "breast" of the bird. Muscles which open and close the wing are attached to the humerus.

The *gastrocnemius* muscle on the back of the leg is connected with tendons which enable the bird to maintain itself upon a perch even while asleep. If the hind limb is bent, a pull is extended on a tendon which flexes all of the toes and bends them automatically round the perch. When resting, the mere weight of the body bends the hind limbs and consequently causes the toes to grasp the perch and hold the bird firmly in place.

The *diaphragm* of the fowl is rudimentary and does not form a partition between the thoracic and abdominal cavities as in mammals. The muscle is represented by a tendinous membrane, lying on the ventral surface of the lungs.

The *dermal* muscles extending to the base of feathers make feather movement possible.

Muscles are supplied by nerves and blood vessels. Oxidations in muscles with resulting heat and energy production are determined by the blood circulation. Both the blood vessels and muscles are controlled by nerves. When nerves are destroyed, or paralyzed by toxins, there is a loss of muscular activity and the bird becomes paralyzed. Abnormal muscle development or control is responsible for such body defects as wry tail and split wing (Chapter Two).

The white and dark meat of a fowl are dependent upon the blood vessels coursing the muscular tissue. The chicken walks more than it flies. There are therefore many blood vessels extending into the leg muscles and few into the wing muscles on the breast. Breast meat of the chicken is white and leg meat is dark.

The Digestive System

The digestive system consists of the alimentary tract and its accessory organs—the liver, pancreas, and spleen. It differs very materially from that of mammals.

The digestive system serves for food intake, storage, digestion, and elimination of body waste products.

The alimentary tract. The alimentary tract (Fig. 28) consists of the mouth, gullet, crop, glandular stomach, gizzard, small intestine, ceca, large intestine, cloaca, and anus.

The *mouth* is characterized by the absence of lips, cheeks, and teeth. The chicken is provided with a beak which is used in tearing apart and picking up its food. The pointed tongue is provided with barbed-like projections which serve the purpose of forcing the food back to the gullet. A small cup-like projection is made in the tongue for holding water when drinking. The bird must raise its head when swallowing or the water will run out through the nostrils, which open into the roof of the mouth. Numerous mucous glands in the mouth provide saliva for moistening the food for ease in swallowing.

The *gullet* is the tube leading from the back part of the floor of the mouth (pharynx) to the glandular stomach. It is characterized by its great expansibility.

The *crop* is the enlargement of the gullet just before it enters the body cavity. It serves for the temporary storage of food. Here the food is softened by saliva that was swallowed with the food, and by secretions from the crop wall.

The *glandular stomach* (proventriculus) is the thickened portion of the tube connecting the gullet and the gizzard. As the food passes from the crop to the gizzard, the glandular cells of the proventriculus secrete a pepsin-hydrochloric acid mixture into the canal which passes with the food to the gizzard.

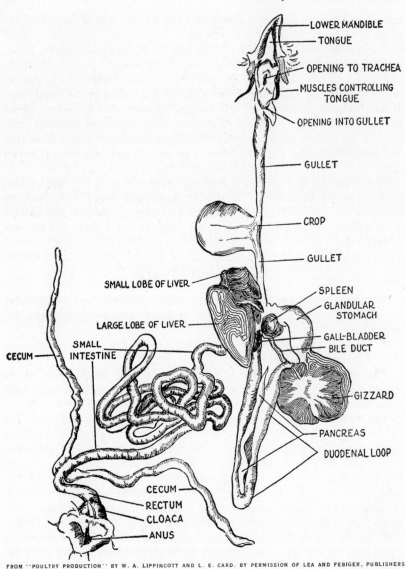

- LOWER MANDIBLE
- TONGUE
- OPENING TO TRACHEA
- MUSCLES CONTROLLING TONGUE
- OPENING INTO GULLET
- GULLET
- CROP
- GULLET
- SMALL LOBE OF LIVER
- SPLEEN
- GLANDULAR STOMACH
- LARGE LOBE OF LIVER
- GALL-BLADDER
- BILE DUCT
- SMALL INTESTINE
- CECUM
- GIZZARD
- PANCREAS
- DUODENAL LOOP
- CECUM
- RECTUM
- CLOACA
- ANUS

FROM "POULTRY PRODUCTION" BY W. A. LIPPINCOTT AND L. E. CARD. BY PERMISSION OF LEA AND FEBIGER, PUBLISHERS

Fig. 28. The intestinal tract and accessory organs.

The *gizzard* or muscular stomach joins the glandular stomach and the duodenal loop of the small intestine. Its walls consist of large, red, thick powerful muscles and its lining is a thick horny epithelium. The gizzard crushes food particles and mixes them with the pepsin-hydrochloric acid solution. Proteins are partly digested and minerals are dissolved in the gizzard. The *small intestine* extends from the gizzard to the large intestine. It consists of the duodenal loop and coils of the free portion. The coils are held by a thin membrane, the mesentery. The small intestine of the average hen is about sixty-two inches in length.

Digestive juices are secreted into the duodenal loop from the pancreas for digestion of carbohydrates, proteins and fats. Alkaline bile is secreted into this region from the gall bladder to neutralize the acids and create a favorable alkaline condition for the action of the digestive enzymes. Digestion is completed in the small intestine. (See Chapter Nine for digestion details.) Absorption of digested food into the blood stream takes place in the coiled portion of the small intestine.

The *ceca* are two blind pouches extending forward from their point of origin at the juncture of the small and large intestine. They are about seven inches long and are usually filled with soft, pasty undigested food (fecal material). The function of the ceca is unknown. They may be removed without impairing the health of the bird.

The *large intestine* extends from the small intestine to the cloaca. It has about twice the diameter of the small intestine and is about four or five inches long. The large intestine holds the fecal matter until it is excreted into the cloaca.

The *cloaca* is the enlarged portion of the alimentary canal connecting the large intestine and the anus or vent. Fecal material from the large intestine, eggs from the oviduct, and urine from the kidneys all pass into the cloaca and are then eliminated by way of the vent.

The *anus* or vent is the external opening from the cloaca.

The accessory organs. The *liver* consists of two large brown lobes of tissue lying by the gizzard and duodenal loop. It produces a greenish alkaline fluid, the bile, which is stored in the gall bladder, a thin, dark-green sack located under the right lobe of the liver. The liver serves as a purification plant for digested food before it enters the general circulation, stores glycogen or animal starch, and transforms protein waste products into uric acid and other products suitable for elimination by the kidneys.

The *pancreas* is a narrow strip of pinkish tissue lying between the folds of the duodenal loop. It secretes the enzymes—amylase, trypsin, and lipase —into the duodenal loop for the digestion of carbohydrates, proteins, and fats. The pancreas also secretes a hormone, insulin, which regulates sugar metabolism.

The *spleen* is generally regarded as one of the accessory organs of the digestive system. It is a reddish-brown body shaped like a buckeye. The spleen lies in a triangle formed by the liver, gizzard, and glandular stomach. The function of the spleen is not definitely known. It removes broken-down red blood cells and is capable of storing iron and blood.

The Respiratory System

The respiratory system of the chicken is quite different from that of mammals. The lungs connect with air sacs which in turn connect with hollow

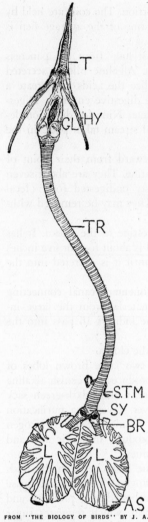

Fig. 29. Trachea and lungs of the fowl: T, tongue; HY, horns of hyoid; GL, glottis; TR, trachea or windpipe; S.T.M., sternotracheal muscles; SY, syrinx or voice box; BR, bronchial tubes; L, cavity of lungs; A.S, mesobronchus leading into the abdominal air sac.

spaces in the bones. The lungs are inexpansible. The active part of breathing is expiration rather than inspiration.

The respiratory system supplies oxygen for body oxidation, removes carbon dioxide, eliminates water from the body, and aids in the control of body temperature.

The respiratory system (Fig. 29) consists of the external and internal nares, pharynx, larynx, trachea, syrinx, bronchi, lungs, and air sacs.

The *external nares,* or openings just back of the upper mandible, open into the cleft in the roof of the mouth.

The *pharynx* is the back part of the floor of the mouth. Air is drawn through the nasal cavities into the pharynx, where it passes on through an opening into the trachea.

The *larynx* is the slitlike opening, surrounded by a ring of cartilage, in the floor of the pharynx. It is attached to the upper end of the trachea. The larynx is kept closed when swallowing food and water. It may become clogged with phlegm when a bird has bronchitis, and cause death by strangulation.

The *trachea* or windpipe is the tube leading from the larynx to the syrinx or voice box. It is a long tube surrounded by rings of cartilage.

The *syrinx* or voice box is the constricted portion of the air passage at the lower end of the trachea. It is a flexible valve which is vibrated when air is forcibly expelled from the lungs, thus producing sounds. A number of muscles make it possible to alter the tension of this valve and consequently the number of its vibrations and the pitch of the note produced.

The *bronchi* are the two branches leading from the syrinx to the lungs.

The *lungs* consist of pinkish spongy masses of tissue imbedded in the dorsal thoracic wall on both sides of the spinal column. The lungs are coursed by many branches of the bronchi, which lead into minute canals beset with thin membranous pouches. There is a rich vascular circulation in the membranes of the walls of the lungs. Oxygen passes from the lungs into the blood and carbon dioxide passes from the blood to the lungs.

The *air sacs* are accessory lungs. There are four pairs and a large single air sac in the fowl (Fig. 30). They connect the lungs with the hollow spaces in the bones of the limbs and other parts of the skeleton. The air sacs serve for respiration, impart lightness and buoyancy to the body, and permit diffusion of water from the blood to be excreted from the lungs in the form of vapors. It is estimated that one hundred hens secrete about a gallon of water daily by way of the lungs.

The *interclavicular* air sac connects the hollow spaces in the bones of the wings with the anterior ends of the lungs. The large abdominal air sacs occupy the spaces between the abdominal organs and the body walls. They connect the hollow spaces of the leg bones with the lungs. The *anterior* and *posterior thoracic* air sacs lie in the chest cavity. They connect with the lungs only. The *cervical* air sacs lie close to the interclavicular air sac, and connect the cervical and thoracic vertebrae with the lungs. Birds have been found injured by shot, which were breathing through a splintered wing

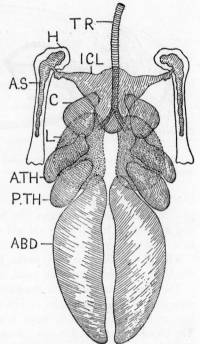

FROM ''THE BIOLOGY OF BIRDS'' BY J. A. THOMPSON. BY PERMISSION OF THE MACMILLAN CO., PUBLISHERS

Fig. 30. The system of air sacs in a bird: L, the right lung; C, a cervical air sac; ICL, the interclavicular air sac; A.S, an outgrowth into the humerus bone; A.TH, anterior thoracic air sac; P.TH, the posterior thoracic; ABD, the abdominal air sac; TR, the trachea.

bone when the trachea was clogged with blood excluding the passage of air.

In respiration, as the abdominal muscles relax and the rear of the sternum drops down, air is drawn in through the lungs and into the abdominal air sacs. As the abdominal muscles contract and the rear of the keel is drawn up, air is forced out of the abdominal air sacs and on out through the lungs. The average respiration rate of the hen is 36 per minute and that of the male 20 per minute.

The Circulatory System

The circulatory systems consist of the blood and lymph circulations. The blood circulation is in a closed system under pressure (90 to 180 mm.) while the lymph circulation is a more open system with little or no pressure. The blood circulation serves for the transfer of digested food, waste products, oxygen, carbon dioxide, water, and hormones to and from the body cells. It

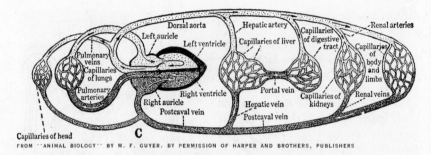

FROM ''ANIMAL BIOLOGY'' BY M. F. GUYER. BY PERMISSION OF HARPER AND BROTHERS, PUBLISHERS

Fig. 31. A diagram of the blood-circulating system of the fowl and mammal. The heavier shading represents unoxygenated blood; arrows indicate the direction of flow.

also aids in the regulation of body temperature, the control of body neutrality, and protection against disease. The lymph circulation bathes the cells, serves as a medium of transfer of food and waste products between the blood capillaries and body cells, and carries fats.

The blood circulatory system. The blood circulatory system consists of the heart, arteries, capillaries, veins, and blood (Fig. 31).

The *heart* is the pump for the blood circulation. It consists of two entirely separated muscular ventricles and two thin-walled auricles. The heart receives the impure blood through veins leading from the head and body regions. The blood is pumped through the lung circulation where it gives off carbon dioxide and takes in oxygen. The blood returns to the heart and is pumped out through the aortic arch and its arterial branches to all parts of the body. The heart beat or pulse rate ranges from about 192 to 396 per minute, with an average of about 282.

The *arteries* carry blood away from the heart. Pulmonary arteries carry blood to the lungs. The carotid arteries supply blood to the head; the brachial arteries supply the wings; and the dorsal aorta gives off branches which supply the liver, digestive tract, kidneys, and legs. Arterial blood is a brighter red than venous blood because of its increased oxygen content. Arterial blood is also under greater pressure than venous blood. The average pressure in the femoral artery is 135 mm.

The *capillaries* are very small blood vessels which connect arteries and veins.

The *veins* carry blood to the heart. They are usually located close to the corresponding arteries and generally bear the same names. For instance, there is a brachial artery and brachial vein in the wing. Blood is returned to the heart from the head regions through the jugular and precaval veins and from the body regions through the postcaval vein. When birds are killed and bled for market, the jugular vein is severed at the point of union of the two branches at the base of the head. The knife blade is directed against the neck wall. Blood samples are taken for the pullorum agglutination test by puncturing a branch of the brachial vein. In caponizing birds one must use extreme

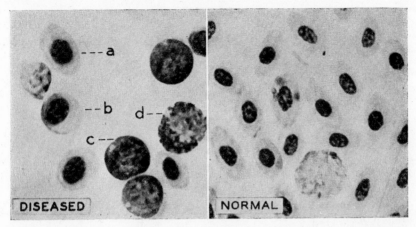

Fig. 32. Blood cells from a normal and leucemic fowl: a, erythrocyte; b, erythroblast; c, lymphocyte; d, polymorphonuclear leucocyte. Magnified 1350 ✕. (Illinois Station Circular 467.)

care to avoid puncture of the postcaval vein. It passes along very close to the testes.

The blood. The blood is the mixture of liquid and cells flowing in the blood circulatory system. The liquid part of the blood is called *plasma*. It carries digested food in solution to the cells, waste products from the cells, solutions of salts for maintaining body neutrality, hormones, and the blood cells.

There are two principal kinds of cells floating in the blood, the red cells or *erythrocytes* and the white cells or *leucocytes* (Fig. 32). The erythrocytes are small and oval in shape with large nuclei. They carry oxygen from the lungs to the body cells and carbon dioxide from the body cells to the lungs. The oxygen and carbon dioxide are carried in the red cells in loose chemical combination with an iron-containing protein, hemoglobin. The leucocytes are larger and fewer in number than the red cells. They may be subdivided into several different groups. The leucocytes help to protect the body against disease; in case of an infection the leucocyte count in the blood increases.

The blood constitutes about 5 per cent of the empty live weight of the fowl. It consists of about 75 per cent water and 25 per cent solids. The blood contains from 2,000,000 to 4,000,000 red cells and 15,000 to 35,000 white cells per cubic milliliter. The plasma contains a substance, fibrinogen, which is essential for blood clotting. The blood of the fowl clots quickly. The liquid which separates from the clot is known as *serum*. It is used in making the tube agglutination test for pullorum disease (Chapter Eleven).

The lymph circulatory system. The lymph circulatory system consists of the lymph vessels, the white cell-forming organs, and the lymph. The lymph capillaries collect the lymph fluid and pour it into the lymph veins, and these in turn, carry it to the large veins adjacent to the heart. The lymph

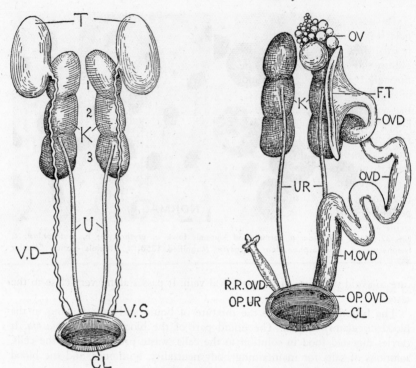

Fig. 33. The urinary and reproductive systems of the fowl: male, left; and female, right. T, testes; K—1, 2, and 3, lobes of the kidneys; V.D, vas deferens; U, ureters; V.S, seminal vesicle; CL, cloaca; OV, ovary; F.T, funnel of oviduct; OVD, oviduct; M.OVD, uterus of the oviduct; UR, ureters R.R.OVD, rudimentary right oviduct; OP.UR, opening of the right ureter; OP.OVD, opening of the oviduct; CL, cloaca.

vessels in birds are numerous. The lymph glands are few. They may be seen in the anterior breast and the neck region, and sometimes in the wings.

The Urinary System

The urinary system is located close to the reproductive system, as in mammals. It serves for the elimination of body waste products which are chiefly protein in nature. The chicken does not have a urinary bladder. It excretes very little liquid urine.

The urinary system consists of the kidneys and ureters (Fig. 33). The *kidneys* are large three-lobed, soft, brown organs attached to the vertebral column just back of the lungs. Many small blood vessels course the kidneys. Protein waste products and water (forming the urine) filter through the walls of the blood vessels into the collecting tubules of the kidneys. The *ureters* are the urinary tubes leading from the kidneys to the cloaca. A single tube leads from each kidney.

The urine passed from the kidneys to the ureters daily by the normal-sized fowl amounts to 700 to 800 cc. As it passes along through the ureters, in the region of the large intestine, much of the water is reabsorbed into the body circulation. The urine passes from the ureters into the cloaca and becomes mixed with the fecal material deposited from the large intestine. The urine and fecal material are eliminated together from the cloaca. The urine, which is chiefly uric acid, is the white pasty material seen on the droppings.

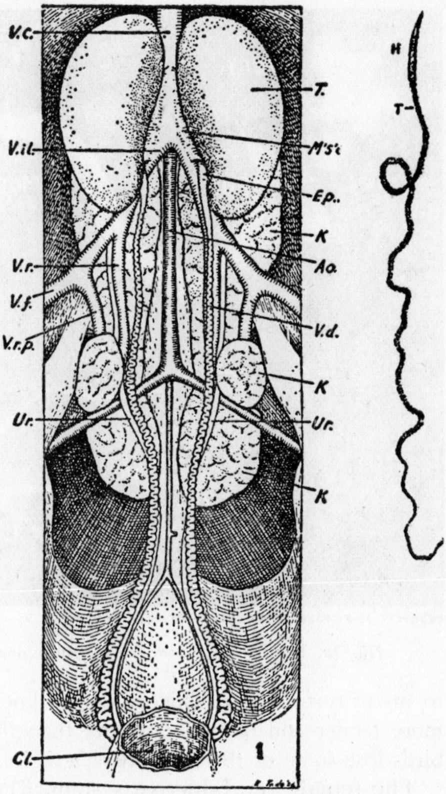

The Reproductive System

The male reproductive system. The male reproductive system produces male reproductive cells (spermatozoa), introduces them into the oviduct of the female for fertilization of the egg, and produces a hormone which influences sex characters.

The male reproductive system consists of the testes, vas deferens, and papillae or rudimentary copulatory organs (Fig. 34). The

COURTESY L. V. DOMM, UNIVERSITY OF CHICAGO

Fig. 34. The male reproductive and urinary systems: T., testis; V.d., vas deferens; K, kidney; Ur., ureter; Cl., cloaca; H, head of reproductive cell or sperm; T, tail of sperm.

testes are two small ovoid organs situated at the anterior end of the kidneys in the dorsal body wall. Some of the cells produced in the testes differentiate into gametes or reproductive cells. They enter the seminiferous tubules and are carried out of the testes by the seminal fluid, which is also produced in the testes. The spermatozoon is a long, slender, motile cell with a head, which contains the nucleus, a neck, and a tail. Millions of these cells are produced and expelled in the seminal fluid. The *vas deferens* are the two tubes pursuing a wavy course from the testes to the cloaca. They convey the spermatozoa and seminal fluid from the testes to the cloaca. The *papillae* or rudimentary copulatory organs are located in the cloacal wall. The vas deferens open on the summit of the papillae. During the process of mating, the spermatozoa are introduced by the papillae into the oviduct opening in the cloacal wall of the female.

The testes are sometimes removed from cockerels if they are to be raised

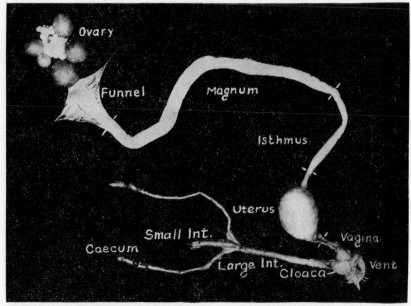

Fig. 35. The female reproductive system and a portion of the intestinal tract.

to maturity for meat. This process is known as caponizing. Capon meat is more tender and of better quality than that from old cockerels. Caponized birds lose some of their sex characteristics.

The female reproductive system. The female reproductive system differs greatly from that of mammals. The reproductive cell, also known as a gamete, ovum, or egg, is an article of food. It is large because it is enclosed with a food supply for embryo development. Most of the development of the bird embryo takes place outside of the body (Chapter Six).

The reproductive system of the female consists of the ovary and oviduct (Fig. 35). At hatching time the female chick has two ovaries and two oviducts. The right ovary and oviduct soon degenerate. The left ovary and oviduct develop as the bird grows. The *ovary* appears as a cluster of tiny gray yolks or ova situated at the anterior end of the left kidney and attached to the dorsal body wall. When a bird reaches sexual maturity, or comes into production, some of the ova develop to mature yolks. The yolk ruptures the membrane or follicle which holds it and falls into the funnel of the oviduct. This process is known as *ovulation*. The ovary also secretes a hormone which influences sex characteristics. The *oviduct* is a long glandular tube leading from the ovary to the cloaca. It consists of five parts: the *funnel* or infundibulum, which receives the yolk; the *magnum*, which secretes the thick albumen or white; the *isthmus*, which adds the shell membranes; the *uterus*, which secretes the thin white, the shell, and the shell pigment; and the *vagina*, which holds the egg until it is laid. Details of the formation of the egg are given on pages 68–70. The egg passes from the oviduct to the cloaca and then out of the body through the vent at the time of laying.

Abnormal conditions of the reproductive system are very common. The ovary may contain abnormally shaped and colored ova as a result of pullorum infection or tumors. The oviduct is easily ruptured and may pass out with the egg or permit eggs to fall into the body cavity.

The Nervous System

The fowl has a highly developed nervous system with a keen sense of sight, hearing, touch, taste, and smell. The nervous system is often called the master tissue of the body because it controls body activities. It receives messages from the outer world through its sense organs, adjusts the body to its environment by controlled movements, and harmonizes the vital activities.

The nervous system (Fig. 36) consists of the brain, spinal cord, branches leading to the sense organs, and sympathetic nerves, which control the viscera. It may be compared to a telephone system with the sense organs of sight, hearing, touch, taste, and smell as telephones; the nerve fibers as wires; and the brain as the switchboard.

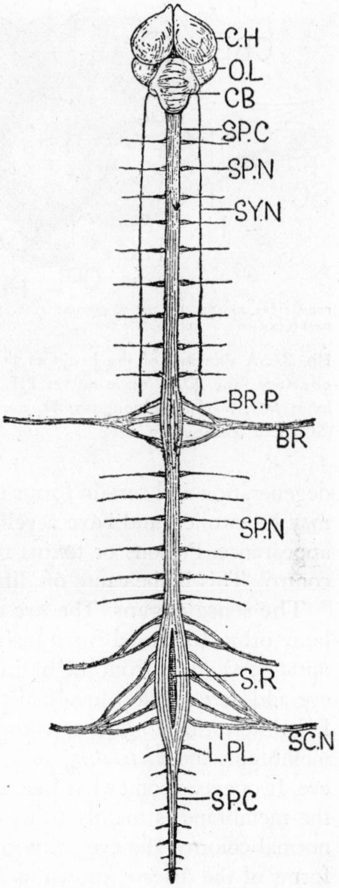

The central nervous system. The *brain* (Fig. 37) consists of three principal parts: the cerebral hemispheres, the cerebellum, and the medulla oblongata. The two *cerebral hemispheres* constitute the front and most conspicuous part of the brain. The olfactory nerves from the nose extend to the cerebral hemispheres. The

FROM "THE BIOLOGY OF BIRDS" BY J. A. THOMPSON. BY PERMISSION OF THE MACMILLAN CO., PUBLISHERS

Fig. 36. The nervous system of the fowl: C.H, cerebral hemispheres of the brain; O.L, optic lobes; CB, cerebellum; SP.C, spinal cord; SP.N, spinal nerves; SY.N, sympathetic nervous system; BR.P, brachial plexus to wing; S.R, rhomboidal sinus; L.PL, lumbar plexus of nerves uniting to form the sciatic nerve (SC.N).

elongated oval *cerebellum* lies upon the medulla oblongata and extends forward to the cerebral hemispheres. The *medulla oblongata* is the back part of the brain which is continuous with the spinal cord. Most of the cranial nerves take origin from it. The medulla oblongata is severed or crushed in debraining birds for dry picking. This releases the muscular tension on the feathers.

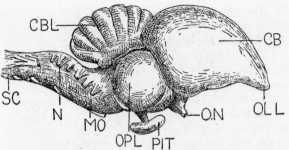

FROM "THE BIOLOGY OF THE FOWL" BY J. A. THOMPSON. BY PERMISSION OF THE MACMILLAN CO., PUBLISHERS

Fig. 37. A sideview of the brain of the fowl: CB, cerebrum; OL.L, olfactory lobe; O.N, optic nerve; PIT, pituitary body; OP.L, optic lobe; MO, medulla oblongata; N, nerve issuing from spinal cord (SC); CBL, cerebellum.

The *spinal cord* is the main trunk line of the nervous system, extending from the brain to the body trunk. It sends out branches to the wings, legs, and peripheral nerves of the skin, and connects with the sympathetic nerves, which control the viscera.

Vitamin deficiency results in nerve degeneration and certain forms of paralysis. In neurolymphomatosis the nerves may be swollen and have a yellowish color instead of the characteristic gray appearance. Poisons or toxins result in nerve paralysis and a lack of muscle control. This is the cause of "limberneck" in chickens.

The sense organs. The *eye* of the bird is relatively large and lodged in a bony orbit. It is used for transforming light waves in visual perception. The optic nerve leads from the brain to the eye. The details of the structure of the eye and nerve action in visual perception are beyond the scope of this book. It is interesting to note that the eye has a third eyelid in the form of a thin membrane, the *nictitating membrane,* which can be drawn quickly over the eye. It operates somewhat like the lens shutter of a camera. When not in use, the membrane is mainly concealed within the medial angle of the eye. The normal color of the eye in most breeds of chickens is a reddish-bay. In some forms of the disease known as leucosis, the color becomes pearl-gray. Toxins resulting from tapeworm infestation and other troubles may cause blindness.

The *ear* of a bird does not form any external appendage to the head as in mammals. An opening surrounded by a fringe of feathers leads into a canal which ends at the tympanic membrane. The inner ear contains the essential parts of the organ of hearing. It is imbedded in the temporal bone. The ear system serves for the transformation of sound waves into nerve impulses and for maintaining body equilibrium. The auditory nerve leads from the brain to the ear.

The *nose* serves not only for respiration but also for the sense of smell. Olfactory nerves lead from the brain to the membranes in the walls of the nasal passages.

The Regulatory System

The regulatory system is composed of endocrine glands. The glands secrete substances, known as hormones, into the blood stream. These chemical sub-

Fig. 38. A Plymouth Rock cockerel on the right and a capon on the left.

stances are carried to other organs of the body and exert a profound influence on their activities.

The *testes* secrete a hormone which is responsible for the marked difference between males and capons. When a cockerel is caponized, the comb and wattles fail to develop normally and the hackle, saddle, and tail feathers grow longer than in normal males (Fig. 38). If a normal testis is grafted into a capon it recovers its normal male characteristics. The same effects are produced by the injection of the male hormone extract or one of the synthetic products, such as androsterone. Male sex hormone products are assayed for strength by testing their ability to produce comb growth in capons. The male sex hormone is responsible for a higher red blood cell count in males than females. It may also be responsible for the higher metabolism in males than females.

The *ovary* produces a hormone which helps to differentiate the two sexes. The female hormone exerts an inhibitory effect on the development of the secondary sex characteristics. If the ovary is completely removed from a female, the bird has a tendency to develop male plumage and sex characteristics. The injection of female hormone extract into males causes them to take on the plumage color characteristic of the female rather than that of the male.

Diethylstilbestrol and other derivatives of stilbene are synthetic hormones which produce effects somewhat similar to the female hormone estrogen. When injected into growing cockerels or old males, they cause the birds to quit crowing and begin to sing; the pelvic bones to spread; the vent to become moist; the lipoid content of the blood to increase; and fat to collect under the skin and in the abdomen. The males appear and act something like pullets that are about to begin egg production. Synthetic female hormone injection, pellet implant beneath the skin, and addition to the feed have been advocated for fattening poultry (p. 277) and for stopping broodiness among layers.

Tumor growths and other abnormalities may impair the testes or ovary to such an extent that the bird gradually loses its normal sex characteristics and assumes more of the characteristics of the opposite sex.

The *adrenals* are small oval or elongated yellowish bodies located on the dorsal body wall just in front of the kidneys. One of the adrenal hormones is adrenalin, which influences carbohydrate metabolism and regulates blood pressure. The adrenal glands are also believed to influence sex-gland activity.

The *pancreas* functions as an endocrine gland as well as an accessory organ of the digestive system. In man it secrets a hormone, insulin, which regulates sugar metabolism. The pancreas probably also regulates sugar metabolism in the bird.

The *thyroids* are two small oval brown bodies a little larger than a grain of wheat located close to the jugular veins near the base of the neck (Fig. 39). They secrete a hormone known as thyroxin, which influences feather growth and coloration as well as the rate of body metabolism.

Thyroprotein, also known as iodinated casein or protamone, is an artificial thyroxin-like compound, which produces some of the accelerated metabolic effects of thyroxin. There is some evidence that its use in the ration at the rate of about 10 grams per 100 pounds of feed will stimulate egg production of old hens and produce faster and more uniform growth of broilers. Thiouracil produces the opposite effect of thyroprotein. It blocks the action of the thyroid gland; reduces the metabolic rate; and causes fat deposition. While early feeding of thiouracil stunts growth, its use later in the growing period has increased body weight and improved market appearance of broilers and roasters. Its use is not permitted, except for experimental work, at the present time.

The *parathyroids* are small glandular bodies located close to the thyroids. They secrete a hormone which regulates calcium and phosphorus metabolism. Parathyroid secretion is an important factor for laying hens because of the large amount of calcium needed for eggshell formation. Birds in production need to carry much more calcium in the blood stream than those out of production.

The paired *thymus* glands occur as thin pinkish lobes along the neck. They are large in chicks but diminish in size with the age of birds. The function of the thymus is unknown. It may play a part in growth.

The *pituitary* or hypophysis is a small kidney-shaped gland located at the base of the brain. It is composed of different kinds of tissue, each secreting a specific hormone substance. One product stimulates both male and female gonad activity. Artificial lights increase egg production by stimulating the

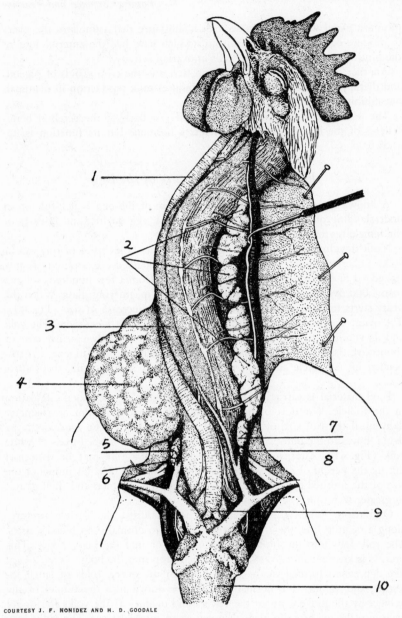

Fig. 39. Structures of the neck region of the fowl: 1, trachea; 2, thymus; 3, gullet; 4, crop; 5 and 7, thyroids; 6 and 8, parathyroids; 9, syrinx or voice box; 10, heart.

pituitary gland which in turn secretes a substance that stimulates the ovary to produce eggs. Use of lights on birds which have had the anterior lobe of the pituitary removed does not result in ovarian activity.

Another pituitary hormone, prolactin, activates the crop glands of pigeons and thereby produces "pigeon milk." It induces milk production in mammals but inhibits ovarian development.

The *pineal body* is a small round gland just back of the cerebral hemispheres of the brain. It probably secrets a hormone but its function is unknown.

Formation and Structure of the Egg

A knowledge of the formation and structure of the egg is helpful for an understanding of fertility, embryo development, egg quality, and diseases of the female reproductive system.

Yolk development. The ovarian tissue appears as a cluster of tiny ova or yolks. Other ova, too small to be seen with the unaided eye, are more deeply imbedded in the ovarian tissue. One may count from a few hundred to more than 3,000 ova in an ovary without the aid of a magnifying glass. When the ovary starts to function, a few of the ova start to increase in size (Fig. 40). The ovum is enclosed in a thin membrane, the *vitelline membrane.* The yolk and its vitelline membrane are in turn enclosed in a highly vascular coat of connective tissue, the *follicle.* As the ovum or yolk increases in size it is suspended in its follicle and held to the ovary by a slender stalk, the *follicle stalk.*

Food material is carried to the developing ovum by the blood circulation in the follicle. The developing yolks increase about four mm. in diameter daily until the full size of about forty mm. is reached. The *nucleus* of the ovum moves to the outer edge, leaving behind it a flask-shaped mass of white yolk (Fig. 41). Alternate layers of *dark and white yolk* may be deposited during the period of rapid yolk development. The size of yolks influence the size of the finished eggs. Large yolks stimulate the albumen and shell glands to greater secretion.

Ovulation. When the yolk has reached maturity, the follicle ruptures along a definite line, the *stigma,* where there are normally no blood vessels. The yolk falls into the funnel of the oviduct or into the body cavity. This process is known as *ovulation.* Yolks which drop into the body cavity, a cuplike depression formed in the angle between the ovary, folds of small intestine, and oviduct, are normally pushed or drawn into the funnel of the oviduct by the movements of the viscera and oviduct. If the yolks fail to get back into the oviduct the bird is known as an internal layer. The yolks may rupture and the liquid be reabsorbed into the circulation, leaving an abnormal deposit of yellow solids covering the intestine, or the yolks may dry up, leaving masses of caked egg-yolk material in the body cavity.

Fertilization. If the hen has been mated and male sperm cells are present in the oviduct, fertilization takes place in the funnel region. The yolk remains in this region for a few minutes. Details of fertilization and the transmission of hereditary characters are discussed in Chapter Four.

Embryo development in the body. The fertilized ovum starts cell division and embryo development soon after fertilization. It continues during the approximate twenty-four hours that the egg remains in the oviduct. The germ spot or blastoderm increases in size and there is some change in the consistency of the white and yolk. Unless the fertile egg is held below 82° F. after it is laid, there will be further germ development. It is therefore desirable to produce infertile eggs at all times except when they are needed for hatching. The details of embryo development are discussed in Chapter Six.

Addition of the thick white and chalaza. After the yolk has been engulfed by the funnel of the oviduct, it moves along with a turning motion through the magnum. It requires about three hours for the yolk to pass through this region. Here the thick white and the dense ropy material known as the chalaza (Fig. 41) are added. The thick white

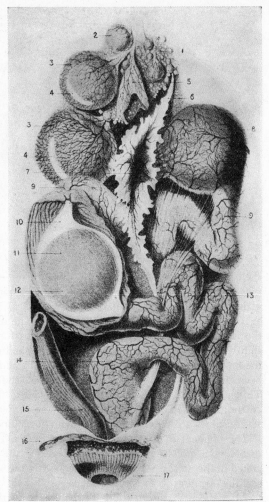

AFTER DUVAL. FROM "POULTRY PRODUCTION" BY W. A. LIPPINCOTT AND L. E. CARD. BY PERMISSION OF LEA AND FEBIGER, PUBLISHERS

Fig. 40. The reproductive system of the female fowl. 1, The ovary. 2, A partly developed ovum. 3, Still larger ova—the lower one nearly ready to leave the ovary. 4, The stigma—a region in which there are normally no blood vessels. 5, An empty follicle from which the yolk has entered the oviduct. 6, Lip or margin of the funnel. 7, Opening or mouth of the funnel. 8, A yolk which has just entered the oviduct. 9, Albumen-secreting portion of the oviduct. 10, Albumen which is secreted around the yolk. 11, Yolk. 12, The germinal disc. 13, Anterior end of the isthmus, in which the shell membranes are formed. 14, The uterus, or shell gland. 15, The large intestine. 16, The abdominal wall, cut and laid back. 17, Anus or vent.

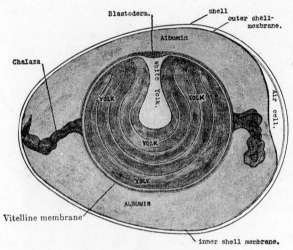

Fig. 41. Structure of the egg.

has a tendency to adhere to the yolk when an egg is broken out. It constitutes about 50 per cent of the total white by volume.

Formation of the shell membranes. The yolk, surrounded with its thick white, passes from the magnum through a short section of the oviduct known as the isthmus. Here the two shell membranes are added and the shape of the egg is determined. An isthmus of large diameter tends to result in thick round eggs while one of small diameter tends to result in long slender eggs.

Addition of thin white and the shell. The developing egg passes from the isthmus into the uterus, where it remains for about twenty hours. The thin white, largely water, passes through the shell membranes into the egg in the first portion of the uterus. Even before the addition of the thin white has been completed, the shell glands of the uterus start the secretion of the shell. This is largely calcium carbonate. It is carried to the uterus by the blood circulation. The size of the oviduct in a laying hen and its blood circulation are several times greater than that of a hen out of production.

The pigment in brown-shelled eggs is secreted in the uterus. The cuticle or bloom, a moist substance noticed covering the newly laid egg, is also secreted in the uterus. Soon after the egg is laid the substance dries and tends to seal the openings in the porous shell.

After the egg reaches the hard-shell stage in the uterus, it is possible to detect it by pressing on the walls of the abdomen. By handling all the birds early in the morning, one can determine the hens that will lay during the day.

The egg remains in the vagina for a short time after completion or until it is laid. Most eggs are laid small end first. They pass from the vagina into the cloaca and are expelled at once.

Abnormal eggs. *Double-yolked* eggs result from two ova ripening at the same time, or one ovum being pushed back into the oviduct at the same time that another ovulation takes place. Eggs with double yolks are more common among pullets than among older birds. It takes time for the newly functioning ovary and oviduct to become properly adjusted and to work normally.

Meat spots may be observed on the yolk covering or in the white of the egg. They are generally degenerated blood clots resulting from hemorrhages in the ovary or oviduct.

Blood spots may be found in some eggs. They result from the hemorrhage of a small blood vessel in the ovary or oviduct. A blood or meat spot on the yolk indicates a hemorrhage in the ovary or funnel region of the oviduct. The follicle probably did not rupture along the stigma, where there are normally no blood vessels, or else a rupture occurred before ovulation (Fig. 40). If the spot is in the white of the egg, it indicates a hemorrhage in the wall of the oviduct. Bloody eggs are probably the result of more severe hemorrhages. The reproductive system of the female may be easily ruptured when in production. Selection of hatching eggs from families that produce eggs with a low incidence of blood spots will do much to correct this egg abnormality.

Soft-shelled eggs may result from failure of the shell glands to secrete; or they may result from the peristaltic constrictions becoming so violent as to hurry the egg through the uterus. Most shell-less eggs are probably laid at night. This would indicate that certain ways in which birds roost may cause abnormal pressure on nerves leading to the oviduct.

Small yolkless eggs may result from the stimulus produced by some foreign substance, such as a blood clot or piece of membrane, gaining entrance to the oviduct and passing along in the same manner as the yolk. The passage of the particle will stimulate the albumen, shell membrane, and shell glands to secrete their particular products.

An egg within an egg is sometimes found. After an egg has been formed it may be forced back up into the funnel region by reverse peristaltic action. As it again traverses the oviduct, albumen, shell membranes and shell are added. When the egg is opened a complete egg is found where the yolk is normally present.

If the reverse peristaltic action is very strong, the egg may be forced entirely out of the oviduct into the body cavity. An accumulation of eggs in the body cavity causes a bird to walk like a penguin and will finally result in death.

REVIEW QUESTIONS

1. What are the structural peculiarities of birds which differentiate them from other vertebrates?
2. Why are chickens more sensitive to changes in environment than other farm animals?
3. Differentiate between the skin of the domestic fowl and that of other farm animals.
4. Differentiate between new and old feathers.
5. How are feathers an aid in determining the sex of chickens?
6. What hormones influence feather growth?
7. In what order are the feathers on a bird molted?
8. Compare the skeleton of the fowl with that of other farm animals.

9. What are the functions of the skeleton?
10. Name two bone diseases.
11. Why is the breast meat of a wild duck dark and that of the chicken light?
12. How do muscles produce locomotion?
13. Explain how a bird is able to sleep in a tree or on a perch pole without falling off.
14. Trace the path traveled by food through the alimentary canal.
15. What are the accessory organs of the digestive system?
16. What are the functions of the liver?
17. What are the functions of the pancreas?
18. What products from the body are passed into the cloaca?
19. What part of the intestinal tract is acid and what part is alkaline?
20. What part of the intestinal tract in birds corresponds to the paunch in ruminants?
21. What are the functions of the air sacs in birds?
22. How are sounds made by birds?
23. What is the normal respiration rate of the chicken?
24. Which has the brighter color, arterial or venous blood? Why?
25. How are blood samples obtained for the pullorum agglutination test?
26. Differentiate between the functions of the erythrocytes and the leucocytes.
27. What happens to the relatively large amount of liquid urine produced by birds?
28. What endocrine glands are located at the anterior end of the kidneys?
29. Differentiate between the characteristics of male and female reproductive cells.
30. What changes in sex characteristics are noticed as a result of caponizing birds?
31. How may one differentiate between the vas deferens and the ureters?
32. Describe the process of ovulation.
33. Where does fertilization take place?
34. Trace the formation of the egg from the time of ovulation until it is laid.
35. What part of the brain should be destroyed when birds are to be dry picked?
36. What are hormones?
37. What are the functions of the pituitary body?
38. What is the cause of blood spots in eggs?
39. Explain the formation of double-yolked eggs.

REFERENCES

ASMUNDSON, V. S.: FORMATION OF THE HEN'S EGG. Sci. Agr., 11: 590–606; 662–680. 1931.

BIRD, S.: EFFECTS FOLLOWING ESTROGEN ADMINISTRATION TO MALE BIRDS. Proc. Eight World's Poultry Cong. pp. 131–136. 1948.

BRADLEY, O. C.: The Structure of the Fowl. A. and C. Black, Ltd., London. 1915.

CALHOUN, M. LOIS: THE MICROSCOPIC ANATOMY OF THE DIGESTIVE TRACT OF GALLUS DOMESTICUS. Iowa State Col. Jour. Sci., 7: 261–382. 1933.

CHAMBERLAIN, F. W.: ATLAS OF AVIAN ANATOMY: OSTEOLOGY, ARTHROLOGY, MYOLOGY. Michigan Sta. Mem. 5. 1943.

CONRAD, R. M., AND SCOTT, H. M.: THE FORMATION OF THE EGG OF THE DOMESTIC FOWL. Physiol. Rev., 18: 481–494. 1938.

COOK, S. F.: A STUDY OF THE BLOOD PICTURE OF POULTRY AND ITS DIAGNOSTIC SIGNIFICANCE. Poultry Sci., 16: 291–296. 1937.

FRANK, R. T., KLEMPNER, E., AND HOLLANDER, F.: THE COMB OF THE BABY CHICK AS A TEST FOR THE MALE SEX HORMONE. Soc. Exp. Biol. and Med. Proc., 38: 853–856. 1938.

FRONDA, F. M.: SOME OBSERVATIONS ON THE BODY TEMPERATURE OF POULTRY. Cornell Vet., 15: 8–20. 1925.

GLAZENER, E. W., SHAFFNER, C. S., AND JULL, M. A.: THYROID ACTIVITY AS RELATED TO STRAIN DIFFERENCES IN GROWING CHICKENS. Poultry Sci., 28: 834–849. 1949.

GODFREY, E. F., AND JAAP, R. G.: ESTROGENIC INTERRUPTION OF BROODINESS IN THE DOMESTIC FOWL. Poultry Sci., 29: 356–361, 1950.

GODFREY, GEORGE: THE EFFECT OF FEEDING THYROPROTEIN ON EGG SHELL QUALITY AND HATCHABILITY. Poultry Sci., 28: 867–873. 1949.

GRAY, J. C.: THE ANATOMY OF THE MALE GENITAL DUCTS IN THE FOWL. Jour. Morph., 60: pp. 393–405. 1937.

HARMON, I. W., OGDEN, E., AND COOK, S. F.: THE RESERVOIR FUNCTION OF THE SPLEEN IN FOWLS. Amer. Jour. Physiol., 100: 99–101. 1932.

HEGNER, R. W.: COLLEGE ZOOLOGY, 5th ed. The Macmillan Co., New York. 1942.

HERRICK, E. H., AND TORTSTVEIT, O.: SOME EFFECTS OF ADRENALECTOMY IN FOWLS. Endocrinology, 22: 469–473. 1938.

HOFFMAN, E., AND WHEELER, K. S.: THE VALUE OF THYROPROTEIN IN STARTING, GROWING, AND LAYING RATIONS. Poultry Sci., 27: 609–612. 1949.

KAUPP, B. F.: ANATOMY OF THE DOMESTIC FOWL. W. B. Saunders Co., Philadelphia. 1918.

KAUPP, B. F.: BLOOD PRESSURE AND PULSE OF THE FOWL. Vet. Med., 18: 919–922. 1923.

KAUPP, B. F.: THE RESPIRATION OF FOWLS. Vet. Med., 18: 36–40. 1923.

KELLY, J. W., AND DEARSTYNE, R. S.: HEMATOLOGY OF THE FOWL. N. C. Agr. Expt. Sta. Tech. Bul. 50. 1935.

LILLIE, F. R.: ON THE DEVELOPMENT OF FEATHERS. Biol. Rev., 17: 247–266. 1942.

MACDONALD, E., AND TAYLOR, L. W.: THE RUDIMENTARY COPULATORY ORGAN OF THE DOMESTIC FOWL. Jour. Morph., 54: 429–499. 1933.

MCNALLY, E. H.: HEART RATE OF THE DOMESTIC FOWL. Poultry Sci., 20: 266–271. 1941.

MCNALLY, E. H.: THE ORIGIN AND STRUCTURE OF THE VITELLINE MEMBRANE OF THE DOMESTIC FOWL'S EGG. Poultry Sci., 22: 40–43. 1943.

NALVANDOV, A. V., AND CARD, L. E.: THE PROBLEM OF BLOOD AND MEAT SPOTS IN CHICKEN EGGS. Poultry Sci., 26: 400–409. 1947.

PARKER, J. T., AND HASWELL, W. A.: A TEXTBOOK OF ZOOLOGY, 6th ed., Vol. 2. Macmillan & Co., London.

PAYNE, F.: ANTERIOR PITUITARY-THYROID RELATIONSHIPS IN THE FOWL. Anat. Rec., 88, No. 4: 337–350. 1944.

PHILLIPS, R. E., AND WARREN, D. C.: OBSERVATIONS CONCERNING THE MECHANICS OF OVULATION IN THE FOWL. Jour. Exp. Zool., 76: 117–136. 1937.

ROMANOFF, A. L., AND ROMANOFF, A. J.: THE AVIAN EGG. John Wiley & Sons, Inc., New York. 1949.

SURFACE, F. M.: HISTOLOGY OF THE OVIDUCT OF THE HEN. Me. Agr. Expt. Sta. Bul. 206. 1912.

THOMPSON, J. A.: THE BIOLOGY OF BIRDS. The Macmillan Co., New York. 1923.

TURNER, C. W.: FEEDING THYROPROTEIN AND SEX HORMONES TO LAYING HENS. Poultry Sci., 27: 613–620. 1949.

VAN DER MEULEN, J. B.: HORMONAL REGULATION OF MOLT AND OVULATION. Proc. Seventh World's Poultry Cong., pp. 109–112. 1939.

WARREN, D. C., AND CONRAD, R. M.: GROWTH OF THE HEN'S OVUM. Jour. Agr. Res., 58: 875–893. 1939.

WILSON, W. O.: HIGH ENVIRONMENTAL TEMPERATURES AS AFFECTING THE REACTION OF LAYING HENS TO IODIZED CASEIN. Poultry Sci., 28: 581–592. 1949.

CHAPTER 4 ||||||||||||||||||||||||||||||||||||||||||||||||||||||||||||

Breeding Principles

▼

Heredity

Heredity accounts for the fact that offspring tend to resemble their parents. Not only do the offspring hatched from a single-comb White Leghorn mating resemble birds and chickens, but also the specific single-comb White Leghorns. A chicken is composed of many characters. Its *physical characters,* such as size, shape, type of comb, and color of plumage, are easily seen. Its *physiological characters,* such as rate of growth, early maturity, and egg production, cannot be seen by looking at the individual. The parents transmit both physical and physiological characters to their offspring through their *gametes* (reproduction cells). The science which deals with heredity and the origin of individuals is *genetics.*

The Genetic Basis of Reproduction

The cell. The component substance of living things is *protoplasm.* In higher forms of plant and animal life it is organized into small, usually microscopic units called *cells.* The higher forms of living things consist of millions of cells, which vary greatly in shape, size, and composition, depending on the functions to be performed. For instance, cells range all the way from bacterial cells so small that it is impossible to see them even when magnified 1,000 times, to nerve cells more than a foot long and ostrich eggs weighing 45 ounces.

The cell is a complicated structure (Fig. 42). The *cell wall* is the boundary of the cell separating it from other cells. The light staining area within the cell wall is the *cytoplasm.* It contains many interesting structures, but most of them are of more interest to cytologists than to poultrymen. The dark staining area in the cytoplasm is the *nucleus.* It varys greatly in size, shape, and structure in different cells. The nuclei of reproductive cells are vital for the transmission of hereditary characters.

Continuity of germ plasm. The gametes and the cells which give rise to them constitute the *germ plasm.* The cells which take no direct part in the production of gametes are known as *somatic cells.* While the somatic cells

75

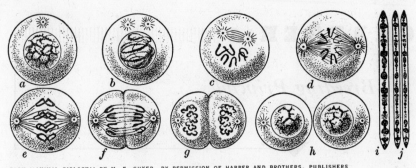

FROM "ANIMAL BIOLOGY" BY M. F. GUYER. BY PERMISSION OF HARPER AND BROTHERS, PUBLISHERS

Fig. 42. Diagram of the cell and mitosis: a and h, resting cells; b—g, stages in cell division; i and j, the halving of each chromosome.

cease to exist with the death of the individual whose body they constitute, the germ plasm may live on indefinitely in succeeding generations.

In the higher vertebrates, including the fowl, the germ plasm of a single individual cannot survive by itself; there must be successful union of the male and female gametes. The two cells pass on all the hereditary characters of the parents to the new offspring.

The quality of the germ plasm of any one individual is only half of the story; of equal importance is that from the opposite sex. If either gamete brings defective germ plasm, the body and the germ plasm of the offspring will suffer accordingly.

Early history of the gametes. Even before it is possible to tell whether the new individual will be a male or female, certain large cells in the embryo differentiate from their neighbors to become the primordial sex cells. They differentiate in the walls of the yolk sac and migrate to the developing gonads (reproductive organs). Sexual differentiation of the embryo becomes observable shortly after the germ cells become established in the gonads.

Development of male gametes. Part of the germ line, which migrated to the walls of the seminiferous tubules of the male gonads, becomes active when a cockerel reaches sexual maturity. These parent cells grow and divide (undergo mitosis) to form new cells. Part of the new cells remain like the parent cells and take the place of others which grow, undergo maturation division (Fig. 43), and differentiate into slender mature *spermatozoa* (male gametes).

The nuclear material collects in the head of the male gamete. The flagella-like tail makes its appearance in the protoplasm and grows far beyond the original confines of the cell. Thus, a mature male gamete is a cell consisting essentially of a very compact nucleus provided with a flagellum which gives it the power of locomotion in a fluid medium.

Development of female gametes. In the growing ovary of the embryo, the female germ cells grow and divide much the same as the male germ cells grow and divide in the testes. In the mature pullet the development of ova (female gametes) is different from the development of spermatozoa in the

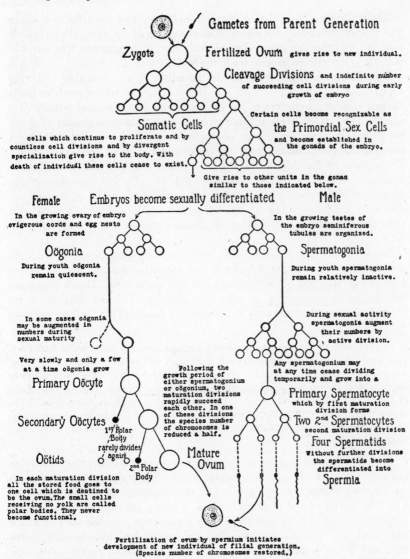

Gametes from Parent Generation

Zygote / Fertilized Ovum gives rise to new individual.

Cleavage Divisions and indefinite number of succeeding cell divisions during early growth of embryo

Somatic Cells
cells which continue to proliferate and by countless cell divisions and by divergent specialization give rise to the body. With death of individual these cells cease to exist.

Certain cells become recognizable as the Primordial Sex Cells and become established in the gonads of the embryo.

Give rise to other units in the gonad similar to those indicated below.

Female   Embryos become sexually differentiated   Male

In the growing ovary of embryo ovigerous cords and egg nests are formed

In the growing testes of the embryo seminiferous tubules are organized.

Oögonia
During youth oögonia remain quiescent.

Spermatogonia
During youth spermatogonia remain relatively inactive.

In some cases oögonia may be augmented in numbers during sexual maturity

During sexual activity spermatogonia augment their numbers by active division.

Very slowly and only a few at a time oögonia grow

Primary Oöcyte

Secondary Oöcytes
1st Polar Body rarely divides again

Oötids

2nd Polar Body

In each maturation division all the stored food goes to one cell which is destined to be the ovum. The small cells receiving no yolk are called polar bodies. They never become functional.

Following the growth period of either spermatogonium or oögonium, two maturation divisions rapidly succeed each other. In one of these divisions the species number of chromosomes is reduced a half.

Mature Ovum

Any spermatogonium may at any time cease dividing temporarily and grow into a

Primary Spermatocyte
which by first maturation division forms

Two 2nd Spermatocytes
second maturation division

Four Spermatids
Without further divisions the spermatids become differentiated into

Spermia

Fertilization of ovum by spermium initiates development of new individual of filial generation. (Species number of chromosomes restored.)

FROM "EARLY EMBRYOLOGY OF THE CHICK" BY B. M. PATTEN. BY PERMISSION OF THE BLAKISTON CO., PUBLISHERS

Fig. 43. Chart outlining, for one generation, the history of the gametes and the germ plasma from which they are derived.

mature male because of the amount of food stored as yolk in the cells. The food material, destined to be used by the embryo in its growth, is gradually accumulated in the ovum before it is liberated from the ovary. The accumulation of yolk requires about ten days. As the yolk accumulates, the nucleus and the cell cytoplasm are forced toward the surface. This is the germinal disc. It becomes the germ spot (blastoderm) on the yolk of the egg.

About the time of ovulation, the cell undergoes two maturation divisions. The yolk material does not divide. Therefore, one of the new cells has all the yolk and the other has none. The one without yolk degenerates. The one with the yolk is the mature gamete ready for fertilization.

Significance of chromosomes in heredity. When a resting cell (Fig. 42, a) starts to grow and divide, the dark-staining chromatin particles in the nucleus arrange themselves in one or more long, deeply stained threads (Fig. 42, b). The threads break up into pairs of dark-staining segments of different shapes and sizes. These pairs of segments are the *chromosomes*. The number and shape of chromosomes are constant for a given species of animal. The nucleus of the chicken male gamete contains at least thirty-six chromosomes and that of the female thirty-five (Fig. 44). The chromosomes arrange themselves about the equatorial plate between the two poles of the cell and then split lengthwise (Fig. 42, d). When the cell divides, each new cell contains the same kind and number of chromosomes as the parent cell (Fig. 42, h).

In one of the last cell divisions, before mature gametes are formed, the chromosomes do not split lengthwise but are redistributed instead. Half of each pair go into one of the new cells and half to the other. This is sometimes referred to as *maturation* or *reduction division*. The distribution of the chromosomes in the new cells is a matter of chance. Thus, in the words of Patten,[1]

In the game of life, the maturation processes virtually shuffle the hereditary pack and deal out half a hand to each gamete. A full hand is obtained by drawing a partner from the "board"—by combining with some other gamete of the opposite sex. Hence, offspring resemble their parents because they play the game of life with the same kind of cards, but not, however, with the same hands. The minor differences in offspring, or the variations from the standard type that always go with these basic resemblances, are due to variations in the distribution of genes during maturation.

There are several sources of evidence which indicate that the hereditary characters are carried by the chromosomes: (1) The male and female gametes are the only things directly involved in the formation of a new individual. (2) The nuclei of the male and female gametes are the only parts of the gametes that are directly concerned with fertilization, and the start of a new individual. (3) The chromosomes are the only things that are alike in the male and female gamete nuclei, and it is known that both parents contribute equally to the characters of the offspring. (4) There is one more chromosome in a male gamete than in a female gamete. It will be seen (p. 80) that a difference of one chromosome accounts for the difference between a male and a female chicken. (5) Sometimes the shape of one of the chromosomes of an animal is seen to be different from the chromosomes of its parents when that animal differs from them in a certain character. It therefore may be assumed that this particular chromosome carries the determining hereditary factor for

[1] B. M. Patten, *Life, Heredity and Evolution.*

the new character. The work of mapping the chromosomes and tying up specific hereditary traits with them is a relatively new and interesting field for study.

Fertilization. The sperm ducts in the testes produce a fluid, the semen, in which the spermatozoa are carried. The semen and its spermatozoa are deposited in the oviduct at the time of mating. The spermatozoa are very motile and work their way to the anterior end of the oviduct, where they wait to fertilize the ovum.

Fig. 44. The chromosomes of the fowl. (After Hance.)

Once the swarm of spermatozoa reach the neighborhood of the ovum, they tend to remain there, held by some chemical interaction which is not fully understood. A cone of ovum cytoplasm rises up to meet one of the sperm cells and draws it into the ovum. Once a sperm has penetrated the ovum, the surface covering appears to undergo a chemical change and thickening which keeps out other sperm cells.

The tail of the sperm cell drops off when it enters the ovum. There are now two nuclei in the ovum, one carrying the maturation division number of chromosomes (seventeen or eighteen) from the female parent, and the other carrying eighteen chromosomes from the male. The fertilized egg now carries the same number of chromosomes (thirty-five or thirty-six) as a cell from one or the other of its parents. The fertilized ovum is known as a *zygote*. It is now ready to undergo cell growth, mitosis, differentiation, and development into a new individual. For details of embryo development, refer to Chapter Six.

The Inheritance of Sex

Sex chromosomes. The chromosomes are of two kinds. Those dealing with sex are known as Z or *sex chromosomes,* and all the others are *autosomes.* The male zygote contains seventeen pairs of autosomes and one pair of sex chromosomes (Fig. 45). The female zygote contains the same number of autosomes, but only one sex chromosome. When maturation division takes place, one chromosome of each pair goes into the mature gamete, so that each mature male gamete contains seventeen autosomes and one sex chromosome. The mature female gametes contain seventeen autosomes, with half of them containing a sex chromosome, and the remainder containing none. If a male gamete fertilizes a female gamete which contains a sex chromosome, the resulting zygote will contain two sex chromosomes and will, therefore, develop into a male. On the other hand, if the male gamete fertilizes one of the female gametes which does not contain a sex chromosome, the resulting zygote will contain only one sex chromosome and will develop into a female. When large numbers of fertilizations are considered, one should expect as many males as females among the offspring.

80   *Poultry: Science and Practice*

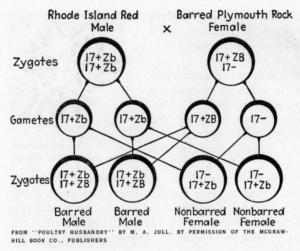

Fig. 45. A diagram illustrating the inheritance of sex and the sex-linked character for barring. The Rhode Island Red male has 17 pairs of autosomes and 2 sex chromosomes, designated Z, associated with each of which is the gene b for non-barring. The Barred Plymouth Rock female has 17 pairs of autosomes but only one sex chromosome Z, associated with which is the sex-linked gene B for barring, which is dominant to non-barring. The male progeny are barred, whereas the female progeny are non-barred.

FROM "POULTRY HUSBANDRY" BY M. A. JULL. BY PERMISSION OF THE MCGRAW-HILL BOOK CO., PUBLISHERS

Sex-linked inheritance. An individual is equal to the total of its genes. Since there are more characters that make up a bird than there are chromosomes in each of its cells, each chromosome must carry more than one character. The unit for a character is known as a *gene*. One might compare each chromosome to a string of beads and each bead on the string to a gene. The characters (genes) carried on the Z or sex chromosomes are known as sex-linked characters.

Sex-linked characters are transmitted from the dam to her sons but not to her daughters, although these same characters are transmitted from the sire to his sons and daughters alike. The results of mating a Barred Plymouth Rock hen and a Rhode Island Red male may be used to illustrate sex linkage. The male offspring from such a mating are barred and the females are black. When the Barred Plymouth Rock female's gametes containing the sex chromosomes unite with those from the male's, which also contain the sex chromosomes, zygotes result which contain two sex chromosomes. These unions result in males with barring. The female's gametes without the sex chromosomes, upon uniting with the male gametes, result in zygotes with only one sex chromosome. These unions result in black females. Barring is therefore a sex-linked gene, two sex chromosomes in an individual resulting in barring and one sex chromosome resulting in the absence of it. Other sex-linked characters of practical importance are broodiness, slow feathering, and early maturity.

Sex-linked matings for the determination of sex at hatching time. The knowledge of sex linkage can be used in mating birds so that the sex of the chicks can be determined at hatching time by the down patterns. If Barred Plymouth Rock females are mated with Buff Plymouth Rock, Rhode Island Red, or White Wyandotte males, the male offspring will be black on top of the body with a white spot on the head and yellow shanks and beak.

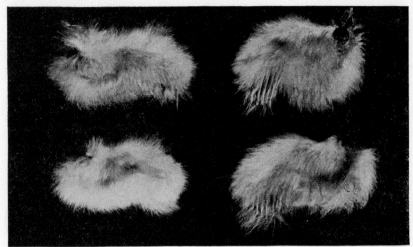

COURTESY D. C. WARREN, KANSAS STATE COLLEGE

Fig. 46. Flight feather development in day-old male and female chicks from crossing a White Leghorn male with a Rhode Island Red female. Note the well-developed flight feather of the female (right) and the very short flight feathers of the male (left).

The females will be solid black on top of the body with dark shanks and beak.

If males of the Mediterranean class are mated with slow feathering females of the American, English, and Asiatic classes, the female day-old chicks will have well-developed wing feathers (Fig. 46). The males will have very short primary wing feathers or else none.

Strains of most common breeds may show either slow or rapid feathering. At hatching time it is possible to determine the sex of the chicks from either of these strains by wing feathers, as noted above. The same thing should be possible with any breed or variety.

The sexes of Barred Plymouth Rock chicks can be determined with 90 to 95 per cent accuracy by the down color on the top of the head of the chicks and by shank color. The cockerel head spot is irregular in outline and scattered in appearance. The color of the shank is lighter than that of the female and blends with that of the foot. The pullet head spot is more regular in outline and does not exhibit the scattered appearance present in the cockerel head spot. The pullet shank is usually black or dark amber in color. The dark color in the typical female chick terminates abruptly at the base of the shank or a short distance out on the toes and the remainder is lighter in color.

The Inheritance of Characters

Mendelism. The discovery of the law governing the inheritance of a pair of characters was made by Gregor Mendel and published in 1865. Mendel-

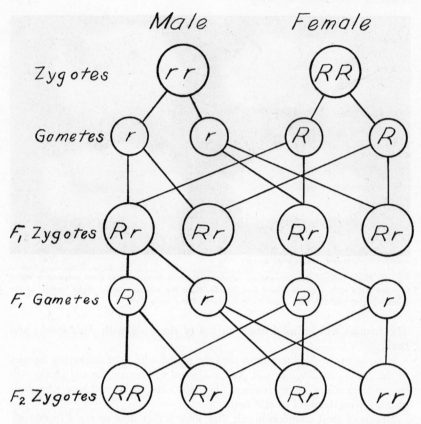

Fig. 47. Inheritance of a pair of characters. When a rose-comb (R) female is crossed with a single-comb (r) male, the first generation birds have rose comb (dominant character). When the F_1 birds are mated among themselves, about 75 per cent of the F_2 generation will have rose combs and the remainder will have single combs.

ism simply means the biological theory of heredity first formulated by Mendel. He also discovered that every pair of characters is inherited independently of every other pair. Mendel worked with hereditary characters of various kinds of garden peas, but the principles he discovered are of universal application to both plants and animals.

The inheritance of a pair of characters. The mating of a White Wyandotte hen and a White Plymouth Rock male may be taken as an example (Fig. 47). Wyandottes have rose combs, and Plymouth Rocks have single combs. One may designate the gene for rose comb by R and that for single comb by r. The gametes from the pure hens will carry the factor R for rose comb and those from the pure male will carry the factor r for single comb. When the birds are mated, the offspring, or F_1 generation, will all have rose combs. When two different characters that are pure are mated, the one that appears in the offspring is *dominant*. The one that does not appear is *reces-*

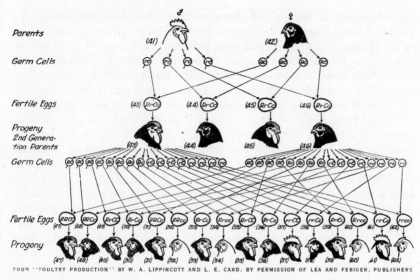

FROM ''POULTRY PRODUCTION'' BY W. A. LIPPINCOTT AND L. E. CARD. BY PERMISSION OF LEA AND FEBIGER, PUBLISHERS

Fig. 48. Diagram showing the transmission of two independent simple characters from generation to generation.

sive. In this case, rose comb is dominant to single comb, or single comb is recessive to rose comb.

Half of the gametes from the F_1 generation will carry the factor R and the others will carry r. If birds of the F_1 generation are mated among themselves, part of their offspring will have rose combs and part will have single combs. The ratio, subject to sampling error, will be three rose combs for each single comb. If an R gamete from one sex unites with an R gamete from the other sex, the resulting zygote will carry the factor RR which is pure for rose comb. If an R gamete of one sex unites with an r gamete from the opposite sex, the resulting zygote will carry the factor Rr. Since R is dominant to r, the offspring will have rose comb, but it will be impure. If an r gamete from one sex unites with an r gamete from the opposite sex, the resulting zygote will carry the factor rr, which is pure for single comb. The birds RR and rr are *homozygous;* that is, they are pure for the comb character. The birds Rr are *heterozygous;* that is, they are impure for the comb characters. The ratio of rose-comb birds to single-comb birds as they appear in the F_2 generation is three to one. This is the *phenotypic* ratio. The ratio with reference to purity for comb character is $1:2:1$. This is the *genotypic* ratio.

Inheritance of two pairs of characters. The crossing of a Black Wyandotte with a White Plymouth Rock may be used to illustrate the inheritance of two pairs of characters.

It is customary to designate dominant characters by capital letters and recessive characters by small letters. Rose comb (R) is dominant to single comb (r), and black (B) is dominant to white (b). The F_1' generation produces four possible kinds of gametes (Fig. 48) instead of only two, as in the inheritance of one pair of characters. Since four kinds of gametes are produced by each sex, the possibilities for the segregation and recombination of the characters is four times as great as in the case when only two kinds of gametes are formed. The F_2 zygotic ratios then become 9 rose-comb black, 3 rose-comb white, 3 single-comb black, and 1 single-comb white, or 9:3:3:1. If comb alone is considered, there are 12 rose combs and 4 single combs, a 3:1 ratio. If color alone is considered, there are 12 blacks and 4 whites, or a 3:1 ratio. These ratios are what would be expected when two pairs of characters are inherited independently of each other. Of the sixteen zygotes formed, one is homozygous for rose comb and black color, and one is homozygous for both single comb and white color. These zygotes are different from those of the original parents and of the F_1 generation and could have been produced only through the random assortment of the chromosomes. All the other zygotes are genetically different from those of the original parents.

The inheritance of several pairs of characters. When more than two pairs of characters are involved and the different genes producing the characters are on different chromosomes, the segregation and assortment of characters behave in the same way as the inheritance of one or two pairs of characters. The number of different kinds of gametes formed by the F_1 generation is doubled with each additional character involved. On the other hand, for each additional character involved there is an increase by four in the number of F_2 individuals required to secure the appearance of the various combinations of characters resulting from the chance combination of the different kinds of F_1 gametes. (Table 12.)

Table 12

INFLUENCE OF THE NUMBER OF CHARACTERS INVOLVED ON THE
NUMBER OF F2 INDIVIDUALS NECESSARY THAT ONE MAY
BE HOMOZYGOUS FOR ALL OF THEM

Number of Pairs of Characters	Number of Different F_1 Gametes Formed	Number of F_2 Individuals Required to Secure One Homozygous for All the Characters
1	2	4
2	4	16
3	8	64
4	16	256

Dominant and recessive characters. Some of the characters whose inheritance has been determined are listed in Table 13. Most of them are simple characters. A few are more complicated than they appear in the table. White in the White Leghorn, for instance, is dominant to colored plumage. If a White Leghorn is mated to a colored bird, the F_1 generation will all be white but some of the birds will have black flecks in a few of the feathers. The dominance of white in the Leghorn is due to the presence of a gene which inhibits color; otherwise the bird would be barred, for it carries genes for barring, color, and black pigment.

Table 13

SOME DOMINANT AND RECESSIVE CHARACTERS IN CHICKENS

Character	Dominant or Recessive	Sex-Linked
White plumage.............	In White Leghorns, dominant to color In Plymouth Rocks and Wyandottes, recessive to color	
Black plumage.............	Dominant to recessive white	
Buff plumage..............	Dominant to recessive white	
Barred plumage............	In Plymouth Rocks, dominant to nonbarring	Yes
White skin and shank color..	Dominant to yellow skin and shank color	
Rose comb................	Dominant to single comb	
Side sprigs................	Dominant to normal comb	
Feathered shanks...........	Dominant to nonfeathered shanks	
Close feathering...........	Dominant to loose feathering	
Slow feathering............	Dominant to rapid feathering	Yes
Early sexual maturity.......	Dominant to late sexual maturity	Yes
Broodiness................	Dominant to nonbroodiness	Yes
Winter pause..............	Dominant to continuous laying	

It is interesting to note that white is not always dominant. It depends on the breed. While white is dominant to color in the Leghorn, it is recessive to color in the Wyandotte and Plymouth Rock.

The inheritance of about fifty characters has been determined to date. With some characters the determination of their Mendelian inheritance is slow because many genes are involved. Furthermore, the expression of characters may be influenced by environment, hormones, feeding, and management practices. For instance, a bird may have inherited the genes for high egg production but may not lay well because it is fed a poor ration.

Testing for purity of characters. An impure recessive character may be carried in a flock for generations without being detected, if matings are made with birds which are pure for the dominant gene. The impurity may crop out unexpectedly when two impure individuals are mated.

Some White Wyandotte flocks produce a few single-comb chicks. This indicates a single-comb impurity in the flock, as Wyandottes have rose combs. Since rose comb is dominant to single comb, the birds that appear with single comb are homozygous for this character. They should be culled out. Part of the rose-comb birds in the flock will be homozygous and part will be hetero-zygous. To test for impurity, mate each bird with a recessive single-comb bird and hatch about six chicks. If no single-comb chicks appear in the lot, the rose-comb bird was pure for this character.

A general rule that may be applied for testing genetic constitution is to mate the bird to be tested with one that carries the pure recessive character. If none of the offspring show the recessive character, the animal was pure for the dominant character.

Modifications of Mendelian Inheritance

Linked genes. Some characters possessed by a bird in an original cross may be carried on into the F_2 generation. They do not follow the Mendelian laws of inheritance. The genes giving rise to these characters are said to be linked together on the same chromosome. The genes for single comb and short legs (creeper condition) exhibit linkage. The opposite to linkage is crossing over. Here there is an interchange of parts of the same pair of chromosomes. The practical significance of linkage and crossing over in poultry breeding work is yet to be demonstrated.

Lethal genes. Recent studies have shown that certain genes, when in homozygous condition, kill the chick embryo. An example is the cross between creeper and normal chickens. The creeper condition is a dominant factor. The F_2 generation should give 3 creepers to 1 normal chicken. Instead, there are 2 creepers for each normal bird. The pure homozygous individual dies in the embryonic state. Sticky embryos are recessive to normal. The "sticky" character is lethal when homozygous.

Complementary genes. The normal 9:3:3:1 ratio for the inheritance of two pairs of characters is sometimes changed by different genes producing like effects or having complementary effects. The mating of White Silkies and White Dorkings may be used for illustration. The F_1 generation is colored. The F_2 generation shows 9 colored for every 7 white birds. The last three groups of the usual 9:3:3:1 series cannot be distinguished by appearance because an individual containing only one of the dominant genes, whether in homozygous or heterozygous form, looks exactly like an individual that carries neither of them.

Mutations. A new character may appear unexpectedly in one generation and be transmitted through inheritance to succeeding generations. The new character is called a "sport" or a "mutation." It is brought about by a change in a gene. The White Plymouth Rock originated as a "sport" from the barred variety.

Complex characters. Not all characters are due to single genes. For instance, laying performance is a complex character in which several genes are involved. Genetically, the number of eggs a bird will lay depends on such characters as early maturity, intensity, persistency, and nonbroodiness. These and other characters will be discussed in the following chapter.

WINTER   PAUSE

REVIEW QUESTIONS

1. Differentiate between the physical and physiological characters of a chicken.
2. What are the principal parts of a cell?
3. What are gametes?
4. Where are hereditary characters carried in gametes?
5. Differentiate between ordinary mitosis and reduction or maturation division of gametes.
6. What are some of the proofs that hereditary characters are carried in the chromosomes?
7. Explain the process of fertilization or the formation of a zygote.
8. Differentiate between autosomes and sex chromosomes.
9. What is a gene?
10. What are sex-linked characters?
11. What use is made of sex-linked matings?
12. Differentiate between dominant and recessive characters.
13. List some dominant and recessive characters of practical significance.
14. List some sex-linked characters of practical significance.
15. How would one test for impurity of a character in a flock of birds?
16. Name some lethal genes.
17. What is a mutation or sport?
18. What is Mendelism?
19. Why is it difficult to breed for more than one or two characters at a time?
20. Differentiate between the functions of autosomes and sex chromosomes.
21. Why are there often marked variations among offspring from the same parents?
22. The female transmits sex-linked characters to which sex of her offspring? Explain.
23. Is the same character dominant in all breeds? Give an example.

REFERENCES

BRESSMAN, E. N., AND HAMBRIDGE, G.: FUNDAMENTALS OF HEREDITY FOR BREEDERS. U. S. D. A. Yearbook, pp. 1419–1449. 1937.

COOK, ROBERT: A CHRONOLOGY OF GENETICS. U. S. D. A. Yearbook, pp. 1457–1477. 1937.

DAVENPORT, C. B.: INHERITANCE IN POULTRY. Carnegie Inst. of Washington, Pub. 52, pp. 1–136. 1906.

DAVENPORT, C. B.: INHERITANCE OF CHARACTERISTICS OF THE DOMESTIC FOWL. Carnegie Inst. of Washington, Pub. 121, pp. 1–100. 1909.

DUNN, L. C.: A METHOD OF DISTINGUISHING THE SEX OF YOUNG CHICKS. Storrs Agr. Expt. Sta. Bul. 113. 1923.

GULICK, A.: WHAT ARE THE GENES? II. THE PHYSICO-CHEMICAL PICTURE: CONCLUSIONS. Quart. Rev. Biol., 13: 140–168. 1938.

GUTHRIDGE, H. S., AND O'NEIL, J. B.: THE RELATIVE EFFECT OF ENVIRONMENT AND HEREDITY UPON BODY MEASUREMENTS AND PRODUCTION CHARACTERISTICS IN POULTRY. I. PERIOD OF GROWTH. Sci. Agr., 22: 378–389. 1942.

GUYER, M. F.: STUDIES ON THE CHROMOSOMES OF THE COMMON FOWL AS SEEN IN THE TESTES AND IN EMBRYOS. Biol. Bul. 31: 221–268. 1916.

HANCE, R. T.: SEX AND THE CHROMOSOMES IN THE DOMESTIC FOWL. Jour. Morph. and Physiol., 43: 119–145. 1926.

HUTT, F. B.: GENETICS OF THE FOWL. McGraw-Hill Book Co., New York. 1949.

JULL, M. A.: POULTRY BREEDING. John Wiley & Sons, Inc., New York. 1940.

JULL, M. A.: SUPERIOR BREEDING STOCK IN POULTRY INDUSTRY. U. S. D. A. Yearbook, pp. 947–995. 1936.

KEMPTON, J. H.: HEREDITY UNDER THE MICROSCOPE. U. S. D. A. Yearbook, pp. 165–182. 1936.

LERNER, I. M.: LETHAL AND SUBLETHAL CHARACTERS IN FARM ANIMALS. Jour. Hered., 35: 219–224. 1944.

LUSH, J. L.: ANIMAL BREEDING PLANS, 3rd ed. Iowa State College Press, Ames, Iowa. 1945.

PUNNETT, R. C.: HEREDITY IN POULTRY. Macmillan & Co., Ltd., London. 1923.

SINNOTT, E. W., AND DUNN, L. C.: PRINCIPLES OF GENETICS, 3rd ed. Mc-Graw-Hill Book Co., New York. 1939.

SNYDER, L. H.: THE PRINCIPLES OF HEREDITY, 3rd ed. D. C. Heath & Co., New York. 1946.

WARREN, D. C.: CROSSBRED POULTRY. Kan. Agr. Expt. Sta. Bul. 252. 1930.

WARREN, D. C.: SEX-LINKED CHARACTERS OF POULTRY. Genetics, 13: 421–433. 1928.

YAMASHIMA, M. Y.: LATEST CHROMOSOME COUNT. Cytologia 13: 270–296. 1944.

CHAPTER 5 |||||||||||||||||||||||||||||||||||||||||||||||||||||||||||||||||

Breeding Practices

▼

Poultry-breeding work during the period 1860–1910 was largely concerned with the development of new breeds and varieties. That the work was quite successful is evidenced by the many classes, breeds, and varieties of chickens (Chapter Two). Since about 1910, interest in poultry-breeding work has centered around the improvement of poultry for meat and egg production purposes. Birds with a first-year production of three hundred eggs are now as common as two-hundred-egg birds were thirty years ago. Yet, in the light of newer knowledge of breeding methods, it appears that poultry breeders are merely on the threshold of the possibilities that lie ahead. There is a need for a larger number of breeders more thoroughly informed concerning the fundamental factors involved in the selection of breeding stock for the development of superior strains.

Selection of Breeding Stock

Selection of males and hens for the breeding flock is more of a problem than is generally believed. Like individuals do not always beget like individuals, as shown in the preceding chapter. Physical characters, such as size, shape, and color, may be seen and judged by looking at the individual. Physiological characters, such as livability, egg production, and hatchability, cannot be seen and measured by looking at the bird.

Selection of breeding stock should be based on the laws of hereditary transmission of characters. Attempts should be made to segregate individuals pure for desirable genes, and then to assemble in new individuals desirable combinations of genes by proper mating. Information regarding a bird's genetic makeup may be obtained from the individual, its ancestry, its sibs, its reproductive performance, and its progeny. The latter two are by far the most important. Much more emphasis should also be placed on the selection of males than females, because each male is mated with from ten to twenty females and produces several times as many offspring.

Selection of individuals. The first step in poultry-breeding work is the selection of males and females to be used as breeders. The selection should be based on (1) vigor, (2) breed and varietal characteristics, and (3) production characteristics.

89

Fig. 49 A Leghorn cockerel with high vitality (on the right) and one with low vitality (on the left).

Vigor. Good health or vigor is the first prerequisite for a bird that is to be used in the breeding pen. It is shown by behavior and body characteristics (Fig. 49). The contrasts in characters, as shown by birds with good and poor vigor, are summarized in Table 14.

Birds with good vigor are interested in things going on around them and are active. They walk, run, fly, forage, scratch, sing, cackle or crow, and show sex interest. It was observed at Cornell University that a group of five males with good vigor mated 132 times with hens during twenty hours of observation, while a similar number of average vitality mated 64 times, and the group with low vitality only 39 times. Birds with low vitality have just the opposite behavior traits of those with good vitality.

Birds with good vigor have a broad, long, deep body, with a good capacity for handling feed and manufacturing eggs (Fig. 50). Other things being equal, birds with good, compact body size are better able to withstand long, intensive egg production than birds with small body size.

The head gives a good indication of the health of the bird. Rice has said, "The bird carries its health certificate on top of its head," meaning the comb. A large, bright red comb indicates good vigor, while a small, pale, or dark comb indicates low vitality or a diseased condition. If the comb is large and bright red, the eyes will be bright and prominent, the face well colored, and the wattles red.

The plumage of vigorous birds is close and the feathers are "well kept," glossy, and unbroken. Vigorous birds generally molt late and quickly. Birds

Table 14

VIGOR CHARACTERISTICS OF BREEDING BIRDS

	Good Vigor	Poor Vigor
Character Behavior		
Activity	Very active	Inactive, tired
Attitude	Alert	Drowsy
Voice	Crow or cackle and sing	Quiet
Sex interest	Gallant or coquettish	Lack of interest
Appetite	Eat well, full crop	Eat little
Roosting	Up early, retire late	Spend much time on perches
Body Characteristics		
Shape	Parallelogram	Triangle
Back	Broad, extends well back	Narrow, wedge shaped
Keel	Long, extends well forward	Short
Breast	Full, plump	Shallow, thin
Abdomen	Deep, full	Tucked up
Size	Generally large, compact	May be small
Head	Broad, round	Long, thin, flat
Beak	Short, heavy, curved	Long, thin, flat
Comb	Large, bright red, warm	Small, pale, or purple
Eye	Large, bright, prominent	Dull, sunken
Plumage	Close, glossy	Loose, dull
Wings	Folded against body	Drooping
Tail	Upright	Drooping
Shanks	Short, thick	Long, thin

with poor vigor may not molt, and the plumage may be irregular and thin. One should take past production into consideration when judging vigor by plumage. Oftentimes birds that have been laying for a long period of time will have poorly kept plumage. They apparently are so busy producing eggs that their plumage is neglected.

Breed and variety characteristics. Individuals should be selected that are free from general disqualifications (p. 42) and that conform to the description of the breed and variety as given in the American Standard of Perfection.

While it is true that there is probably very little relation between the refinement of type and color of a bird and its production, yet one should retain the identity of the breed and variety in the flock. The buyers of poultry will pay more for Standard-bred stock than for birds that lack a definite breed and variety identity.

The breeding problem is simplified by choosing a variety with a solid color, such as white, in preference to one with shaded or mixed color (barring). The white color does not create a breeding problem. Barring is a problem because definite dark and light and narrow bars are preferred. As illustrated by the principle of segregation of characters in the preceding chapter, if a bird with small-egg size is crossed with one for large-egg size and the F_1 generation mated among themselves, about one bird out of every four

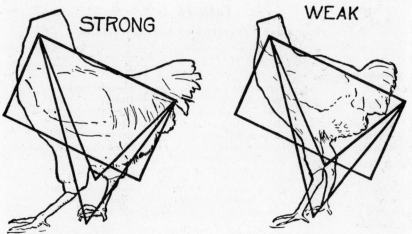

REPRINTED BY PERMISSION FROM ''JUDGING POULTRY FOR PRODUCTION'' BY RICE, HALL, AND MARBLE, PUBLISHED BY JOHN WILEY AND SONS, INC.

Fig. 50. The way in which birds of high and low vitality fill a parallelogram and two triangles. This clearly brings out the points of weakness in development of keel, breast, and abdomen in the low-vitality bird.

will be pure for large-egg size. If one had to select for a desirable type of barring as well as egg size, only about one bird out of sixteen would have the proper egg size and barring.

Production characteristics. It is possible to secure an indication of a hen's present, past, and future egg production by physical examination of the bird. Characteristics observed and their significance are summarized in Table 15.

Distinguishing layers from nonlayers. In selecting good producers and culling the unprofitable birds, it is necessary to be able to distinguish hens that are laying from those that are not laying.

The color of comb and wattles gives some indication of present production. When the ovary starts to function and yolks start to develop, the comb and wattles increase in size and become bright red in color. If a bird is about ready to lay or is in production, she has a large, bright red, smooth, glossy comb, and full, smooth wattles (Fig. 51). Near the end of a laying period and when production stops, the comb shrinks and becomes dull, dry, and shriveled.

Condition of the vent is used to indicate production. The vent of a hen in production is large, oval or elliptical, and moist. When a bird is out of production, the vent is shrunken, puckered, and dry (Fig. 52).

The space between the pubic bones indicates the laying condition of a pullet or hen. As a fowl comes into laying condition, the pubic bones (Fig. 53) spread apart. The distance between them, when a bird is in production, will be at least one and one-half inches, even in small fowls, and may be as much as three inches in the larger breeds. A space equal to the width of one finger (about three-fourths of an inch) between the pubic bones indicates

Table 15

CULLING AND SELECTION OUTLINE

Distinguishing Layers from Nonlayers

CHARACTER	LAYING HEN	NONLAYING HEN
Comb	Large, red, full, glossy	Small, pale, scaly
Eye	Bright	Dull
Vent	Large, dilated, oblong, moist	Small, contracted, round, dry
Pubic bone spread	Two or more fingers	Less than two fingers
Abdomen and spread	Soft, pliable	Full, hard
	Three or more fingers between pubic bones and keel	Less than three fingers between keel and pubic bones

Estimating Past Production

	LONG LAYING PERIOD	SHORT LAYING PERIOD
Vent	Bluish white	Flesh colored
Eye	Prominent, sparkling	Dull, sunken
Eyelids	Thin, edges white	Thick, yellow tinted
Earlobes	Enamel white *	Yellow tinted
Beak	Pearly white	Yellow tinted
Shanks	White, flat	Yellow, round, smooth
Plumage	Worn, soiled, close feathered	New, glossy, clean, loose feathered

Estimating Merits of Good and Inferior Layers

	GOOD LAYER	POOR LAYER
Pigmentation	Well bleached	Yellow pigment
Molt	Late, rapid, laying during molt	Early, slow
Persistency of production	Laying in August and September	Out of production in August and September

* Mediterranean class birds.

that the hen is not laying. A space greater than the width of two fingers usually shows that she is laying.

Long production causes the pubic bones to become thin and pliable. In nonlayers these bones are thick and less flexible.

A soft, pliable abdomen indicates that a bird is in production. A full, hard abdomen indicates a nonlaying bird. A pullet or a nonlaying bird has a depth of only about two fingers between the pubic bones and the keel (Fig. 54). As the fowl comes into production, the abdomen expands, the keel drops down, and the space between the pubic bones and keel has a depth of three or more fingers.

Indications of good layers. The selection of hens should not be based on their present laying condition alone. The fact that a hen is laying at the time of examination is no proof that she is a good producer. Almost any hen

COURTESY THE EARLY AND DANIEL CO.

Fig. 51. Head of a good Barred Plymouth Rock layer (left) and poor layer (right). Note the large comb and wattles and short beak on the good layer.

will lay during the spring. If she is not laying in July and August of the year after she was hatched, she is likely to be a poor layer.

Although trap-nesting is the best way to ascertain the exact number of eggs a hen has laid, there are easily observed changes in physical appearance which indicate a bird's past laying performance. These include pigmentation and molt.

Pigmentation gives some information regarding a bird's past production, in case of hens having yellow skin and shanks. During the period of production, the yellow xanthophyl pigment in the feed eaten is used for coloring the yolks and the body gradually loses its reserve supply of yellow pigment. The order of disappearance of pigment from the body and the approximate period of egg production required to bleach the body structures are as follows:

Vent	1– 2 weeks
Eye rings and earlobes	2– 4 weeks
Beak	6– 8 weeks
Shanks	12–20 weeks

The pigment first leaves those structures having the best blood circulation. It leaves the beak from the base towards the tip and the front of the shanks before the back part. When a bird stops production, the pigment returns in the same order as it left and approximately twice as fast.

The rate of production and the kind of ration alter the rapidity with which pigment is lost from the body. Birds laying at a high rate lose pigment more rapidly than those laying at a low rate. Birds kept in confinement or fed very little yellow corn or alfalfa lose pigment much more rapidly than those re-

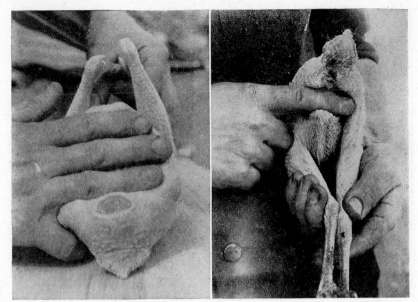

Fig. 52. The influence of egg production on the condition of the abdomen and vent. Left, a bird in production. Note the large space between the pubic bones and keel, and the large, oval vent. Right, a bird out of production. Note the small space between the pubic bones and keel, and the small, flat vent.

ceiving an abundance of xanthophyl pigment from green grass range, yellow corn, or alfalfa.

Molt may be used to indicate a bird's laying ability. Both the time and duration of molt should be considered.

The early molter is usually a poor layer. The normal molt occurs during the summer and fall of each laying year. Poor producers frequently stop laying in June or July and begin to drop their feathers. They usually take a long time to complete their molt and as a rule lay no eggs during this period. They seldom start to lay before December or January. Late molters, after a rest of only a month or two, also begin to lay in December or January.

It takes about six weeks for a new feather to grow out in either a low or a high producer, but the latter grows more feathers at a time, thereby completing the molt much more quickly than a low producer. Exceptionally good hens may molt and lay at the same time.

The order of the molt is as follows: head, neck, breast, body, wings, and tail. If birds are selected in the early fall, the plumage of the good layers will show wear and tear, and is usually soiled. The early molting hens will have a growth of new feathers. The webs of the new feathers are glossy and bright in contrast to the dry, frayed webs of the old ones. The new quills are large, full, and soft. The quills of the old feathers are small, hard, and nearly transparent. A few pinfeathers in the neck may indicate a short molting period without

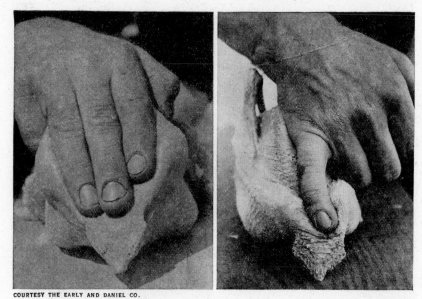

Fig. 53. The influence of egg production on the condition of the pubic bones and abdomen. Left, a bird in production. Note the wide space between the pubic bones, and the loose abdomen. Right, a bird out of production. Note the small space between the pubic bones and the tight abdomen.

a stop in egg production. When the molt extends to the body and wings, the hen usually stops laying and the molt becomes complete.

It is possible to estimate when the molt began by counting the number of wing feathers. The primary feathers are the stiff flight feathers seen on the outer part of the wing when it is spread out (Fig. 55). They are separated from the secondary feathers by a short feather (axial feather). There are usually ten primary feathers on each wing, and they are molted from the axial feather toward the tip of the wing. Early and slow molters generally drop one or two primary feathers at a time. Late and fast-molting birds shed three or more primary feathers at a time. Since it takes about six weeks to grow a new wing feather, and two-thirds of the growth is made during the first three weeks, one can estimate the time of wing molt by observing the number and length of the new primary wing feathers. The new feathers will be clean and bright with a soft quill and broad outline. The old primaries are much more faded, soiled, worn, and pointed.

The trap-nest record. The trap-nest record gives the true picture of a bird's egg-laying performance. It not only gives the number of eggs laid, but is necessary for a study of egg characters and individual reproductive performance (p. 120).

Ancestry. A good individual with good ancestry is to be preferred to one with poor ancestry because it is more likely to carry the genes for the desired character. It should be remembered that good ancestry only betters the

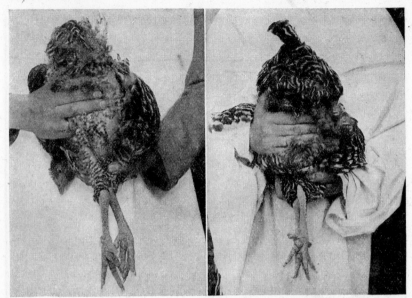

COURTESY THE EARLY AND DANIEL CO.

Fig. 54. The space between the pubic bones and the keel indicates the laying condition of a bird. Left, a bird out of production, with a narrow space between the pubic bones and keel and a hard, full abdomen. Right, a bird in production, with a wide space between the pubic bones and keel and a soft, pliable abdomen.

chances; it does not guarantee purity. The greater the variation in the environmental conditions, the ration, and management practices, the less the reliance that can be placed upon the ancestors' records of production in the selection of progeny for future breeding purposes.

Sibs. The records of the brothers and sisters in a family furnish further evidence of an individual's desirability as a breeder. The probability is greater that the bird under consideration is pure for the genes for the characters he carries when his brothers and sisters have the characters.

Reproductive performance. A bird will be of little value as a breeder unless it reproduces well. It may lay many eggs but still be of little value as a breeder if it has few or no progeny.

Fertility of eggs is the first limiting factor determining the number of offspring. Low fertility may result from sterility or partial sterility of the male, barrenness of the female, aversion or favoritism on the part of the male, or a lack of sex interest in either sex. Insofar as known, fertility is an individual characteristic which is not hereditary. It remains more or less constant in an individual from year to year. There appears to be no relation between fertility and hatchability.

Hatchability is an inherited character. A hen may lay a large number of fertile eggs, yet many of the embryos will die in the shell. The poor hatchability may be due to lethal genes. Some of these are stickiness, deformed mandibles, and malpositions of embryos.

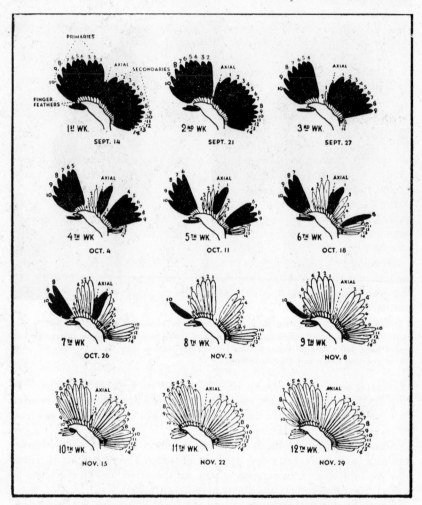

Fig. 55. A diagram showing weekly stages of the wing molt. The black portions represent the old feathers, while the new ones are represented by the feather outlines. (Cornell Bulletin 503.)

Livability of chicks hatched is the final measure of a bird's reproductive performance. Chicks from certain matings are known to live well, while those from different matings, kept under identical conditions, have high mortality. It is not known definitely that livability is inherited. However, it is a good practice to use only breeders whose progeny live well.

Progeny. The final proof of a bird's value as a breeder is its ability to transmit desirable characters that it possesses to its offspring. Selection of female breeders on the basis of their first year trap-nest records failed to improve egg production in the Maine Experiment Station flock. When selection of cockerels and pullets for breeders was made from the best families of that year, a steady increase in production was obtained.

Systems of Breeding Poultry

Once individual breeders have been selected, they are bred according to one of three systems. These are: inbreeding, crossing, and closed flock breeding.

Inbreeding. Inbreeding is the mating together of relatives. Since there are different degrees of relationship, there are also different degrees of inbreeding. The term "close inbreeding" is used to refer to the mating of brothers and sisters or parent to offspring.

The purpose of inbreeding is to intensify desirable characters—that is, to secure them in more homozygous condition. Inbreeding is used on poultry farms to develop strains for high egg production, large eggs, good meat type, good livability, etc.

Inbreeding may result in reduced vigor and a decline in hatchability unless the birds are selected for good vigor and hatchability, as well as the particular character that is to be improved. It must be remembered that, if a bird is selected for a good character and it should happen to have a bad one and if it is inbred to intensify the good one, the bad one will also be intensified.

At the University of Wisconsin, Rhode Island Red pullets and cockerels were selected on the basis of plumage color. Vigor, egg production, and hatchability were not considered. After four years of inbreeding, in which brothers and sister matings were used, the experiment had to be discontinued because of the decline in vigor, egg production, and hatchability. The decline in hatchability is shown in Table 16.

Table 16

INFLUENCE OF CLOSE INBREEDING ON HATCHABILITY AMONG
RHODE ISLAND REDS [1]

Mating	First Year	Second Year	Third Year	Fourth Year
	Per Cent			
Inbred line.........	67	49	41	18
Control line.........	67	31	56	64

Inbred poultry, according to the National Poultry Improvement Plan (page 115) is the first generation poultry, chicks, or eggs, produced by a mating of poultry of known relationship, related to the degree of first cousins or closer. *Inbred line* is a group of inbred poultry, or chicks, or eggs, resulting from at least four generations of inbreeding. The poultry constituting the line must be individually identified as to origin and so interrelated that the mating of any pair within the line would result in progeny with an amount of inbreed-

[1] Cole and Halpin, 1922.

ing exceeding that resulting from three successive generations of full brother-sister matings.

Coefficient of inbreeding is the measurement of the intensity of inbreeding or the decrease in heterozygosity. It is exactly one-half of the relationship between the parents unless these parents are themselves inbred, in which case some correction should be made. For instance, if a bird is heterozygous for 100 pairs of genes and it is inbred so that its inbreeding coefficient is 25 per cent, it will probably be heterozygous for only 75 pairs of genes. The formula for determining the coeffcient of inbreeding is complicated and need not be considered here.

Crossing is: (1) The crossing of two different breeds or varieties. (2) Crossing first generation poultry resulting from the combination of two different breeds or varieties with another and different breed or variety. (3) Crossing the first generation poultry resulting from the combination of two different breeds or varieties with the first generation poultry resulting from the combination of two other different breeds or varieties.

Crossing is used to determine the sex of chicks at hatching time and to produce chicks for commercial broiler and egg production. It may result in better hatchability, livability, and growth rate of chicks. It does not have much influence on egg production and livability of laying birds. (Table 17.) Results obtained may be expected to vary with the breeds or varieties crossed and also their purity.

Table 17

INFLUENCE OF CROSSING RHODE ISLAND REDS AND BARRED ROCKS [2]

Characters Studied	Rhode Island Reds	Barred Plymouth Rocks	Red and Rock Cross
Fertility (per cent).	63	70	74
Hatchability (per cent).	54	62	65
Mortality first 24 weeks (per cent).	13	17	10
Egg production first 11 months (no eggs). . .	108	171	127
Mortality during 11 months egg production (per cent).	33	29	43

Hybrid chickens as used at present refers to stock produced by crossing of breeds with or without previous inbreeding.

Outcrossing is a form of breeding in which one family line is crossed with that of another of the same variety. The object is to hold the good traits already in the one family line and to capture the good ones from the other one. Or, it may be to attempt to get rid of the undesirable traits in one line and obtain only the good ones from another line.

Outgrading is a breeding plan used by many commercial hatcheries to improve the quality of the chicks sold. They buy improved males of some breed or variety, Single-Comb White Leghorns for instance, and place them in hatchery flocks comprised of Single-Comb White Leghorns. (Fig. 56.) The object is to improve the quality of the chicks produced from the flocks.

[2] Jeoffrey, 1939.

Backcrossing is the mating of a crossbred animal back to one of the pure parent races which were crossed to produce it. It is not widely used.

Incrossing is: (1) The crossing of two inbred lines of the same or of different breeds or varieties. (2) The crossing of first generation poultry resulting from the combination of two other inbred lines when each line used is of different breed or variety than any other used. The production of commercial incrossbreds is usually accomplished by this method. (Fig. 57.) Some incrosses improve the quality of the resulting stock while others do not. The problem is to find desirable inbred lines for making desirable crosses.

Closed flock breeding. This system of breeding begins with the selection of individuals and families within a flock. The individuals from different families are mated. No new strains of stock are introduced. No crossing is practiced except between the different families within the flock. The objective of the closed flock system of breeding is to combine or intensify the desirable characters in the different families within the flock and at the same time reduce or eliminate the undesirable ones.

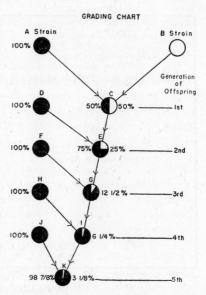

GRADING CHART

Fig. 56. Flock improvement by the purchase of improved males (outgrading).

Methods of Mating

The method of mating used will haγe a marked influence on fertility and consequently on the number of offspring used. The two most common methods of mating are flock and pen mating. Stud mating and artificial insemination are sometimes used in experimental work.

Flock mating. Flock or mass mating means that a number of males are allowed to run with the entire flock of hens. This system of mating is used on most farms. In flock matings the parentage of the chicks hatched is unknown.

Other things being equal, better fertility is obtained from flock matings than from pen matings. There is an opportunity for birds to mate with those they like in flock mating; in pen mating there is no choice. Competition among males in flock mating also results in more matings and better fertility.

The number of hens that should be mated with each male will vary with the size and age of the birds (p. 103).

Pen mating. In pen mating a pen of hens is mated to a single male. If the birds are trap-nested and the hen's leg-band number recorded on the egg, it is possible to know the parents of every chick hatched from a pen mating.

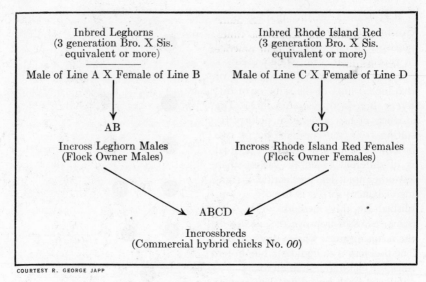

Fig. 57. Production of incrossbred hybrids.

About the same number of hens are mated with a male as in the case of flock mating. Fertility is generally not so good in pen mating as in flock mating. This is because certain hens may not like the male, or vice versa.

Stud mating. In stud mating the females are mated individually with a male kept by himself in a coop or pen. In this system of mating more females can be mated with a male than in pen matings. Stud mating involves more labor than flock or pen mating. The birds should be mated at least once each week in order to maintain good fertility.

Stud mating may be used where hens are kept in laying batteries. It is also used when a very valuable male is being used as a breeder. By the use of stud mating, more offspring can be obtained from the male.

Artificial insemination. Artificial insemination is possible but not practical in ordinary poultry-breeding work. It is used in experimental work and may be used in turkey breeding where poor fertility is encountered.

A method has been developed at the National Agricultural Research Center and elsewhere for securing sperm from the male by artificial stimulation and for transferring it to the oviduct of the female. Doses of .1 cc. of semen injected once a week give good fertility.

Securing Good Fertility

Once high egg production has been secured, fertility is the first factor which determines the number of offspring that may be obtained from a given individual. As in the case of other animals, both males and females among poultry may be sterile. It is a good plan to test the fertility of males and females at least a month before the beginning of the breeding season. Factors influencing fertility include the number of females mated to one male, the age of breeders, the length of time between mating and saving eggs for hatchability, and management practices.

The number of birds mated to one male. In mating birds of the light or egg breeds, such as Leghorns, it is customary to use one male for fifteen to twenty hens. In case of the general-purpose breeds, such as Plymouth Rocks, it is customary to use one male with ten to fifteen hens. About eight to twelve hens are mated with one male in case of the heavy breeds, such as the Brahmas.

Age of breeders. Young birds are more active than old ones. Fertility is better among pullets and cockerels during the first year than later on. Males are not very satisfactory as breeders after they are about three years old.

Fertility can be improved by using cockerels with old hens or pullets with old males. When both old hens and old males are used in the breeding pen, fewer hens should be used with each male than generally recommended.

Length of time after mating. It is possible to secure fertile eggs about twenty-four hours after males have been placed in the pen. However, a maximum percentage of fertility is not reached until about ten days after the birds have been mated.

It is possible to secure fertile eggs as long as twenty-one days after the males have been removed from the flock. Reasonably good fertility may be expected for about a week after removal of the males. In case a male bird dies or is replaced by another male in a breeding pen, one should wait about three weeks before saving eggs for hatching in order to be sure that none of the eggs were fertilized by the sperm of the preceding male.

It is true that when other things are equal, the newest sperm in the oviduct will be most likely to fertilize the eggs.

Influence of flock management. The health of the flock and housing conditions influence fertility. Good fertility cannot be expected unless the birds are vigorous and active.

Extremely cold weather will result in poor fertility and poor hatchability unless housing conditions are such that the birds will be comfortable. In cold climates, where breeders are kept in unheated pens, it is a good plan to dub the combs and wattles of the males to prevent freezing. Birds with frozen combs or wattles are inactive because of the soreness of the affected parts.

The poultry house should be kept clean, dry, well ventilated, and free from filth.

Breeding for Hatchability

It is known that feeding and management practices affect hatchability. Aside from these, there are a number of breeding practices which influence hatchability. Chief among these may be mentioned the age of breeders, egg production, method of breeding, egg characters, and lethal genes.

Age of breeders. Eggs from pullets show a little better hatchability of fertile eggs than those from hens. Since fertility of eggs from pullets is higher than that from hens, the number of chicks obtained from each one hundred eggs set is higher from pullets than from hens. This fact tempts some hatcherymen to hatch from pullets rather than from hens. The chicks from pullets will not be so large or uniform as those from hens.

The University of Missouri has made a study of the hatchability of eggs from hens and pullets, comprising several different breeds. The results are summarized in Table 18.

Table 18

THE PER CENT HATCHABILITY OF PULLET AND HEN EGGS [3]

Breed	Pullets	Hens
White Leghorns........................	83	75
Rhode Island Reds....................	79	71
Barred Plymouth Rocks...............	62	57
White Plymouth Rocks...............	76	69

The hatchability of eggs of the same group of birds used two or more breeding seasons in succession tends to decline. Studies made at the Kansas Experiment Station are summarized in Table 19.

Table 19

PER CENT HATCHABILITY OF EGGS FROM THE SAME
GROUPS OF BIRDS IN SUCCEEDING YEARS [4]

Breed	Pullet Year	Second Year	Third Year	Fourth Year
White Leghorns......	75	66	70	...
White Leghorns......	...	78	72	61
Rhode Island Reds...	60	53	49	...
Rhode Island Reds...	...	69	66	54

Egg production. Good hatchability is associated with good egg production. There is a common belief that if birds have been laying very long before the hatching season, hatchability of eggs and livability of chicks will be lower than from birds that have not laid so many eggs. A study of this factor was made at the National Agricultural Research Center. The results are summarized in Table 20. From it, one may conclude that the length of time birds have been in production before the hatching season does not influence the hatchability of the eggs set or the livability of the chicks hatched.

[3] Funk, 1934.
[4] Warren, 1934.

Table 20

EFFECT OF PREVIOUS PRODUCTION ON HATCHABILITY
AND LIVABILITY OF CHICKS [5]

Previous Production of Birds from October to Hatching Season	Per Cent Hatchability of Fertile Eggs	Per Cent Chick Mortality First Four Weeks
Barred Plymouth Rocks		
Those laying 0–29 eggs	77	4
30–59 eggs	72	3
60–89 eggs	71	...
Rhode Island Reds		
0–29 eggs	73	1
30–59 eggs	71	2
60–89 eggs	64	...
White Leghorns		
0–29 eggs	74	3
30–59 eggs	73	3
60–89 eggs	69	2

Methods of breeding. Hatchability is influenced by the method of breeding. Close inbreeding tends to lower hatchability (p. 99), while cross-breeding increases it. If birds are selected for high hatchability as well as for the character to be intensified in line breeding, no harm results from this system of breeding.

Egg characters. Egg characters, such as size, shape, and interior quality, affect hatchability.

Standard-weight eggs, those weighing two ounces each, hatch better than those much above or below this weight.

Long pointed and short bulging eggs do not hatch well. They should be culled out from eggs that are to be used for hatching purposes anyway. If a pullet is hatched from such an egg, it will likely lay the same kind. Long pointed and short, thick eggs are unsatisfactory for packing for market.

Double-yolked eggs do not hatch. Embryos may develop in such an egg until near the hatching day. The chicks are too cramped and there is not enough space for respiration and movement in the pipping process.

Eggs with shells of medium strength hatch better than eggs with shells that are too thick or too thin. Evaporation is too rapid from thin-shelled eggs during the period of incubation. Chicks have difficulty in pipping in eggs with extremely thick shells.

Eggs with good interior quality, as judged by candling appearance, hatch better than those with poor interior quality. Eggs with a large proportion of white in proportion to yolk do not hatch so well as those with less white.

Records were obtained on the relationship between the candling grade of eggs and their hatchability in connection with chicks produced for the An-

[5] Jull, 1931.

nual Baby Chick Show, held at Ohio State University. Some of the data obtained are summarized in Table 21.

Table 21

INFLUENCE OF EGG QUALITY ON HATCHABILITY

Quality of Eggs	1938	1939	1940	Total for Three Years
Grade A				
Number set...................	1147	4547	5825	11519
Number chicks hatched........	825	3364	4192	8381
Per cent hatch of eggs set.......	72	74	72	73
Grade B				
Number set...................	1733	2155	1001	4889
Number chicks hatched.........	1229	1550	744	3523
Per cent hatch of eggs set.......	71	72	74	72
Grade C				
Number set...................	97	30	4	131
Number chicks hatched.........	50	19	1	70
Per cent hatch of eggs set........	52	63	25	53
Blood and Meat Spots				
Number set................	9	19	37	65
Number chicks hatched.........	4	11	23	38
Per cent hatch of eggs set........	44	58	62	58
Checks				
Number set...................	14	30	2	46
Number chicks hatched.........	4	16	1	21
Per cent hatch of eggs set.......	29	53	50	46

Lethal genes. Lethal genes affecting hatchability have been discovered in recent years (p. 86). In studying hatching records on breeding farms, the dead embryos should be examined in order to locate sires and dams carrying the lethal genes in heterozygous condition. A sire and a dam each carrying a lethal gene in a heterozygous condition will produce offspring in the proportion of three normal to one carrying the lethal character. The same sire, mated to his daughters, produces five normal to one lethal or seven normal to one lethal embryo.

Hatchability improvement through breeding can be secured only by trapnesting and selection of individuals and families. The farmer who experiences low hatchability as a result of breeding can improve it by the use of males which were produced by families having high hatchability.

Breeding for Livability

Livability is influenced greatly by feeding and management practices. It is also influenced, in many cases, by low resistance of the stock to disease invasion.

Experimental evidence has shown that there are family differences as regards the susceptibility to and resistance against pullorum, fowl typhoid, range paralysis, roundworm infestation, crooked keels, and reproductive troubles.

Breeds and strains. Chicks obtained from different breeds and strains but reared under identical conditions show marked differences in livability. In the Nebraska flock-testing project in 1935, differences in mortality among chicks from different flocks during the first four weeks varied from 1 to 70 per cent. The variation was from 13 to 70 per cent among strains of general-purpose breeds, and from 1 to 31 per cent among Leghorns. A large part of the mortality was probably due to pullorum. These and other data indicate that general-purpose breeds are more susceptible than Leghorns to pullorum infection.

Age of breeders. Chicks hatched from hens are more uniform in size and vigor and live better than those hatched from pullets (Table 22). This

Table 22

MORTALITY OF PULLETS DURING THE FIRST LAYING
YEAR, HATCHED FROM HEN AND
PULLET BREEDERS [6]

Kind of Breeders	Mortality of Pullet Progeny (per cent)	
	Total	*Due to Paralysis*
Hens		
Trial 1............	35	20
Trial 2............	34	14
Pullets		
Trial 1............	62	32
Trial 2............	48	24

may be expected, since pullet mortality is higher than hen mortality. Pullet and cockerel parents may die before the end of the first year of production. The offspring will, therefore, be from parents whose livability has not been determined. When chicks are hatched from year-old stock or older, it is known that the birds are from parents that were able to live and produce well through at least one year of production.

The fact that pullets lay more eggs and that the hatchability of their eggs is better has led hatcherymen to use mostly pullet eggs for hatching. This has no doubt been a major factor in shortening the life and increasing mortality among laying flocks. More attention is now being given to the hatching of chicks from breeders that have been through one or more years of production.

System of breeding. Inbreeding results in reduced vigor and increased mortality (p. 99). Crossbreeding has the opposite effect. If care is used in the selection of breeding stock for livability, as well as for the character to be intensified, inbreeding may be practiced without harmful effects on livability.

---

[6] Kennard, 1934.

Fig. 58. Chicks showing contrasting feather growth. Left, slow feathering chick at age of 10 days: right, fast feathering chick at same age. (U. S. D. A. Leaflet 233.)

In breeding for livability, only birds from families that have shown good livability should be used in the breeding pen. This is especially true in case of the male bird. Theoretically, at least, it would be possible to improve livability by the system of breeding known as outcrossing (p. 000). The use of hens rather than pullets for breeders and mating them with males from families that have shown good livability will no doubt do much to reduce adult mortality.

Breeding for Growth and Feathering

Rate of growth and adult body size are both inherited characters. They may be influenced greatly by the selection of breeding stock. The rate of growth of body flesh and feathers is also influenced by the protein and vitamin content of the ration (Chapter Nine) and the temperature used in brooding.

It is known that lightweight breeds, such as Leghorns, reach maturity about a month earlier than general-purpose breeds, such as Plymouth Rocks. Within a given breed or variety it has been observed that some strains grow much faster and reach sexual maturity earlier than others. Strains with narrow feathers generally mature more slowly than those with broad feathers. Birds with narrow feathers in the Barred Plymouth Rock and Rhode Island Red breeds may produce chicks that have bare backs most of the time during the first six to eight weeks of the growing period.

The breeding stock should be selected on the basis of the rate of growth up to eight weeks. The young stock should be inspected for weight and feathering at this age. Underweight and poorly feathered birds should be removed or marked and removed later on. If the records on growth and feathering are not recorded until the birds are housed, many of the undesirable birds will be missed. They will have completed a normal plumage and possibly will have grown to normal size by the time they are placed in the laying house.

COURTESY CANADA DEPARTMENT OF AGRICULTURE

Fig. 59. A good body type for meat production. The legs are short; the breast broad; and the keel is carried well forward.

Early-feathering chicks are found within a breed and strain as indicated by the length of the wing and tail feathers at about ten days of age (Fig. 58). By picking out these chicks and using them as breeders, it is possible to develop an earlier-feathering strain of birds.

Crossbred poultry generally make better growth during the first eight to twelve weeks than the Standard-bred birds from which they were hatched. The adult size is generally intermediate between that of the two breeds that were crossed. Data obtained at the California Experiment Station indicate that the shank length measurement of live birds is a true indication of heritable differences in body size.

Breeding for Meat Production

Breeding chickens for meat production has been overshadowed by breeding for egg production. As we shall see, selection of birds for egg production is very complicated. Very little may be learned about the egg production of a hen by looking at her. It is quite different in selecting birds for meat production. Birds are selected for type in breeding for meat production.

Extensive studies have been made in Canada on the selection and breeding of birds for meat production. Contrasts in good and poor types for meat production are shown in Figures 59 and 60. Good birds have a broad back and the keel is carried well forward. The legs are short and thick and set well apart. The neck is short. Poor meat-type birds have narrow backs and shallow breasts; the legs are long, thin, and close together. Birds selected as breeders for meat production should have shown rapid growth and good feathering during the first eight weeks.

Breeding for Egg Production

Most of the income from chickens is from the sale of eggs for food and for hatching purposes. The higher the egg production secured, the lower the feed and total cost per dozen of eggs. Consequently, poultrymen are interested in high egg production. Good feeding and management practices will result

COURTESY CANADA DEPARTMENT OF AGRICULTURE

Fig. 60. A poor body type for meat production. The legs are long; the breast shallow; and the body is short and narrow.

in an increase in egg production from about 80 or 90 eggs per year to 150 or 160. Greater production will depend largely on careful selection of breeders on the basis of the trap nest, sib, and progeny records.

Selection on the basis of the trap-nest record. Inherited characters for high egg production include early sexual maturity, rate of production, lack of pauses, nonbroodiness, and persistency in production. Accurate records regarding these characters can be secured only through trap-nesting the birds. Once prospective breeders have been selected on the basis of vigor and breed and variety characteristics, they should be leg-banded and trap-nested; and the records should be analyzed on a family basis before the breeders are selected.

Early maturity. Early sexual maturity, the age at which egg production begins, is an inherited character. It shows dominance and some sex linkage in which several genes are probably involved. By selecting the early-maturing birds in a flock each year, it is possible to materially reduce the time required to reach sexual maturity in a flock. At the Kansas Experiment Station the time required for a strain of Rhode Island Reds to reach sexual maturity was reduced from 269 to 222 days in the course of six years of selection and breeding for early maturity.

If light breeds, such as Leghorns, are to lay approximately two hundred eggs during the pullet year, they should come into production when about five and one-half months old. In the case of general-purpose breeds, such as Rhode Island Reds, production should start when the birds are about six months old.

In a flock of birds in which all of them are the same age, the first 75 per cent that come into production will be the best layers.

Rate of production. A bird that lays at a high rate has a shorter interval between ovulations, the eggs remain in the oviduct for a shorter period of time, and laying takes place more nearly at the same hour each day than in the case of a low-rate layer. In other words, the best layers lay in long clutches with few intervals, while the poor layers lay in short clutches with numerous intervals of varying length between the clutches. At the National Agricultural Research Center it has been observed that full sisters lay at more nearly the same rate than half sisters and less related birds, and half sisters lay at more nearly the same rate than less related birds.

The rate of production is figured on a percentage basis, using the number of eggs laid from the date of the first egg to a given date in relation to the total number of days involved. If a flock of birds is to average about two hundred eggs during the first year of production, they should lay at the rate of 60 per cent, or at least four eggs per clutch.

Lack of pauses. Some birds lay well for a while and then go out of production for varying lengths of time. A pause is regarded as an interval of more than seven days between clutches of eggs. Some pauses may be caused by digestive disturbance, a cold or other respiratory trouble, parasites, etc. Other pauses are encountered which cannot be accounted for on the basis of disease, environment, and management. They are believed to be herditary. One of these pauses is encountered during the winter and is commonly referred to as the winter pause.

In selecting birds to be used for breeders, those with the fewest pauses and of the shortest duration should be selected.

Nonbroodiness. If a bird is to lay well, it must not be broody much of the time. Broodiness is a dominant sex-linked character. Unless breeders are selected for nonbroodiness, the offspring will show more broodiness each year with a decline in egg production.

Light breeds, such as Leghorns, are less broody than general-purpose breeds, such as Plymouth Rocks. Within a given breed or variety there are strains with much less broodiness than is found in others.

When two breeds are crossed, the progeny generally show more broodiness than that shown by either of the parent breeds.

A record should be made of each period that a bird is broody. If the broody period is often or of long duration, the bird should not be used in the breeding pen. It is a common practice to reject Leghorns that are broody two or more times during the year, as well as general-purpose birds that are broody three or more times.

Persistency in production. Persistent layers are those that lay well during the summer and fall of the year following that in which they were hatched.

The termination of the first year of laying is closely related to the first annual molt. Most birds quit laying and then molt. A few birds will lay and molt at the same time; these are usually very desirable birds for use in the breeding pen.

Birds should be selected for persistency of production that lay approximately twenty-five eggs during August and September of the year following that in which they were hatched.

At the Massachusetts Experiment Station, Rhode Island Red breeders have been selected for egg production for a number of years on the basis of early maturity, rate of laying, nonbroodiness, and persistency. Each of these characters has been improved along with an increase in egg production (Table 23). Selection for nonbroodiness has shown more progress than selection for the other factors.

Selection of breeders on the basis of the first year of egg production alone is not a satisfactory measure of their breeding value (Table 24). The data show no apparent relationship between the egg production of the dams and that among the daughters among the Rhode Island Reds, but there is seen a slight relationship between the egg production of the dams and that of the daughters among the White Leghorns. Inheritance of a character in one breed may be different in another one.

Table 23

IMPROVEMENT IN EGG PRODUCTION WITH IMPROVEMENT IN
INHERITED CHARACTERS FOR EGG PRODUCTION [7]

Year	Sexual Maturity Days	Rate of Laying (number eggs per clutch)	Nonbroodiness (per cent)	Persistence Days	Average Egg Production
1920	200	2.7	54	331	200
1921	211	3.3	55	304	198
1922	197	2.7	71	322	200
1923	209	2.4	73	323	189
1924	196	2.5	67	327	196
1925	192	3.1	58	330	205
1926	199	2.7	81	331	205
1927	185	3.5	90	321	197
1928	196	3.4	72	335	215
1929	197	3.1	87	330	208
1930	191	3.7	78	340	214
1931	189	3.8	84	344	234
1932	202	3.3	88	338	222
1933	194	3.3	95	342	214
1934	186	3.7	92	344	225
1935	192	2.9	95	343	216
1936	196	2.9	90	345	220
1937	197	3.0	98	339	205
1938	196	3.2	92	343	221

Table 24

THE   AVERAGE   FIRST-YEAR   PRODUCTION   OF   THE
DAUGHTERS OF DAMS CLASSIFIED ACCORDING
TO THE RANGE IN EGG PRODUCTION
OF THE DAMS [8]

RANGE IN EGG PRODUCTION OF DAMS	AVERAGE EGG PRODUCTION OF DAUGHTERS	
	Rhode Island Reds	White Leghorns
181–190	...	162
191–200	...	157
201–210	188	168
211–220	205	161
221–230	192	173
231–240	192	176
241–250	199	169
251–260	201	188
261–270	200	209
271–280	197	188
281–290	179	208
291–300	...	222
301–310	...	228
311–320	...	220

[7] Hays, 1939.
[8] Jull, 1938.

Selection on the basis of the family records. A bird with a good pedigree or family history of good production is to be preferred to one whose pedigree is unknown. A study of the egg-production records of ancestors back as far as three generations is useful in estimating the breeding value of an individual. However, the records of the brothers and sisters, are as important or more so than that of the parents and grandparents, in predicting the breeding value of a male or female.

Selection on the basis of the progeny test. The final and most valuable test for a breeder is the kind of progeny that it produces. It is not how many eggs a hen lays that counts, but the number her daughters will lay. If a bird is to be valuable as a breeder, it must be able to transmit desirable characters to its offspring.

Poultry-breeding work at the Maine Experiment Station became the foundation for modern poultry breeding and progeny testing. Nine years of poultry breeding in which females were selected for breeders on the basis of their first-year trap-nest records failed to produce an increase in the level of egg production among the pullets raised each year. When pullets and cockerels were selected for breeders each year from among the best families of that year, a steady increase in the level of egg production was achieved.

It is highly important to select sires of superior breeding value because the average sire has about ten times as many chicks as the average dam. It is also important to be able to identify females of superior breeding worth, if for no other reason than to produce more superior males. Some actual case records are presented in Table 25. Sire Number 1 is far more valuable than Number 3 as a breeder, even though his mates did not have quite so high an egg production. In like manner, dam Number 4 is superior to Number 5. Register of merit breeders (p. 116), both male and female, are most likely to produce the best progeny.

In carrying on a progeny test program the first step is to determine which of the different male birds used proved to be the best breeders. The daughters of each male should be compared with those of other males with respect to sexual maturity, rate of laying, lack of pauses, nonbroodiness, and persistence

Table 25

VARIATIONS IN EGG PRODUCTION OF DAUGHTERS
OF DIFFERENT SIRES AND DAMS

Sire or Dam Number	Average Production of Mates or Self	Number of Daughters	Average Egg Production of Daughters
Sire 1	264	76	219
Sire 2	276	108	191
Sire 3	285	114	163
Dam 4	281	8	278
Dam 5	312	19	203
Dam 6	234	11	186

of production. Having determined the best males, the next step is to determine the female progeny of each of the hens to which a superior male was mated.

The breeding program should be based on the selection of outstanding families. Sires and dams of outstanding value should be used as many years as possible. Their progeny should also be given preference when selecting future breeders.

Since the life of chickens is relatively short, and their breeding period pretty well over by the time records on the progeny are known, the records of the full sisters are given considerable weight in selecting cockerels for the breeding pen. If the first part of the pullet laying year is outstanding, as judged by sexual maturity, rate of laying, lack of pauses, and nonbroodiness of all the sisters in the family, the brothers can be used as breeders that year with a good degree of assurance that they will prove satisfactory.

Selection on the basis of long-time egg production. Birds that lay well the first year have a tendency to do so the second year. There are some notable exceptions, however. Naturally a bird that lives and continues to lay well for two, three, or four years is more desirable as a breeder than one with a shorter record of production.

Under ordinary circumstances, the decline in egg production is about 20 per cent of that of the preceding year. For instance, if a bird laid 200 eggs during the pullet year, it may be expected to lay about 160 eggs the second year and 130 the third year. If the first-year egg production has been retarded by improper feeding or management, a bird may lay more eggs the second year than during the first one if the poor management practices are corrected.

Breeding for Egg Quality

The number of eggs laid is not the only thing to be considered in breeding for egg production. The markets and consumers are interested in egg size and shape, shell color and texture, and interior quality.

Egg size. Egg size is correlated with body size. Egg size increases from the time pullets start to lay in the summer or fall until the month of February. The size of eggs declines during the hot summer months. Eggs produced during the second year of production are larger than first-year eggs. Those laid at the beginning of a clutch are larger than those laid at the end. There is also a tendency toward a decline in egg size with the total number of eggs laid in a year.

It is possible to secure and maintain good egg size even with high egg production by mass selection of breeders that have good body and egg size as well as good egg production.

Eggs of uniform shape and weighing between twenty-four and twenty-eight ounces per dozen should be set in order to maintain standard-weight eggs of twenty-four ounces per dozen in the succeeding generation. There is a tendency for birds to revert to the laying of small eggs like those of their ancestors, unless one continually selects eggs of good size for hatching.

Leghorns should weigh at least three pounds, Rhode Island Reds four and one-half pounds, and Plymouth Rocks five and one-half pounds at the time production begins, if good egg size is to be obtained. The size of the pullet, rather than the age at which it starts to lay, is the more important factor influencing egg size.

Shell color. Shell color is more important in white eggs than in brown ones. Varying shades of color are expected among brown eggs. Tinted shells should be avoided among white eggs; they do not influence the food value of the eggs, but do have an unfavorable effect on the appearance of packs of white eggs. White eggs that have tinted shells should not be set. Birds that lay eggs with tinted shells or poor shell texture should not be used for breeders. The use of the trap nest enables one to detect the birds that lay undesirable eggs.

Eggshell texture declines with age and the length of the laying period. A breeder may have laid eggs with good shell texture in the pullet year and with thin or rough shells in later years. Shell thickness declines toward the end of the laying year, often becoming quite poor in the late summer. Birds should be selected for breeders that lay well during the months of August and September, and that produce good shells during this period.

Interior quality. Interior quality of eggs is influenced by breeding as well as by management. The percentage of thick white to total white, presence of blood spots, and possibly yolk color, are influenced by the genetic constitution of the bird. Hatching eggs should be graded for size and shape, and candled for shell texture and interior quality.

The National Poultry Improvement Plan

Most states have had some kind of breed improvement programs for a number of years. Some have been supervised by state regulatory agencies, some by poultry extension service agencies, and others by dues paid by members of the association. The programs have lacked uniformity in terminology and supervision.

In 1935 the United States Department of Agriculture established the National Poultry Improvement Plan in co-operation with state poultry improvement associations. The objectives of the plan are to improve the breeding and production qualities of poultry and to reduce losses from pullorum disease. This is being accomplished by (1) the development of more effective state poultry improvement programs; (2) the identification of the quality of breeding stock, hatching eggs, and chicks by authorized terms that are uniform and applicable in all parts of the country; and (3) the establishment of an effective co-operative program through which newer knowledge and practical experience can be applied to the improvement of poultry and poultry products.

Acceptance of the plan is optional with the states and with individual members of the industry within the states. The plan is administered in each state by an official state agency, cooperating with the Bureau of Animal Industry, United States Department of Agriculture.

The National Poultry Improvement Plan is divided into two parts: breeding stages and pullorum control and eradication classes

Breeding stages. 1. *U. S. Approved Stage:* The females are rigidly and thoroughly selected once each year for constitutional vigor and for egg production, such selected females to combine Standard-bred and production qualities to a reasonably high degree. Males are selected especially for constitutional vigor and Standard-bred qualities. The selection of the flocks is approved by an official state inspector. The hatching eggs must weigh at least one and eleven-twelfths ounces each, except during the months of July through November when they may weigh as low as one and ten-twelfths ounces each, or 22 ounces per dozen.

2. *U. S. Certified Stage:* These flocks fulfill all the requirements of the U. S. Approved flock and are mated to U.S.R.O.P. males.

3. *U. S. Record of Performance Stage:* U.S.R.O.P. females must lay two hundred eggs during the first laying year. The eggs must average not less than twenty-four ounces per dozen for pullets and twenty-five ounces for yearlings or older hens.

U.S.R.O.P. males must come from U.S.R.O.P. eggs. These weigh twenty-five ounces or more per dozen.

The males and females qualifying for U.S.R.O.P. must be of normal size, free of disqualifications, and have the standard characteristics for the breed.

4. *U. S. Register of Merit Stage:* A U.S.R.O.M. male is a U.S.R.O.P. male which has at least one-half of his daughters qualify for U.S.R.O.P. and a minimum of twenty.

A U.S.R.O.M. female is a U.S.R.O.P. female which has at least one-half of her daughters qualify for U.S.R.O.P. and a minimum of four.

Pullorum control and eradication classes. 1. *U. S. Pullorum-Controlled Class:* All chickens over five months of age to be used as breeders shall be tested for pullorum disease under the supervision of an official state agency and contain fewer than 2 per cent of reactors, the last test being made within twelve months immediately preceding the date of sale of hatching eggs or chicks from such flocks. Three official pullorum tests are recognized in the National Plan. These are the standard tube, rapid serum, and whole blood-stained antigen tests. The last test is the most practical for general use.

2. *U. S. Pullorum-Passed Class:* Flocks shall be tested as described for the U. S. Pullorum-Controlled Class and shall contain no reactors on the last test.

3. *U. S. Pullorum-Clean Class:* The flocks shall be tested as directed for the U. S. Pullorum-Controlled Class and shall contain no reactors in two consecutive tests not less than six months apart or in three consecutive tests not less than 30 days apart, the last being made within the testing year immediately preceding the date of sale of hatching eggs or chicks from such flocks.

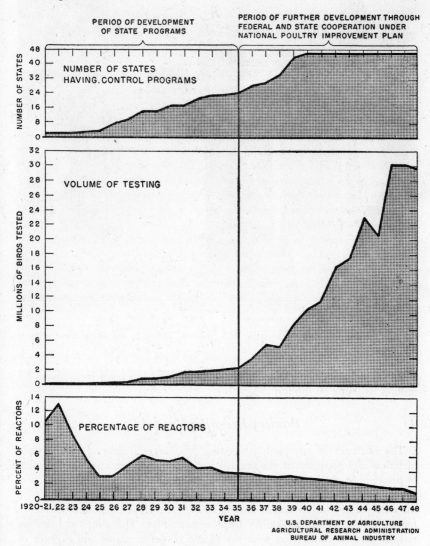

Fig. 61. Pullorum testing under the National Poultry Improvement Plan.

Accomplishments of the Plan. The average annual egg production in the United States increased only seven eggs during the twenty-five-year period before the National Plan was started. During the first twelve years of its operation the average annual egg production has increased 15 eggs (Fig. 10).

The per cent of pullorum reactor chickens in flocks when official pullorum testing was started in the United States in 1920 was about 11 per cent. By 1948 it had been reduced to about 1 per cent (Fig. 61). Since the National

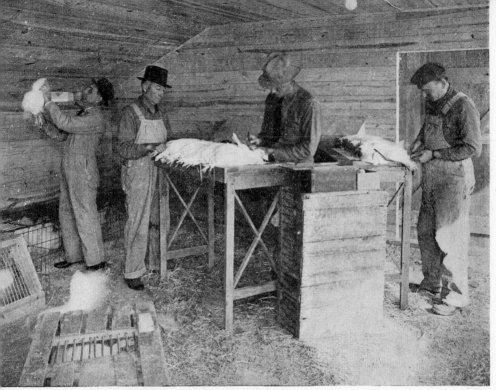

Fig. 62. Selecting birds for the breeding flock; pullorum testing by the whole blood method; and banding approved birds.

Plan was started, the number of breeders tested has increased from about 2.5 million to about 29 million.

Poultry-Breeding Records

The efficiency of any poultry-breeding program will depend on the completeness and accuracy of the records kept. They are essential for selection of breeders on the basis of production, reproduction, family and progeny performance. The United States Department of Agriculture, in co-operation with the state poultry improvement associations, has developed a system of records for use in the National Poultry Improvement Plan. The simplest breeding records used in connection with the record of performance and register of merit stages are (1) the monthly trap-nest record, (2) yearly summary sheet, (3) the breeding-pen record, (4) incubation and chick-banding report, (5) pedigree record, and (6) the female summary record.

The monthly record. Trap-nesting is costly because it requires about twice as much labor to care for birds as if they were not trap-nested. Therefore, in starting a poultry breed improvement program, one should first have a healthy flock of Standard-bred birds with good flock-production records.

The birds to be trap-nested should be selected from the flock, blood-tested, and leg-banded with a sealed band (Fig. 62). The birds should be trapped every hour during the morning and every hour or so during the afternoon

Fig. 63. Trap-nesting. The bird and egg are removed from the nest and the egg recorded on the trap-nest record sheet.

(Fig. 63). When the bird is removed from the nest, the egg is recorded on a monthly record sheet (Fig. 64).

The various characteristics listed at the top and right of the form should be recorded in order to supply as much information regarding individual layers as possible.

The monthly record forms are large enough to provide for the recording of the monthly production of twenty-five to fifty hens.

The yearly summary sheet. The monthly egg production and characteristics of each bird are transferred from the monthly record to the yearly summary sheet (Fig. 65), and the total production determined for the year. Birds to be used in the breeding pen are selected largely on the basis of their health, body size, and egg production records, as shown on the summary sheet.

The breeding-pen record. The records of the females used in the breeding pen are obtained from the yearly summary sheet and recorded on the breeding-pen record (Fig. 66). The record of the male used in the breeding pen is obtained from the pedigree index record.

The females used in the breeding pen are trap-nested. The pen number, the leg-band number of the hen, and the date are marked on the small end of the hatching egg at the time the hen is released from the nest, and the record made on the monthly egg record sheet.

The incubation and chick-banding report. The male's record and the

MONTHLY EGG RECORD

Breeder..   Average Production to Date...

House No..   Pen No...   Variety...   Month..................................., 19.........

Hen Number	1	2	3	4	5	6	7	8	9	10	11	12	13	14	15	16	17	18	19	20	21	22	23	24	25	26	27	28	29	30	31	Month Total	Brot Forw'd	Total to Date	Weight of Egg		

Fig. 64. Monthly trap-nest record sheet.

hen leg-band numbers are taken from the breeding-pen record and recorded on the incubation and chick-banding report (Fig. 67). A separate sheet is used for each breeding pen. If more than six hatches are made from a given pen mating during the season, two sheets may be used and the totals listed on the second sheet. The chick band numbers list the first and last band numbers only. For instance, if five chicks were hatched from a hen on a given

SUMMARY SHEET

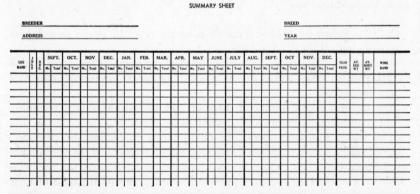

Fig. 65. Yearly egg record summary sheet. The monthly records (Fig. 64) are transferred to this sheet.

date and the last band number that had been listed was 51, the band numbers of the chicks hatched would be 52 to 56.

It is a good plan to separate the hatching eggs by pen numbers at the time they are gathered and by hen numbers in the pen at the time they are set (Fig. 68). The number of eggs set from each hen is recorded at the time they are set and each hen's eggs are set together in the tray. Sometime be-

THE NATIONAL POULTRY IMPROVEMENT PLAN
U. S. R. O. P. BREEDING PEN RECORD

1. Flock owner ....
                (Name)   (Address)

2. Breed and variety .... Pen No. .... Year ....

MALE

U. S. R. O. P. leg-band number of sire ....

U. S. R. O. P. leg-band No. ....
Wing-band No. ....
Body weight ....:...........................
Date hatched ....

U. S. R. O. P. leg band number of dam ....
   Egg production ....
   Egg weight ....
   Body weight..

Fertility and hatchability of eggs from previous season's matings in which this male was used: Percent fertile eggs ....; percent fertile eggs hatched ....

FEMALES

U.S.R.O.P. LEG-BAND NO.	WING-BAND NO.	EGG PRODUCTION	EGG WEIGHT	BODY WEIGHT	REMARKS
		Number	Oz. per dozen	Pounds	

Date ....
                                                          (Official State Inspector)

U. S. GOVERNMENT PRINTING OFFICE   16—9580

Fig. 66. U. S. R. O. P. breeding pen record used in the National Poultry Improvement Plan.

tween the sixteenth and eighteenth day of incubation, the eggs should be candled, the infertile eggs recorded, the dead embryos and infertile eggs removed, and each hen's hatchable eggs placed in a separate pedigree basket or sack for hatching.

At hatching time each hen's chicks are counted, wing-banded (Figs. 69 and 70), and the numbers recorded on the incubation and chick-banding report.

The pedigree record. The wing band, pen and dam's numbers are taken from the incubation and chick-banding report and recorded on the pedigree record (Fig. 71). The wing-band numbers are listed in numerical order.

U. S. R. O. P. INCUBATION AND CHICK-BANDING REPORT

Breeder's name...............
Breed and variety...............
Pen No............... Year...............

Male's { Wing-band No...............
{ U. S. R. O. P. leg-band No...............

Male's { U. S. R. O. P. leg-band No...............
dam's { Egg production...............
{ Egg weight...............

U. S. GOVERNMENT PRINTING OFFICE   16—10440

Hen's U.S.R.O.P. Leg Band		DATE SET / DATE HATCHED				DATE SET / DATE HATCHED				DATE SET / DATE HATCHED				DATE SET / DATE HATCHED				DATE SET / DATE HATCHED				DATE SET / DATE HATCHED				TOTAL			
Série	No.	Number of eggs set	Number infertile	Number of chicks	Chick band No.	Number of eggs set	Number infertile	Number of chicks	Chick band No.	Number of eggs set	Number infertile	Number of chicks	Chick band No.	Number of eggs set	Number infertile	Number of chicks	Chick band No.	Number of eggs set	Number infertile	Number of chicks	Chick band No.	Number of eggs set	Number infertile	Number of chicks	Chick band No.	Number of eggs set	Number infertile

Fig. 67. U. S. R. O. P. incubation and chick-banding record.

U. S. D. A.

Fig. 68. A convenient cabinet for holding hatching eggs until placed in the incubator. The top of the cabinet has indentations so that eggs may be arranged according to the hen or the pen they came from. The two rows of drawers are for holding the eggs from different pens.

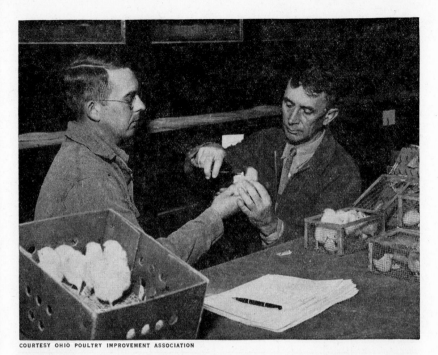

Fig. 69. Pedigreeing chicks. Each hen's eggs are hatched in a separate basket or compartment. Each chick is wing banded and the wing-band number recorded on the incubation and chick-banding report (Fig. 67).

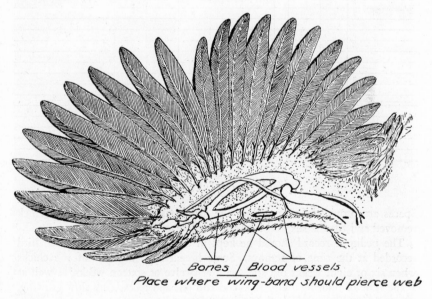

Bones | Blood vessels
Place where wing-band should pierce web

Fig. 70. Structure of the wing, showing location of the wing band. (Cornell Extension Bulletin 117.)

THE NATIONAL POULTRY IMPROVEMENT PLAN
U. S. R. O. P. PEDIGREE RECORD
(For breeders who use serially numbered wing bands)

Name _____ Breed and variety_____ Date of hatch _____

Chick Wing-Band No.	Pen No.	Dam's No.	Sex	Sex-Linked Feathering	At ___ Weeks Feathering	Body Weight	Breast Breadth	Keel Length	Remarks (U. S. R. O. P. Leg Band No., defects, disposal, etc.)
1									
2									
3									
4									
5									
6									
7									
8									
9									
0									
1									
2									
3									
4									
5									
6									
7									
8									
9									
0									
1									
2									
3									
4									
5									
6									
7									
8									
9									
0									
1									
2									
3									
4									
5									
6									
7									
8									
9									
0									

16—18537-4   U. S. GOVERNMENT PRINTING OFFICE

Fig. 71. U. S. R. O. P. pedigree record.

Spaces are provided for recording the date, season, and sex of every chick removed and for the sex and leg-band number of each bird kept.

The pedigree record should be kept in the brooder house and each bird recorded at the time of removal. Some breeders go over all of the chicks when six or eight weeks old and again at twelve or sixteen weeks, as well as at the time of housing (Fig. 72), and cull out and record any slow-growing, poorly feathered, or otherwise abnormal birds.

The female summary record. The breeding pen progeny record (Fig.

COURTESY OHIO POULTRY IMPROVEMENT ASSOCIATION

Fig. 72. Inspecting U. S. R. O. P. cockerels. Those approved for breeders will be leg banded and pedigrees approved by the inspector.

73) is the most important of all the records kept. It shows whether or not birds used in the breeding pen are able to transmit desirable characters to their offspring.

The records of the male and dams may be copied from the breeding-pen and incubation and chick-banding record sheets.

The records of the female progeny may be obtained from the pedigree record and from the pullet year summary sheet.

REVIEW QUESTIONS

1. Compare the body characteristics of birds with good and poor vigor.
2. Why should birds that are bred to lay have Standard breed and variety characteristics?
3. Name two of the most common disqualifications found in Leghorn breeding flocks.
4. Differentiate between the characteristics of a bird that is in production and one that is out of production.
5. Can the egg production of a bird be predicted by its body measurements?
6. Why is it harder to select breeders for egg production than for meat production?
7. What are the records of the sibs?
8. What is the most practical system of breeding for the average farmer?

The National Poultry Improvement Plan

U. S. R. O. P. FEMALE-SUMMARY RECORD

Breeding-pen No._____   Dam's U. S. R. O. P. leg-band No._____

Sire's U. S. R. O. P. leg-band No._____   Dam's U. S. R. O. P. wing-band No._____

16—26031-1

Daughter's No.		Aug.	Sept.	Oct.	Nov.	Dec.	Jan.	Feb.	Mar.	Apr.	May	June	July	Aug.	Sept.	Oct.	Nov.	Off. Egg Production	Off. Egg Weight	Off. Body Weight
	Prod.																			
	E. W.																			
	Prod.																			
	E. W.																			
	Prod.																			
	E. W.																			
	Prod																			
	E. W.																			
	Prod.																			
	E. W.																			
	Prod																			
	E. W.																			
	Prod.																			
	E. W.																			
	Prod.																			
	E. W.																			
	Prod.																			
	E. W.																			
	Prod																			
	E. W																			
	Prod.																			
	E. W.																			
	Prod.																			
	E. W.																			
	Prod																			
	E. W.																			
	Prod.																			
	E. W.																			
F average	Prod.																			
	E. W.																			
Dam's first-year record	Prod.																			
	E. W.																			

Fig. 73. U. S. R. O. P. Female-Summary Record.

9. What are the dangers of line breeding?
10. Which practical system of mating gives best fertility?
11. Why are more hens mated with one male among the light breeds than among the general-purpose breeds?
12. How soon after males are added to the flocks may one expect good fertility of the eggs?
13. What lethal genes result in reduced hatchability?
14. Why are chicks from hens worth more than those from pullets?
15. Compare the fertility and hatchability of pullet and hen eggs.
16. What inherited characters for high egg production are measured by the use of the trap nest?

17. At what age and size should Leghorns start to lay? Rhode Island Reds?
18. Which is more important at the time of sexual maturity in determining egg size—age or body size?
19. At what time of year is egg size the largest? The smallest?
20. If a bird lays two hundred eggs in the pullet year, how many may it be expected to lay the second year? The third year?
21. At what season of the year is eggshell texture the poorest?
22. Compare the shell texture of pullet and hen eggs.
23. Name a characteristic indicating good interior egg quality that is inherited.
24. What is the main function of the National Poultry Improvement Plan?
25. What are the breeding stages in the plan?
26. Which breeding stage involves progeny testing?
27. Differentiate between approved and certified flocks.
28. How many eggs must a bird lay during the first laying year to qualify for U.S.R.O.P.?
29. Differentiate between the size requirements of U. S. Approved and U.S.R.O.P. hatching eggs.
30. Differentiate between pullorum-passed and pullorum-clean flocks.
31. How old should birds be before they are tested for pullorum?
32. What tolerance of pullorum infection is permitted in pullorum-controlled flocks?
33. What methods of pullorum testing are recognized as official?

REFERENCES

ASMUNDSON, V. S., AND LERNER, I. M.: BREEDING CHICKENS FOR MEAT PRODUCTION. Calif. Sta. Bul. 675. 1942.

BALL, R. F.: THE VALUE OF FOUR CHARACTERS USED IN CULLING READY-TO-LAY PULLETS. Poultry Sci., 24: 216–225. 1945.

BOSTIAN, C. H., AND DEARSTYNE, R. S.: THE INFLUENCE OF BREEDING ON THE LIVABILITY OF POULTRY. N. C. Sta. Tech. Bul. 79. 1944.

BRYANT, R. L.: BREEDING LEGHORN CHICKENS TO INCREASE THE LIFE SPAN. Va. Sta. Tech. Bul. 99. 1946.

BURROWS, WILLIAM: ARTIFICIAL INSEMINATION OF CHICKENS AND TURKEYS. U. S. D. A. Circ. 525. 1939.

COLE, L. J., AND HALPIN, J. G.: RESULTS OF EIGHT YEARS OF INBREEDING RHODE ISLAND REDS. Anat. Rec., 23: 97. 1922.

FUNK, E. M.: FACTORS INFLUENCING HATCHABILITY IN THE DOMESTIC FOWL. Mo. Sta. Bul. 341. 1944.

FUNK, E. M., AND FORWARD, J. F.: THE RELATIONSHIP OF EGG SHELL COLOR TO HATCHABILITY IN NEW HAMPSHIRES. Poultry Sci., 28: 577–580. 1949.

GERRY, R. W., AND MISHLER, D. H.: SEXING BARRED ROCK CHICKS. Poultry Sci. 28: 479–485. 1949.

GODFREY, A. B.: POULTRY-BREEDING-STOCK SELECTION FOR DESIRED CHARACTERS. U. S. D. A. Circ. 715. 1944.

GODFREY, A. B.: THREE-DAY-A-WEEK TRAP-NESTING. U. S. D. A. Bur. An. Ind., A. H. D. 121. 1948.

HAYS, F. A.: THE VALUE OF LIMITED TRAP-NESTING IN POULTRY BREEDING. Mas. Sta. Bul. 438. 1947.

HAYS, F. A.: HIGH FECUNDITY IN POULTRY. Poultry Sci., 28: 921–928. 1949.

HAYS, F. A., AND KLEIN, G. T.: POULTRY BREEDING APPLIED. Poultry-Dairy Publishing Co., Mount Morris, Ill. 1943.

HAYS, F. A., AND SANBORN, R.: FACTORS AFFECTING ANNUAL EGG PRODUCTION. Mass. Sta. Bul. 423. 1944.

HENDERSON, E. W.: EGG PRODUCTION AND MEAT TYPE COMPATABILITY. Mich. Sta. Quart. Bul. 29, No. 3: 237–242. 1947.

HUTT, R. B., BRUCHNER, J. H., AND COLE, R. K.: FOUR GENERATIONS OF FOWLS BRED FOR RESISTANCE TO NEOPLASMS. Poultry. Sci., 20: 514–526. 1941.

INSKO, W. M., STEELE, D. G., AND WIGHTMAN, E. T.: REPRODUCTIVE PHENOMENA IN AGING HENS. Ky. Sta. Bul. 498. 1947.

JAAP, R. G.: STRAINS OF WHITE PLYMOUTH ROCKS FOR SPECIFIC ECONOMIC PURPOSES. Poultry Sci., 22: 209–217. 1943.

JEFFREY, F. P.: METHODS OF BREEDING CHICKENS FOR HIGH EGG PRODUCTION. N. J. Sta. Bul. 714. 1944.

JULL, M. A.: STUDIES IN HATCHABILITY. Poultry Sci., 10: 327–331. 1931.

JULL, M. A.: POULTRY BREEDING. John Wiley & Sons, Inc., New York. 1940.

LERNER, I. M.: LETHAL AND SUBLETHAL CHARACTERS IN FARM ANIMALS. Jour. Heredity, 25: 219–224. 1944.

LERNER, I. M., CRUDEN, DOROTHY, AND TAYLOR, L. W.: THE RELATIVE BREEDING WORTH OF FULL SISTERS. Poultry Sci., 28: 903–913. 1949.

LUSH, J. L., LAMOREUX, W. F., AND HAZEL, L. N.: THE HERITABILITY OF RESISTANCE TO DEATH IN THE FOWL. Poultry Sci., 27: 375–388. 1948.

MAW, A. J. G.: CROSSES BETWEEN INBRED LINES OF THE DOMESTIC FOWL. Poultry Sci., 21: 548–553. 1942.

PAYNE, L. F., AND AVERY, T. B.: INTERNATIONAL POULTRY GUIDE FOR FLOCK SELECTION. Int. Baby Chick Assoc., Kansas City, Mo. 1950.

PERRY, F. S.: SELECTING AND CULLING POULTRY. Fla. Sta. Ext. Bul. 132. 1947.

PLATT, C. S.: TEN YEARS OF STANDARD EGG-LAYING TESTS IN THE UNITED STATES. Poultry Sci., 28: 363–371. 1949.

QUINN, J. P.: SELECTING HENS FOR EGG PRODUCTION. U. S. D. A. Farmers' Bul. 1727. 1934.

ROBERTS, E., AND CARD, L. E.: INHERITANCE OF RESISTANCE TO BACTERIAL INFECTION IN ANIMALS. A GENETIC STUDY OF PULLORUM DISEASE. Ill. Sta. Bul. 419. 1935.

STURKIE, P. D.: FIVE YEARS OF SELECTION FOR VIABILITY IN WHITE LEGHORN CHICKENS. Poultry Sci., 22: 156–160. 1943.

TAYLOR, L. W., AND LERNER, I. M.: BREEDING FOR EGG PRODUCTION. Calif. Sta. Bul. 626. 1938.

THE NATIONAL POULTRY IMPROVEMENT PLAN. U. S. D. A. Misc. Pub. 300. 1948.

THOMPSON, W. C.: EGG-PRODUCTION BEHAVIOR OF HENS. N. J. Sta. Bul. 700. 1942.

UPP, C. W.: SELECT COCKERELS EARLY FOR BETTER SIRES. La. Sta. Circ. 30. 1943.

WARREN, D. C.: DEVELOPING EARLY-FEATHERING STRAINS IN HEAVY BREEDS OF POULTRY. Kan. Sta. Circ. 224. 1944.

WATERS, N. F.: THE INFLUENCE OF INBREEDING ON HATCHABILITY. Poultry Sci., 24: 329–334. 1945.

ZUMBRO, P.: IMPROVING POULTRY THROUGH THE NATIONAL POULTRY IMPROVEMENT PLAN. U. S. D. A. Misc. Pub. 317. Revised, 1949.

CHAPTER 6 ||||||||||||||||||||||||||||||||||||||||||||||||||||||||||

Incubation Principles and Practices

▼

Incubation practices may be better understood if the principles underlying them are more thoroughly explained. Those who investigate the factors influencing hatchability should have some knowledge of the structural and physiological development of the chick embryo. Those who operate the incubators should be able to do a better job if they understand the development of a baby chick.

Development of the Chick Embryo

The development of the chick embryo is a very interesting phenomenon. Embryologists are interested in its early development because of the general information about embryology which may be obtained by studying the early stages of development of the chick embryo, these stages being quite similar to those of the mammals. The poultryman is interested in the embryology of the chick because an understanding of its development will supply information as to the requirements for incubation, and will point the way to better incubation practices. In twenty-one days remarkable changes occur inside the egg. During this time a mass of nutritive material is transformed into a complex living organism.

In discussing the development of the embryo it is well to consider the anatomical or structural development as well as the physiological development which the embryo undergoes from fertilization to hatching.

Anatomical Development

The development which takes place in an egg from the time of fertilization to the time of hatching is one of the wonders of nature which man has revealed to himself by the use of the microscope. The complexity of this development cannot be understood without some thorough training in embryology.

Development before the egg is laid. Soon after fertilization, cell division begins. It continues as long as the temperature of the egg is above 82° F. and, after hatching, until growth has been completed. As cell division progresses the blastoderm spreads out over the yolk. The cells are first arranged

129

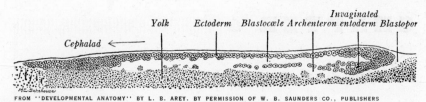

Fig. 74. Gastrulation in the pigeon by which the entoderm is formed. Longitudinal section of the blastoderm.

in a single layer (the ectoderm) but they soon form, by invagination or folding under, another layer—the entoderm. The formation of the entoderm is called gastrulation (Fig. 74).

Development during incubation. After the fertile egg is laid, embryonic development proceeds when the egg is held where the temperature is higher than 82° F. (Fig. 75). The two primary germ layers (ectoderm and entoderm) are usually formed by the time the egg is laid, and the third layer (mesoderm) is formed soon thereafter if a suitable incubation temperature is maintained (Fig. 76). From these three primary germ layers the different parts of the embryo develop. The skin, feathers, beak, claws, nervous system, and the linings of the mouth and vent develop from the ectoderm. The entoderm gives rise to the respiratory and secretory organs and the linings of the digestive tract. The bones, muscles, blood, excretory and reproductive organs have their origin in the mesoderm.

Structure of the chick embryo during the first twenty-four hours of incubation. The primitive streak is visible after about sixteen hours of incubation in the incubator. Thereafter development proceeds rapidly, many new organs arising between the sixteenth and twenty-fourth hours of incubation. The head of the embryo becomes differentiated; the foregut is formed; four somites are visible; the blood islands, which later develop into a blood system, appear in the area vasculosa; the neural fold arises which later forms the neural groove; and the coelom and the pericardial regions make their appearance (Fig. 77).

Development of the chick embryo during the second day. The neural fold closes, forming the neural groove, the anterior part of which develops during the second day into the different parts of the brain: the forebrain, midbrain, and hindbrain. The heart is formed during this period and by the forty-fourth hour of incubation has begun to beat. Two distinct circulatory systems are established, one within the body of the embryo and the other the vitelline circulation extending out from the heart into the egg. The eye and the auditory pits of the ear begin to develop.

The extra-embryonic membranes, the yolk sac, amnion, allantois, and serosa begin developing during the second day. The yolk sac will later envelop the entire yolk which serves as a source of food material for the embryo and the newly hatched chick. A considerable portion of the yolk remains to be taken into the body cavity of the chick shortly before hatching.

The amnion is formed during the second and third days of incubation.

The amniotic fluid fills this cavity and surrounds the embryo also enclosed in the amnion. The embryo is thereby protected from shocks and possibly adhesions. The serosa, which is formed at the time the amnion is formed, surrounds the other extra-embryonic membranes, lies next to the shell membranes, and later fuses with the allantois.

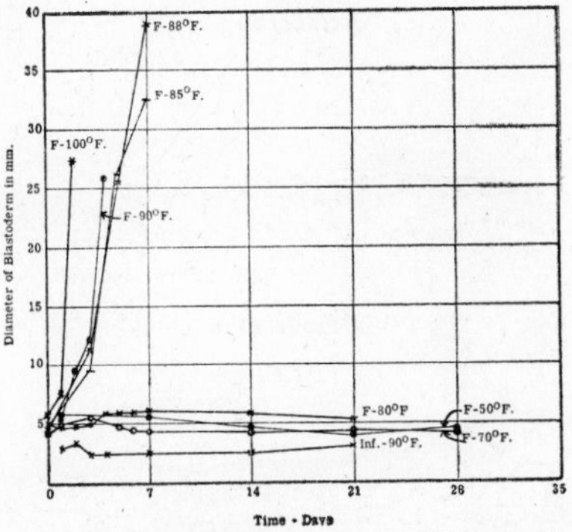

Structure of the four-day-old chick embryo. By the end of the fourth day of incubation the embryo has all of the organs needed for its development and most of the parts of the chick can be identified. However, the embryo cannot be distinguishel from

COURTESY MISSOURI AGRICULTURAL EXPERIMENT STATION

Fig. 75. The effect of temperature on embryonic development. F. refers to fertile and Inf. to infertile.

that of mammals. The allantois appears during the third day of incubation as an evagination of the hind-gut. The allantois later surrounds the entire egg contents and fuses with the serosa to form the chorion. The capillaries of the allantois therefore come in contact with the shell membrane. The allantois serves as a respiratory and also as an excretory organ for the embryo. The allantois circulation is also a medium by which nutrients from the albumen and calcium from the shell are carried to the embryo.

The leg and wing appendages are now visible as limb buds. The tail has made its appearance. Five divisions of the brain can be located. The spinal nerve roots have begun their development. The lens of the eye, the auditory vesicles, and the olfactory pits are visible. The heart has not been enclosed inside the body and can be observed to beat if the egg is opened. The other internal organs have already begun their development.

The embryologist is not interested in the development of the chick embryo beyond the fourth day because from there on only growth takes place. For him the important story is ended, but the poultryman continues to be interested because his objective in incubation is a well-hatched chick and he needs to know more about the development which occurs throughout the entire period of incubation.

By the sixth day the main divisions of the wings and legs are visible. The feather tracts appear on the eighth day and by the ninth day the embryo has a birdlike appearance. On the thirteenth day the color of the chick down may be observed. By the sixteenth day the beak, nails, and scales are well formed. The supply of albumen is now about exhausted and therefore the yolk serves as the sole source of nutrients. Several stages in the development of the embryo of the chick are shown in Figure 78.

Hatching. On the seventeenth day the fluid in the amnion begins to decrease. The yolk is drawn into the body cavity on the nineteenth day. The beak soon thereafter pierces the air cell and pulmonary respiration begins.

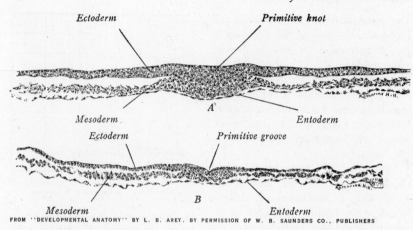

FROM "DEVELOPMENTAL ANATOMY" BY L. B. AREY. BY PERMISSION OF W. B. SAUNDERS CO., PUBLISHERS

Fig. 76. Transverse sections of a chick embryo at the stage of the primitive streak, showing the primary germ layers: A, through the primitive knot; B, through the primitive groove.

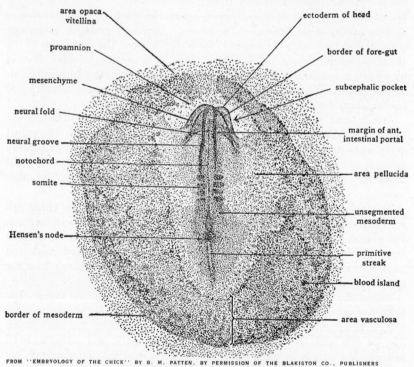

FROM "EMBRYOLOGY OF THE CHICK" BY B. M. PATTEN. BY PERMISSION OF THE BLAKISTON CO., PUBLISHERS

Fig. 77. A chicken embryo showing 24 hours' development.

The normal position of the chick for hatching is with the head under the right wing, in the large end of egg, and the legs drawn up towards the head. Two special mechanisms, the horny cap on the upper mandible and muscles on the back of the neck, are developed for hatching the chick. The horny

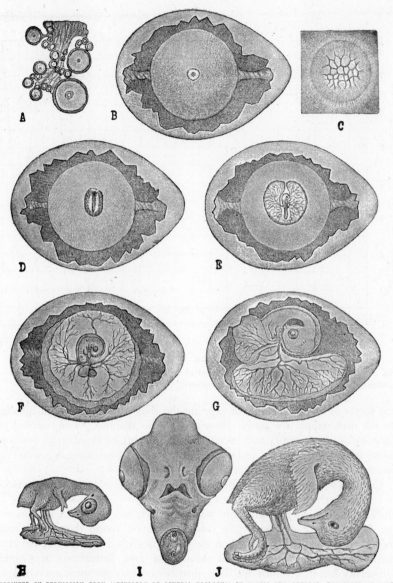

Fig. 78. The development of the chick. A, Part of the ovary showing ova in different stages of development. B, The fertilized egg at time of laying. C, Early cleavage of the blastoderm. D, Egg opened to show the late neural-fold stage and extension of blastoderm over yolk. E and F, Stages during which the circulation is becoming established as the blastoderm extends further over the yolk. The allantois appears as a bladder-like outgrowth at the posterior end of the embryo in F. G, Stage in which the allantois has enlarged and the yolk, surrounded by the yolk sac, has become reduced. In F and G the amnion is shown closely surrounding the embryo. H, Later stage showing yolk stalk. I, Front view of head, showing eyes, nasal openings, mouth, and ears. J, A stage shortly before hatching, showing yolk stalk and remains of yolk.

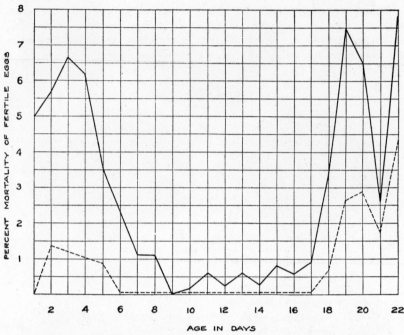

Fig. 79. Daily embryonic mortality, in per cent of fertile eggs, within a high and a low (——) hatching line of White Leghorns. (From Bronkhorst.)

cap serves as an instrument for pipping the shell and the enlarged muscles on the neck supply the power for pipping. The allantois, having served its function as a respiratory and excretory organ during embryological development, is no longer needed and appears in the shell at hatching as a dried up membrane filled with blood vessels.

Critical stages in incubation. There are definite stages in the development of the chick embryo when mortality is highest. These stages occur in chickens during the first and third weeks. As early as 1919 Payne determined the daily embryonic mortality in chicken eggs. He found that of the total mortality 16.2 per cent occurred on the fourth to sixth days, and 48.7 per cent occurred from the eighteenth to twenty-first days. Bronkhorst at Cornell University has determined the daily distribution of embryonic mortality in high and low hatching lines as shown in Figure 79. A satisfactory explanation of the critical stages has not been given, but it will probably be found in the physiological changes which occur in these embryos during the first and third weeks. Much of the mortality which occurs at the end of the incubation period can be attributed to abnormal embryo positions which are caused by inheritance as well as environmental factors and feeding. The early embryonic mortality may arise from the efforts of the embryo to shift its source of energy from a simple compound (glucose) to a more complex substance (protein), which requires deamination.

Abnormal embryo positions. Embryos assume positions in the shell from which apparently they cannot hatch. These abnormal positions are probably caused by inheritance, deficient rations, and faulty incubation. The more common embryo positions have been listed by Asmundson as follows:

CLASSIFICATION OF EMBRYO POSITIONS

A. Head in large end of egg
   1. Head turned right and beak under right wing
   2. Head turned right but beak not under right wing
   3. Head turned right but away from air space
      (a) beak under wing
      (b) beak not under wing
   4. Head buried between thighs
   5. Head turned left and beak under the left wing
   6. Head turned left but beak not under the left wing
   7. Feet over the head (resting on the head)
      (a) beak under right wing
      (b) beak not under right wing but turned right
      (c) beak under left wing
      (d) beak not under left wing but turned left
B. Head in small end of the egg
   1. Head turned right and beak under the right wing
   2. Head turned right but beak not under the right wing
   3. Head buried between the thighs
   4. Head turned left and beak under the left wing
   5. Head turned left but beak not under the left wing
   6. Feet over the head (resting on the head)
      (a) beak under the right wing
      (b) beak turned right but not under the right wing
      (c) beak under the left wing
      (d) beak turned left but not under the left wing

NOTE: Beak not under wing indicates that the beak was either in front of the wing, resting on the wing, or its tip, or that it was back of the wing and resting on the thigh. In the case of embryos with head in the large end and in positions 1, 2, and 7a and b, the head was towards the air cell.

Asmundson not only observed the position at hatching time of chicken embryos which had failed to hatch, but he also observed and classified embryo positions in turkeys, pheasants, and partridge. The most common malpositions he observed in eggs which failed to hatch were, in the order of importance, in chickens—A2, A4, A6, and B1; in Ringneck pheasants—A2, A4, A7a, and B1; in Chukar partridge—A2, A4, A7b, and B4; and in turkeys—A2, A4, A5, and B1.

Physiological Development of the Chick Embryo

The poultryman, as well as the physiologist, is interested in the physiology of the embryo and the physiological changes which occur during incubation.

A more thorough understanding of these phenomena may help solve some of the problems of incubation.

General metabolism of the embryo. Under the heading of general metabolism, pH changes and water metabolism may be considered. Aggazzotti in 1913 reported the measurements he had made of the pH changes which occurred during the process of incubation. He found that the hydrogen ion concentration of unincubated eggs remained fairly constant, but that when fertile eggs were incubated the pH changed considerably. Before incubation the yolks had a pH of 4.5 and the whites a pH of 8.3. During incubation the pH of the yolks rose steadily to a pH of 6 about the tenth day and neutrality (pH7) by the sixteenth day. The pH of the white decreased regularly to neutrality on the tenth day and a pH of 6 on the fifteenth day of incubation. The allantoic liquid remains nearly neutral and the amniotic fluid remains neutral until the eleventh day, after which it becomes decidedly acid in reaction.

The relative water content of chick embryos decreases from about 94 per cent on the fifth day to about 80 per cent at hatching time. The egg of the domestic fowl loses water by evaporation at a constant rate (about 5 per cent weekly) during the process of incubation, the rate being governed by the relative humidity of the atmosphere of the incubator and the physical characteristics of the egg. During the first ten days water passes from the white into the yolk, the water content of the white decreasing and that of the yolk increasing. From the tenth day until hatching the yolk loses water, and by the twenty-first day the water content is about the same as that of the yolk of a fresh-laid egg.

Energy for embryonic development. The chick embryo requires energy for its development. The sources of energy for the developing embryo are, in the order of their usage, carbohydrates, proteins, and fats. Needham says:

> It is possible that carbohydrate is first combusted because it requires no preparation. Proteins must be deaminated, fats must be desaturated, and probably the embryo in its earlier stages cannot do either of these things, but, on the other hand, glucose lies ready for use, and it is significant that what is combusted is free, not combined, carbohydrate. There is already evidence that the power of desaturation of fats only arises at the comparatively late stage of development, e.g., the tenth to the fifteenth day in the chick. And we may look on the unsaturated fatty acids which are notably present in the yolk as a preparation for these conditions.

Carbohydrate metabolism. Though the egg contains only a small amount of carbohydrate material and this is used throughout the incubation period, it is the chief source of energy during the early development of the embryo. The carbohydrates found in the chick embryo during the early stages are very largely glucose in combination with protein. During the first week glycogen increases outside the embryo and free sugar increases within the embryo. During the second week the free glucose continues to increase and the glycogen of the yolk sac increases. Between the seventh and eleventh days some fat is transformed into carbohydrates by the embryo. By the tenth day the pancreas is secreting insulin. Beginning at about the eleventh day the liver is able to store glycogen.

Fat metabolism. Fat is not utilized by the embryo until after the fifth day of incubation and it is not deposited in the embryo until after the tenth day. Fat serves as an important source of energy for the embryo, particularly during the later stages of development when most energy is needed. About 99½ per cent of the fat of the egg is contained in the egg yolk. About one-third of the fat of the egg is lost by combustion and the other two-thirds is transferred to the embryo.

Protein metabolism. The proteins of the embryo are derived from the proteins of the egg. A number of investigators have shown the decrease of the different amino acids in the egg white and yolk during incubation and the increase of these amino acids in the embryo as it develops. The amino acids essential for embryonic development must be present in the white and yolk of the egg. Those which have been identified are tryptophane, tyrosine, histidine, arginine, lysine, and cystine.

The percentage of nitrogen excreted by the chick embryo in different forms are ammonia 1 per cent, urea 7.6 per cent, and uric acid 91.4 per cent. During the first week the nitrogen is excreted principally as ammonia and urea, but after the first week it is excreted almost entirely as uric acid, which is the form in which the adult bird excretes nitrogen.

Mineral metabolism. A number of investigators have worked on calcium metabolism in the hen's egg during the process of incubation. It has been shown that in fertile eggs which are incubated the shell loses calcium and that the calcium content of the interior of the egg increases. This change occurs only when an embryo is developing in the egg. More calcium is transferred from the shell to the embryo when the relative humidity is high than when it is low. The transfer of calcium from the shell to the embryo is also influenced by the amount of vitamin D present in the egg.

Phosphorus is an important constituent of the embryo. Most of the metabolism of phosphorus occurs after the fifteenth day of incubation and is associated with bone formation.

The sodium, potassium, and chlorine content of the white decrease throughout the incubation period, while the quantity of these elements present in the embryo increases steadily. In the yolk these elements increase until the seventh day and then decrease, thus indicating a greater movement of these elements from the white to the yolk during the first week than from the yolk to the embryo. All minerals needed by the chick embryo are obtained from the egg.

Enzymes in embryonic development. Enzymes play an important part in the development of the chick embryo, reducing substances of the egg to less complex structures so that they may be utilized by the developing embryo. Some are present in the egg and others are secreted by the embryo.

Hormones in chick development. Very little is definitely known about the function of hormones in the development of the chick embryo. Most of the hormones are not present in the freshly laid egg but are found after the endocrine glands develop to a stage where they are capable of secreting them. Insulin and the estrogenic hormone are present in the yolk of the freshly laid egg. This yolk insulin may play an important part in carbohydrate metabolism before the insulin-secreting cells of the pancreas become functional. After the eleventh day the embryo is capable of insulin secretion. Adrenalin, which is secreted by the adrenal glands, is first formed in the embryo on the eighth day of incubation.

Pigment metabolism. The fresh egg contains only a few pigments but the chick contains several that are unlike those of the fresh egg. The embryo during its development is capable of synthesizing hemoglobin, bile pigments from the breakdown of hemoglobin, the carotenoid pigments (red and greenish yellow), and the melanin pigments of the dark-colored chicks.

Vitamin production by the embryo. Fresh eggs laid by hens properly fed for the production of hatching eggs contain all of the vitamins essential for hatching. Unless these vitamins are provided by nutrition of the breeding stock the embryo could not develop and hatch. Some of the vitamins, however, are synthesized by the embryo. Those reported to be synthesized are inositol, nicotinic acid, and ascorbic acid.

Factors Influencing Hatching Results

The incubation of an egg is a complex biological process influenced by a large number of factors, many of which man does not know or understand. Hatching results depend not alone upon proper incubation but upon the breeding stock and its management as well as the care the eggs receive from the time they are laid until they are set. Research workers are adding to the store of existing knowledge on this subject and, as in many other scientific fields, it is necessary for those interested in incubation to read and evaluate the reports continually being issued on this subject.

Breeding Stock

Those factors associated with the care and management of the breeding stock may be considered first because they influence the inherent hatching properties of the egg and are therefore of prime importance.

Inheritance. Hatchability of eggs of the domestic fowl has been shown to be an inherited characteristic and therefore amenable to the laws of heredity. Those hens which possess the ability to lay eggs which hatch well also have the power to transmit this character to their offspring (Table 26). Therefore, by following proper breeding procedure poultry breeders can establish high-hatching families and strains.

At least nineteen lethal genes which cause the death of chick embryos have been reported in at least six different breeds of poultry. The first of

Table 26

THE DIFFERENCE IN HATCHABILITY BETWEEN GROUPS OF DAUGHTERS, THE
COMPOSITION OF THE GROUPS BEING DETERMINED BY THE
HATCHABILITY OF THE DAMS, IN WHITE LEGHORNS [1]

Range in Per Cent Dams' Hatchability	Number of Dams	Mean Per Cent Dams' Hatchability	Number of Daughters	Mean Per Cent Daughters' Hatchability
74.0–94.5	36	81.24±0.36	62	63.40±1.92
53.0–73.5	24	64.36±0.76	43	52.33±1.94
Difference		16.88±0.84		11.07±2.73

these was found in Wyandottes at the Storrs Agricultural Experiment Station
in 1923. Since then lethal genes have been found in the Creeper chicken,
crosses between Barred Plymouth Rocks and Rhode Island Reds, Dark
Cornish, and two strains of White Leghorns. These genes are lethal only
when they are present in the homozygous condition and therefore have
been inherited from both parents. The maximum embryonic mortality
which could result from such inheritance would be 25 per cent.

Inbreeding where no specific selection for hatchability has been practiced has resulted in lowered hatchability (p. 99). But at the Iowa Agricultural Experiment Station, where in inbreeding experiments selection
was made for high hatchability, satisfactory hatchability was maintained
in inbred lines. Crossing breeds or inbred lines tends to increase hatchability, particularly if the strains being crossed have relatively low hatchability. This is one of the expressions of hybrid vigor.

Matings. The matings are likely to influence fertility (p. 103) and
thereby the percentage of hatch of all eggs set.

Age of breeding stock. Hens are generally recommended as more desirable for breeding purposes than pullets. The hen has proved her ability
to survive and if she has been in a flock which is trap-nested she has a
known production record, whereas these qualities in the pullet are unknown. It should be noted, however, that more chicks can be produced
from a given number of eggs laid by pullets than from a similar number
of eggs produced by hens.

Some hatcherymen have abandoned the use of cock birds for use in
hatchery supply flocks where chicks are desired during the winter and
early spring months. Cockerels produce a much higher percentage of
fertile eggs than do old males, especially during cold weather. The breeder
who is doing progeny testing should use valuable males as long as they retain
their vitality.

Egg production. The experimental evidence which has been collected
on the relationship of egg production and hatchability shows that those
birds which lay well also produce eggs which hatch better than eggs laid
by poorer producers (p. 104). The Missouri Agricultural Experiment Station

[1] Jull, 1930.

has shown, as indicated in Table 27, that eggs laid in multiple egg clutches (three to six consecutive eggs) hatch better than eggs laid in one or two egg clutches. Since both high egg production and good hatchability may be considered as measures of vitality, it appears logical that these two traits should be associated.

Physical Characteristics of Eggs

A number of investigations have been made for the purpose of determining the relationships between physical characteristics of eggs and hatchability. The earlier work was on exterior characteristics but more recently studies have been made on the relation of certain interior characters and hatchability.

Exterior characteristics. Several investigators have found that medium-sized eggs weighing from twenty-three to twenty-six ounces per dozen hatch better than do larger or smaller eggs (Fig. 80). What experimental evidence there is available indicates that shape of egg within marketable limits is not related to hatchability, but since egg shape is an inherited characteristic, all eggs abnormally shaped should be discarded and not used as hatching eggs.

Shell texture. The mottled appearance of the eggshell as observed by candling does not appear to be related to hatching results, as will be observed in Table 28. Mottling is not necessarily an indication of porous eggshells. The California station found that an uneven distribution of moisture in the eggshell would cause mottling. Poor shell texture resulting from a deficiency of calcium or vitamin D would, of course, be associated with low hatchability.

Color of shell. Observations at the Ohio, Massachusetts, and Missouri stations have shown that medium and dark brown eggs hatch better than light brown eggs.

Defective eggs. It has long been recognized that defective eggs should not be set not only because of poorer hatching results from such eggs but also because many of these physical characters of eggs are inherited and therefore the stock producing such eggs should be eliminated. The National Agricultural Research Center (Table 29) reported hatching results which showed that the average percentage hatch of all such eggs was only 44.4 per cent as compared to a hatch of 71.7 per cent for normal eggs used as controls.

Interior quality. There is some evidence that the color of the egg yolk is associated with hatchability. Since the richer-colored yolks generally contain more vitamin A than the light-colored yolks, the increase in hatchability associated with increased yolk color could be an effect of vitamin A.

Some observations made at the Missouri Agricultural Experiment Station and at Ohio State University (Table 21) indicated that those eggs which showed the most rapid movement of interior contents when rotated before an egg candler did not hatch so well as eggs which showed less movement. Workers at Cornell University have reported that hens which lay eggs that

Table 27

RELATION OF POSITION OF EGG IN THE CLUTCH TO HATCHABILITY OF ALL FERTILE EGGS SET. ALL BREEDING STOCK. 1935 AND 1936 [2]

CLUTCH	First Egg		Second Egg		Third Egg		Fourth Egg		Fifth Egg		Sixth Egg		Total		Chi-Square Value
	Eggs Set	Per-centage of Hatch	Eggs Set	Per-centage of Hatch	Eggs Set	Per-centage of Hatch	Eggs Set	Per-centage of Hatch	Eggs Set	Per-centage of Hatch	Eggs Set	Per-centage of Hatch	Eggs Set	Per-centage of Hatch	
One Egg	845	58.93	…	…	…	…	…	…	…	…	…	…	845	58.93	18.541
Two Egg	879	67.01	848	68.28	…	…	…	…	…	…	…	…	1727	67.63	6.043
Three Egg	589	69.10	581	70.39	506	75.49	…	…	…	…	…	…	1676	71.48	.264
Four Egg	289	70.24	290	68.97	285	74.74	265	75.85	…	…	…	…	1129	72.36	.287
Five Egg	139	73.38	149	71.14	146	70.55	135	68.15	129	72.87	…	…	698	71.20	
Six Egg	83	67.47	67	80.60	76	80.26	79	82.28	73	80.82	86	77.91	464	78.02	6.719

[2] Data of Funk.

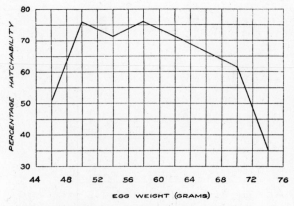

Fig. 80. Relationship between percentage hatchability and average egg weight per bird, based on the records of 367 hens and for one hatching season. (From Godfrey.)

have a low albumen score hatch better than eggs which have relatively high scores. Thus it appears that good albumen quality and high hatchability are associated.

Testing hatching eggs before incubation. The testing of hatching eggs before regular incubation to determine fertility, sex, etc., has been advocated from time to time but most of such claims have been discredited. However, within recent years some progress has been made on such tests.

The National Agricultural Research Center at Beltsville, Md., has reported that eggs preincubated for about eighteen hours can be candled and the infertiles removed with an accuracy of about 90 per cent. They have also found that such eggs can be cooled and shipped and then incubated to give satisfactory hatches. The elimination of infertiles before shipping hatching eggs would result in a considerable saving in transportation costs and would also save space in the incubators.

Table 28

RELATION OF SHELL TEXTURE AND HATCHING RESULTS [3]

Year	Shell Texture	Eggs Set	Percentage Hatch	
			All Eggs	Fertile Eggs
1931	Good	1011	54.8	67.1
	Poor	336	60.0	72.2
1933	Good	1797	59.0	76.3
	Poor	925	57.1	77.4

Other observations made at Beltsville show that by tapping eggs to detect checked eggs and by candling to eliminate tremulous air cells hatching eggs can be separated into groups having significantly different hatchability.

The Central Experimental Farm of Canada (1940) reported that eggs having high specific gravity hatched 15 to 20 per cent better than eggs of a low specific gravity. The relative amount of shell is most important in determining the specific gravity of an egg.

[3] Mo. Agr. Expt. Sta. Bul. 341.

Table 29

PERCENTAGE INFERTILITY AND PERCENTAGE HATCHABILITY OF VARIOUS
TYPES OF DEFECTIVE EGGS.[4]

Type of defective eggs	* Number of Eggs Set	* Percentage of Total Eggs Examined	In- fertile Eggs	Per- centage of Eggs In- fertile	Number of Chicks Hatched	Percentage Hatch Fertile Eggs Set	Percentage Hatch Total Eggs Set
Cracked eggs..........	610	1.27	155	25.4	242	53.2	39.7
Extra large eggs (65 gr. or more)...........	332	.69	113	34.0	155	70.8	46.7
Small eggs (45 gr. or less)...............	155	.32	80	51.6	60	80.0	38.7
Misshapen eggs.......	68	.14	21	30.9	23	48.9	33.8
Poor shells...........	102	.21	28	27.5	35	47.3	34.3
Loose air cells........	47	.10	13	27.7	11	32.4	23.4
Misplaced air cells.....	406	.85	89	21.9	216	68.1	53.2
Large blood spots.....	174	.36	37	21.3	98	71.5	56.3
All defective eggs......	1,894	3.95	536	28.3	840	61.8	44.4
Control eggs..........	3,031		537	17.7	2,174	87.2	71.7

* The first two columns of figures in Table give the numbers and percentages of eggs of various types found among 47,950 newly laid White Leghorn eggs.

Romanoff of Cornell University has by the use of a high frequency field found differences between fertile and infertile eggs.

Nutrition. Unless the egg contains all of the essential materials for developing and hatching a normal chick, it will fail to hatch. The chick embryo must obtain everything necessary for its development, except air, from the egg itself. All of the nutrients needed for developing the chick embryo must be placed in the egg by feeding the breeding stock. An influence of the presence of a toxic substance in the ration on embryo development is shown in Figure 81.

Weather conditions. Every experienced hatchery operator knows that his hatches are greatly influenced by weather conditions. There are several ways in which the weather affects hatching results, but at this point only its effect on the breeding stock will be considered. Severe "cold waves" which often sweep over the United States during the winter months freeze the combs and wattles of the breeding stock and reduce the fertility of eggs laid during the second and third weeks following the cold weather. Since the hatchability of fertile eggs is also reduced by these "cold waves," it appears that the metabolism of the bird may be an important factor affecting hatchability.

Care of Hatching Eggs

The hatchability of eggs containing all the materials required for chick development can be completely destroyed by improper care.

[4] Olsen and Haynes, 1949.

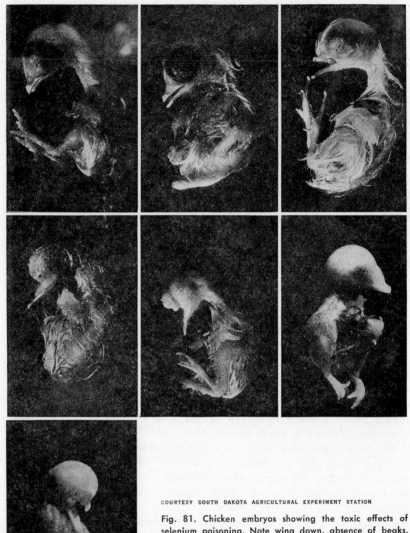

Fig. 81. Chicken embryos showing the toxic effects of selenium poisoning. Note wing down, absence of beaks, and other deformities.

Temperature. The hatchability of an egg can be destroyed by holding it either at too high or too low a temperature. During cold weather eggs intended for hatching purposes are frequently held at temperatures injurious to their hatchability. While eggs may be held at relatively low temperatures for some time, there are definite limits beyond which one does not dare go if satisfactory hatchability is to be secured, as indicated by the results shown in Table 30. However, the Maryland Agricultural Experiment Station in 1945 reported results which showed that temperatures of 32° F. and 38° F. for one to seven days were not detrimental to the hatchability of eggs laid by New Hampshires.

Table 30

EFFECT OF LOW TEMPERATURES BEFORE INCUBATION ON HATCHABILITY. 1931 [5]

Time held at 32°F. to 38°F.	Eggs Set	Percentage of Infertile	Percentage of Dead Embryos	Chicks Hatched	Percentage Hatch	
					All Eggs	Fertile Eggs
6	194	9.8	21.6	133	68.6	76.0
12	131	11.5	20.6	89	67.9	76.7
48	105	9.5	17.1	77	73.4	81.1
96	193	31.1	23.8	87	45.1	65.4
120	58	12.1	51.7	21	36.2	41.2
144	78	48.7	48.7	2	2.6	5.0
168	59	35.6	64.4	0	0	0
192	63	31.7	68.3	0	0	0
Controls *	752	9.0	20.1	533	70.9	77.9

* The controls were held in a basement at a temperature of 45°–60°F. The other eggs were held in an electric household refrigerator where the temperature varied from 32°F. to 38°F.

The ideal holding temperature appears to be a constant temperature somewhere between 50° F. and 55° F. (Table 31). The Kansas State Agricultural College found that Leghorn eggs held at 54° F. maintained excellent hatching quality for as long as twenty days.

Table 31

INFLUENCE OF HOLDING TEMPERATURE ON HATCHABILITY [6]

Days Held	At 50° F.		At 55° F.	
	Of All Eggs	Of Fertile Eggs	Of All Eggs	Of Fertile Eggs
7	67.9	80.4	67.1	80.0
14	67.2	77.0	63.9	72.1
21	54.5	60.1	56.7	60.4
28	43.2	50.0	24.2	26.3
35	17.8	22.2	4.7	5.9
42	3.3	6.5	0.0	0.0

Temperatures above 82° F. are not satisfactory for holding hatching eggs, because slow embryonic development occurs which weakens the embryos and results in high embryonic mortality during preincubation and during incubation. Hatcheries located where high summer temperatures prevail usually

[5] Mo. Agr. Expt. Sta. Bul. 341.
[6] Olsen and Haynes, 1948.

get relatively poor hatches during this period. Holding eggs at high temperatures contributes to these poor results.

Before eggs are placed under regular incubation, considerable development of the chick embryo frequently occurs because the eggs are subjected to conditions suitable for such development. That the incubation process is cumulative and that any preincubation shortens the regular incubation period an equivalent amount is shown by Table 32. Preincubation of eggs beyond

Table 32

EFFECT OF PRE-INCUBATION TEMPERATURE UPON THE LENGTH OF THE INCUBATION PERIOD. SETTING MADE APRIL 6, 1934 [7]

Time Held After Laying at 101°F. Before Cooling	Regular Incubation	Total Hours of Incubation	Number Chicks
Hours	*Hours*		
0	532	532	54
6	523	529	64
12	519	531	61
18	514	532	39
24	498	522	39

the equivalent of fourteen to eighteen hours of regular incubation is harmful to hatching results (Table 33). This offers one explanation of the relatively poor hatches which usually occur during the summer months when eggs are held at temperatures well above 80° F.

Table 33

EFFECT OF PRE-INCUBATION OF EGGS ON HATCHING RESULTS. EGGS LAID APRIL 13–20 AND SET APRIL 21, 1934 [8]

Time Held at 101°F. After Laying Before Cooling	Eggs Set	Percentage Hatch of All Eggs
0 hours	85	64.7
6–8 hours	88	72.7
12–14 hours	89	68.5
18–20 hours	84	46.4
24–26 hours	82	47.6

Age of egg. The length of time eggs can be held without reducing their hatching power depends somewhat upon the environmental conditions which prevail. Work at the Missouri Agricultural Experiment Station (Table 30) showed that eggs held as long as seven days in a household refrigerator where the temperature varied from 32° F. to 38° F. failed to hatch, and that the

---

[7] Mo. Agr. Expt. Sta. Bul. 341.
[8] Mo. Agr. Expt. Sta. Bul. 341.

hatchability of eggs held under these conditions for ninety-six hours was lowered. Eggs cannot be held so long either at high or low temperatures as at optimum (50° F. to 60° F.) temperatures without reducing hatchability.

Observations made at the Kansas Agricultural Experiment Station showed that by holding eggs at a relatively constant temperature (54.2° ± .26° F.), hatchability was not reduced when Leghorn eggs were held as long as twenty days and turkey eggs were held as long as twenty-eight days. Work at the Missouri Agricultural Experiment Station showed that when chicken eggs were stored in a basement room where the temperature varied from 45° F. to 60° F., hatchability was lowered after two weeks and was completely destroyed after four weeks (Table 34). Hatcherymen find that best results are obtained when the eggs from each flock are set once each week during the regular hatching season and more often during the summer months.

Table 34

EFFECT OF AGE OF EGG ON HATCHABILITY—1933 [9]

AGE OF EGG WHEN SET	EGGS SET	INFERTILE	HATCHED	PERCENTAGE HATCH	
				All Eggs	Fertile Eggs
1–7 days.........	3253	816	1856		
Per cent..........		25.1		57.1	76.2
8–14 days........	930	206	536		
Per cent..........		22.2		57.6	74.0
15–21 days.......	109	27	53		
Per cent..........		24.8		48.6	64.6
22–28 days.......	61	36	8		
Per cent.........		59.0		13.1	32.0
29–31 days.......	19	19			
Per cent.........		100	...	0	...

Handling. Excessive shaking or jarring of eggs is detrimental to hatchability. Results obtained at the National Agricultural Research Center showed that eggs with tremulous air cells had a hatchability of 56.5 per cent as compared to a hatchability of 77.3 per cent for eggs with normal air cells. Their results also showed that eggs jarred with the small end down hatched as well as eggs which were not jarred, but that eggs which were jarred with the large end down developed tremulous air cells and the hatchability was decreased more than 20 per cent. Eggs which are being saved for hatching purposes should be packed in cases with the small end down.

Turning. It is considered good management to turn eggs which are intended for hatching purposes if they are held for more than one week. It is not necessary to turn hatching eggs which are being held for one week or less.

---

[9] Mo. Agr. Expt. Sta. Bul. 341.

A simple way to facilitate turning is to place the eggs in a case with the small end down and tilt the case daily by placing a block under one end of the case. Work (unpublished) at the Missouri Station showed that for eggs held at 55° F. turning was of no benefit unless they were held ten days or longer.

Cleaning soiled eggs. Eggs that become soiled do not hatch well. Such eggs may be dry cleaned or they may be cleaned by washing without affecting hatchability. The Missouri Station found that soiled eggs cleaned by washing in a disinfecting solution slightly warmer than the eggs, hatched as well as unwashed clean eggs. The use of a warm disinfecting solution tends to prevent bacterial penetration through the shell. Eggs cleaned by washing in warm water also hatched well.

Requirements for Incubation

Four environmental conditions are necessary for successful incubation: proper temperature, adequate ventilation for respiration, sufficient humidity, and correct position of the eggs. For best results each of these conditions must be controlled and kept within definite limits. The sciences of physics and engineering have developed modern incubators which make possible intelligent control of the environment of the egg during incubation.

Temperature. Investigators have attempted to establish the correct operating temperature for incubators by determining the temperature at which eggs are kept when incubated naturally. Since the body temperature of hens varies from hen to hen and for individual hens during the day, the results obtained have not been uniform. Electric resistance thermometers were used at the Montana Agricultural Experiment Station for determining the temperature of the egg during natural incubation. That station reported in 1925 that in natural incubation the average temperature at the top of the egg on the outside of the shell was 102.3° F. The temperature at the bottom of the egg was from fifteen to eighteen degrees lower during the first few days of incubation, but during the last few days of incubation it was only ten to twelve degrees lower. At the Missouri Agricultural Experiment Station in 1936 an attempt was made to measure by means of a thermocouple the temperature of the egg between the shell and shell membranes at the top and bottom of eggs being incubated naturally. These results, as shown by Figure 82, indicate that soon after the hen goes on the nest that portion of the egg near the germ spot is warmed; and after a few hours the bottom of the egg may be only 10° F. lower than the top of the egg. For determining the temperature of the incubating egg, temperatures taken beneath the shell are more satisfactory than temperatures taken outside of the shell.

It is a popular notion that the temperature of broody hens is higher than that of nonbroody hens. Investigations, however, show that this is not the case. The internal body temperature of the broody hen is usually lower than that of the nonbroody hen. Anyone who handles broody hens which have been broody for some time will observe that they have few feathers on the breast and that the breast appears quite warm. The loss of feathers from the breast facilitates the warming of the eggs by the broody hen; and for ability

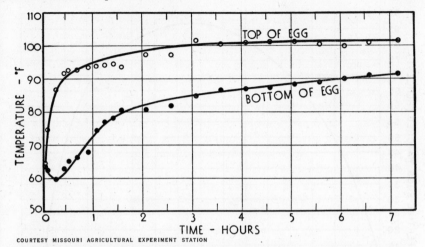

COURTESY MISSOURI AGRICULTURAL EXPERIMENT STATION

Fig. 82. The temperature between the shell and shell membranes of an egg soon after being placed under a broody hen.

to transmit heat to the egg the broody hen, no doubt, excels the nonbroody hen. Poultrymen observe this condition and conclude that the temperature of the broody hen is higher than that of the nonbroody hen.

While the difference in temperature between the top and bottom of an egg incubated under a hen may be 10° F. or more, the difference in the temperature at similar positions in an incubator may be only 4° F. in "still-air" machines and the same temperature in forced-draft incubators. Since humidity and ventilation influence temperature requirements, the application to artificial incubation of knowledge gained of temperature under natural incubation is rather limited. The most valuable contributions have therefore been made by those who have incubated eggs under controlled artificial conditions and determined the response of the embryos to definite experimental conditions.

The Purdue Agricultural Experiment Station investigated the effect of temperature on the occurrence of dead embryos in "still-air" incubators. The investigators reported best hatching results when eggs were incubated for three weeks at 101° F. when the bulb of the thermometer was 1½ inches above the bottom of the egg tray. When the temperature was lowered to 100° F. or lower, or raised to 103° F. or higher, the percentage of dead embryos was greatly increased. The National Agricultural Research Center has investigated the temperature requirements for eggs incubated in machines where the relative humidity was 60 per cent, the concentration of oxygen 21 per cent, the concentration of carbon dioxide less than 0.5 per cent, and air movement 12 cm. per minute. Under these conditions it was found that a temperature of 100° F. gave the best hatchability. The work of Barott (Figs. 83 and 84) shows quite clearly the detrimental effects on hatchability of both high and low temperatures. That the temperature requirements are not the same throughout the incubation period is indicated by work reported by Cornell University in 1936, which showed that by lowering the temperature

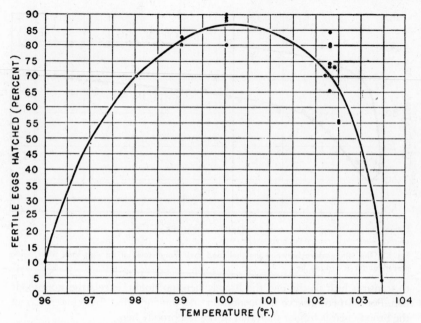

Fig. 83. Effect of temperature of incubation on percentage of fertile eggs hatched—relative humidity 60 per cent, oxygen 21 per cent, carbon dioxide below 0.5 per cent. (Barott, 1937.)

as much as 3° C., during the last few days of incubation, hatchability was increased and the quality of the chicks was improved.

Both high and low temperatures result in abnormal development and reduced hatchability. High temperatures at first accelerate but later retard the rate of growth and the CO_2 output, while low temperatures retard growth and reduce the output of CO_2. Low temperatures cause an early mortality peak, while both high and low temperatures cause heavy mortality on the nineteenth and twentieth days of incubation. The total length of the incubation period in a forced-draft incubator may be varied from nineteen to twenty-four days by incubating eggs at temperatures from 103.5° F. to 96° F. By incubating eggs in a "still-air" machine at 95° F., hatching may be delayed until the twenty-eighth day. Best hatches are produced, however, when the chicks hatch on the twenty-first day of incubation. In commercial hatchery operation it is desirable that all chicks be out of the incubators by the end of the twenty-first day so that settings may be made on a three-weeks' schedule.

It should be noted that satisfactory hatches are often obtained with farm incubators though the temperature may have run up to 108° F. or 110° F. for a short time. These results may be explained on the basis that such temperatures did not prevail long enough for the embryos to be heated to such high temperatures.

Cooling eggs. For many years after the advent of the small farm-type incubator, cooling eggs during incubation to duplicate the conditions which

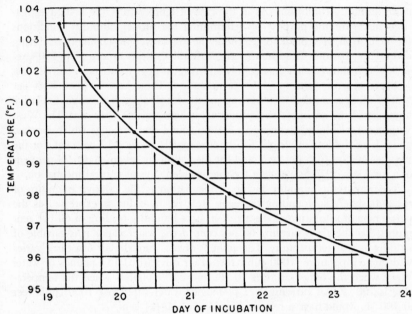

Fig. 84. Effect of incubation temperature on the time of hatching chicken eggs. (Barott, 1937.)

prevail when the hen leaves the nest was generally recommended. Poultrymen believed that removing the eggs from the incubator and cooling the eggs improved hatching results and in many cases this belief was well founded. Most manufacturers of the early farm incubators recommended operating temperatures which were higher than those later found to be optimum, and as a result of cooling the average incubating temperature was reduced and the hatch was thereby improved. It has been demonstrated by commercial hatcherymen that cooling eggs is not essential for successful hatching when the incubators are properly ventilated and operated at the correct temperature.

The effect of prolonged cooling on the hatchability of eggs is of interest to the hatchery industry because occasionally storms and floods cause electric current interruptions to the hatcheries. The California Agricultural Experiment Station investigated the effect of a twelve-hour electric current interruption on hatching results where the room temperature was approximately 70° F. This station reported in 1933 that such interruptions (twelve hours) on one day during the incubation period reduced the hatch 3.4 per cent and increased the number of unsalable chicks from 1.8 per cent to 3.4 per cent. These results show that electric current interruptions for several hours do not seriously affect hatching results. During current interruptions the temperature in the top of the incubator may go too high.

Humidity. While humidity in the incubator may vary considerably without reducing hatching results appreciably, there are definite limits and optimum humidity conditions. As in the case of temperature, the first investigations made for the purpose of determining the proper humidity conditions for incubation were made to determine the loss in weight which occurs during natural incubation. The Ontario Agricultural College reported in 1908 results which showed that during July and August eggs incubated naturally lost 12.0 per cent of their weight by evaporation. These hens hatched 71.5 per cent of all eggs set and 86.0 per cent of the fertile eggs. The average relative humidity of the air in the nests under these hens was 59.2 per cent. The West Virginia Agricultural Experiment Station found that for eggs which hatched under hens the loss in weight for the first five days was 4.17 per cent, for the next seven days 6.35 per cent, and for the following seven days 6.98 per cent or a total loss of 16.54 per cent for the nineteen days of natural incubation.

The important humidity factor in incubation is the relative humidity of the atmosphere surrounding the eggs. Relative humidity is expressed as the percentage of saturation of the air. A relative humidity reading of 60 per cent means that the air is carrying 60 per cent of the water vapor it is capable of holding at that temperature. The amount of moisture the air can carry varies with the temperature; 1000 cubic feet of air can carry 1.153 pounds of water vapor when the temperature is 70° F., and 2.855 pounds when the temperature is 100° F. Air carrying 1.71 pounds of water vapor per 1000 cubic feet at 100° F. would have a relative humidity of 60 per cent.

The gauge used for determining humidity conditions in the modern incubator is the wet bulb thermometer. The principle involved in estimating moisture conditions from the wet bulb reading is that when the atmosphere is dry evaporation from the wet bulb is increased, and therefore the bulb of the thermometer is cooled to a lower temperature than the dry bulb thermometer records. High wet bulb readings indicate high humidity in the incubator whereas low wet bulb readings indicate dry atmospheric conditions. The relative humidity as indicated by certain differences between dry bulb and wet bulb thermometer readings is given in Table 35.

Hatchability of eggs is very definitely affected by moisture conditions

Table 35

RELATIVE HUMIDITY AS DETERMINED BY DIFFERENCES IN WET BULB
AND DRY BULB THERMOMETER READINGS [10]

Dry Bulb Reading (Degrees F.)	Degrees F. Wet Bulb Is Below Dry Bulb Temperature							
	1.8	3.6	5.4	7.2	9.0	10.8	12.6	14.4
95.0	94	87	81	75	69	64	59	54
96.8	94	87	81	75	70	64	59	54
98.6	94	87	82	76	70	65	60	55
100.4	94	88	82	76	71	66	61	56
102.2	94	88	82	77	71	66	61	57

[10] Adapted from 22nd edition of Hodgman's Handbook of Chemistry and Physics, 1937.

during incubation. The Storrs Agricultural Experiment Station reported in 1918 the results of artificial incubation experiments with still-air machines in which the relative humidity was varied from 15 per cent to 80 per cent. The results obtained were as follows:

RELATION OF THE RELATIVE HUMIDITY TO LOSS IN WEIGHT OF EGGS DURING INCUBATION AND HATCHABILITY

Per Cent Relative Humidity	Average Loss of Weight per Egg, in Grams	Per Cent Loss of Weight	Per Cent Hatch of Fertile Eggs
70 to 80	3.03	5.3	45.5
60 to 70	4.96	8.7	62.1
50 to 60	5.61	9.8	69.3
40 to 50	5.82	10.2	68.6
30 to 40	6.57	11.5	68.6
20 to 30	8.29	14.5	60.6
15 to 20	9.94	17.4	48.0

Investigations made at Cornell University and the National Agricultural Research Center (Fig. 85) showed that most satisfactory hatches were obtained when the relative humidity of the egg chamber was 60 per cent. The results of experiments reported in 1938 by the Iowa Agricultural Experiment Station showed that in modern mechanically ventilated incubators where the temperature was 99.7° F. the growth of the embryo was not significantly different when the relative humidity was 40 per cent, 62 per cent, or 80 per cent.

That there is a definite relationship between humidity and temperature is shown by the work of Townsley. He found that when large forced-draft incubators were operated at 99° F. and wet bulb readings of 75° F., 85° F., and 90° F., the chicks hatched where the humidity was high (90° F. wet bulb reading) came out about twenty-four hours earlier than those hatched where the wet bulb reading was 85° F. The chicks hatched where the humidity was low (wet bulb reading of 75° F.) were twenty-four hours later in hatching than those in the machine where the wet bulb reading was 85° F. The chicks produced where the humidity was high and also where it was low were small and showed "stickiness." It was found that the length of the incubation period could be adjusted to twenty-one days by operating the incubators with the following dry bulb and wet bulb temperatures, respectively: 98° F. and 90° F., 99° F. and 85° F., and 100° F. and 75° F.

Humidity is an important factor in the control of pullorum disease during incubation. Relatively high humidity at hatching time minimizes the circulation of down in the incubator and thereby reduces the spread of pullorum Fumigation of incubators is more effective when humidity is high.

Most experienced incubator operators try to keep the wet bulb temperature about twelve to fourteen degrees below the dry bulb reading during the first eighteen days of incubation and only ten degrees lower than the dry bulb temperature while the chicks are hatching. Reducing the humidity of the incubator or separate hatcher after the hatch is complete strengthens the chicks

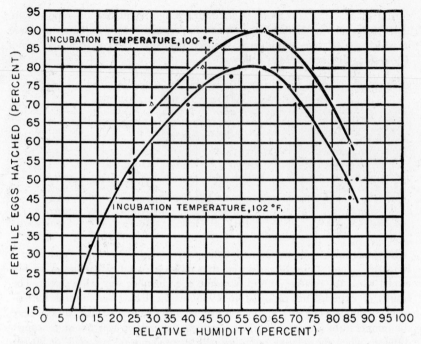

Fig. 85. Effect of relative humidity during incubation on hatchability, oxygen 21 per cent and carbon dioxide below 0.5 per cent. (Barott, 1937.)

and improves their appearance when they are removed from the trays and placed in chick boxes.

Ventilation. Since the chick embryo is an animal organism and therefore requires oxygen for its development, adequate ventilation is essential for successful incubation. A normal fertile hen's egg contains all of the materials necessary for embryonic development, except air. The embryo obtains the oxygen necessary for growth from the air which passes through the pores of the eggshell. Closing these pores causes suffocation of the embryo.

Carbon dioxide as a factor in incubation. The detrimental effect of CO_2 on hatchability has sometimes been questioned. Some investigators were led to believe that CO_2 depressed hatchability only to the extent that it replaced oxygen and therefore lowered the oxygen content of the air. Recent research work by Barott shows that CO_2 has a detrimental effect on embryonic development, though the oxygen content of the air is held constant at the most desirable level (Fig. 86).

Early work at the Ontario Agricultural College showed that the CO_2 content of air in the hen's nest during incubation was .32 per cent, in an incubator .10 per cent, and in the air in the incubator room .07 per cent. Since the hens were more successful than the incubators in incubating the eggs, attempts were made to improve artificial incubation by introducing some CO_2

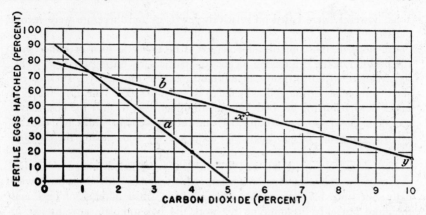

Fig. 86. Effect of carbon dioxide on hatchability. a, The percentage of carbon dioxide was kept constant throughout incubation. b, The percentage of carbon dioxide was kept constant at .5 per cent and allowed to accumulate to 5.5 per cent (x) and to 10 per cent (y) and then kept constant. (Barott, 1937.)

into the incubators. The results obtained indicated that introducing CO_2 into incubators did not improve hatching results.

Ventilation of incubators is essential for the removal of CO_2 produced by the developing embryos and for supplying fresh air containing a normal quantity of oxygen. Results obtained at Cornell University showed that when the carbon dioxide content of the air was 1.0 per cent or more and the oxygen was reduced accordingly, the growth of the embryos was slow; and such abnormalities as crooked toes, deformed beaks, and malpositions were common and mortality was high. The Wyoming Station found that increasing the oxygen content of the air in incubators at high altitude (5200 to 7200 feet) increased hatchability of both chicken and turkey eggs.

Position of the egg and turning. Best hatching results are obtained when the large end of the egg is uppermost. This is the natural position of an egg incubated by a hen, since the egg has a shape which causes it to assume such a position and the concave shape of the nest forces the eggs into a slightly tilted position. As early as 1886 Dareste reported that eggs incubated in a vertical position with the large end up developed normally, whereas those incubated with the small end up showed abnormal development. Research work at the National Agricultural Research Center reported in 1931 showed that when eggs were incubated with the large end up, only about 2 per cent of the embryos developed with their heads in the small end of the egg, but that when eggs were incubated with the small end up, about 60 per cent of the embryos developed with their heads in the small end of the egg. The position of the embryo is determined during the second week of incubation, gravity being an important factor in determining the position of the embryo in the egg. As early as 1907 Eycleshymer reported that eggs standing on the small ends at an angle of 45° hatched better than those eggs laid flat. His results, however, were based on relatively few eggs and therefore were inconclusive.

For normal embryonic development it is necessary to turn or rather shift the position of the egg during incubation, particularly during the first twelve days. Failure to do so results in mortality because the embryos stick to the shell membranes or the yolk adheres to the allantois. The hen turns the eggs under her by shifting her body and by using her beak to shift the position of the eggs. Observers have found that the broody hen may turn her eggs as often as ten times in two hours and at least every hour during the day and night.

Eycleshymer reported data in 1907 which showed the advantage of turning eggs and also the advantage of turning eggs five times daily instead of twice daily, but since his data were obtained with a small number of eggs and therefore probably insignificant, his work did not stimulate any interest in multiple turning. Later work reported in 1921 from the Massachusetts Agricultural Experiment Station showed that turning eggs six times daily as compared to turning eggs twice daily increased hatchability from 3 to 10 per cent. A number of other investigations have contributed data which show that hatchability is increased by turning up to eight times daily. (See list of references.) In commercial hatcheries where forced-draft incubators are used, eggs are not turned but merely shifted in position by tilting the eggs about their short axis. As long as eggs were incubated in incubators where hand turning was required, twice daily was considered sufficient turning; but with the invention of simple egg-turning devices attention was centered upon the extra chicks which could be produced by turning the eggs more frequently.

Natural Incubation

Although the tendency is for artificial methods of incubation to replace natural methods, a relatively high percentage of the chicks produced in some sections of the United States continue to be hatched by hens. With the eggs of some species natural methods of incubation remain most efficient. However, in the case of the chicken, duck, and turkey, man has perfected artificial methods of incubation which give results superior to those obtained when natural incubation is used.

Even though natural incubation may be used, the poultryman usually prefers to render assistance which he believes will improve the results.

Date of hatch. One of the disadvantages of natural incubation is that hens usually go broody too late for the production of early chicks. However, those that do go broody first may be set and those which go broody later may be placed in broody coops, and therefore the time of hatch may be controlled somewhat.

Selecting broody hens. The best hens to use for incubating chicken eggs are such general-purpose breeds as the Rhode Island Reds, Plymouth Rocks, Wyandottes, and Orpingtons. The Mediterranean breeds such as the Leghorns are unreliable sitters, even when they go broody. The hens should be healthy and, if possible, free from external parasites.

Preparing the nest. A nesting box about 16 inches square and 6 inches deep placed in a cool, quiet place where the hen will be protected against rain provides a satisfactory nest when it is partially filled with straw, fine hay, or leaves. The nest should be shaped so that the entire setting (about fifteen hen eggs, depending upon the size of the hen and the season) is in one layer and with the center of the nest lower than the outside so that the eggs in the nest will conform to the shape of the hen's body and not roll out of the nest.

Setting the hen. It is usually best to place eggs under a hen at night, because she will be disturbed less at that time.

Care of the hen. Grain (corn, wheat, or oats or a mixture of these), grit, and fresh water should be kept near the hen so that she will not be required to leave the nest for a long period to get feed and water. Hens selected for incubation purposes should be examined carefully for lice, and if any are found, two applications of sodium fluoride powder should be administered to the hens at ten-day intervals. This will rid the hens of this parasite and prevent them from being spread later to the newly hatched chicks.

Artificial Incubation

The art of hatching chickens by artificial methods has been known by man for several thousand years but only within the last fifty years has this method been applied within the industry on a large scale. The economical commercial production of poultry and eggs is dependent upon artificial incubation because the time of hatching can be controlled; the spread of diseases and parasites can be reduced; and the amount of labor required for incubation is reduced.

History of artificial incubation. To trace the history of artificial incubation, it is necessary to delve into the early history of the Chinese and Egyptian civilizations. This has been done by a number of writers. The Chinese developed the method as shown in Figure 87 in which they heated the eggs with a charcoal fire. The Chinese also used the hot-bed method (decomposition of manure) for heating incubators. The Egyptians constructed large incubators heated by fires built in the rooms where the eggs were incubated. These Egyptian hatcheries were constructed of brick and had a capacity of 90,000 eggs. They were operated on a toll basis, two chicks for each three eggs set being returned to the flock owner. Reaumur in 1750 constructed an incubator and hatched chicks successfully by using fermenting horse manure as a source of heat. It is interesting to note that in southern Australia there is a bird, *Leipoa ocellata,* which incubates its eggs by preparing a nest of vegetable matter in the sand, which later provides by fermentation sufficient heat to incubate its eggs. In 1770 an Englishman, John Champion, hatched chicks by passing hot air through the room where the eggs were located. Bonneman, a French physician, in 1777 hatched chicks by heating a hatching oven with

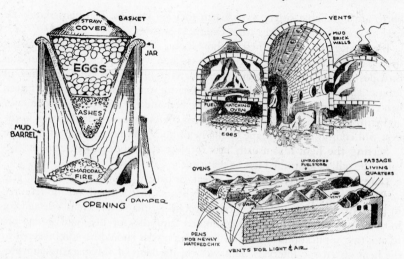

Fig. 87. Early incubators. Left: cross section of barrel type Chinese incubator. Right—upper: cross section of an ancient Egyptian incubator. Right—lower: drawing of an Egyptian hatchery. (From "The Baby Chick.")

circulating hot water. The first American incubator, a hot water machine, was built in 1844. The first mammoth incubator in America was built by Charles A. Cyphers in 1895. It was a 20,000-egg duck incubator of the room type. Dr. S. B. Smith apparently built the first forced-draft incubator, which he patented in 1918. The Petersime Incubator Company introduced in 1923 the first all-electric incubator. In recent years several new machines have been developed and all makes have been improved.

Modern Incubators

Incubators serve two distinct purposes: the production of chicks for the use of the operator, and the commercial production of chicks for sale. Those used for the first purpose are known as farm incubators and those used by the commercial chick hatcheries are called mammoth incubators.

Farm incubators. While the percentage of chicks hatched in small incubators has decreased since the development of commercial chick hatcheries, many producers still use small incubators for producing chicks for their own use. With the development in recent years of more rural electric power lines the use of small electric incubators has been increasing. Many of these small incubators are now of the forced-draft type.

Mammoth incubators. The invention of the mammoth incubator made possible the development of the modern chick hatchery which now produces more than 90 per cent of the chicks hatched in the United States. Two types of incubators are used in hatcheries—sectional and forced-draft machines. Before the invention of the cabinet or forced-draft incubator, commercial hatcheries were equipped with sectional incubators. Sectional machines have the advantage of being independent of electricity and therefore can be operated in rural areas where electricity is not available.

Cabinet or room-type incubators have these advantages: (1) They require a minimum of floor space. (2) The control of temperature, humidity, and ventilation are simplified and the turning of eggs made easier. (3) They are better adapted to use in business districts than the sectional machines because less space is required.

These advantages have caused most hatcherymen to turn to the cabinet or forced-draft incubators. In recent years practically all new incubators purchased for use in hatcheries have been of this type (Figs. 88 and 89).

A recent development has been the separate hatcher. These units are designed for hatching purposes only. The eggs (chicken) are incubated elsewhere until the eighteenth day, when they are transferred to the separate hatcher, such as shown in Figure 90. Some of the incubator companies have built compartments into their machines which are used only for hatching and therefore are separate hatching units.

Fuels used for heating incubators are oil, coal, gas, and electricity. Small farm incubators are usually heated with kerosene. Coal and gas are used for heating sectional machines which are heated by hot water. Forced-draft machines require electricity for the operation of the fans which are necessary for circulating the air in these machines. In most cases these machines are also heated with electricity. However, some large incubating units are heated by hot water which is warmed by coal-burning heaters. Fuel cost is a considerable item in the cost of producing chicks and should be considered when selecting an incubator.

Management of the Incubator

Proper management of the incubator is essential for the production of chicks. Unless all the requirements for the developing chick embryo are satisfied, poor hatches will result.

Regulating the temperature. The temperature of an incubator must be controlled within very narrow limits. The instructions of the manufacturer should be followed, keeping in mind the temperature requirements previously discussed as factors influencing hatching results. All incubators are equipped with temperature-regulating mechanisms which are sensitive to temperature changes inside the incubator. In the electrically heated machines the thermostat makes and breaks the electric circuit and thereby the temperature can usually be kept within very narrow limits. In incubators heated by other sources, a thermostat is used which regulates the amount of heat entering the compartments where the eggs are located.

If, for some reason, the source of heat is cut off for several hours, little damage may be done. In case of such interruptions, the room temperature should be kept up and the heat inside the incubator conserved by closing the ventilators on the machine. Precautions should be taken to prevent the temperature in the top of the incubator from going too high.

Fig. 88. Evolution in modern incubators. Top left, small home incubator. (Courtesy Smith Incubator Company.) Top right, early sectional type incubators. (U. S. D. A.) Center, partial view of hatchery equipped with cabinet type forced-draft incubator for a million egg capacity. (Courtesy Smith Incubator Company.) Bottom, mammoth sectional type incubators. (Ohio Poultry Improvement Association.)

Ventilation. Proper ventilation is essential for incubation so that the embryos will be supplied with air containing an adequate amount of oxygen and less than $1\frac{1}{2}$ per cent of carbon dioxide. The operator of an incubator should

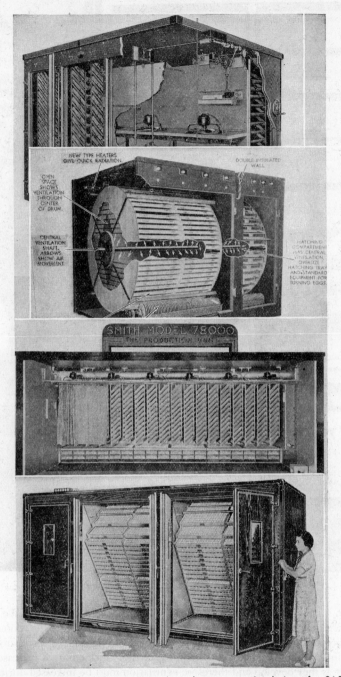

Fig. 89. Some forced-draft incubators. From top to bottom: a sectional view of a 24,000-egg Buckeye incubator (Buckeye Incubator Company); a Petersime incubator with separate hatching compartment (Petersime Incubator Company); a Smith 78,000-egg capacity incubator (Smith Incubator Company); a Robbins incubator with a separate hatching compartment (Robbins Incubator Company).

Fig. 90. Baby chicks ready to leave a separate hatcher.

bear in mind that the incubator cannot be properly ventilated unless the room in which the machines are located contains fresh air. Therefore the room must be ventilated before any progress can be made in ventilating incubators located in such rooms. The oxygen requirements of chick embryos increase very rapidly as they develop and therefore ventilation must be increased during the later stages of incubation.

The rate of circulation of the air in the incubator does not appear to be a factor affecting the incubation of the eggs of most species; but apparently pheasant eggs hatch better in "still air" than in the circulating air of forced-draft incubators. The Pennsylvania Agricultural Experiment Station reported that pheasants hatched better when the eggs were transferred from forced-draft incubators to "still-air" sectional machines for hatching.

Turning the eggs. Turning during the early stages of incubation is necessary for normal embryonic development. Best hatching results are obtained when the eggs are turned at least five times daily up to the eighteenth day. Mammoth incubators and some small machines are equipped with turning devices which reduce to a minimum the labor required for turning the eggs. Small sectional farm incubators do not usually have such devices and therefore the eggs must be turned by hand. Eggs should be turned gently so that the delicate chick embryos will not be injured.

Control of moisture. For most satisfactory hatches with incubators it is usually necessary to supply moisture to keep the relative humidity rather high (about 60 per cent) during incubation and slightly higher (about 70 per cent) at hatching time. Mammoth machines are equipped with various devices for supplying moisture, such as burlap panels from which moisture evaporates or automatic devices for liberating or spraying moisture into the incubator. The relative humidity of forced-draft incubators is gauged by wet bulb thermometer readings. Moisture conditions in small incubators can be judged by the size of the air cell or by the percentage loss in weight of the eggs. The normal loss in weight for eggs incubated under proper conditions is from 4 to 5 per cent per week. One hundred eggs weighing 200 ounces when first set should lose from 8 to 10 ounces in weight each week while being incubated. The skilled operator learns from experience the moisture conditions which give best results.

Taking off the hatch. The hatch should be completed by the end of the twenty-first day of incubation, if the incubator has been operated correctly. If the hatching trays are crowded, some chicks should be removed before the hatch is completed. None of the chicks should be taken out of the incubator before they have dried off or "fluffed out." Chicks removed from incubators after hatching should not be placed where they will be chilled (Fig. 91). The ventilation of the chick boxes is important. In cold weather only a few holes should be punched in the boxes but during hot weather the chicks will need all of the ventilation they can be given.

Hatchery Management

Although the Egyptians have used commercial hatcheries (Egyptian ovens operated as public institutions on a toll basis for hatching chicks) for centuries, the development of the chick hatchery in America did not occur until the twentieth century. The number of commercial hatcheries in 1918 was estimated as 250 but in 1943, when a relatively accurate count was taken by the U. S. Department of Agriculture, there were 10,112 breeder and commercial hatcheries which sold chicks. The total egg capacity of these hatcheries was 504,640,000 eggs. Eighty-eight of the largest of these hatcheries had

Fig. 91. Sorting and boxing chicks for shipment. Note the storage racks on the left and openings in the chick boxes for ventilation.

a total egg capacity of 74,788,000 eggs. The hatchery industry of America is more highly developed than that of any country in the world.

Location for a hatchery. The type of chick business (local, mail order, or wholesale) the hatcheryman expects to do will govern somewhat the location for the hatchery. The local hatchery which depends on selling practically all chicks at the hatchery must be located where there is a good demand for chicks and must be readily accessible to chick buyers who call for the chicks. Hatcherymen who hope to develop a mail-order business should locate where good shipping facilities are available. Wholesalers of chicks should be located near their dealer or jobber customers. The hatchery should be located where there are enough good flocks to supply satisfactory hatching eggs. A location on or near "farmers' street" in a town where the farmers do their trading is usually a good location for a hatchery. Parking space at or near the hatchery is a great convenience to chick customers and flock owners. A hatchery which has space available for a window display of chicks can use such space to good advantage in advertising chicks if they are located in the business district of town.

The hatchery. The building which houses the hatchery should be built of substantial material and so constructed that it will withstand outside temperature fluctuations reasonably well. It should be kept in good repair, well painted, and present an attractive appearance (Fig. 92). A well-drained concrete floor is conducive to cleanliness in the hatchery. The hatchery should be well lighted and properly ventilated. Good lighting improves the work of

Fig. 92. A modern hatchery.

employees and makes a good impression on customers. A well-ventilated building makes possible proper incubator ventilation. Forced ventilation is necessary in larger hatcheries, particularly in warm weather, to remove stale air and excess humidity, and to reduce the temperature. The building should be so arranged and a schedule of work so planned that the hatchery will be clean when customers come in. Every commercial hatchery should have at least separate rooms for the office, incubators, and for started or display chicks. Usually it requires only a little material and a small amount of labor to provide these minimum facilities. Other desirable rooms are egg receiving and traying room, chick sorting and boxing room, room for chick boxes and other supplies, and a display room for equipment and feed.

The modern hatchery will likely be equipped with the cabinet type of incubator because such equipment requires less floor space. Old incubators which do not give satisfactory hatches are too expensive at any price for the progressive hatcheryman. Separate hatchers or incubators with separate hatching compartments are gaining in popularity.

Battery brooders are used by most hatcheries for holding surplus chicks which accumulate because of weather conditions, order cancellations, or oversettings.

The manager. The most important single factor making for success in the hatchery business is the manager. A good manager may build a profitable hatchery business even where the conditions are unfavorable, but a poor manager may ruin the best hatchery. The management problem is the chain hatchery operator's greatest worry. The most successful manager is one who knows the poultry business as well as the hatchery business, possesses a strong personality, and has business ability.

Hatching egg supply. A supply of hatching eggs from healthy, well-bred flocks is essential to the continued operation of a hatchery. Few hatcherymen own enough birds to supply all the eggs required by their hatcheries and therefore they must purchase eggs from co-operating flock owners. In many communities good breeding flocks are not available and therefore it becomes necessary to ship in part or all of the eggs required. The most satisfactory arrangement is to get eggs from flocks located nearby so that the eggs can be delivered to the hatchery by the flock owner. The number of birds required to supply hatching eggs to a commercial hatchery is approximately one tenth of the egg capacity of the hatchery.

Fig. 93. An official hatchery flock inspection.

The servicing of hatchery supply flocks is essential if reliable sources of hatching eggs are to be maintained. Those hatcheries which hope to produce quality chicks must select good breeding flocks and know how they are managed. The cost of competent servicing for flocks is more than paid for by the improved quality of the chicks. The hatcheries generally make a service charge to the flock owner for culling and blood testing. Too often this is the only servicing the flock receives. All flocks should be visited before the hatching season begins and a careful check made as to the condition of the males and females in the flock and the feeding and management of the flock (Fig. 93).

Many hatcherymen prefer to have some of the flock servicing done by trained state inspectors. These inspectors have or develop a background which is valuable in advising flock owners about their poultry problems. Forty-seven states in 1946 had organized state poultry programs with state inspectors. Agreements between the hatcherymen and flock owners are desirable so that each party may understand his responsibilities. Many hatcherymen have oral agreements with their flock owners which both parties respect.

The premium paid for hatching eggs varies with the quality of stock, the locality, the competition, the hatchability of the eggs, and the value of other services rendered. Most hatcheries pay a straight premium but some hatcherymen grade their flocks and pay a premium based on the quality of the flock, while others base the premium on the hatchability of the eggs.

The hatcheryman should make the flock owner a definite part of his hatchery organization. He should assist the flock owners with their poultry problems and make the flock owners feel that they have a definite responsibility to the hatchery. Flock owners should be boosters in their neighborhoods for the hatchery.

Hatchery sanitation. Cleanliness and sanitation in the hatchery are essential for continued success in putting out chicks which live and do not spread disease. Unfortunately, some hatcheries through their chicks spread such poultry diseases as pullorum and bronchitis and thereby create a bad reputation for hatchery chicks. Frequently chicks infected with bronchitis are shipped in the same car with other chicks or mixed with healthy chicks in the brooders, thus spreading this disease to chicks which were free of this trouble. It is to the interest of each hatchery that all hatcheries produce chicks free from such diseases as bronchitis.

Pullorum is the most common chick disease which may be spread through the hatchery. However, modern methods of blood testing the breeding stock and fumigating the incubators make possible the control of this disease. Progressive hatcherymen blood test the breeding stock used for producing hatching eggs. They also fumigate the hatching compartments of their incubators between hatches, using formaldehyde gas, which kills any pullorum organisms left by the previous hatch. Between hatching seasons the incubators, incubator room, brooder room, and brooding equipment should be thoroughly cleaned and disinfected. Movable parts should be scrubbed with a 2 per cent solution of commercial lye. (Rubber gloves should be worn.) The inside of the incubators, the incubator room, and brooding room should be sprayed with a 5 per cent solution of formalin. The temperature should be as much above 60° F. as convenient, and the incubators and rooms should be kept closed for twelve hours or longer.

Between hatches during the hatching season the hatching compartment should be fumigated with formaldehyde gas, using 40 cc. of a 40 per cent solution of formalin and 20 grams of potassium permanganate for each 100 cubic feet of space inside the compartment. The potassium permanganate should be placed in a glass or earthenware container and the formalin poured over it. Another method for liberating the formaldehyde gas is to saturate cheesecloth with the formalin and then hang the cloth near the fans in the incubator. To be most effective, fumigation should be done with both the temperature and humidity of the machine at the highest levels used in incubation. If the dry bulb reading is 100° F., the wet bulb thermometer should register at least 90° F. Since chicks which live well are excellent advertising for a hatchery and since pullorum disease is the most common cause of early chick mortality, it behooves every hatcheryman to control this disease. Time and money expended in blood testing breeding stock and for sanitation in the hatchery may be considered advertising expense.

To prevent the spread of pullorum disease in the incubator, the chicks may be fumigated according to the following procedure:

Calculate the exact number of cubic feet in the compartment to be fumigated. Use 35 cc. of fresh formalin and 17.5 grams of potassium permanganate per 100 cubic feet of space inside the compartment to be fumigated. Make the first fumigation when about 10 per cent of the chicks are out and before any have dried off. Twelve hours later repeat the fumigation. After each fumigation keep all ventilators closed for from 8 to 10 minutes, *but no longer.*

Remove all chicks hatched soon after the second fumigation. Twelve hours after the second fumigation make a third fumigation and again soon thereafter remove the chicks.

Be sure that the wet bulb reading shows about 70 per cent relative humidity throughout the hatch. *High humidity is very important.* Chicks may appear to suffer but if the correct amounts of materials are used and the above instructions are followed, results will be entirely satisfactory.

The prevention and control of infectious bronchitis has during recent years become an important problem in hatchery management. Every hatcheryman should follow practices designed to keep the disease out of the hatchery. Chicks should not be brooded in the incubator room; chick boxes and poultry coops previously used and adult birds should not be brought on the hatchery premises, and the hatchery room and equipment should be kept clean. In case of an outbreak in the hatchery plant, all affected chicks should be killed, other chicks moved from the incubator room, and all equipment used for brooding chicks thoroughly cleaned and disinfected, and the building fumigated with formaldehyde gas, using two and one-half times the amount recommended for incubator fumigation. The walls and floors should be wet thoroughly to increase the humidity of the room and the temperature should be raised to 90° F. to make the gas more effective. The room should be closed tightly for twenty minutes following fumigation. Fans should be operated in the room to distribute the gas during fumigation and to eliminate it after twenty minutes of fumigation. It has been observed that an outbreak of this disease spreads quite generally in a territory. Hatcherymen located in such a territory should exercise extreme caution in preventing an outbreak in their plants.

Hatching season. The hatching season varies with the geographical location and weather conditions. In the United States most chicks are sold during March, April, and May. Most hatcheries make their first settings in January or February and bring off their last hatches in June. Severely cold weather may delay the opening of the chick season and an early drought may abruptly end the season. Some hatcheries operate throughout most of the year and a considerable number now operate during the fall months to supply the chicks demanded for winter broiler production.

Surplus chicks. The modern hatchery is prepared to handle some surplus chicks. Floods and snow and ice storms frequently cause the demand for chicks to be postponed and the hatcheryman who had anticipated the demand on the basis of normal weather conditions finds that more chicks hatch than can be sold. By carrying these chicks in battery brooders until favorable weather prevails, they can be moved through the regular chick sales without dumping them on auctions or selling them at reduced prices.

Surplus chicks are the greatest menace to the maintenance of chick prices. If surpluses occur early in the season, they may demoralize the price structure for most of the season.

Surplus chicks are sometimes sold at auctions for much less than the cost of production. The disposal of surplus chicks leads to unethical trade practices.

The booking of chick orders for future delivery is decreasing, particularly late in the season. This condition has arisen because buyers find that hatcheries carry chicks on hand or can fill orders on short notice. Therefore, the hatcheryman must anticipate the demand for chicks in the light of his past experience and the current season demand and govern his settings accordingly.

Sexing chicks. The sexed-chick business has developed since it was first introduced into the commercial hatcheries of the United States in 1934, into a very important phase of the chick business. In certain regions, notably the commercial egg-producing sections of the Pacific Coast, it is estimated that 90 per cent of the chicks are sexed by an examination of the rudimentary copulatory organs (Fig. 94). Sexed pullets are particularly desirable in Leghorns if there is a poor market for Leghorn broilers. In the East, Middle West, and South where suitable markets for broilers usually prevail or where the farmers can use the males to good advantage as table poultry, sexing has not gained any great headway. Since the price of sexed pullets is usually about twice the price of straight-run chicks, the farmer does not care to pay for the cockerels and leave them with the hatcheryman for his disposal. It is usually profitable for the farmer to raise the cockerels.

To be an efficient sexer one must have good eyesight, be adept with his fingers, be trained, and keep in practice by working at the job. Most efficient sexers are those who do this work continually during the hatching season. The hatcheryman will do well to employ a sexer for such work. Several small hatcheries may arrange a schedule so that they can use the services of the same person.

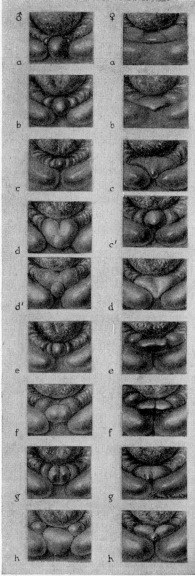

Fig. 94. Chick sexing. Diagrams of the everted cloacas of chicks showing the different structures observed in male chicks (left) and female chicks (right). Note the great variation in the appearance of both the males and females.

Custom hatching. Many community hatcheries incubate eggs for poultry raisers, making a charge for this service. For the small local hatchery this source of income is relatively high and therefore prized by these hatcherymen. The cost of incubating hen eggs is about $2.00 per 100 eggs. Hatcheries which have expanded their capacity beyond their chick demand often bid for custom hatching with prices far below the actual cost of the service. Much of the custom hatching is now being done on such a basis and a hatchery located in such a region may well abandon custom hatching and devote its time to the production and sale of chicks. The hatcheryman as well as the poultryman should realize that pullorum disease is spread in incubators when healthy chicks and diseased chicks are hatched in the same machines. Therefore, eggs from stock blood tested for pullorum disease should not be hatched with eggs from nontested stock. Both parties should insist upon this.

Custom hatching is a service which the poultryman who has stock he wants to reproduce can well afford to use. Custom hatching is usually less expensive for the poultry raiser than hatching the chicks at home.

Culling chicks. It is just as important to cull chicks as to select laying stock (Fig. 91). All weak and crippled chicks should be destroyed. They mar the appearance of the group and often succumb to the attacks of disease and thereby spread infection to healthy chicks. It is also important that "off-colored" chicks be removed from the group, particularly if the chicks are to be sold. Chick cus-

Fig. 95. Chicks are delivered by truck, parcel post, express, and airplane. A shipment of chicks for South America.

tomers are quite critical of chicks that show impurity of breeding, often judging the entire group by one or two "off-colored" chicks. The Standard of Perfection contains color descriptions of the different varieties of chicks. The producer of baby chicks should be familiar with these descriptions. Complaints may be reduced by acquainting customers with the proper color markings of the chicks they purchase as chick customers are often misinformed as to the correct color of baby chicks.

Delivering chicks. Small local hatcheries deliver most of the chicks they sell directly to the buyer at the hatchery. The hatcheryman is therefore relieved of the costs of transportation and the hazards of shipping. Some hatcheries are now making local deliveries by truck to the poultryman. As competition increases, this practice will likely become more common.

Chicks are shipped by express and parcel post (Fig. 95). During the spring months losses are negligible but in hot weather losses may run quite high. Hatcheries make a practice of guaranteeing 100 per cent live delivery.

The ventilation of the boxes is quite important. It should be kept in mind that in cold weather the chicks are kept warm in the boxes by their body heat. In cold weather very few holes should be punched in the boxes, but in hot weather the boxes should be well ventilated. Some hatcheries replace most of the top of the box with screen wire when shipping chicks during the summer months.

The standard containers for delivering chicks are cardboard boxes in sizes suitable for 25, 50, and 100 chicks. The standard chick box for 100 chicks is 22" x 18" x 5½". For hot weather shipments larger boxes (24" x 18" x 6") are used. Special chick box supply houses provide the hatcheries with their shipping supplies.

Business methods. Financial success in the hatchery business, as in all business enterprises, is dependent upon good business methods. A complete set of records should be kept in every hatchery. Such records should not only show all financial transactions but should also show the inquiries received, the name and address of customers, the number and grade of chicks sold to each customer, the date of each sale, and a record of all hatching eggs purchased.

Marketing chicks. The marketing of chicks is the hatcheryman's sales problem. There are three common methods of selling chicks: local sales at the hatchery, mail orders direct to customers, and wholesale. The wholesale method is the least satisfactory and most destructive of chick quality. This method prevents contact between the producer and customer, an arrangement vital to the improvement of quality. Local chick sales are most satisfactory and are less expensive than mail order sales. In every community there is a demand for high-quality chicks that can be supplied by the local hatchery.

Advertising. The best advertisement any hatchery can have is the chicks it produces. Quality chicks sell themselves and also stimulate repeat orders. Many hatcheries sell their entire output primarily upon the reputation of the chicks produced in previous seasons. A satisfied customer not only buys the next year but also influences others to buy. This form of advertising should be carefully guarded by every producer of chicks.

A neatly kept plant is another inexpensive but very effective method of advertising. Visitors are interested in cleanliness around the hatchery. Every visitor is a prospective customer and should be considered as such.

Attractive advertising signs and buildings are good advertising particularly for the local demand. Well-painted and well-kept buildings should be considered a part of the advertising program of every hatchery. Advertisements in the local newspaper stimulate local demand and should be used as a means of reaching this outlet. Often news stories of local interest about the hatchery or its products serve as splendid advertising. Advertising on a statewide or nation-wide scale should be conducted by an advertising specialist whose services are available to the hatcheryman through various advertising agencies. Catalogs and other advertising material should be prepared by advertising specialists.

Shipping hatching eggs. Some states have developed important hatching egg outlets because of their favorable climatic conditions and location in the United States. Hatching eggs are shipped by express and by truck. Eggs intended for the use of hatcheries should be carefully graded for size, and eggs weighing less than twenty-three ounces per dozen should never be sold to hatcherymen without a very definite understanding about the size of the eggs. Extra long or large eggs which are likely to be broken in transit should not be shipped as hatching eggs. Hatching eggs should also be graded for shape

Fig. 96. A scene in the exhibit area of an International Baby Chick Association convention. The association meets annually with thousands of hatcherymen and members of allied industries in attendance.

and color. Eggs from varieties which lay white-shelled eggs should be chalk white and reasonably free from tints. For best results the eggs should not be over one week old. They should be packed with the small end down in new cases, with flats and fillers. Eggs shipped with the small end up do not hatch well. The use of new flats and fillers will prevent damage to the eggs. The case tops should be nailed down at each end but not in the middle, with four-penny cement-coated egg-case nails. Each case should carry a label showing the name of the buyer, the name of the shipper, and the fact that the eggs are hatching eggs. If the eggs are from a hatchery co-operating with the National Poultry Improvement Plan and are being shipped to another hatchery operating under the plan, they should carry an official label indicating the breeding stage and pullorum control class. Inside the case on top of the eggs there should be a slip showing the number of dozens and the breed and variety of chickens which produced the eggs.

Hatching-egg stations. Large hatcheries have need for stations at which hatching eggs from flocks located in different communities may be assembled before being shipped or trucked to the hatchery. The most satisfactory arrangement appears to be a co-operative arrangement between hatcherymen, by which the operator of the local hatchery assembles the eggs and ships them to the larger hatcheries. In communities where there are no hatcherymen, a co-operative arrangement may be made with a feed store or produce house as a place for the hatching eggs to be assembled. If a produce dealer co-operates with the hatcheryman, a separate room should be set aside during the hatching season where only hatching eggs are received and held. The room should be cool and damp.

REVIEW QUESTIONS

1. Is a knowledge of embryonic development of any value to a hatcheryman?
2. Which of the primary germ layers of the embryo are present when the egg is laid?
3. When does the primitive streak make its appearance?
4. Name some of the functions of the extra-embryonic membranes.
5. Why is the embryologist interested primarily in the first four days of incubation?
6. What special mechanisms are developed for hatching a chick?
7. Why do critical stages occur during incubation?
8. What is the relative water content of the chick embryo during incubation?
9. What are the sources of energy for the developing chick embryo?
10. Do eggs contain hormones?
11. What are lethal genes? Are they dominant or recessive?
12. What relation exists between egg production and hatchability?
13. What physical characters of hen's eggs are associated with hatchability?
14. What vitamins influence hatching results?
15. At what temperature should hatching eggs be held? Why?
16. Should soiled hatching eggs be cleaned?
17. Why is a forced-draft incubator operated at a lower temperature than a sectional machine?
18. What is relative humidity? How is the percentage of relative humidity calculated?
19. Does a wet bulb thermometer reading of 85° F. or 90° F. in an incubator operated at 100° F. represent a higher humidity? Explain.
20. By diagrams illustrate the relation of temperature, humidity, turning, and CO_2 content of air to hatchability.
21. Are there any illustrations of artificial incubation found in nature?
22. Where do commercial hatcheries obtain their supply of hatching eggs?
23. Why has chick sexing grown in popularity?
24. What is custom hatching? What precautions should be taken with eggs custom hatched?

REFERENCES

ALDER, H. G.: DETERMINING THE SEX OF DAY-OLD CHICKS. Neb. Sta. Circ. 51. 1935.

BAROTT, H. G.: EFFECT OF TEMPERATURE, HUMIDITY, AND OTHER FACTORS ON HATCH OF HENS' EGGS AND ON ENERGY METABOLISM OF CHICK EMBRYOS. U. S. D. A. Tech. Bul. 553: 1–45. 1937.

BUSHNELL, L. D., AND PAYNE, L. F.: DISSEMINATION OF PULLORUM DISEASE IN THE INCUBATOR. Kan. Tech. Bul. 29. 1931.

CANFIELD, T. H.: A TECHNIQUE FOR THE SEX DETERMINATION OF CHICKS. Minn. Sta. Misc. Rpt. 3. 1944.

CHICKENS IN NATIONAL POULTRY IMPROVEMENT PLAN HATCHERY SUPPLY FLOCKS AND THEIR DISTRIBUTION BY STATES AND VARIETIES. 1941–42, 1944–45, and 1947–48. U. S. D. A. Bur. An. Ind., A. H. D. 69. 1949.

COONEY, W. T.: PREINCUBATION HUMIDITY VARIATION EFFECTS ON CHICKEN EGG HATCHABILITY. Ore. Sta. Tech. Bul. 2. 1943.

FORSYTH, R. M.: Chick Sexing Made Easy. Pacific Coast Motorist, Ltd., Vancouver, British Columbia, Canada. 1934.

FUNK, E. M.: FACTORS INFLUENCING HATCHABILITY IN THE DOMESTIC FOWL. Mo. Agr. Expt. Sta. Bul. 341: 1–22. 1934.

FUNK, E. M., AND BIELLIER, H. A.: THE MINIMUM TEMPERATURE FOR EMBRYONIC DEVELOPMENT IN THE DOMESTIC FOWL. Poultry Sci., 23: 538–540. 1944.

GIBBS, C. S.: A Guide to Chick Sexing. Orange Judd Co., New York. 1935.

GODFREY, A. B.: THE EFFECT OF EGG WEIGHT, QUANTITY OF TOTAL ALBUMEN PER EGG, AND QUANTITY OF THICK ALBUMEN PER EGG ON HATCHABILITY. Poultry Sci., 15: 294–297. 1936.

GODFREY, G. F., AND JAAP, R. G.: THE RELATIONSHIP OF SPECIFIC GRAVITY, 14-DAY INCUBATION WEIGHT LOSS, AND EGG SHELL COLOR TO HATCHABILITY AND EGG SHELL QUALITY. Poultry Sci., 28: 874–889. 1949.

GRAHAM, R., AND MICHAEL, VIOLA: INCUBATOR HYGIENE. Ill. Sta. Circ. 403. 1933.

HALPIN, J. G., AND HOLMES, C. E.: PRODUCING GOOD HATCHING EGGS. Wis. Agr. Expt. Sta. Bul. 433. 1936.

HARTMAN, ROLAND C., AND VICKERS, G. S.: Hatchery Management, Revised. Orange Judd Co., New York. 1950.

HENDERSON, E. W.: HATCHING ABILITY OF POULTRY. III. THE MARKET QUALITY CRITERION—MOBILITY OF YOLK AND HATCHABILITY. Mich. Sta. Quart. Bul. 25: 151–156. 1942.

JEFFREY, F. P., AND PLATT, C. S.: A THREE-YEAR STUDY OF OUT-OF-SEASON HATCHING. N. J. Sta. Bul. 687. 1941.

JEFFREY, F. P., AND THOMPSON, W. C.: SIGHT-SEXING OF NEWLY HATCHED CHICKS OF STANDARD BREEDS. N. J. Sta. Bul. 705. 1943.

JULL, M. A., AND LEE, A. R.: INCUBATION AND BROODING OF CHICKS. U. S. D. A. Farmers' Bul. 1538. Revised 1946.

KING, D. F.: THE DETECTION OF INFERTILE EGGS AND ITS APPLICATION TO HATCHERY MANAGEMENT. Ala. Agr. Expt. Sta. Circ. 82. 1939.

KIMBALL, E. S., MOORE, R. F., AND SMITH, P. W.: COMMERCIAL HATCHERY CHICK PRODUCTION. U. S. D. A. Sta. Bul. 81. 1945.

KOSIN, I. L.: THE ACCURACY OF THE MACROSCOPIC METHOD IN IDENTIFYING FERTILE UNINCUBATED GERM DISCS. Poultry Sci., 24: 281–283. 1945.

LANDAUER, W.: THE HATCHABILITY OF CHICKEN EGGS AS INFLUENCED BY ENVIRONMENT AND HEREDITY. Storrs Sta. Bul. 262. 1948.

LILLIE, F. R.: The Development of the Chick. Henry Holt & Co., New York. 1930.

LYONS, M., AND INSKO, W. M.: CHONDRODYSTROPHY IN THE CHICK EMBRYO PRODUCED BY MANGANESE DEFICIENCY IN THE DIET OF THE HEN. Ky. Agr. Expt. Sta. Bul. 371. 1937.

MESHEW, M. H.: THE USE OF OXYGEN IN THE HATCHING OF CHICKEN AND TURKEY EGGS AT HIGH ALTITUDES. Poultry Sci., 28: 87–97. 1949.

MUNRO, S. S.: FURTHER DATA ON THE RELATION BETWEEN SHELL STRENGTH, POTENTIAL HATCHABILITY AND CHICK VIABILITY IN THE FOWL. Sci. Agr., 22: 698–704. 1942.

NEEDHAM, J.: Chemical Embryology. 3 Vols. The Macmillan Co., New York. 1931.

OLSEN, M. W.: EFFECT OF SHIPMENT ON PREINCUBATED FERTILE EGGS. Poultry Sci., 29: 731–738. 1949.

OLSEN, M. W., AND BYERLY, T. C.: MULTIPLE TURNING AND ORIENTING EGGS DURING INCUBATION AS THEY AFFECT HATCHABILITY. Poultry Sci., 15: 88–95. 1936.

OLSEN, M. W., AND KNOX, C. W.: EARLY IDENTIFICATION OF FERTILITY IN HENS' EGGS. Poultry Sci., 17: 472–477. 1938.

OLSEN, M. W., AND HAYNES, S. K.: THE EFFECT OF DIFFERENT HOLDING TEMPERATURES ON THE HATCHABILITY OF HENS' EGGS. Poultry Sci., 28: 420–426. 1948.

OLSEN, M. W., AND HAYNES, S. K.: EGG CHARACTERISTICS WHICH INFLUENCE HATCHABILITY. Poultry Sci., 28: 198–201. 1949.

PATTEN, B. M.: The Early Embryology of the Chick, 3rd ed. P. Blakiston's Son & Co., Philadelphia. 1929.

PENQUITE, R.: INFLUENCE OF TEMPERATURE AND HUMIDITY UPON THE GROWTH OF CHICK EMBRYOS IN A MECHANICALLY VENTILATED INCUBATOR. Iowa Agr. Expt. Sta. Res. Bul. 232: 1–39. 1938.

PHILLIPS, R. E.: HATCHABILITY AS INFLUENCED BY ENVIRONMENTAL AND DIFFERENT STORAGE TEMPERATURES. Poultry Sci., 24: 25–28. 1945.

POFFENBERGER, P. R., AND DEVAULT, S. H.: AN ECONOMIC STUDY OF THE HATCHERY INDUSTRY IN MARYLAND. Md. Agr. Expt. Sta. Bul. 426. 1939.

REAUMUR, M.: The Art of Hatching and Bringing Up Domestic Fowls. Published for C. Davis, London. 1750.

ROMANOFF, A. L.: BIOCHEMISTRY AND BIOPHYSICS OF THE DEVELOPING HEN'S EGG. I. INFLUENCE OF HUMIDITY. Cornell Agr. Expt. Sta. Mem., 1932: 1–27. 1930.

ROMANOFF, A. L.: EFFECT OF COMPOSITION OF AIR ON THE GROWTH AND MORTALITY OF THE CHICK EMBRYO. Jour. Morph. and Physiol., 50: 517–525. 1930.

ROMANOFF, A. L.: WHY SOME EGGS DO NOT HATCH. Cornell Ext. Bul. 205. 1931.

ROMANOFF, A. L.: RECENT PROGRESS IN ARTIFICIAL INCUBATION. Proc. Eighth World's Poultry Cong., pp. 43–59. 1948.

ROMANOFF, A. L., AND BAUERNFEIND, J. C.: INFLUENCE OF RIBOFLAVIN-DEFICIENCY IN EGGS ON EMBRYONIC DEVELOPMENT. Anat. Rec. 82: 13–23. 1942.

ROMANOFF, A. L., AND ROMANOFF, ANASTASIA: The Avian Egg. John Wiley & Sons, Inc., New York. 1948.

ROMANOFF, A. L., SMITH, LAURA L., AND SULLIVAN, R. A.: BIOCHEMISTRY AND BIOPHYSICS OF THE DEVELOPING HEN'S EGG. III. INFLUENCE OF TEMPERATURE. Cornell Agr. Expt. Sta. Mem., 216: 1–42. 1938.

RUDNICK, D.: EARLY HISTORY AND MECHANICS OF THE CHICK BLASTODERM: A REVIEW. Quart. Rev. Biol., 19: 187–212. 1944.

SCOTT, H. M.: THE EFFECT OF AGE AND HOLDING TEMPERATURES ON HATCHABILITY OF TURKEY AND CHICKEN EGGS. Poultry Sci., 12: 49–54. 1933.

SKOGLUND, W. C., TOMHAVE, A. E., AND MUMFORD, E. W.: THE HATCHABILITY OF EGGS OF VARIOUS SIZES. Poultry Sci., 27: 709–712. 1948.

TAYLOR, L. W.: EDITOR: The fertility and hatchability of chicken and turkey eggs. John Wiley & Sons, Inc., New York. 1949.

TAYLOR, L. W., GUNNS, C. A., AND MOSES, B. D.: THE EFFECT OF CURRENT INTERRUPTION IN ELECTRICAL INCUBATION. Calif. Agr. Expt. Sta. Bul. 550: 1–19. 1933.

TERMOHLEN, W. D., WARREN, C. C., AND LAMSON, G. G.: CHICK HATCHERY SURVEY 1937–38. U. S. D. A. Div. of Marketing and Marketing Agreements. 1940.

THOMPSON, W. C., AND BLACK, L. M.: THE PROBLEM OF DISTINGUISHING THE SEX OF DAY-OLD CHICKS. N. J. Agr. Expt. Sta. Circ. 433. 1942.

Trade Practice Rules for the Baby Chick Industry. Federal Trade Commission, Washington, D. C. 1948.

UPP, C. W.: STUDIES ON EMBRYONIC LETHAL CHARACTERS IN THE DOMESTIC FOWL. La. Agr. Expt. Sta. Bul. 255. 1934.

WARREN, D. C.: DISTINGUISHING THE SEX OF CHICKS AT HATCHING. Kan. Sta. Bul. 307. 1942.

WARREN, E. L., AND WERMEL, M. T.: AN ECONOMIC SURVEY OF THE BABY CHICK INDUSTRY. U. S. D. A. Pub. G-33: 1–64. 1936.

CHAPTER 7 |||||||||||||||||||||||||||||||||||||||||||||||||||||||||||||

Rearing Principles and Practices

▼

The success of the poultry enterprise depends quite largely upon the results achieved in rearing the young stock. This is true of egg production as well as broiler and capon production. Pullets must be properly grown out if they are to become economical producers of eggs. Birds infested with parasites and disease should not be placed in the laying houses.

Natural Brooding

Natural brooding, once the only method used in brooding chicks, has been quite largely displaced by artificial methods. The natural method is used on farms where only a few chickens are raised each year (Fig. 97). Under these conditions this method is probably an economical and convenient method to follow, otherwise it would have been replaced by artificial methods. Broody hens may be used for raising hen-hatched or incubator-hatched chicks. If used for raising incubator-hatched chicks the broody hen should have a few eggs placed under her four or five days before the chicks are placed with her. The chicks can best be placed with the hen at night. It is well to place one or two chicks with the hen at first to see if she will accept them.

Before placing chicks with a hen she should be examined for lice. If infested with lice she should be treated with sodium fluoride at least twice at ten-day intervals, making the first treatment three or four days before the chicks are placed with her.

The general-purpose breeds such as the Rhode Island Reds, Rocks, Wyandottes, and Orpingtons make good mothers. These hens can brood from fifteen to twenty chicks, depending upon weather conditions. Early in the season where cold weather prevails the hens and chicks should be confined to a building, but later in the season the chicks should be given range while the hens are confined to brood coops. The hen should be confined to the brood coop as long as the chicks need her care. The floor should be covered with some short cut litter or sand. This litter should be changed at least once each week so that the floor will be kept clean. Brood coops should be moved often so that the ground around the coop remains in sanitary condition. A good location for a brood coop is in the shade and on a grass sod.

178

Fig. 97. Evolution in chick brooding. Top, colony brooder houses. (U. S. D. A.) Center, natural brooding with hens. (U. S. D. A.) Bottom left, multiple-unit brooder house with central heating plant. Bottom right, battery brooding. (Courtesy Hawkins, "Million Dollar Hen.")

Artificial Brooding

Artificial methods of brooding have made possible large-scale poultry production and have replaced natural brooding on most farms where one hundred or more chicks are raised annually. Thousands of chicks are now brooded by a single person, an unheard of feat before the adoption of artificial methods of brooding. Chicks can now be brooded at any season of the year. Artificial brooding combined with artificial incubation enables poultry raisers to control production.

Brooding Requirements

There are certain requirements for brooding which must be provided if success is to be attained. These requirements are proper temperature, adequate ventilation, control of moisture, sanitation, and adequate brooding space.

Temperature. Control of temperature, which provides sufficient heat in cold weather and minimizes the excess temperatures which prevail during the summer months, is essential for success in brooding chicks. The thermoregulatory mechanism of the young chick is not capable of maintaining the normal body temperature when the chick is exposed to high or low temperatures. The young chick, when exposed to such abnormal temperatures for even a short time, will develop intestinal disturbances which are manifested by a diarrhea.

In brooding chicks it is desirable to provide a range of temperature so that the chicks may have some choice in selecting a temperature most suitable to them. For day-old chicks the maximum temperature should be kept between 90° F. and 100° F. When first placed in the brooder, the chicks should be confined near the heat so they may learn where the source of heat is located. The temperature may be reduced about 5° F. each week as the chicks become older. It is most important that chicks be kept comfortable at all times. Chicks will not be overheated if they can get away from the high temperatures.

Chicks have very little reserve energy to protect themselves against low temperatures. Huddling or crowding is an indication that the brooder is too cool for the chicks. Temperatures in the brooder should be determined with an accurate thermometer and controlled with a reliable thermostat.

Ventilation. Sufficient ventilation to supply plenty of oxygen and remove carbon dioxide, excess moisture, and carbon monoxide is essential in brooding chicks. These conditions can be controlled in most climates by having an open-front brooder house which is partially closed with a muslin frame in cold weather. When chicks are brooded in tightly closed brooder houses with fuel-burning brooder stoves, carbon monoxide gas may increase in concentration to a point which is fatal to chicks and poults. Slow poisoning may occur when the air contains .01 per cent carbon monoxide. In acute cases the symptoms of this poisoning are gasping, head thrown back, and spasms at death. When the poisoning is slow the birds may show only a stunted and unthrifty condition.

The injurious effects of CO poisoning are caused by asphyxiation, which results from the CO combining with the hemoglobin of the blood and thereby destroying the ability of the blood to carry oxygen to the tissues.

The moisture content of the air in the brooder room can be controlled by ventilation and heating. In cold weather the litter in a brooder room where electric brooders are used will become damp within a few days. This may be partially overcome by increasing the ventilation of the room and frequent changing of litter.

Dougherty and Moses of the California Agricultural Experiment Station investigated the relation of ventilation in electric brooders to health and growth of chicks. They concluded that a flow of two cubic feet of air per minute per one hundred chicks would meet the requirements of the chicks as well as larger amounts but would not keep the hover and litter dry after the chicks were three weeks old. They found that ventilation which would keep the brooder reasonably dry would assure the chicks an ample supply of fresh air. Additional ventilation increased the cost of electricity but did not benefit the chicks.

Moisture. Though the relative humidity in a brooder room may vary considerably without harmful effects, extremely low or high humidity is not conducive to best results. It is desirable that the litter in the brooder house be kept dry to prevent the spread of disease among the chicks. An excessively dry atmosphere, however, results in poor feather development and increases the occurrence of "bare backs." The Pennsylvania Agricultural Experiment Station reports results which show that where the relative humidity in the brooders varied from 30 per cent to 75 per cent, growth was not affected.

Sanitation. Sanitation is essential for success in brooding chicks. Losses from diseases and parasites can be quite largely prevented by proper sanitary measures. For best results chicks should not be exposed to infectious diseases and parasites. To carry out a sanitary program which will prevent exposure of chicks to disease organisms and parasites implies a clean environment. This means that the brooder house as well as the range shall be clean and relatively free from organisms which cause chick diseases and infestations.

Space. Overcrowding causes slow growth and heavy mortality. One-half square foot of floor space should be provided for each chick on the brooder floor. Table 36 shows how mortality is increased by overcrowding chicks in the brooder house. Each chick should be provided with at least eight square inches of floor space beneath the hover. A fifty-six-inch hover should not be used for brooding more than 300 chicks, which is a maximum number for good growth and livability.

Table 36

RELATION BETWEEN FLOOR SPACE AND MORTALITY OF CHICKS [1]

Floor Space per Hundred Chicks	Number of Chicks	Number of Deaths	Per Cent Mortality to Three Months of Age
35 square feet or less........	73,077	19,257	26.3
35 to 50 square feet.........	25,371	4,122	16.2
50 square feet or more......	25,044	3,484	13.1

[1] Calif. Agr. Extension Service Circ. 28, 1929.

Colony Brooding Systems

The colony brooding system is quite generally used by farmers and commercial poultry raisers. It is an economical system adaptable to most poultry farms. One advantage of this system is that it can be started on a small scale and expanded each year as desired.

Colony brooder houses. These houses are small portable houses large enough to provide room for about three hundred chicks but small enough so that they can be moved to clean ground each year. They may be built on skids or constructed to be moved on a tractor-trailer. Muslin curtains are usually used to cover the open front during cold weather. The houses generally are built of matched lumber and the walls and floors are of a single thickness of this material. In some sections where native lumber is cheap, rough lumber direct from the sawmills is used for constructing these houses, the walls being covered on the outside with a cheap grade of composition roofing.

All openings should be covered with poultry netting to keep out birds and predatory animals.

Instead of moving the colony brooder house each year many producers leave the colony house near the residence where it is more convenient to care for the chicks and use a sun porch to keep the chicks from contacting any contaminated soil. A range shelter can be used as a sun porch.

When the chicks no longer need heat they are moved to clean range. The cockerels not needed for breeding can be kept in the brooder house and finished for market.

Location of the brooder house. In selecting a location for the brooder houses one should avoid using land that has been occupied by chickens during the previous two years or traversed by drainage water from old poultry runs, or where droppings from the laying or brooder houses have been deposited within the last two or three years. A three- to four-year rotation of runs for the brooder houses makes an ideal arrangement for growing healthy chicks.

The barren ground adjacent to a stationary brooder or laying house is usually contaminated with worm eggs and coccidia. Thus, chicks brooded in such a place are likely to become badly infested with intestinal worms and coccidiosis. Under these conditions it becomes almost impossible to raise a large number of healthy pullets or cockerels. The brooder house should be located where there is growing green feed and near some natural shade such as is available or can be grown.

Colony brooders. Brooders used for brooding chicks in colony houses are heated with oil (kerosene or distillate), coal, wood, gas, and electricity (Fig. 98). These stoves are generally equipped with hovers for holding the heat near the floor. The drum-type, oil-burning brooder radiates heat from the drum down to the chicks on the floor. Distillate or fuel oil is usually burned in these stoves. The temperature of oil-burning brooders is governed by a

Fig. 98. Colony brooders. Top left, oil brooder. (Courtesy Simplex Brooder Stove Company.) Top right, electric brooder. (Ohio Extension Service.) Center, coal brooder. (Ohio Extension Service.) Bottom, wood brooder. (Courtesy Shenandoah Manufacturing Company.)

thermostat which regulates the flow of oil to the brooder. Coal-burning brooder stoves are perhaps more commonly used than any other type of brooder. They are very dependable, may be operated economically in most sections of the United States, are easy to operate, and seldom get out of order.

The temperature of such stoves is controlled by a thermostat which regulates the draft through the stove. Hard coal is the most satisfactory fuel for such stoves but briquettes and soft coal may be used if the stove is large and equipped with a large pipe which is not easily clogged with soot. When soft coal is used the stove will require close attention. A damper or automatic wind-damper placed in the pipe will help prevent high winds from setting up a strong draft and burning out the fire during the night.

Wood-burning brooder stoves have in recent years become popular in those sections of the United States where wood is plentiful. The draft on these stoves is thermostatically controlled so that they require little attention, holding fire throughout the night. Wood is an economical fuel in many sections of the United States and such stoves will very likely gain in popularity as the public becomes aware of their merits.

Electric brooders are now used in all sections of the United States, in cold weather as well as in mild weather. They have certain decided advantages: (1) The temperature can be accurately controlled; and (2) they require very little attention if there is a dependable source of electricity. A thermostat which makes and breaks the electric circuit controls the temperature of these brooders. The increase in rural electrification has resulted in a corresponding increase in the use of electric brooders. In most sections of the United States where electric power is available the cost of operating an electric brooder compares favorably with that of operating other brooders. The electric consumption of electric brooders is given in Table 37.

Table 37

CURRENT CONSUMPTION OF ELECTRIC BROODERS [2]

Kind and Operation of Brooders	House Insulation	Temperature		Electricity used 6 wks. kwh
		Brooder Av. ° F.	Outdoor Mean ° F.	
Standard Nebr. rectangular..............	Yes	91.6	39	116
Fan ventilation standard................	Yes	92.8	39	155
Round, conical top, curtains, uninsulated...	Yes	93.0	39	147
Same as above but insulated.............	Yes	92.1	39	93
Standard............................	Yes	99.5	34.5	141
Round, conical top, curtains insulated......	Yes	97.6	34.5	100
Standard............................	No	98.4	34.5	171
Standard with tube ventilator............	Yes	101.7	34.5	195
Standard, 1 foot longer.................	No	99.7	34.5	180
Standard with strip heaters.............	Yes	98.8	34.5	139

The use of gas brooders, both natural and "bottle gas," are quite popular in some regions. These brooders like electric brooders require very little attention and are quite economical to operate. But also like electric brooders they do not provide sufficient heat to keep the brooder pen always dry.

[2] Nebraska Sta. Circ. 80. 1945.

Preparing for the chicks. Before the chicks are hatched or received, the brooder house and all brooding equipment should be thoroughly cleaned and disinfected. The first step in cleaning is to remove from the house all removable equipment. Thorough scraping and sweeping of the floor and walls will remove most of the visible dirt, and lye water (one can concentrated lye to twelve gallons of water) liberally applied with a coarse broom will free the house of contamination, although in some instances two applications may be necessary. The feeders and other equipment should not be overlooked but should be given the same treatment that is applied to the house. If the house is not cleaned before it is moved, some of the filth from the previous year is almost certain to be scattered and to contaminate the new range. The floor should be covered with litter such as cut straw, clover, alfalfa, shavings, peat moss, or coarsely ground corncobs. The fire in the stove should be started at least twenty-four hours before the chicks are ready to be placed in the house. This will make it possible to have the house at the right temperature and will give the operator an opportunity for making necessary adjustments.

At the time the chicks are placed in the brooder house they do not know how to find the source of heat. For this reason a circular guard of hardware cloth or some other materials, about twelve inches high, should be set up around the stove. This enclosure should be about two feet from the edge of the hover. This arrangement should always be used for a few days to confine the chicks to a limited area of the brooder house floor until they become accustomed to their quarters.

A well-balanced ration should be placed in chick feeders, allowing about one inch of feeding space per chick. Chicks may be encouraged to start eating by filling the feeders full for the first day or so. Enough waterers should be provided so the chicks have access to fresh water at all times.

Operating the brooder stove. Prior to the brooding season the stove should be examined to see that it is in proper working condition. The drafts must open and close easily in order to permit the thermostat to work effectively. The thermostat wafers should be tested by placing them in warm water to determine whether or not they retain their power to expand and contract. Damaged wafers are worthless and should be replaced.

No specific set of rules can be offered that will apply to operating the various brooder stoves on the market. Therefore, it is suggested that the instructions of the manufacturer be followed closely until experience dictates a change in operation.

As a rule, when hard coal is used it is usually not necessary to fill the brooder stove more than twice each day (morning and night). Before adding fresh fuel it is advisable to remove all the ashes. In refilling the stove one should avoid extinguishing the fire by adding too much coal at one time. This precaution is especially necessary when the fire is burning slowly.

Brooder stoves in which soft coal is used have to be filled more often and require closer attention in order to equal the results obtained with anthracite coal. In addition to keeping the clinkers and ashes removed, it is advisable to clean the stovepipe at least once a week to insure a good draft. As

Fig. 99. A long brooder house used for brooding chicks in confinement.

a general rule it is a mistake to build a hot fire just as the chicks are becoming settled for the night. This condition causes the chicks to nestle too far from the stove with the consequent piling up or possibly chilling as the fire burns down and the stove cools.

The drum-type, oil-burning brooders have large fuel tanks and consequently they do not require refilling more than once a day. The fuel line should be kept unobstructed so that the thermostat can regulate the flow of oil to the burner and thereby maintain a uniform temperature.

The ashes should be removed from wood stoves often enough to keep the draft open and the fire burning uniformly. Green wood produces much "tar" and the stovepipe may become clogged with this material unless the operator keeps the pipe reasonably clean.

Electric brooders require very little attention if the electric service is dependable. The operator of an electric brooder should adjust the thermostat and the height of the brooder from the floor so that sufficient heat and ventilation can be supplied at a minimum cost. Electric brooders can be adjusted very easily to meet the chicks' needs. In mild weather and as the chicks become older the electricity can be turned off during the day to reduce brooding costs. Double floors particularly beneath the hover are desirable when electric brooders are used in cold weather.

Stationary Brooding Systems

Stationary brooding systems were developed in the nineteenth century but were abandoned because poultrymen did not know what to feed or how to rear chicks in confinement. Colony brooding systems replaced permanent brooders because chicks could be raised on clean range even when deficient or incomplete rations were fed, because the chicks were exposed to the direct rays of the sun and were also able to supplement the ration with succulent green feed. Since the discovery of the vitamins and other fundamental principles of nutrition and with a better knowledge of the control of diseases, the stationary brooder house has again found a place in brooding.

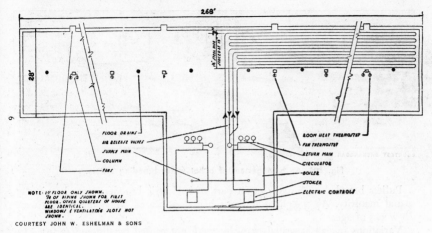

COURTESY JOHN W. ESHELMAN & SONS

Fig. 100. Simple diagram of radiant-heated poultry house, showing arrangement of hot water pipes and other details.

Long brooder houses (such as shown in Figure 99) divided into pens are used on many commercial poultry farms. They are often equipped with sun porches to prevent the chicks from coming in contact with contaminated soil. Such brooder houses are desirable for broiler production or for raising pullets as long as they need artificial heat or the protection of a building. These brooder houses may be heated with hot water heating systems as shown in Figure 101, or by using a colony brooder stove in each pen.

The long brooder house, when compared with the colony system of brooding, has the advantage of reducing the labor required for raising chicks; but it may have the disadvantage of a greater investment per one hundred chicks.

Radiant heating. Within recent years radiant heating has been advocated and used in permanent brooder houses (see Fig. 100). This is a system of floor heating where hot water pipes are placed in the concrete floor of the brooder house, spacing them about 12 to 16 inches apart. Since this is a relatively expensive method of heating it has not gained widespread adoption.

A comparison of brooding systems. The Pennsylvania Agricultural Experiment Station in 1937 made a comparison of brooding systems for raising pullets, in which were included the following brooders: hot water, hot water and electric, coal, oil, gas, electric, and batteries. The conclusions which were reached are as follows:

Brooder pen temperature and relative humidity did not affect: (a) growth as measured by body weight at 10 and 16 weeks of age; (b) sexual development as measured by age at first egg; (c) plumage growth and condition as measured by:
(1) Primary wing feather development of Barred Plymouth Rock pullets at 10 and 16 weeks of age; or
(2) Plumage condition of Barred Plymouth Rock cockerels graded when eight weeks old.

COURTESY SHENANDOAH MANUFACTURING CO.

Fig. 101. An arrangement of a hot water brooding system.

Pullets brooded exclusively or in part with electric brooders were heaviest at sexual maturity. All weight differences had disappeared when the pullets were 70 weeks of age.

Variations in age at sexual maturity were not caused by differences in: (1) protein level of the total ration consumed; (2) brooder pen temperature; or (3) relative humidity in the brooder pen.

The environmental conditions supplied by electric brooders in unheated colony houses or in pens using auxiliary hot water heat did produce more rugged, vigorous, and healthy pullets.

No beneficial effects were observed from the application of auxiliary hot water heat to pens in which electric brooders were used.

No method of brooding employed was definitely superior to others in the development of layers.

Pullets brooded exclusively with electric brooders laid heavier eggs at sexual maturity and throughout the pullet year. Differences in initial egg weight, as measured by weight of the first 10 eggs laid, probably were an indirect effect of variations in body weight.

Single-Comb White Leghorn pullets brooded exclusively or in part with electric brooders, using exposed "black heat" resistance coils as the source of heat, required approximately 20 days longer to attain sexual maturity than comparable pullets brooded with hot water or coal stove brooders.

Barred Plymouth Rock pullets brooded exclusively with a similar electric brooder required approximately 30 days longer to attain sexual maturity than comparable pullets brooded with hot water, coal, oil, or gas brooders, and 14 days longer than those brooded under an electric brooder in a pen supplied with auxiliary hot water heat.

The evidence leads to the conclusion that proper management of a good brooder, not the particular style of brooder or the kind of fuel used, is the most important consideration in successful pullet rearing.

Time of Hatching

The time to hatch chicks for a given poultry enterprise is an important management problem. The nature of the poultry business and the objectives to be obtained must be kept in mind, as well as the climatic conditions which prevail where the enterprise is to be undertaken.

Some general considerations. For a time the question of date of hatching appeared to be settled and the general recommendation was that chicks should be hatched during the spring months (February to May). In recent years broiler raisers have found that fall and winter chicks are more profitable than spring-hatched chicks and commercial poultrymen have found that egg production can be maintained at a relatively high level throughout the year by having pullets coming into production at different seasons of the year.

The Oklahoma Agricultural Experiment Station hatched chicks every two weeks throughout the year from December 31, 1923, to December 15, 1924. This station reported some very interesting observations on the problem of time of hatch which are repeated here.

The best hatches were secured between December 31 and April 7, inclusive.

The summer and fall hatches gave markedly poorer results.

The chick mortality was greater for the summer and fall hatches than for the winter and spring hatches. The late winter hatches gave the lowest per cent mortality.

The winter-hatched birds grew more rapidly than did the spring-, summer-, or fall-hatched chicks.

The spring-hatched individuals maintained a faster rate of growth and were heavier throughout the first laying year than were the summer- or fall-hatched pullets.

The "summer weather handicap" was especially noticeable in the growth of summer-hatched chicks. The growth of the fall-hatched chicks was checked due to winter weather before they attained maturity.

The spring-hatched individuals were heavier at the beginning of production and were also older when laying began than were the birds hatched at other seasons.

The birds that were hatched during the winter, summer, and fall months matured sexually at an earlier age than did those hatched during the spring season.

A tendency was noted for seasonal variation in egg weight regardless of when the birds were hatched and the date that production started. All groups showed an upward trend in egg weight from September to February and a downward trend from this point to July or August.

The spring-hatched pullets produced the heaviest eggs, on the average, with the winter- and summer-hatched birds next in order named; and the eggs produced by the fall-hatched birds averaged lightest in weight.

There was little difference in the average egg production between the winter and spring hatches. The summer- and fall-hatched birds gave decidedly lower production.

When the seasons were ranked according to the value of eggs produced by the birds hatched during each, spring is the most desirable, followed by winter, summer, and fall in the order named.

Table 38

SIZE AND VALUE OF EGGS PRODUCED BY WHITE LEGHORN PULLETS HATCHED
AT DIFFERENT SEASONS OF THE YEAR [3]

PULLETS HATCHED IN—	WEIGHT OF EGGS			
	30 to 44 Grams	45 to 54 Grams	55 Grams & Over	All Eggs
Per Cent of Total Yearly Production Falling in Each Size Group				
May................	2.4	45.6	52.0	100.0
July................	4.8	80.5	14.7	100.0
September...........	18.5	69.4	12.1	100.0
November...........	37.2	43.6	19.2	100.0
January.............	16.4	61.9	21.7	100.0
March..............	6.9	64.0	29.1	100.0
Average Value per Dozen of All Eggs Falling in Each Size Group				
May................	31.1¢	30.7¢	29.2¢	29.4¢
July................	18.5	24.7	31.1	25.3
September...........	15.6	24.1	36.3	24.0
November...........	15.6	25.4	29.4	22.6
January.............	18.6	25.8	30.8	25.7
March..............	22.8	26.5	28.4	26.9

Card investigated the effect of date of hatching on egg size and value of eggs laid. Table 38 shows the results he obtained. Leghorns hatched during the spring months produced larger eggs and eggs which commanded a higher price than eggs laid by pullets hatched during the summer and fall months.

Broiler production. Since the commercial broiler raiser should produce fresh broilers and fryers at a time when few young chickens are being marketed from the general farm flocks, broiler chicks should be started during the fall and winter months when few chicks are being started in the general farm flocks. Many commercial broiler growers now operate throughout the year.

Commercial egg flocks. In commercial flocks where egg production is the principal objective, the practice of hatching layers at different seasons of the year has developed within recent years. Such a practice has the following advantages: (1) levelling out the production curve through the year; (2) better utilization of laying houses and equipment; and (3) more efficient use of brooding facilities.

Commercial poultrymen are hatching two or three times per year. If three hatches are made, January, April, and September are preferred. If two hatches are made, February and May, March and June, or April and September are preferred. Jeffrey of the New Jersey Agricultural Experiment Station reported in 1940 data which are tabulated as follows:

---

[3] Card, 1922.

EFFECT OF DATE OF HATCH ON GROWTH, FEED CONSUMPTION, MORTALITY,
EGG PRODUCTION, AND COST OF PRODUCTION—
SINGLE-COMB WHITE LEGHORNS

Date of Hatch	Feed Consumed to 24 Weeks (Lbs.)	Body Weight at 24 Weeks (Lbs.)	Mortality to 24 Weeks (Per Cent)	Cost Per Pullet Raised (Cents)	Annual Egg Production
Jan. 15	20.2	3.1	19.9	87	151
April 1	18.8	2.9	12.2	70	172
June 15	18.6	2.9	11.8	50	166
Sept. 1	21.8	3.0	8.5	70	151
Nov. 1	22.5	3.2	16.5	87	151

These data indicate that under conditions which prevail in New Jersey, satisfactory egg production may be obtained with pullets hatched at different seasons of the year. Pullets started in the winter cost considerably more to produce than pullets started during the spring and summer months.

The Management of Young Stock

The successful poultryman knows when and how to do the things which should be done at any given time. The best poultrymen are born as well as trained. There are many details that must be attended to and the good poultryman never neglects his poultry. Fortunate indeed is the poultry farm that has an experienced and "born" poultryman.

Feeding the Young Stock

It is essential that the young stock be properly fed during the brooding and rearing period. Both starting and growing rations are given in Chapter Ten. The rations recommended in any state may be obtained by residents of the state by writing to the department of poultry husbandry of their state agriculture college, as listed in the Appendix.

Feeding methods. A well-balanced starting mash should be placed before the chicks as soon as they are received—if purchased, or soon after they are removed from the incubator—if hatched on the premises of the poultry raiser. Chicks do not need to be starved after hatching, though they do have a reserve food supply in the form of recently absorbed egg yolk.

For the first eight to ten weeks it is advisable to use only a starting mash, keeping it before the chicks. After that time the chicks should have both a growing mash and grain before them in hoppers. Chicks will select a suitable ration if they have an opportunity to choose the proper ingredients.

Feeding and watering equipment. Many chicks develop into culls because they never have an opportunity to become anything else. It is a mistake to raise more chicks than the equipment on the farm will accommodate. At least one inch of feeding space at the hoppers should be provided for each chick for the first six weeks and after that time the feeding space should be doubled. Each chick should be provided with about one-half inch of space at the waterers, and this should be increased, as the chicks grow older, to always provide plenty of fresh water.

Outdoor feeders should be placed on wire frames or moved frequently to prevent the ground around them from becoming contaminated. Obviously, feeders should be so constructed that there will be a minimum loss of feed.

Growing green feed. Better pullets can be grown when the young stock has access to growing green feed. The poultryman should so manage the range as to provide succulent green feed throughout the growing period. In some sections of the United States this is no easy task as several crops must be planted during the season and a summer drought interferes with plant growth.

Where alfalfa range can be provided the pullets have ideal conditions for obtaining succulent green feed. Bluegrass is an ideal pasture crop for poultry during the spring and late fall. The clovers provide good pasture for poultry. Sudan grass, rape, and the cereal grains can be planted for summer pasture. Poultry can utilize pasture crops to best advantage when they are planted in rows so that the birds can range between the rows.

A suitable pasture system for growing stock will reduce the cost of producing pullets and improve the quality of the stock matured.

Finish cockerels and pullets separately. For best results in growing young stock the cockerels and pullets should be separated at an early age. In Leghorns and similar breeds the males can be identified by their comb development by the time they are three or four weeks old. Heavy breed males and particularly those with rose combs usually cannot be identified before they are eight to twelve weeks of age. The males which are to be sold for broilers should be separated from the pullets by the time they are eight weeks old, if they can be identified. The males will have larger heads, coarser features, and shorter and more blunt tails than the pullets. They can be continued on a starter or broiler mash until they are sold. The pullets will have more room and they can be placed on a growing mash and otherwise managed for the production of layers.

Cockerels intended for breeding purposes should be separated from the pullets to provide additional room for both the pullets and cockerels and prevent the cockerels from treading the pullets. Where a large number of cockerels are kept together precautions must be taken to minimize fighting.

Cannibalism. This trouble, manifested by chicks by toe picking, tail picking, or feather pulling, frequently occurs when the brooder house is overheated, overcrowded, or the birds are too closely confined. Cannibalism is more often reported among white than among colored chicks. This is probably due to the fact that blood shows more plainly through the quills of white feathers. Chicks become ravenous when they get a taste of blood and will continue pecking the injured chick until it has been removed or completely devoured.

In case these habits are developed the affected chicks should be isolated, and it may be necessary to darken the brooder house by hanging curtains over the windows. Chicks slightly wounded may be returned to the brood within a day or two if the injured parts are covered with tar or other antipick preparations.

Cannibalism can be most effectively prevented by not overcrowding the house and by keeping the chicks busy. A fresh sod of grass placed in the house for the chicks to work over encourages exercise and may reduce toe picking and tail picking. Darkening the room and painting the windows with a ruby water-color paint are also helpful in preventing cannibalism. It is also well to supply the proper amount of protein, salt, and green feed in the ration to prevent unusual craving because of deficiencies in the diet. Cannibalism usually disappears as soon as the chicks are given fresh range.

Crowding or piling. Chicks which have been chilled frequently crowd at night. Serious losses from smothering result when chicks develop the habit of crowding and piling. This trouble can be largely prevented by teaching the chicks to roost at an early age.

Early roosting should be encouraged by providing low roosts when the chicks are about three weeks old. Chicks seldom cause trouble by crowding after they have learned to use the roosts. Narrow boards laid on bricks at the rear of the house make excellent starting roosts. As the chicks become accustomed to roosting, the boards may be raised gradually until they are two or three feet from the floor. Some poultrymen use roosting frames (Fig. 102). A roosting frame fits into the rear end of the house and is covered with narrow roost boards spaced about five inches apart. Inch mesh poultry netting fastened underneath the roost poles and down the front side prevents the chicks crowding under the frame. Sixty feet of roosting space should be provided for each one hundred birds kept in the house or range shelter after twelve weeks of age. A satisfactory roost is a 2" x 2" with the upper corners rounded.

Grow healthy pullet programs. Most states, through their agricultural extension service, have developed programs designed to produce better pullets for the laying flock. These programs have been instrumental in reducing mortality in the young stock. The essentials of these programs are:

1. Clean Chicks
    (a) Chicks from stock officially tested for pullorum disease.
    (b) They should be free from other diseases as far as known.
    (c) They should be from stock which has demonstrated ability to produce vigorous, livable chicks.
    (d) Chicks hatched in clean incubators.
2. Clean Brooder Houses
    (a) Clean, scrape, and scrub, with lye water.
    (b) Disinfect with government-approved disinfectants.

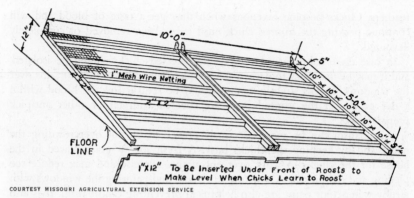

FLOOR LINE

1"x12" To Be Inserted Under Front of Roosts to Make Level When Chicks Learn to Roost

Fig. 102. Low roosts in the brooder house encourage early roosting. Wire netting under the roost poles keep the chicks out of the droppings.

  (c) Clean all equipment used for brooding.
3. Clean Litter
    (a) Change litter when it becomes damp, or once each week for the first eight weeks.
    (b) Keep litter dry at all times.
4. Clean Feed and Water
    (a) Place all feeders and waterers on wire platforms in the house.
    (b) Move hoppers and movable water pans to a clean spot on range each week.
    (c) Use platform and dry well beneath automatic water fountains.
5. Clean Range
    (a) Land not used by poultry for two years or more.
    (b) Land not contaminated by drainage water or by the spreading of poultry manure.
    (c) Clean brooder house before moving to clean range.
6. Clean Management
    (a) Maintain a quarantine between young and old stock.
    (b) Avoid crowding both in the house and on range.
    (c) Teach chicks to range by moving feed and water.

The use of sun porches. Where the ground around the brooder house is contaminated with disease-producing organisms or parasites, the use of sun porches makes possible the growing of healthy chicks even when permanently located brooder houses are used. In recent years many poultrymen have constructed sun porches (Fig. 103). They are also used in connection with long brooder houses which are used for brooding chicks or poults.

The floor should be covered with wire sufficiently strong to withstand the use which will be made of it. For small chickens a one-half inch mesh hardware cloth makes a desirable floor but for older chicks and turkeys a 1" x 1" or a 1" x 2" mesh wire of about 12½-gauge material makes a substantial floor. Sun porches should be constructed so that feeders and waterers can be placed along the sides, thus increasing the amount of feeding and watering space available.

COURTESY L. L. RUMMEL

Fig. 103. Screened brooder houses and sun porches. The birds receive fresh air and sunshine without the dangers of contaminated range and diseases carried by flies, mosquitoes, and other insects.

The use of range shelters. The development of the summer range shelter has done much to improve the quality of young stock being grown by poultry raisers. The range shelter serves a very useful purpose because it provides ideal roosting quarters for pullets started in permanent brooder houses or for surplus stock from colony brooder houses. A range shelter 10′ x 12′ as shown in Figure 104 provides room for 125 pullets to mature. It can easily be moved to clean range several times during the summer, thereby keeping the pullets on clean range and providing them with growing green feed.

One-inch mesh, 18-gauge poultry netting may be used for the sides and ends. The floor should be 1½-inch mesh, 14-gauge poultry netting, or 1″ x 2″, 12½-gauge wire. The roof may be metal, shingles, or composition roofing.

Shade. It is very necessary that growing stock during hot weather be provided with either natural or artificial shade. The range shelter provides some shade; other means may be used to provide artificial shade. Natural shade as provided by trees, shrubs, or growing crops such as corn and sunflowers makes an excellent arrangement for shade.

Moving the pullets to laying quarters. The pullets, if grown on range, should be left in the colony house or range shelter until they are ready to begin laying. Their sexual maturity may be judged by comb and body development. Since pullets of the same age vary considerably in their age at sexual maturity it is well to leave the immature birds on range until late in the fall. Undeveloped and slow-maturing pullets should be marketed. The laying house should be cleaned thoroughly and the pullets should be given separate quarters.

COURTESY MISSOURI AGRICULTURAL EXPERIMENT STATION

Fig. 104. A well-constructed range shelter built on skids to facilitate moving.

It is advisable to make changes gradually in rations and feeding methods. Sudden changes will cause laying pullets to stop production. Pullets should be caught and handled carefully. The colony house or range shelter should be closed the night before the pullets are to be moved. The pullets should be carefully driven into catching coops or chutes early the next morning. They should be culled when handled, the best pullets being sent to the laying pens, the inferior prospective layers being sent to market, and immature but good prospects being left.

Battery Brooding

Within recent years battery brooding of chicks has developed quite extensively. The advantages of battery brooding of chicks may be listed as follows: (1) This system may be used where it is impossible to use other systems of brooding. (2) Chicks can be supervised more closely. (3) Chicks can be kept away from organisms that cause disease better than if they were on range. (4) Chicks of different ages can be separated more easily. (5) Battery brooding is ideally adapted to feeding investigations with chicks where accurate feed and growth records are required.

The disadvantages of batteries for brooding are the following: (1) The average operator cannot produce satisfactory pullets with them. (2) Battery equipment should be supplemented with floor brooders if pullets for flock replacement are raised. (3) There is more trouble with cannibalism with chicks brooded in batteries than with chicks raised on range. These disadvantages may be overcome when the nutritional and other requirements of chicks become better known.

The principal users of batteries for brooding chicks are hatcheries for brooding surplus or started chicks; broiler raisers near or in cities who sell dressed broilers; and laboratories that conduct feeding tests with chicks.

Types of batteries. There are two general types of batteries—the warm room battery brooder and the battery equipped with a heating system. If the warm room type of battery brooder is used for raising broilers, it is necessary to have at least two and preferably three rooms where the chicks may be brooded: one for starting the chicks where the temperature is about 90° F., reducing it about seven degrees each week; one for growing the chicks from the third to sixth week where the temperature is from 75° F. down, being reduced as the chicks become older; and a room where the temperature is 60° F. or less but where the chicks are comfortable.

Batteries equipped with heating systems, usually electric, are more expensive than warm room brooders but they are generally preferred. The temperature of these batteries can be regulated accurately.

The battery brooder room. Batteries are used in many kinds of rooms with results which indicate that the building or room is an important factor in the successful brooding of chicks in batteries. Most operators overcrowd the battery room. A room or building used for battery brooding should be so located and so arranged that it is convenient for the work to be done. It should have a concrete floor to facilitate cleaning. The building should be ratproof and mouseproof. The ceiling should be at least eight feet high and preferably nine or ten feet high. There should be three or four feet of space between the tops of the batteries and the ceiling. The battery building should be insulated to conserve heat during the winter and keep the room cool in summer. Windows should be so arranged as to provide sufficient natural light for the chicks to eat and drink. The room should be ventilated so that the chicks have sufficient fresh air at all times.

The batteries should be arranged in the room so that the work involved in caring for the chicks can be reduced to a minimum. Aisles at least three feet wide should be left between the brooders. Running water in the room and to the batteries saves much labor.

Since battery brooding is a recent development and the requirements rather difficult to determine, very little has been known about the conditions which influence the results obtained with battery brooders. Most recommendations have been based on experience. The Larro Milling Company in recent years has investigated the space requirements for chicks brooded in batteries.

Space required. Results obtained at the Larro Research Farm show that the cubic space as well as the floor space per chick should be considered. For most satisfactory growth 450 cubic inches of space in the batteries should be provided for each pound of live weight. One hundred chickens weighing two pounds each would require 90,000 cubic inches of space in the batteries or eight compartments 30" x 30" and 12½ inches high. The floor space requirement per chick is about as follows:

Age in Weeks	Square Inches Floor Space per Chick
1 and 2	10
3 and 4	20
5 and 6	30
7 and 8	40
9 and 10	60
11 and 12	75

Temperature. Chicks must be kept comfortab!e, but too much heat is detrimental to growth and development. The brooder room where heated batteries are used should be kept between 60° F. and 70° F., and the temperature of the batteries regulated to suit the comfort of the chicks. A proper temperature for starting chicks is from 90° F. to 95° F. This can be reduced about seven degrees each week as the chicks develop. More important than an exact degree of temperature is the reaction of chicks; they should not huddle or otherwise appear uncomfortable.

Ventilation. Fresh air is essential for growth and health in chicks. Where chicks are brooded in small rooms, windows located on the sides of the buildings may provide sufficient ventilation to supply the oxygen needed and carry away the carbon dioxide produced as well as the excess moisture which accumulates in rooms where chicks are brooded. In large plants, specially built ventilators with forced-draft circulation are necessary to ventilate the battery room adequately.

Moisture. Too dry an atmosphere in the battery room will cause poor feathering, slow growth, and increased mortality. Extremely high humidity may also cause poor results. A relative humidity of 60 to 70 per cent will give very satisfactory results. In cold weather or when the outside air is very dry, it will be necessary to sprinkle the floor to increase the humidity inside the room. Excess moisture may be carried away by increasing the ventilation of the room.

Feeding and watering space. Sufficient feeding and watering space must be provided for each brooder compartment to give the chicks room to eat and drink when they so desire. Most batteries are equipped with feeders and waterers on all sides. There should be at least one inch of feeding space per chick for the first six weeks and one and one-half inches per chick for the second six weeks. Baby chicks can be encouraged to eat by filling the feeders full during the first two or three days.

Sanitation in the battery room. Sanitation in the battery room is necessary to prevent disease and to provide the chicks with suitable growing conditions. The feeders should be kept clean and the waterers should be scrubbed as often as is necessary to keep them clean but at least twice each week. The droppings pans should be cleaned daily and the pans covered with acid phosphate. After each lot of chicks is removed from the batteries, all

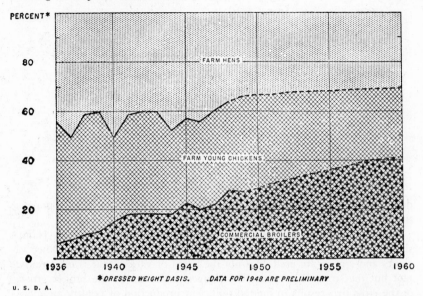

PERCENT*

U. S. D. A.

Fig. 105. Chicken meat: Percentage of total consumption by types, 1936 to 1948, and estimated 1949 to 1960.

parts of the brooders should be thoroughly cleaned and disinfected. The brooder room should also be cleaned thoroughly. If there has been an outbreak of disease, the room and all equipment should not only be thoroughly cleaned but the room containing all equipment used should be fumigated with formaldehyde gas before other chicks are placed in the batteries. (See page 168 for recommendations.)

Broiler Production

There has developed in the United States within recent years a very large specialized poultry meat-producing industry known as the broiler industry. This industry in 1948 produced twenty-eight per cent of the poultry meat in the United States as compared to only 8 per cent in 1936. The expansion of this industry and estimated future production is shown in Fig. 105. The development of this industry has made available fresh frying chickens throughout the year and thereby stimulated the consumption of poultry meat.

Producing and consuming areas. The broiler industry has tended to develop near the consuming centers and toward the southeastern part of the United States. The expansion of the broiler industry by areas as indicated by Table 39 shows that the greatest expansion has occurred in the East and Southeast. Northwest Arkansas and Texas have also developed relatively large broiler industries.

Broiler breeds and strains. The grower of broilers needs a rapid growing, fast feathering, early finishing bird that will make economical gains and

Table 39

CHICKS PLACED IN THE SEVEN PRINCIPAL COMMERCIAL
BROILER AREAS IN 1948

Area	Number Chicks Placed
Del.–Mar.–Va.	117,230,000
North Georgia.	41,588,000
Shenandoah Valley.	27,526,000
Northwest Arkansas.	24,593,000
Texas.	17,702,000
North Carolina.	12,061,000
Eastern Connecticut.	8,524,000

dress out an attractive carcass. The demand for such a bird has stimulated the breeders to produce some very fine broiler strains and crosses.

The more common breeds used in broiler production are the New Hampshires, broiler crosses, White Rocks, and Delaware (Table 40). Other varieties and crosses are used. It is not the breed or variety that is most important but the strain that carries the characters desired by the broiler grower or the cross that results in the most efficient production of poultry meat.

Table 40

BREEDS OF CHICKS RAISED FOR BROILERS [4]

BREED	NUMBER OF LOTS	PER CENT OF TOTAL CHICKS STARTED			
		All Cockerels	All Pullets	Straight Run	All Broilers
Broiler Cross.	115	32	13	81	60
Rhode Island Red.	65	25	5	5	12
Sex-Linked Cross.	53	25	69	...	10
New Hampshire.	35	9	13	7	8
Plymouth Rock.	22	4	...	2	3
Mixed lots.	18	5	...	5	7
Total.	308	100	100	100	100

Houses and equipment. The buildings and equipment generally used by the commercial growers are practical and not necessarily expensive. Native rough lumber covered with composition roofing is quite commonly used. The houses are from 20 to 40 feet wide; the narrow houses have shed roofs and the wider houses are covered with gable or uneven span roofs.

Since broiler houses are now used throughout the year they should be constructed so they can be kept warm in winter and cool in summer.

The floor may be concrete, sand, dirt, wire, or wooden slats. A concrete floor that can be easily cleaned is favored by most growers. The other types of floors have their advocates.

[4] Me. Sta. Bul. 441. 1945.

Many different litters give satisfaction, such as cut straw, sand, shavings, sawdust, peat moss, and ground corncobs. Built-up litter is becoming more common in broiler plants; never changing the litter through the twelve to fourteen weeks growing period. It is essential that the litter be kept reasonably dry to avoid outbreaks of disease such as coccidiosis. An application of 10 to 15 pounds of lime to the litter per 100 square feet of floor space beginning when the broilers are about four weeks of age and repeating this treatment every two to four weeks will help keep the litter dry.

Floor space. From one-half to one square foot of floor space per broiler is used by successful operators. Most producers and especially beginners will do well to allow one square foot of floor space per broiler.

Equipment. Broiler production has become more commercialized than other phases of poultry production and therefore more labor-saving devices and automatic equipment are used than are found on general farms. Automatic waterers are commonly used. A carrier suspended from an overhead track is generally used for moving feed and litter. Automatic feeders are also used. Roosts are not necessary, as the birds grown to broiler size (3 to 4 pounds) and then marketed develop better on the floor.

Success in growing broilers. These are the requirements which appear to be necessary for success in growing broilers commercially:

1. Make a business of the operation by providing full-time employment for at least one person, which means raising 10,000 or more broilers at one time and running two or more lots per year.
2. Use only good broiler strains of chicks that are from U. S. Pullorum passed or clean stock.
3. Use a well-balanced broiler ration. Feed represents about 70 per cent of the cost of producing broilers.
4. Provide adequate housing, using large units to save labor. Use automatic waterers and feed carriers.
5. See that the chicks have feed and water available at all times.
6. Use a dependable brooding system that requires a minimum of labor to operate.
7. Maintain sanitary quarters and keep the plant under quarantine against visitors.
8. Have only one age of broilers on the plant, so that the place can be depopulated and thoroughly cleaned between each brood.

Capon Production

The art of caponizing is exceedingly old, dating back to the pre-Christian era. As early as 37 B.C., Cato and Varro stated in their book *Roman Farm Management* that "the altered males are called capons." Reaumur in his book *The Art of Hatching and Bringing up Domestic Fowls, etc.,* published in 1750 A.D., mentioned the fact that capons can be trained to care for young chicks.

The caponized male as it develops takes on some of the characters of the female. The comb and wattles do not develop, and capons are less active than cockerels.

The objectives of caponizing. The principal objective of caponizing is to improve the quality of the meat produced. This is the same objective the farmer has in castrating male calves or pigs. The improvement in the quality of the meat insures a better price for capons than for cockerels which have become staggy. There is also a slight weight advantage for capons as compared to cockerels when the birds are seven or eight months old, when they are usually sold. Contrary to public opinion, capons will become tough-meated after they are more than one year old.

Breeds to caponize. Since capons are raised for meat, it is evident that only those breeds should be caponized which are efficient producers of high-quality meat. Barred and White Plymouth Rocks, Rhode Island Reds, New Hampshires, and White Wyandottes make good capons. Other general-purpose and heavy breeds may be used for commercial capon production but the above-mentioned breeds give the most consistent profits. Yellow-skinned breeds are preferred on the markets. The strain selected should be rapid growing and early maturing but large enough to demand top prices. Leghorns and other light breeds may be caponized for family use.

Time to caponize. The size of the cockerel is the most important consideration in deciding when to caponize. Cockerels weighing from one and one-half to two pounds are the most satisfactory size on which to operate. The operation is more successful when performed on young birds. Chicks hatched in May can be caponized in July and be ready for the market in December. June-hatched chicks can be finished as January or February capons.

Preparation of the birds for the operation. Feed and water should be withheld from the cockerels twelve to eighteen hours before the operation is performed. This starvation period empties the intestines and thereby gives the operator more room in the body cavity to perform the operation. It is believed that withholding water from the birds will reduce the amount of bleeding. If the feed and water are removed in the late afternoon from the pens where the cockerels are located, the birds will be ready for the operation the following morning.

Only strong, healthy cockerels should be selected for caponizing. Unthrifty and slow-growing birds should be marketed as broilers, as they will not develop into profitable capons.

The operation. The most satisfactory way to learn to caponize chickens is to get instruction and experience by working with an experienced operator. A brief description of the operation will be given here for the benefit of those who desire to learn something about the operation before attempting to do the work. Birds weighing one and one-half to two pounds are about the correct size for caponizing. The bird can be held in place on a barrel head or table by weights attached to the legs and wings.

The operation is simple and almost anyone can do the work after he has had some experience. When the incision is to be made, the skin and muscles be-

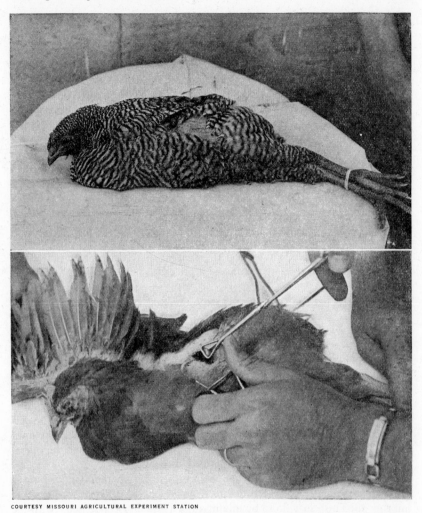

Fig. 106. Caponizing.

neath the skin should be drawn toward the hip and the incision made between the last two ribs. The operator should avoid cutting any large blood vessels in the skin. The incision should be about three-fourths inch in length. Figure 106 shows the incision which has been made, the spreaders in place which hold the ribs apart, and the forceps being used to remove one of the testicles. The danger in the operation lies in rupturing the blood vessels which are located near the gonads. Birds which die soon after the operation should be dressed and used.

Before gaining entrance to the body cavity it is necessary to use a sharp pointed hooked-probe to tear the membranes which line the body cavity.

If the incision is made at the correct location the testicles can be located easily —attached to the back at the forward end of the kidney. The size of the gonads varies with the sexual maturity of the bird, but in birds weighing one and one-half pounds they will be only slightly larger than a grain of wheat. They are usually yellowish in color but may be grayish or black.

The experienced operator can remove both testicles through one opening, but the amateur will have best results by making an incision on each side of the body. The size of the opening should be as small as is convenient for the operator's work.

When the testicles are removed the spreader should be closed and removed from between the ribs. The skin and the muscles underlying it will find their position and form a natural bandage over the incision between the ribs.

Slips. If any part of the testicle is left inside the body cavity the bird is not completely castrated. As it develops, instead of becoming a capon, it shows the characters of the cockerel and is known as a slip. Sometimes these male characters do not appear until just before the birds are ready for market, their development depending upon the amount of testicular material left in the body cavity. Slips usually command a price between that of the capon and cockerel.

Care of the birds after the operation. Soon after the operation the birds should be placed in a house without roosts where they have access to the same ration they have been receiving. They should be kept under these conditions for a week to ten days.

Wind puffs are quite common among recently caponized birds, and their occurrence need not cause any alarm or indicate faulty technique. Wind puffs are caused by air escaping from the air sacs of the abdominal cavity which were punctured by the operation; the air passing through the opening which was made between the ribs collects under the skin which has healed. The only remedy is to puncture these puffs with a sharp knife each day until they cease forming, which will usually be within two weeks after the operation.

Marketing capons. Capons can be finished for market by keeping a growing mash and whole corn before them in hoppers. Those who wish to improve the finish may do so by mixing milk (liquid or condensed) with the mash or grain and giving the birds twice daily an amount they will clean up in from fifteen to twenty minutes. A capon is finished for the market when it is free of pinfeathers and the body is well covered with fat. An examination of the fat under the wing on the side of the breast should show that all blood vessels are hidden by a layer of creamy or yellowish fat.

There is usually a good market for capons from November to April, with the highest prices generally prevailing after January. The general farmer sells capons as live birds to dealers. Poultrymen who produce a large number of capons may sell to dealers in a large city market or kill and dress for special outlets.

Caponizing other species of fowl. Since there is some interest in turkey capons, it is well to mention the results reported on this subject by the Kansas State Agricultural Experiment Station. The experimenters caponized turkeys and guineas and made observations on growth and development of the capons and uncastrated males of these species. They concluded that there was no difference in weight up to one year of age, but that at eighteen months of age the capons were somewhat fatter than normal males. Since turkeys are usually sold on the market before they are one year old and the quality of the meat of young toms is excellent up to that time, there is evidently no advantage in caponizing turkeys. Similar conclusions relative to guineas may be drawn.

Growth and feed consumption. Table 41 shows the relative size of cockerels and capons at twenty-four weeks of age. At this time there is little difference in the size of cockerels and capons. Table 48 shows the amount of feed required to produce one pound of gain with cockerels and capons to thirty-two weeks of age when their average weight was about seven pounds.

Table 41

COMPARISON OF GROWTH OF PUREBRED AND CROSSBRED CAPONS AND COCKERELS. AVERAGE WEIGHT IN GRAMS (454 GRAMS = 1 LB.) AT TWENTY-FOUR WEEKS OF AGE [5]

	1935				1936			
STRAINS	CAPONS		COCKERELS		CAPONS		COCKERELS	
	No.	Wt.	No.	Wt.	No.	Wt.	No.	Wt.
Barred Rocks......	41	2535	43	2839	31	2739	34	2572
Rock x Reds.......	41	2938	39	2851	...	...	...	...
S. C. R. I. Reds...	...	...	...	...	14	2504	14	2536
Red x Rocks.......	...	...	...	...	13	2612	14	2849
New Hampshires...	...	...	...	...	29	3092	27	2917
N. H. x Rocks.....	...	...	...	...	12	2632	12	2662

Feeding and management. The feeding and management of capons is not unlike that of other growing stock. They should receive a good growing mash and grain in hoppers. They should be raised on clean range where there is growing green feed and plenty of shade during the summer, and otherwise receive treatment similar to that given growing pullets.

Chemical caponizing. This process is accomplished by implantation of diethylstilbestrol in pellet form into the neck tissues of the male two to five weeks before the birds are to be marketed. The pellet should be implanted in the neck near the head, so that any remaining portion of the pellet at slaughter time is removed with the head and is not used as human food. This product is an estrogen (female hormone). Experimental work shows that this treatment results in stopping of fighting and crowing, shriveling and paling of comb and wattles, increased deposits of fat throughout the body, improved finish, and a more tender juicy meat. However, with old cock birds, these changes do not always occur.

The Food and Drug Administration office at St. Louis, Missouri, in 1949 made the following statement relative to this use of estrogens:—"No objection to the use of a 15 milligram pellet of diethylstilbestrol to be inserted in

[5] Annin and Halpin, 1938.

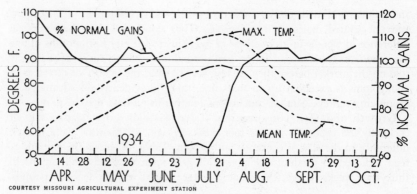

COURTESY MISSOURI AGRICULTURAL EXPERIMENT STATION

Fig. 107. Effect of high temperatures on the growth of chickens.

the neck tissues of cockerels for tenderizing purposes. However, we have objected to the feeding of synthetic estrogens for this purpose, since we have not been satisfied that the treated birds are safe for human consumption."

For those who grow out extra cockerels to make their selection of breeding males in the fall, it would seem that these extra birds to be marketed might be treated to advantage. But the growing of cockerels so they can be chemical-caponized would seem most questionable.

Growth in Chickens

There are a number of factors which influence the rate of growth in chickens. These factors may be classified as hereditary, environmental, and nutritional. Some breeds when mature are large, whereas others are small. Some strains grow more rapidly than other strains and males usually grow more rapidly than females.

Temperature as a factor influencing growth. Supplementary heat is essential for the growth of chicks in cool weather. High temperature exerts a depressing influence on the growth rate of chickens (Fig. 107). It will be observed that when the temperature goes above 90° F. during the growing period, growth is retarded.

Early-hatched (February) pullets grow more rapidly to twenty weeks of age than late April-hatched pullets if hot weather prevails during the summer months. However, at maturity there will be no difference in weight because when growth is retarded by high temperatures it will be accelerated later when more favorable conditions for growth prevail.

Other environmental factors affecting growth. The rate of growth in chickens is influenced by the space available for the growing stock, the ventilation of the brooding room, and the humidity of the atmosphere. Ordinarily growth is not retarded by the ventilation or humidity of the brooder room, but insufficient fresh air and an atmosphere that is either too humid or too dry will retard growth. Failure to provide sufficient room for the growing stock is a common cause of poor growth in chickens.

Nutritional factors influencing growth. The effects of proteins, minerals, and vitamins on growth are discussed in Chapter Nine and may be omitted here. In addition to providing the necessary nutrients for growth, it is necessary that the feed be given in a palatable form and in feeders where the birds have access to liberal quantities of it, as needed. A good feeder can produce more rapid gains than one who is inexperienced.

Feed Consumption of Growing Chickens

The amount of feed required to produce a pound of gain or to grow a pullet to maturity is important to the poultryman. The amount of feed required to grow a pullet to twenty-four weeks of age in complete confinement has been determined for Single-Comb White Leghorns and Barred Plymouth Rocks by the Pennsylvania Agricultural Experiment Station, as shown in Tables 42 and 43.

Table 42

FEED CONSUMPTION PER HUNDRED SINGLE-COMB
WHITE LEGHORN CHICKS, 1929 [6]

Age in Weeks	Lbs. of Mash	Lbs. of Mash to Date	Lbs. of Grain	Lbs. of Grain to Date	Lbs. of Mash and Grain	Lbs. of Mash and Grain to Date
1	14.42	14.42	...	...	14.42	14.42
2	23.56	37.98	...	...	23.56	37.98
3	31.55	69.53	...	...	31.55	69.53
4	46.97	116.50	...	...	46.97	116.50
5	58.21	174.71	...	...	58.21	174.71
6	64.75	239.46	...	...	64.75	239.46
7	80.14	319.60	...	...	80.14	319.60
8	73.73	393.33	...	...	73.73	393.33
9	68.14	461.47	16.38	16.38	84.52	477.85
10	58.62	520.09	22.73	39.11	81.35	559.20
11	55.02	575.11	26.12	65.23	81.14	640.34
12	55.13	630.24	32.11	97.34	87.24	727.58
13	54.36	684.60	37.45	134.79	91.81	819.39
14	48.31	732.91	42.41	177.20	90.72	910.11
15	50.66	783.57	42.44	219.64	93.10	1003.21
16	59.73	843.30	34.37	254.01	94.10	1097.31
17	61.01	904.31	34.43	288.44	95.44	1192.75
18	68.51	972.82	29.31	317.75	97.82	1290.57
19	68.55	1041.37	37.35	355.10	105.90	1396.47
20	68.19	1109.56	40.41	395.51	108.60	1505.07
21	82.85	1192.41	31.34	426.85	114.19	1619.26
22	71.83	1264.24	38.72	465.57	110.55	1729.81
23	66.14	1330.38	56.86	522.43	123.00	1852.81
24	66.91	1397.29	48.13	570.56	115.04	1967.85

AVERAGE WEIGHT OF ABOVE CHICKS

	8 Weeks	16 Weeks
Males.........................	1.36 lbs.	...
Females.......................	1.15 lbs.	2.36 lbs.

[6] Pa. Agr. Expt. Sta. Bul. 246.

Table 43

FEED CONSUMPTION PER HUNDRED BARRED PLYMOUTH
ROCK CHICKS, 1929 [7]

Age in Weeks	Lbs. of Mash	Lbs. of Mash to Date	Lbs. of Grain	Lbs. of Grain to Date	Lbs. of Mash and Grain	Lbs. of Mash and Grain to Date
1	14.23	14.23	...	...	14.23	14.23
2	23.99	38.22	...	...	23.99	38.22
3	27.74	65.96	...	...	27.74	65.96
4	44.10	110.06	...	...	44.10	110.06
5	63.47	173.53	...	...	63.47	173.53
6	77.25	250.78	...	...	77.25	250.78
7	85.20	335.98	...	...	85.20	335.98
8	88.86	424.84	...	...	88.86	424.84
9	79.36	504.20	13.92	13.92	93.28	518.12
10	77.27	581.47	20.69	34.61	97.96	616.08
11	72.48	653.95	24.16	58.77	96.64	712.72
12	66.03	719.98	34.76	93.53	100.79	813.51
13	72.96	792.94	27.41	120.94	100.37	913.88
14	62.45	855.39	38.28	159.22	100.73	1014.61
15	64.02	919.41	43.38	202.60	107.40	1122.01
16	64.28	983.69	52.55	255.15	116.83	1238.84
17	68.51	1052.20	47.56	302.71	116.07	1354.91
18	83.98	1136.18	37.98	340.69	121.96	1476.87
19	81.38	1217.56	41.87	382.56	123.25	1600.12
20	70.18	1287.74	64.13	446.69	134.31	1734.43
21	62.26	1350.00	70.48	517.17	132.74	1867.17
22	74.85	1424.85	75.50	592.67	150.35	2017.52
23	64.25	1489.10	72.59	665.26	136.84	2154.36
24	56.70	1545.80	66.93	732.19	123.63	2277.99

AVERAGE WEIGHT OF ABOVE CHICKS

	8 Weeks	16 Weeks
Males.............................	1.53 lbs.	...
Females...........................	1.33 lbs.	3.10 lbs.

Growth rate and feed consumption of New Hampshires is shown in Table 44.

REVIEW QUESTIONS

1. Should any poultry raiser use natural methods of brooding?
2. List the requirements for artificial brooding. Discuss each.
3. Define a colony brooding system.
4. Name the types of brooder stoves and list some advantages of each type.
5. How much feeding space at the hoppers is recommended for chicks?
6. Why were stationary brooding systems abandoned for some time?
7. Is the brooding system used or the management of the brooder most important in growing chicks? Explain.
8. When should chicks be hatched for growing layers? Explain.

[7] Pa. Agr. Expt. Sta. Bul. 246.

Table 44

GROWTH AND FEED CONSUMPTION OF NEW HAMPSHIRES [8]

WEEK	WEIGHT		FEED CONSUMPTION	
	Males	Females	Male	Female
Initial	.09	.09		
1	.12	.12	.10	.10
2	.20	.20	.21	.21
3	.30	.30	.37	.37
4	.44	.44	.41	.41
5	.64	.64	.52	.52
6	.91 *	.91 *	.74 *	.74 *
7	1.35	1.20	1.25	1.23
8	1.75	1.51	1.30	1.22
9	1.96	1.70	1.40	1.28
10	2.39	2.05	1.42	1.62
11	2.82	2.32	1.69	1.36
12	3.17	2.73	1.89	2.06
13	3.48	2.93	2.10	1.59
14	3.95	3.35	2.21	2.31
15	4.35	3.52	1.93	1.79
16	4.48	3.69	2.09	1.92
17	4.93	3.97	1.52	1.72
18	4.90	4.34	2.04	1.98
19	5.28	4.45	1.70	1.80
20	5.53	4.62	1.56	1.70
21	5.60	4.82	2.23	2.34
22	5.82	4.89	2.22	1.75
23	5.95	5.00	1.98	2.23
24	6.20	5.04	1.84	2.03
Total			34.71	34.28

* Records for the sexes were not kept separately until after the sixth week.

9. How can cannibalism among chicks be reduced?
10. How can crowding be prevented?
11. List the essential practices of a healthy pullet program.
12. Why are sun porches used in growing chickens?
13. What are some of the advantages and disadvantages of battery brooders?
14. How much room should be provided per chick raised in batteries?
15. What breeds are most popular for broilers?
16. Why are chickens caponized?
17. When should they be caponized?
18. How can wind puffs be controlled?
19. How much feed does it take to grow an eight-pound capon?
20. Compare the rate of growth of cockerels and capons.
21. What effect does hot weather have on the growth of chickens?
22. How much feed is required to grow a Leghorn pullet to twenty-four weeks of age?

[8] N. H. Sta. Circ. 52.

REFERENCES

ACKERMAN, W. T., CHARLES, T. B., FOULKROD, G. M., TEPPER, A. E., AND DURGIN, R. C.: ELECTRIC BROODING OF CHICKS. II. HEAT REQUIREMENTS. N. H. Agr. Expt. Sta. Bul. 303: 1–31. 1938.

ANNIN, G. E., AND HALPIN, J. G.: COMPARATIVE GROWTH AND FEED CONSUMPTION OF ROOSTERS, CAPONS, AND PULLETS. Poultry Sci., 17: 419–422. 1938.

BAILEY, C. F., GRIESBACK, L., AND RANKEN, J. A.: HOMEMADE ELECTRIC BROODERS. Canad. Dept. Agr. Pub. 756. 1943.

BAUSMAN, R. O.: INFLUENCE OF MANAGEMENT PRACTICES ON COST OF PRODUCING BROILERS IN DELAWARE. Del. Sta. Bul. 270. 1947.

BIRD, S.: EFFECTS FOLLOWING ESTROGEN ADMINISTRATION TO MALE BIRDS. Proc. Eighth World's Poultry Cong., pp. 131–136. 1948.

CALLENBACH, E. W., NICHOLAS, J. E., AND MURPHY, R. R.: ELECTRIC BROODING UNDER WINTER CONDITIONS. Pa. Sta. Bul. 416. 1941.

CALLENBACH, E. W., NICHOLAS, J. E., AND MARGOLF, P. H.: POULTRY BROODING SYSTEMS. Pa. Agr. Expt. Sta. Bul. 340: 1–40. 1937.

CALLENBACH, E. W., AND NICHOLAS, J. E.: EFFECT OF REARING ENVIRONMENT ON SEXUAL DEVELOPMENT OF FOWLS. Pa. Agr. Expt. Sta. Bul. 368. 1938.

CLARKE, J. H.: THE BROILER INDUSTRY IN WEST VIRGINIA. W. Va. Sta. Bul. 338. 1949.

DAVIDSON, J. A., McCRAY, C. M., AND CARD, C. G.: SUMMER BROILER PRODUCTION. Mich. Sta. Quart. Bul. 26. 1944.

ESHELMAN, J. W., AND SONS: BULLETIN ON RADIANT HEATING. Lancaster, Pa. 1947.

HALL, G. E.: EXTERNAL TEMPERATURE AS A FACTOR IN THE PRODUCTION OF DIARRHEA IN YOUNG CHICKENS. Poultry Sci., 11: 250–254. 1932.

HEYWANG, B. W.: EFFECT OF COOLING HOUSES FOR GROWING CHICKENS DURING HOT WEATHER. Poultry Sci., 26: 20–24. 1947.

HIENTON, TRUMAN E.: ELECTRIC BROODERS ON INDIANA FARMS. Purdue Agr. Expt. Sta. Circ. 187 (rev.). 1934.

HOFFMANN, E., AND JOHNSON, H. A.: Successful Broiler Growing. Watt Pub. Co., Mt. Morris, Illinois. 1946.

IRWIN, M. B.: PRODUCING AND MARKETING CAPONS. Mo. Sta. Bul. 495. 1946.

JOHNSON, H. A.: THE BROILER INDUSTRY IN DELAWARE. Del. Sta. Bul. 250. 1944.

KEMPSTER, H. L.: THE NORMAL GROWTH OF CHICKENS. Mo. Sta. Bul. 423. 1941.

KENNARD, D. C., AND CHAMBERLAIN, V. D.: HOMEMADE ELECTRIC LAMP BROODER. Ohio Sta. Spec. Circ. 63 (rev.). 1943.

KING, D. F.: HOMEMADE LAMP BROODER. Ala. Sta. Leaflet 19. 1941.

KNANDEL, H. C., CALLENBACH, E. W., AND MARGOLF, P. H.: MANAGING CONFINED FOWL. Pa. Agr. Expt. Sta. Bul. 246. 1930.

LEE, A. R.: CAPONS AND CAPONIZING. U. S. D. A. Farmers' Bul. 849. 1932.

LENNARTSON, R. W.: ECONOMIC FORCES THAT BUILD A SUCCESSFUL BROILER INDUSTRY. Amer. Egg and Poultry Rev. 10, No. 2, 32. 1949.

MEHRHOF, N. R., WARD, W. F., AND MOORE, O. K.: COMPARISON OF PUREBRED AND CROSSBRED COCKERELS WITH RESPECT TO FATTENING AND DRESSING QUALITIES. Fla. Sta. Bul. 410. 1945.

MEHRHOF, N. R., WARD, W. F., AND MOORE, O. K.: EFFECT OF METHOD OF REARING S. C. WHITE LEGHORN CHICKS UPON RATE OF GROWTH, FEED EFFICIENCY, AND MORTALITY. Fla. Sta. Bul. 394. 1943.

MEHRHOF, N. R., AND O'STEEN, A. W.: FLOOR SPACE REQUIREMENTS FOR BROILER PRODUCTION. Fla. Sta. Bul. 451. 1948.

MITCHELL, H. H., CARD, L. E., AND HAMILTON, T. S.: A TECHNICAL STUDY OF THE GROWTH OF WHITE LEGHORN CHICKENS. Ill. Agr. Expt. Sta. Bul. 367: 81–139. 1931.

NORTH, M. O.: THE A B C'S OF PROFITABLE BROILER PRODUCTION. U. S. Egg and Poultry Mag. 55, No. 4, 16. 1949.

PARKER, J. E., AND MCSPADDEN, B. J.: GROWTH OF BARRED-ROCK CHICKENS. Tenn. Sta. Bul. 180. 1942.

PAYNE, L. F.: CAPON PRODUCTION. Kan. Sta. Bul. 315. 1943.

PERRY, A. L., AND DOW, G. F.: COSTS AND RETURNS IN BROILER PRODUCTION. Me. Sta. Bul. 441. 1945.

POFFENBERGER, P. R., AND DEVAULT, S. H.: AN ECONOMIC STUDY OF THE BROILER INDUSTRY IN MARYLAND. Md. Agr. Expt. Sta. Bul. 410: 1–54. 1937.

POULTRY COMMITTEE OF THE RUTGERS UNIVERSITY FARM BUILDINGS INSTITUTE. YOUNG-STOCK POULTRY HOUSES. N. J. Ext. Bul. 246. 1947.

POULTRY COUNCIL OF THE STATE COLLEGE OF WASHINGTON. SUN PORCHES FOR CHICKENS AND TURKEYS. Wash. Ext. Bul. 376. 1948.

PRICE, F. E., KIRK, D. E., AND COSBY, H. E.: HOMEMADE ELECTRIC BROODERS. Ore. Sta. Circ. 146. 1943.

STILES, G. W.: CARBON MONOXIDE POISONING OF CHICKS AND POULTS IN POORLY VENTILATED BROODERS. Poultry Sci., 19: 111–115. 1940.

SWINK, E. T.: TESTS OF CHICK BROODERS. Va. Agr. Expt. Sta. Bul. 306: 1–16. 1936.

TEMPERTON, H., AND DUDLEY, F. J.: THE REACTIONS OF BABY CHICKS TO CHILLING AND OVERHEATING IN BROODER UNITS. Harper Adams Utility Poultry Jour. 31: 42. 1946.

TERMOHLEN, W. D., KINGHORNE, J. W., WARREN, E. L., AND RADABAUGH, J. H.: AN ECONOMIC SURVEY OF THE COMMERCIAL BROILER INDUSTRY. U. S. D. A. Pub. G-61: 1–54. 1936.

THOMPSON, R. B.: CHICK RAISING IN OKLAHOMA. Okla. Sta. Bul. 254. 1942.

THOMPSON, W. C.: CARE AND MANAGEMENT OF BABY CHICKS. N. J. Sta. Circ. 474. 1944.

TITUS, H. W., AND JULL, M. A.: THE GROWTH OF RHODE ISLAND REDS AND THE EFFECT OF FEEDING SKIM MILK ON THE CONSTANTS OF THEIR GROWTH CURVES. Jour. Agr. Res., 36: 515–540. 1928.

TOMHAVE, A. E.: BROILER FEEDING EXPERIMENTS. Del. Agr. Expt. Sta. Bul. 210: 1–20. 1938.

TOMHAVE, A. E., AND SEEGER, K. C.: FLOOR SPACE REQUIREMENTS OF BROILERS. Del. Sta. Bul. 255. 1945.

WARREN, D. C.: PHYSIOLOGIC AND GENETIC STUDIES OF CROOKED KEELS IN CHICKENS. Kan. Agr. Expt. Sta. Tech. Bul. 44: 1–32. 1937.

WEST, H. O.: BROILER PRODUCTION. Miss. Sta. Bul. 370. 1942.

WIANT, D. E., AND DAVIDSON, J. A.: ELECTRIC CHICK BROODER OPERATION. Mich. Sta. Ext. Bul. 237. 1942.

YUNG, F. D., AND MUSSEHL, F. E.: ELECTRIC CHICK BROODING STUDIES. Neb. Sta. Circ. 80. 1945.

CHAPTER 8 |||||||||||||||||||||||||||||||||||||||||||||||||||||||||||||

Housing Principles and Practices

▼

Poultry is housed for comfort, protection, efficient production, and convenience of the poultryman.

The chicken, as a wild jungle fowl, sought safety and rest on the high limb of a tree or in the thick underbrush. The jungle served for protection against the hot sunlight. The bird tucked its head under its wing and drew its feet up under its body and was well protected against cold by its covering of feathers. Line breeding to fix desirable characters and management to secure continued high egg production have so reduced the vitality of poultry that housing is necessary for the birds to survive. Artificial protection is necessary to offset the general reduction in bodily vigor. The more birds are forced for production, the more attention that will have to be given to improved housing conditions.

If birds are housed in comfortable quarters where they are neither too warm nor too cold, they will lay more eggs. The more springlike conditions that can be maintained in the house, the greater production that may be expected. More birds suffer and die as result of extremely hot summer weather than as a result of extremely cold weather. Both extremes of temperature cause a slump in egg production. If birds are kept comfortably warm in the winter, less feed will be required to maintain body temperature and a bigger percentage of the feed eaten will be used for egg production.

Birds that are housed and confined to yards are more easily cared for. Eggs are laid in nests rather than in some hidden spots, and are more easily gathered. Proper housing protects birds from predatory animals and from destruction by larger domestic animals.

Housing Requirements

Birds must be housed comfortably in order to produce well. They need adequate room in the house, sufficient air space and ventilation to prevent "stuffiness" in the house, a moderate temperature, dry living quarters, and daylight.

Floor space. The floor space allotted per bird is important from the standpoint of results obtained with both growing stock and laying hens. The space required for growing stock has been discussed in the preceding chapter.

There has been very little experimental study of the floor space required

212

for laying hens. Practical poultrymen differ widely in their opinion regarding the most practical floor space per hen. It is customary to allow about three square feet per bird in case of the light breeds, such as the Leghorns, and four square feet per bird in case of the general-purpose breeds, such as the Plymouth Rocks.

More floor space is needed for birds kept in confinement than for those given range part of the time. It is customary to increase the floor space about 25 per cent over the above recommendations for birds kept in strict confinement.

The amount of floor space needed per bird will vary with the size of the flock. If the pen is large enough to accommodate one hundred or more birds, less floor space is needed per bird than in a pen that will accommodate only ten to twenty birds.

Overcrowded birds are less contented. Feather picking and cannibalism are more likely to occur in overcrowded pens. Lowered egg production and egg eating are other troubles that are more likely to be encountered in overcrowded pens. Egg production, of the weaker individuals in particular, is likely to suffer. The more individuals in a pen, the more "bossy" birds present and the greater the number that will be bullied.

The more floor space per pen, the less the labor required to care for the birds. It requires nearly twice as much labor to care for birds in pens of twenty to one hundred as it does to care for them in pens that accommodate five hundred to one thousand each. The customary size of pen will accommodate about two hundred birds. However, on commercial farms the pens often accommodate five hundred to one thousand birds. The more birds kept in a pen, the greater the chances of spreading disease and poultry vices. In a small pen the trouble can spread only to the fifty to one hundred birds in the pen, but in the large pen it can spread to the entire five hundred to one thousand birds.

Ventilation. Ventilation in the poultry house is necessary to provide the birds with fresh air and to carry off moisture. It needs to be provided without exposing the birds to drafts.

Since the fowl is a small animal with a rapid metabolism, its air requirement per unit of body weight is high in comparison with that of other animals (Table 45). A hen weighing 2 kilograms, and on full feed, produces about 52 liters of CO_2 every 24 hours. Since the CO_2 content of expired air is about 3.5 per cent, the total air breathed amounts to .5 liter per kilogram live weight per minute.

The amount of air space needed per bird will vary with the rate of movement of the air. The greater the difference between the inside and outside temperature of a house, the greater the movement of air between the inside and outside. A house that is tall enough for the attendant to move around in comfortably will supply far more air space than will be required by the birds that can be accommodated in the given floor space.

In providing ventilation, drafts should be avoided as they make birds susceptible to colds, roup, and bronchitis.

Exchange of air between the inside and outside of the house will help to

Table 45

ESTIMATED AIR CONSUMPTION OF DIFFERENT
ANIMALS [1]

Species of Animal	Liters of Air per Kilogram of Weight per Minute
Man	.1
Goat	.2
Rabbit	.4
Chicken	.5
Guinea pig	.6
Rat	1.5
Mouse	5.1

keep the pens dry. Hens exhale a lot of moisture in respiration as well as eliminating some by way of the excreta. This needs to be carried away by proper ventilation.

Temperature. Hens need a moderate temperature of 50 to 70° F. They suffer from extreme heat or cold. Birds need a warmer temperature at night, when they are inactive, than during the day.

Temperature regulation in the house should be based on the critical temperature and management of the birds. The critical temperature may be as high as 62° F. for hens on the roosts at night and with no feed in the intestinal tract to be digested. It may drop to 15° F. during the day for laying hens that have access to feed.

Aids toward keeping the house at a comfortable temperature during cold weather include the elimination of excessive air space, keeping the house filled to capacity, insulation of the house, and restricted ventilation. There are times during the winter when artificial heat is desirable. It increases the water-holding capacity of the air, creates a movement between air inside and outside of the house, and aids in keeping the house dry.

The use of insulation not only keeps the house warmer during the winter months but cooler during the summer months. Cross ventilation also aids in keeping the house comfortable during hot weather.

Dryness. Dryness in the poultry house is desirable. Birds require a lot of water as well as air because of their rapid metabolism. Most of it is eliminated by the lungs in the form of vapor or by way of the excreta in the form of liquid. If it is not removed by proper ventilation or frequent cleaning of the litter, it is a menace to the health and management of the birds.

Disease-producing organisms thrive better in damp quarters than in dry ones. On the other hand, they are not distributed so easily by dust particles if the house is fairly damp. However, it is likely that more disease germs are picked up from wet litter than inhaled from dusty litter.

If the house is damp and the litter wet, more soiled eggs will be produced. The use of thick litter on the floor and stirring it up frequently will help prevent floor condensation of moisture in the spring. The use of insulation

---

[1] Mitchell and Kelley, 1934.

will prevent wall and ceiling condensation of moisture. The windows or ventilators should be opened just enough to prevent window condensation of moisture. The use of a little artificial heat will increase the water-holding capacity of the air, aid air movements, and remove moisture from the house.

Light. Daylight in the house is desirable for the comfort of the birds. They seem more contented on bright, sunshiny days than on dark, cloudy ones. Birds do fairly well when kept under artificial lights.

The tendency today is to reduce the amount of window space in poultry houses to one square foot for each twenty to forty square feet of floor space. It cuts down the light intensity and thereby reduces the troubles from such vices as feather picking and cannibalism. Reducing the amount of window space also reduces the heat loss from the house. Insulation is not very effective if there are a lot of windows for heat loss.

Sunlight in the poultry house is desirable for the destruction of disease germs and for supplying vitamin D. However, ordinary window glass shuts out the beneficial rays. The windows should extend from near the floor to near the ceiling so that when they are open during the summer, sunlight can shine on the floor and on the birds.

Location of the House

In planning a poultry house, the location should be taken into consideration. The location with respect to the other buildings, the exposure, the soil and drainage, shade and protection, and a number of other factors should be considered.

Relation to other buildings. The poultry house should not be so close to the home as to create unsanitary conditions. If the birds are to be given range, sufficient space should be provided around the house for a double yarding system. The house should not be too far away from the home because this will require more time in going to and from the house in caring for the birds. At least three trips should be made daily to the poultry house in feeding, watering, gathering the eggs, etc. Also, if the poultry house is too far away from the home, it is more likely to be visited by thieves. The poultry house should not be located in the barnyard. The chickens are a nuisance around the barn lot. They may be killed or injured by the larger livestock. It is impossible to provide a clean range for the birds when they have the run of the barnyard.

The old idea seems to have been to fence the yard, garden, orchard, etc., to keep the chickens out. The new idea is to fence the chickens in. They should be provided with a double system of yarding (p. 481) or kept in total confinement. If the latter system is practiced, and it is increasing in popularity, the location of the house is of less importance.

Exposure. The poultry house should face south or east in most localities. A southern exposure permits more sunlight to shine in the house than any of the other possible exposures. This is especially true of winter sunlight.

An eastern exposure is almost as good as a southern one. Birds prefer morning sunlight to that of the afternoon. The birds are more active in the morning and will spend more time in the sunlight.

Western and northern exposures are objectionable in most localities. The prevailing winds and storms come from the west or north in most cases. The house needs to be faced so that the prevailing winds and rain do not blow in the open windows. Reducing the window space helps control this trouble.

Soil and drainage. The poultry house should be placed on a sloping hillside rather than on a hilltop or in the bottom of a valley. A sloping hillside provides good drainage and affords some protection. A hilltop location leaves the house exposed; it is harder to ventilate without drafts and more difficult to keep warm. A valley location means more dampness from fog and poorer drainage.

The type of soil is important if the birds are to be given range. A fertile, well-drained soil is desired. This will be a sandy loam rather than a heavy clay soil. A sandy soil is well aerated and drains well. Pathogenic microörganisms do not live well in sandy soil. A fertile soil will grow good vegetation, which is one of the main reasons for providing range. A heavy clay soil is objectionable because it does not drain well, and pathogenic microörganisms, such as coccidia, parasite eggs, and bacteria, will live in it for a long time.

If the poultry house is located on flat, poorly drained soil, the yards should be tiled. Otherwise, the birds should be kept in total confinement.

Shade and protection. Shade and protection of the poultry house are just as desirable as for the home. Trees serve as a windbreak in the winter and for shade in the summer. They should be tall, with no low limbs. It is better to have no shade than that produced by low shrubbery. The soil becomes contaminated under the shrubbery, remains damp, and sunlight cannot reach it to destroy the disease germs.

Protection of the poultry house from prevailing winds by a hillside, a barn, or other large buildings, will make it easier to ventilate and to keep warm in the winter.

Kinds of Poultry Houses

Poultry houses are classified in several different ways. These include size, portability, purpose, style, and type of construction.

Sizes of houses. Houses vary in size, depending on the number of birds to be housed and the size of units in which they are to be kept (Fig. 108).

Colony houses are one-room buildings intended for housing single flocks or colonies of birds. They are usually some distance from each other on range (Fig. 97).

Multiple-unit houses are long houses consisting of several rooms. Each room is like every other room and is known as a pen. In fact, a multiple-unit house is essentially several colony houses built into a single structure.

Multiple-story houses consist of two or more stories. They are popular on large commercial poultry farms where it would be impractical to provide range. Multiple-story houses require less ground, less roofing, and are easier

Fig. 108. Some differences in poultry houses. From top to bottom: a poor colony house; a modern colony house; a multiple-unit house; a multiple-story house.

to heat than multiple-unit houses. On the other hand, they require heavier timbers for construction, increased labor in getting materials to the upper floors, and are more difficult to ventilate.

Portability of houses. Houses may be constructed so that they are movable or so that they must remain in one place.

Fig. 109. Small portable trap-nest house.

Portable houses are small one-room colony houses that are built on runners or skids so that they may be moved from place to place. By moving the houses from place to place, clean green range may be provided. Portable houses are generally used for brooding chicks.

Permanent houses are built on a permanent foundation and are, therefore, immovable. They usually have cement floors. Permanent houses are generally multiple-unit or multiple-story houses.

Purpose of houses. Houses are constructed for several purposes on the poultry farm.

Brooder houses are used for brooding chicks. Colony houses are used for this purpose on general farms and breeding farms. These houses are generally 10 to 12 feet wide and 12 feet deep. The houses may be moved from place to place to provide clean grass range. Where several colony houses are scattered over a range, much labor is required in caring for the birds.

Multiple-unit brooder houses are used on large commercial farms. The pens are close together and often a centralized heating plant is used. These factors reduce the labor required for caring for the birds. Range is generally not provided because it soon becomes contaminated, since the buildings are immovable.

Rearing houses are used to shelter the chicks from the time they no longer need brooder heat until they are placed in the laying house. This period will vary from two to four months, depending on the season of year and the breed of chickens. Colony and multiple-unit brooder houses are often used for this purpose. Range shelters (Fig. 110) are popular for housing pullets on range after they no longer need heat. The colony houses generally contain more pullets than can be cared for comfortably as they approach maturity. The range shelters make it possible to separate the birds in smaller groups.

Laying houses hold the laying hens. They vary all the way from one-room colony houses to multiple-story houses. Instead of being provided with

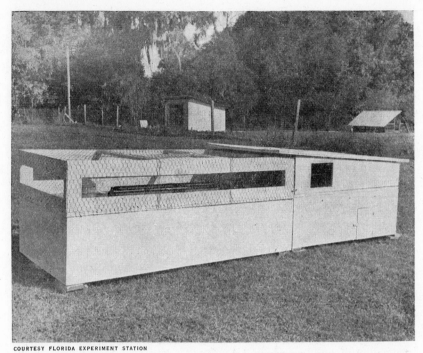

COURTESY FLORIDA EXPERIMENT STATION

Fig. 110. Oil heated chick brooder and sunporch in foreground. Colony brooder house and range shelter in background.

brooding equipment, they are provided with nests and equipment more suitable for older birds. Laying houses also serve for breeding houses. If pen matings are used, smaller pens are made in the laying house, or the breeders are kept in separate small houses.

Styles of poultry houses. The style of the poultry house makes little difference as long as the comfort of the birds is provided. There are several styles of poultry houses with reference to types of roofs (Fig. 111).

Shed-type houses have single-pitch roofs. They are the simplest style of poultry house construction and require the least number for a given floor space. Shed-type poultry houses are the most popular type among poultrymen.

Gable-type houses require more material and labor for construction. They are suitable for straw-loft type of construction. Some poultrymen put a ceiling floor in gable roof houses and use the space in the gable for storage. Multiple-story houses often have gable roofs.

Combination-type houses have double-pitch roofs in which the ridge between the two slopes is not midway from front to back. Most of the houses have the long slope to the rear. Like the gable type, the combination roof requires more material and labor than the shed roof.

The monitor and semi-monitor type houses are expensive and not practical.

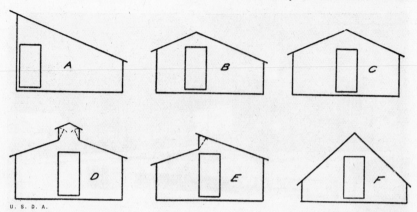

U. S. D. A.

Fig. 111. Types of roofs for poultry houses: A, shed; B, combination; C, gable; D, monitor; E, semi-monitor; F, A-shaped.

They were popular in the early days of poultry house construction. Both types have a large amount of air space and are hard to keep warm.

Types of construction. Several different types of building materials are used in constructing poultry houses. These include wood, hollow tile, concrete blocks, and metal.

Wood houses are most popular because of ease of construction and general availability of building material (Fig. 112). The outside wall is generally drop siding (Fig. 113). There is considerable heat loss through single wall wood construction. The use of sheathing or insulation board on the inside, to provide double wall construction, greatly reduces the heat loss. Wood houses require frequent painting.

Hollow tile houses are popular in areas where tile is produced and is cheap. The heat loss through hollow tile walls is less than through single wall wood construction. The tile is durable, the outside does not require paint, no inside insulation is used, the walls are ratproof, and the house is fireproof.

Concrete block houses are not widely used because they are costly and permit considerable heat loss through the walls. Some houses are built of lighter blocks made of cinders and concrete.

Metal houses are sold by some commercial firms. If of single wall construction, they are cold. Some of them have double wall construction and insulation material between the walls. Metal houses are expensive but durable and easy to keep clean.

House Construction

There are many different kinds, sizes, and types of construction of poultry houses. The 25′ x 30′ shed-type wood poultry house is probably the most popular house in use on general farms. It will accommodate a flock of 200 to 250 birds. It can be increased in length with an increase in the size of the

Fig. 112. Some types of poultry-house construction. Top, metal. (James Manufacturing Company.) Center left, concrete blocks. (Portland Cement Company.) Center right, tile. (U. S. D. A.) Bottom, wood. (U. S. D. A.)

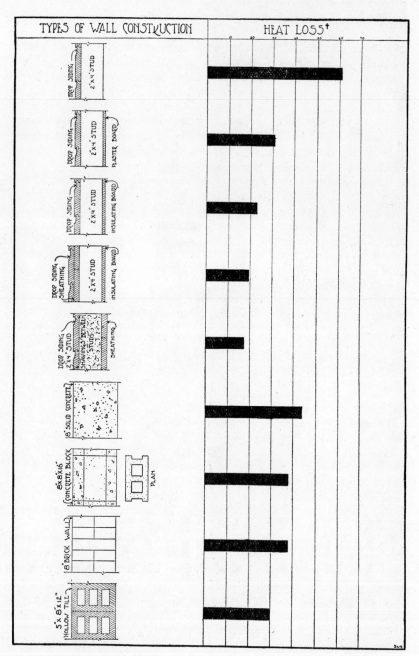

Fig. 113. Heat loss through different types of wall construction. The use of sheathing on the inside of the studs, with the spaces between the studs filled with shavings, as shown above, provides one of the best methods of practical insulation for poultry houses. (Ohio Extension Bulletin 94.)

flock. Since the 25' x 30' shed-type wood house is a typical practical poultry house, the general details of its construction will be discussed.

The foundation. Most permanent poultry houses have concrete foundations and floors. They are durable, ratproof, and easily cleaned. Before starting to dig the ditch for the foundation, square the corners by fixing one side of the site of the proposed house. With this as a base, locate the other corner posts by using the 6-, 8-, and 10-foot combination, measuring 6 feet from one end of the fixed line and 8 feet from the same line at right angles. The angle between the two lines is fixed by measuring 10 feet from the 6-foot mark of the fixed line to the end of the 8-foot line, thereby making a square corner.

The depth at which the ditch should be dug for the foundation for the walls will depend upon the height of the house and the dangers of heaving as a result of freezing. Generally, the foundation should be at least 6 inches thick, and extend about 18 inches below the surface of the ground. If the soil is firm and does not cave in, it will not be necessary to build a form beneath the surface of the ground. The top of the foundation wall should extend at least 12 inches above the ground level (Fig. 114).

The concrete mixture should be a 1:2½:3½ mixture with 5 to 6½ gallons of water per sack of cement. The foundation and post footings for a 25' x 30' house will require about 4½ cubic yards of concrete, consisting of the following:

Portland cement.................	26 sacks
Sand (fine aggregate)............	2½ cubic yards
Stone (coarse aggregate)..........	3½ cubic yards

The floor. The top of the concrete floor should be at least 10 inches above the outside ground level. The space inside the foundation and beneath the floor should be built up about 8 inches above the outside ground level with gravel covered with cinders, and well tamped. A layer of tar paper may be placed on top of the cinders before the concrete is poured in order to further inhibit the possible capillary rise of water through the floor.

The concrete floor should be sloped to a floor drain at one side of the house. The layer of concrete should be 2 to 3 inches thick. The cement mixture consists of a 1:2:3 mixture with 4½ to 5½ gallons of water per sack of cement. The entire thickness of the floor may be poured at one time. The top of the floor should be finished with a wooden trowel in order to produce a smooth surface, and the finish should be made with a light trowel. The floor should be kept wet for several days after being laid in order to permit the concrete to harden without cracking.

A floor for a 25' x 30' house will require about 6½ cubic yards of concrete, consisting of the following:

Portland cement.................	45 sacks
Sand (fine aggregate)............	3½ cubic yards
Stone (coarse aggregate)..........	5 cubic yards

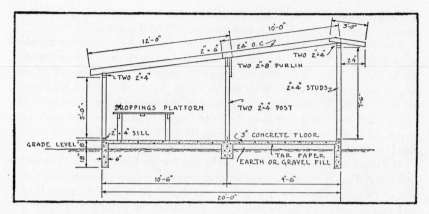

Fig. 114. Side view of shed-type poultry house. (Ohio Extension Bulletin 94.)

The framework. The sills are usually 2 x 4 inches, laid on the broad side and bolted to the concrete foundation by bolts inserted in the concrete foundation at the time it was poured. Heavier sills are used for multiple-story houses. Sometimes two 2 x 4's are spiked together for sills.

Runners, 3 x 4 or 4 x 6 inches in size are used as sills for portable houses. Portable houses that are to be moved on runners must be braced extra well in the corners to stand the strain of moving.

Joists for wooden floors are either 2 x 4 or 2 x 6 inches, depending on the span. They should be 16 to 20 inches apart. If the space is over 10 feet, a center support should be used for 2 x 4-inch joists.

Studdings are 2 x 4 inches and spaced 2 to 4 feet apart and to fit windows and doors wherever necessary. They are toe-nailed on the sill and should be set plumb with a spirit level and braced well until sheathed. The corner studs are generally doubled, making them 4 x 4 inches.

Plates are 2 x 4 inches laid flat on top of the studding. They are halved or spliced and nailed together at the ends or over a post or stud. The plates are spiked to the top of the studding. Sometimes 4 x 4 plates are used. They are made by spiking two 2 x 4's together.

Rafters are 2 x 4 or 2 x 6 inches, depending on the size of the building. The larger rafters should be used where the clear span is 12 feet or more or in climates where the roof must support much snow. The rafters are generally spaced 2 feet apart.

Purlins are 2 x 4's or 2 x 6's set on edge on posts to support the roof. They are placed lengthwise of the house and about midway of the length of the rafters, which rest on them.

About 1200 B.M. feet of lumber are required for the framework for a 25' x 30' laying house.

Walls and partitions. The walls in shed-type houses are usually 5 feet high in the rear and 8 feet high in the front. In gable-type houses, they are usually 6 to 7 feet high in both the front and rear. Wood wall construction is generally used. Drop siding, Pattern No. 106, makes a very desirable outside wall (Fig. 113).

Partitions are generally spaced every 20 or 30 feet in multiple-unit or long laying houses. About every other partition should be solid. The middle partition may be wire netting. Drafts are created by wind entering one end of the house and sweeping through it, unless checked by solid partitions.

Windows. Windows are used for admitting light and may be used for ventilation.

The front windows should extend from near the floor to near the ceiling in order to secure the best distribution of light on the floor and to carry out the warm foul air from near the top of the pen. The windows should be evenly spaced across the front of the house. One square foot of window space should be provided for about 20 square feet of floor space.

The windows should be so arranged that they may be easily opened and closed and will not have to be removed during the summer. One practical arrangement is illustrated in Figure 115. The top sash is hinged to the bottom one and opens in to provide ventilation. It may be folded down on the lower sash and the entire window turned back against the wall during the warm summer months. The studdings are so spaced at the side of the window that the sash will fold back between them.

Rear windows were placed in poultry houses years ago in order to get better distribution of light over the floor. This was desirable when scratch grain was fed in the litter, but is now no longer necessary with the more sanitary methods of feeding. Either rear windows or ventilators are desirable in poultry houses in order to provide cross ventilation during hot weather. They should be broad but not extend down very far, so that they will not be close to the dropping pits.

Ordinary single-strength window glass in 9″ x 12″ panes is satisfactory for poultry house windows. Single-strength glass permits the passage of more beneficial rays of sunlight than double-strength glass and yet is sufficiently strong when used in small panes. Glass substitutes are not durable and have to be replaced too often to be practical.

The roof. The kinds of roofing most generally used on poultry houses are the so-called "prepared roofing," built-up roofing, metal roofing, and shingles.

Prepared roofing which is available in rolls of different degrees of thickness is widely used on poultry buildings. It is cheap and easily put on. However, it soon becomes loose, strips blow off, and it has to be replaced often. Sheathing is first put on the rafters, the roofing is tacked to the sheathing with large-headed nails, the seams overlapped, and the surfaces cemented together. The thicker the roofing material, other things being equal, the better the product. When the doors or windows are open and the wind blows, some pressure is built up in the house. The wind gets under the roof through cracks and holes in the sheathing, the nailheads are loosened, and strips of roofing are blown off after a year or so. Good grade tongue-and-groove sheathing should be used to prevent this trouble. Prepared roofing will also fit tighter if it is put on during warm weather.

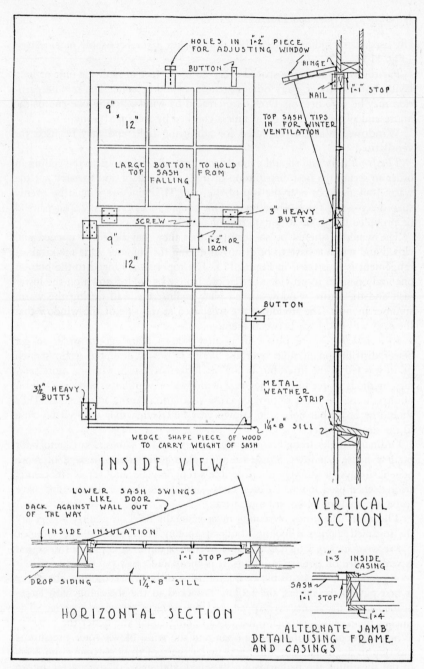

INSIDE VIEW

VERTICAL SECTION

HORIZONTAL SECTION

ALTERNATE JAMB DETAIL USING FRAME AND CASINGS

Fig. 115. In this window arrangement, the top sash is hinged to the bottom sash, which in turn is hinged to the building. A metal weatherstrip should be used between the sill and the lower sash. (Ohio Extension Bulletin 94.)

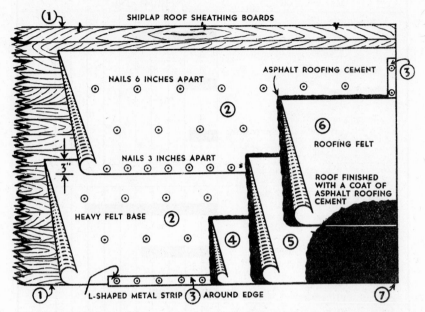

Fig. 116. This diagram shows the manner in which a built-up roof is applied to a board roof (1). The felt base (2) is applied to the sheathing and the edges are protected with a strip of metal. (3) Roofing (4, 5, 6) is applied and asphalt (7) is then applied over the entire roof. (Ohio Extension Bulletin 94).

Built-up roofing consists of several layers of roofing paper and asphalt over wood sheathing. The sheathing should be of tongue-and-groove boards to prevent the wind from blowing through from the underside to loosen the roof. The first weight of roofing paper which should weigh sixty pounds per square, is laid on the sheathing and nailed down tightly with the cap spacing nails. The other layers of roofing paper, varying from two to four in number, are laid horizontal with the sheathing and cemented down with hot asphalt (Fig. 116).

A built-up roof costs no more than a heavy-ply prepared roofing, but lasts much longer. Some poultrymen experience difficulty in applying the asphalt and for that reason prefer one of the other types of roofing.

Metal roofing. Metal roofing for poultry houses is increasing in popularity. It is durable and will last for years before an application of paint is necessary. The rafters need to be lathed to hold the roofing but do not need to be sheathed. This reduces the amount of lumber required.

Modern metal roofing has a double crimped edge. The crimps of one sheet fit over those of the next one. This prevents water from getting through the roof by capillary attraction. Metal roofs do not require a steep slope to prevent leakage. They may be used on shed-type as well as gable-type houses.

Metal roofs do not make the house hotter than other forms of roofs and do not cause condensation of moisture, if the ceiling is insulated.

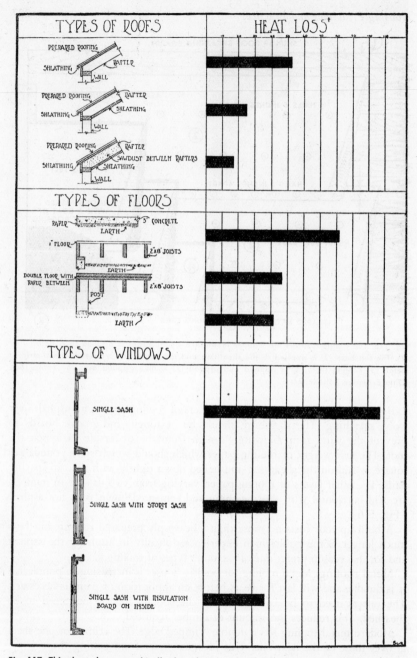

Fig. 117. This chart shows graphically the relative amount of heat loss through different types of ceiling or roof construction, through floors, and through different window arrangements. (Ohio Extension Bulletin 94.)

Fig. 118. A multiple-unit laying house showing straw ceiling insulation.

Insulation. The poultry house should be insulated for protection against both heat and cold. It is more important that the ceiling be insulated than the sidewalls. Most of the heat from the sun comes down through the roof and most of the heat lost from a house goes out through an uninsulated roof. Heat loss through different types of construction is shown in Figure 117. One of the types of insulation for a shed-type house is tongue-and-groove sheathing on the inside of the studding and rafters and the spaces between the inside and outside walls stuffed with shavings, dry sawdust, ground corncobs, or finely cut straw. Metal or hardware cloth may be tacked over the sheathing near the perches and other places where rats may find a place to stand to gnaw through the insulation board.

Metal roofing may be used in place of the tongue-and-groove sheathing to line the inside of the house for insulation purposes. It is durable, ratproof, does not need painting, and is easily cleaned.

Fiber insulation board, while having good insulation value, is unsatisfactory for insulating poultry houses. The material must be thick and soft to have good insulation value. When this type of material is used, it is picked by chickens, easily gnawed through by rats, punctured easily by cleaning equipment, and becomes warped when wet.

Straw loft insulation used in many Midwestern gable-roof poultry houses is satisfactory (Fig. 118). The straw is supported on wire netting and should be 12 to 18 inches deep. At the ends of the house above the straw, there should be ventilators to allow air to pass out from above the straw.

Permanent tongue-and-groove ceiling may be put in gable-roof houses; shavings or other insulation material may be put between the joists; a floor

Fig. 119. A well-equipped poultry house. Note the sanitary metal feeders and waterers, perches and dropping boards, nests, electric lights, insulation, partitions, and oil heater.

may be put on top of the joists; and the gable room space used for storage of litter, feed, or poultry equipment.

Laying-House Equipment

Good laying-house equipment is essential for satisfactory production. It should be simple in construction, movable, and easily cleaned. The perches, nests, feeders, and waterers are of particular importance (Fig. 119).

Perches. Perches are essential for chickens but not for waterfowl for prevention of soilage of feathers by the droppings. They should be as far away as possible from probable drafts.

The perch poles should be spaced about 14 or 15 inches apart and made of 2 x 2-inch material with rounded tops. Heavy 1½-inch poultry netting should be tacked on the underside of the perch section. This will prevent the birds from coming in contact with the droppings on the dropping boards or in the dropping pit. The perch sections should be in 5- to 6-foot sections and not more than 5 or 6 perches wide, for ease in handling. The rear perches should rest a little higher than those at the front, if they are arranged to be horizontal with the length of the house. This will encourage some of the birds that like to roost high to go to the back perches. Otherwise, all of the birds will want to roost on the front perches. Some poultrymen prefer to have the perch poles at right angles to the front of the house. The facing of the perches is of minor importance. Sufficient perch space should be provided to provide 8 to 10 inches per bird.

Dropping boards were formerly recommended, and are still widely used for holding the droppings that are voided during the night while the birds are on the roosts. They are usually built like tables and are about 2½ feet from the floor. The perches rest on short legs on the dropping boards and are about 4 to 6 inches above them. The dropping boards, by retaining nearly half of the droppings voided, aid in keeping the litter clean and living conditions more sanitary. The dropping boards and perches should not be more than three feet from the floor. Birds in heavy production that jump or fly on or off of high perches are more likely to rupture the egg-production organs. High perches may be one factor responsible for an unusual number of blood spots, or eggs loose in the body cavity.

Dropping pits (Fig. 120) are replacing dropping boards in many poultry houses because they have several advantages. Dropping pits are easier and cheaper to construct than dropping boards. The same perches are used in

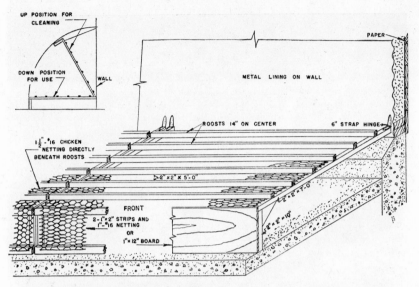

Fig. 120. Details for roosts and dropping pit. (Ohio Extension Bulletin 94.)

both cases. In case of the pits, the droppings are allowed to fall on litter on the floor beneath the perches. The perches are about 18 inches from the floor at the rear and about 12 inches at the front. The front of the perch section rests on a board which keeps the birds from getting in the pit beneath the perches. The dropping pits need not be cleaned as often as dropping boards. Dropping pit perches are lower than those with dropping boards. There is less danger of rupture or bruising the feet in getting on and off of the perches. Trouble encountered in teaching newly housed pullets to roost is eliminated by the use of low dropping-pit perches. At first thought, one would expect dropping pits to take up too much valuable floor space. This is not the case because the birds spend much of the time during the day on the perches, when they are low. The dropping pits act much like a section of the pen with a wire floor. Since birds spend much of the time during the day over the dropping pits, a bigger percentage of the droppings is collected in the pit and the litter remains clean for a longer period.

Nests. Nests should be roomy, movable, easily cleaned, cool and well ventilated, dark, and conveniently located.

Nests are usually constructed 14 inches square, 6 inches deep, and with about 15 inches head room. All-metal nests are preferred to wood nests because of ease of cleaning and less chance of becoming infested by mites. The entire battery of nests should be movable for convenience in cleaning.

One nest should be provided for every five or six hens. In case the birds are trap-nested, one nest should be available for every two or three birds. Dark nests are desirable because birds prefer seclusion when laying. They result in less scratching in the nest, less egg breakage, and less egg eating.

Fig. 121. A community nest. The front part of the lid is hinged for ease of gathering the eggs.

Batteries of nests may be placed against the end walls or partitions and along the posts supporting the roof in the center of the house.

Trap nests differ from regular nests in that they are provided with trap doors by which birds shut themselves in when they enter. Trap nests are essential on poultry-breeding farms.

The large type community nest is becoming widely used in many sections. While the nests seem large, they actually occupy less space in the laying house because fewer nests are required to provide ample nesting space.

The two-section nest shown in Fig. 121 is 8 feet long, 2 feet wide, 14 inches high in front, and 30 inches high in back. The entrance for the birds is 8 inches square. The lid is made 16 inches wide and can be hinged with strap hinges. It will accommodate 80 to 100 birds.

The floor of the nest can be hinged so it will drop for easy cleaning, or the bottom can be made separate and the nest set on the floor. The nest can be fastened to the wall or supported as the one shown in Fig. 121.

The perch should extend beyond the front of the nest 10 to 12 inches.

For convenience of the caretaker, the nest should be placed 18 to 20 inches above the floor.

Wall feed bins. Enough feed is wasted on many farms, by rats and mice tearing open sacks, to pay for enough lumber to construct one or two feed bins in the laying house.

COURTESY OHIO AGRICULTURAL EXTENSION SERVICE

Fig. 122. A wall feed bin in the poultry house saves space, labor, and feed.

If an opening is provided on the outside wall, the bin can be filled from a truck or trailer without going into the laying house.

The bin need not be built more than 18 inches wide, and the bottom should be sloped so the front of the bin is 18 inches lower than the back side of the bin. This will allow more of the feed to run out the slide gates and also facilitate complete removal of all feed in the bin.

A wall bin that will hold 2 or 3 tons of feed can be supported on the wall and ceiling joist without floor supports. It does not take up floor space or hinder in cleaning the house (Fig. 122).

Feeders. The feeders should be easy to fill, easy to clean, built to avoid waste, so arranged that the fowls cannot roost on them, high enough that

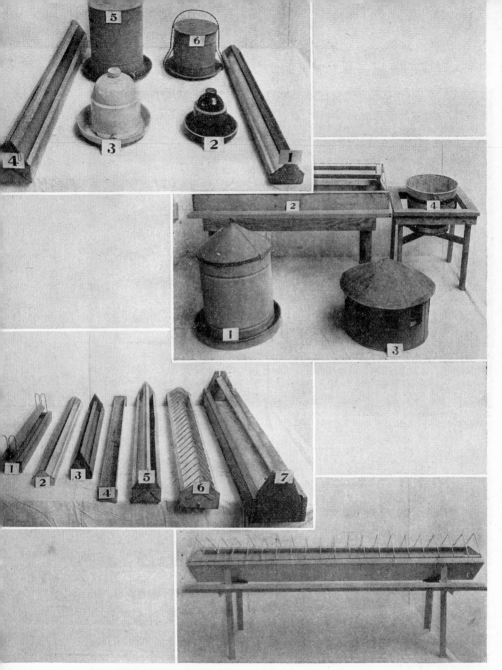

Fig. 123. The use of equipment which keeps the birds out of the feed and water will reduce contamination by droppings, and therefore lessen the spread of bacterial and parasitic diseases. Upper, 2, 3, 5, and 6 in left half and 1 on right half, drinking vessels for small chicks; 3 and 4 in right half, drinking vessels for pullets; 1 and 4, left half, feed hoppers for chicks; 2 right half, feed hopper for mature birds. Lower, 1 to 4, mash hoppers for small chicks; 5 to 7, mash hoppers for pullets. Right, sanitary hopper for mature birds.

Fig. 124. Automatic poultry feeder.

the birds cannot scratch litter in them, and constructed in such a manner that as long as they contain any feed at all, the fowls will be able to reach it.

Sufficient feeders should be available so that there will be one foot of eating space for every three or four birds. More hopper space is recommended now than in former years because both the grain and mash are hopper fed, whereas in former years the scratch grain was fed in the litter. Several different styles of feeders are shown in Figure 123. All metal feeders that slope inward toward the bottom are more desirable than rectangular, boxlike wooden feeders.

A section of the feed hopper may be partitioned for oyster shells or other grit. It is advantageous to have the source of calcium for eggshell formation near the feed hopper.

Automatic feeders (Fig. 124) are now in use in some large broiler and egg-laying houses. They save labor. The feed is moved from a feed bin by a moving belt in a long trough.

Watering devices. Satisfactory watering devices should keep the water clean, be available and easily cleaned, and prevent spillage of water around the vessels.

A hundred hens will drink from three to six gallons of water or milk per day, depending on size of birds, rate of production, salt content of the ration, and weather conditions. Therefore, two or three water buckets or vessels of

Fig. 125. Sanitary drinking vessel and stand. The overflow is carried away in the tile that supports the vessel.

equivalent capacity should be provided for each hundred hens. A rack (Fig. 123) should be provided for holding the bucket, in order that the bird may stand on it and drink until the vessel is empty. Various forms of covers are provided for open pans and crocks to keep birds out of them. Drinking fountains are provided for young chicks, and in some cases for older birds as well (Fig. 125). Troughs with automatic float valves and other automatic watering devices are used on commercial farms where large numbers of birds are kept and running water is available.

Lights. Artificial lights are used in laying houses to stimulate fall production of hens, to bring late- or slow-maturing pullets into production, and to delay or hasten birds through the molt.

About a forty-watt bulb to a pen that will accommodate fifty to one hundred birds is sufficient. The light is usually placed in the center of the pen and over the feeders and water stands. The use of a broad, flatlike reflector will throw more of the light toward the floor and on the birds.

Morning, evening or all-night lights are satisfactory. Morning lights are most generally used. Some automatic device is used for turning on the lights about 3:00 or 4:00 A.M. A simple home-made device attached to an alarm clock may be used for this purpose (Fig. 126).

Catching equipment. Catching coops, hurdles, and catching hooks are valuable equipment for the poultry farm. The birds may be driven into one

Fig. 126. A homemade device for turning on the electric lights in the laying house.

end of the house with the aid of wire frame hurdles and on into rows of catching coops lined up end to end with the doors open at both ends. The birds may be caught with these aids with a minimum of labor and with little fright or injury to the birds. Collapsible, bottomless wire coops are of particular value to hatcherymen for culling and blood-testing work. A catching hook and coop (Fig. 127) are handy devices for catching birds.

Broody coop. A broody coop with a wire bottom, located at one end of the dropping boards or dropping pit, is useful for holding broody birds or those that have been injured. Less labor is involved in removing and caring for broody or injured birds if they can be cared for in the pens where they belong. This is especially true if the birds are on some kind of an experimental test.

Cleaning equipment. Some useful tools for cleaning purposes include shovels, brooms, scrapers, etc.

Spray pump. A spray pump is satisfactory for applying disinfectant after a house or equipment has been thoroughly cleaned.

Fig. 127. Catching coop and hook. The birds may be driven out through the chicken door into the catching coop.

Incinerator. An incinerator should be conveniently located for burning dead or diseased birds.

Manure shed. A screened-in manure shed should be available for holding droppings or litter that cannot be disposed of at once. Manure piles are breeding places for flies. These and other insects are carriers of disease.

Care of the House

The house must be carefully managed if satisfactory results are to be obtained. A good house and equipment are only the first steps toward successful poultry production. Essential everyday poultry house management practices to be carried out include ventilation, temperature control, and sanitation.

Ventilation of the poultry house. The house may be ventilated by means of the windows and without the aid of special ventilators.

In summer both the front and back windows should be kept wide open in order to secure cross ventilation. The doors in the ends of the building should also be left open, and wire or screen-covered doors used to keep the birds confined.

In the fall and spring, when weather conditions are quite changeable, the rear windows or ventilators and the end doors should be kept closed. Ventilation should be provided through the top sash of the windows. These should be opened back or folded down, depending on the season of the year. Most of the troubles from faulty ventilation start in the fall. The house is often filled to capacity and left wide open with cross ventilation. If a cold, chilly storm comes along, the birds are exposed to drafts and may contract a cold developing into bronchitis or roup. Once a few of the weaker birds have become ill, the trouble is easily spread to others in the flock. Correcting the ventilation after the birds have been exposed is too late to prevent the onset of the trouble. Weak, parasitized, or poorly nourished birds are most likely to be affected first.

In the winter the windows should be adjusted to take advantage of all the outside temperature possible. A thermometer should be kept outside of the house as well as inside. When the outside temperature goes above the inside temperature during the day, the upper sash of the front windows should be opened. When the outside temperature starts to drop, the windows should be closed to retain as much heat as possible. During thawing weather, the house will become quite wet unless the windows are opened. If the temperature cannot be kept above freezing in the house, when the building is tightly constructed, the windows should never be completely closed. The more moist exhaled air kept in the house when the temperature is below freezing, the greater the danger of frozen combs and wattles.

Temperature control in the house. Extremes of temperature should be avoided in the house, as far as possible, through practical means. Insulation of the house and cross ventilation will help prevent extreme heat in the pens in summer.

Insulation, elemination of high ceilings or unnecessary air spaces, keeping the house filled to capacity, and proper window ventilation will help keep the inside temperature above that of the outside temperature in winter. In spite of all these practices, the temperature in the house will drop below freezing, at least a few times during the winter, in most of the central and northern states. This will interfere with egg production and in the case of breeders will result in lower fertility and hatchability.

A coal, wood, or oil brooder stove may be used in the laying house during cold winter weather. One stove will provide sufficient heat to keep the temperature from going below freezing in a well-insulated pen that will accommodate five hundred to one thousand birds. There are not many days that supplementary heat will be needed. The use of a little heat will not only make the birds more comfortable but will aid in drying out the house.

Sanitation. Sanitation should be practiced every day in the year. The larger the farm and the more birds in a pen, the more rigidly it should be enforced. Every sick or injured bird should be removed as soon as noticed and put in a separate small building, used as a hospital.

Litter used on the floor, stirred every few days, and the addition of a little new litter from time to time will aid in keeping the floor warm and dry. The accumulated built-up litter provides a place for the synthesis of nutritional factors.

Wire floors may be used in the absence of litter. However, a more complete ration must be fed when birds are kept on wire than when they are kept on litter.

The droppings and litter should be removed as often as necessary to prevent wet, dirty, foul-smelling conditions in the house. They should be removed at once to some distant part of the farm where chickens will not range. If this is impractical, they should be stored in a screened-in manure shed.

The feeders and waterers should be kept clean and partly filled at all times.

Yards

Good range is desirable for healthy birds, good egg production and hatchability, and reduced feed costs. However, the use of range requires that the birds be kept in small groups and in small houses scattered over the farm. This adds to the cost of production through the necessity for land and increased housing and labor costs. Poultrymen find that for commercial egg production, at least, it is more economical to keep the layers in confinement.

Alternate yarding may be used with small groups of birds in small houses. While the birds are ranged in one yard, the other one may be plowed and planted with a cover crop. One yard should extend out on one side of the house and the other one on the opposite side. The yards should be the width of the house and extend fifty to one hundred feet from it. Even with a two-yard system, the vegetation soon disappears near the house and the yard becomes dirty.

Cindered yards may be used to provide sunlight and fresh air without the necessity for range (Fig. 128). They may be used in front of long multiple-unit houses where attempts to supply range would be impractical. They may also be used where the henhouse is in the barnyard with no ground for poultry yards. The cindered yards should extend along the entire front of the house and six to ten feet out from it.

Fencing the old birds off of the range where young chicks or turkeys are to be ranged is an absolute necessity. The old birds are often carriers of parasites, coccidia, and bacterial diseases to which the young stock is very susceptible. A five-foot wire fence is desirable. The large wing feathers on one wing may be clipped to prevent the birds from flying out of the yards.

Laying Batteries

Laying batteries have been advocated in recent years, principally by battery manufacturers. The claims are made that more birds can be housed in a given space, that mortality will be less, egg production better, and labor cost lower.

Housing requirements. Houses for laying batteries need to be of better construction than for birds kept on the floor. More attention needs to be paid to the ventilation and heating of a house which contains laying batteries. The birds are confined to small compartments and are unable to move about to get away from drafts and to keep warm.

By the use of batteries, it is possible to keep from two to three times as many birds in a given floor space. The better type of house construction

Fig. 128. Cindered yards provide fresh air and sunshine where clean range is not available.

required and the cost of batteries add to the housing cost until the actual cost per bird in batteries or on the floor is very little different.

Management of caged layers. Caged layers may be fed whole grains, mash, and oyster shells scattered along in troughs in front of them. They may pick out what they need. Automatic watering devices are generally installed so that a small stream of water is always passing along in the water trough. A layer of paper is generally used in place of dropping pans under the birds. These are pulled out and removed when sufficient manure has collected on them. When eggs are laid, they roll to the front of the cage, where they may be removed.

Losses from cannibalism are prevented by keeping layers in cages. However, the total mortality from all causes is about the same among caged layers and those kept on the floor. It is difficult to keep the laying batteries and the room in which they are kept, clean.

REVIEW QUESTIONS

1. Why house poultry?
2. What seasonal conditions should be attempted in the laying house?
3. A house 20′ x 30′ will accommodate how many laying hens?
4. What are the principal ill effects of overcrowding?
5. What are the advantages and disadvantages of keeping small numbers of birds in a pen?
6. What diseases are likely to develop as a result of birds being exposed to drafts?
7. Should the house be warmer during the day or night? Why?
8. What are the sources of moisture that cause damp houses?

9. What are the advantages of using artificial heat in laying houses?
10. What are the advantages and disadvantages of reducing the amount of daylight in poultry houses?
11. Which direction should the house face? Why?
12. What type of house is easiest to construct?
13. Why are monitor-type houses objectionable?
14. What should be the composition of a concrete mixture for poultry house floors?
15. How are concrete floors constructed to prevent the capillary rise of water through them?
16. What is one of the best types of ceiling insulation?
17. How many feet of perch space are needed for one hundred hens?
18. Why are dropping pits better than dropping boards?
19. How many nests should be provided for five hundred hens?
20. How many feet of eating space should be provided for one hundred hens?
21. Describe an inexpensive practical means of heating a poultry house.
22. What are some of the means used to maintain a satisfactory temperature in the house without the use of supplementary heat?
23. What are the advantages and disadvantages of providing range for layers?
24. What are the advantages and disadvantages of laying batteries?

REFERENCES

ASHBY, W., MILLER, T. A. H., EDICK, G. L., AND LEE, A. R.: FUNCTIONAL REQUIREMENTS IN DESIGNING LAYING HOUSES FOR POULTRY. U. S. D. A. Circ. 738. 1945.

BELTON, H. L., AND ASMUNDSON, V. S.: POULTRY HOUSES AND EQUIPMENT. Calif. Sta. Bul. 476. 1943.

BENTLEY, M. R., AND MARTIN, T.: POULTRY HOUSES FOR TEXAS. Tex. Bul. B–65. 1947.

BERRY, L. N.: THE CAGE SYSTEM FOR MANAGING LAYING HENS. N. M. Sta. Bul. 276. 1941.

BRESSLER, G. O., SPRAGUE, D. C., AND MOWERY, A. S.: AUTOMATIC FEEDING OF POULTRY. Pa. Agr. Expt. Sta. Bul. No. 522. 1950.

BRUCKNER, J. H.: THE EFFECT OF ENVIRONMENTAL CONDITIONS ON WINTER EGG PRODUCTION. Poultry Sci., 15: 417–418. 1936.

CARTER, D. G., AND FASTER, W. A.: FARM BUILDINGS, 3rd ed. John Wiley & Sons, Inc., New York. 1941.

CHARLES, T. B., TEPPER, A. E., ACKERMAN, B. J., FRENCH, B. J., DURGIN, R. C., AND HALPIN, R. B.: THE PROBLEM OF MOISTURE IN POULTRY HOUSE LITTER. N. H. Sta. Bul. 338. 1942.

CHRISTOPHER, R. C., AND KING, D. F.: TYPES OF HOUSES FOR LAYING HENS. Ala. Sta. Circ. 88. 1943.

COLBY, H. N.: BURGLAR-PROOFING THE FARM. N. H. Ext. Circ. 171. 1935.

COONEY, W. T., HOLMES, C. E., HARPER, J. A., AND COSBY, H. E.: BATTERY AND FLOOR MANAGEMENT PRACTICES FOR PULLETS AND HENS. Poultry Sci., 24: 310–313. 1945.

DOBIE, J. B., CARVER, J. S., AND ROBERTS, JUNE: POULTRY LIGHTING FOR EGG PRODUCTION. Wash. Bul. 471. 1946.

FUNK, E. M.: POULTRY HOUSING CONDITIONS IN MISSOURI. Mo. Sta. Bul. 431. 1941.

HEYWANG, B. W., AND JULL, M. A.: THE HOUSELESS METHOD OF POULTRY KEEPING. Poultry Sci., 10: 32–36. 1930.

HINDS, H. B.: ENVIRONMENTAL FACTORS AND THEIR EFFECT ON THE NATURAL EGG CYCLE. Ariz. Bul. 222. 1949.

HOFFMAN, E., AND TOMHAVE, A. E.: A RELATIONSHIP OF SQUARE FEET OF FLOOR SPACE PER BIRD AND EGG PRODUCTION. Poultry Sci., 24: 89–90. 1945.

JEFFERSON, C. H., AND DAVIDSON, J. A.: PORTABLE BROODER HOUSES FOR MICHIGAN. Mich. Ext. Bul. 236. 1942.

JONES, R. E.: THE CONNECTICUT 24' x 24' POULTRY HOUSE. Conn. Sta. Bul. 266. 1938.

KENNARD, D. C., AND CHAMBERLAIN, V. D.: TIME AND LABOR-SAVING EQUIPMENT FOR THE LAYING HOUSE. Ohio Spec. Circ. 51. 1942.

LEE, C. E., HAMILTON, S. W., HENRY, C. L., AND CALLANAN, M. E.: THE EFFECT OF SUPPLEMENTARY HEAT ON EGG PRODUCTION, FEED CONSUMPTION, AMOUNT OF LITTER REQUIRED, AND NET FLOCK INCOME. Poultry Sci., 16: 267–273. 1937.

MARTIN, TED, AND BENTLEY, M. R.: POULTRY YARD EQUIPMENT. Tex. Ext. Bul. 71. 1947.

MEHRHOF, N. R., AND ROGERS, FRAZIER: POULTRY HOUSES AND EQUIPMENT. Fla. Sta. Bul. 126. 1945.

MITCHELL, H. H., AND HAINES, W. T.: THE CRITICAL TEMPERATURE OF THE CHICKEN. Jour. Agr. Res., 34: 549–557. 1927.

MITCHELL, H. H., AND KELLEY, M. A. R.: ESTIMATED DATA ON THE ENERGY, GASEOUS, AND WATER METABOLISM FOR USE IN PLANNING THE VENTILATION OF POULTRY HOUSES. Jour. Agr. Res., 47: 735–748. 1934.

MODERN POULTRY HOUSES. Portland Cement Assoc., Chicago.

MOORE, J. M., AND BELL, A. J.: LAYING HOUSES FOR MICHIGAN. Mich. Ext. Bul. 233. 1941.

MOORE, O. K., AND MEHRHOF, N. R.: PERIODIC INCREASE IN LIGHTING VERSUS CONTINUOUS LIGHTING. Fla. Bul. 420. 1946.

MOWERY, A. S., SPRAGUE, D. C., AND BRESSLER, G. O.: PENN STATE AUTOMATIC POULTRY FEEDER. Prog. Rpt. No. 17. 1949. Pennsylvania State College, School of Agriculture.

MOYER, D. D., AND BLICKLE, J. D.: POULTRY HOUSING IN OHIO. Ohio Ext. Bul. 303. 1949.

MUSSEHL, F. E., AND OLSON, E. A.: A STANDARD POULTRY-LAYING HOUSE. Neb. Sta. Ext. Circ. 1419. 1948.

OTIS, C. K., AND WHITE, H. B.: CONDITIONS IN A TWO-STORY INSULATED POULTRY HOUSE. Agr. Engin., 24: 407–411. 1943.

PATTY, R. L., AND LARSEN, L. F.: NEW HARD-SURFACED FLOORS FOR THE FARM POULTRY HOUSE. S. D. Sta. Circ. 42. 1943.

POLK, H. D.: WATERING EQUIPMENT FOR POULTRY. Miss. Sta. Circ. 119. 1944.

POULTRY COMMITTEE OF RUTGERS UNIVERSITY FARM BUILDINGS INSTITUTE. POULTRY HOUSE REQUIREMENTS. N. J. Bul. 732. 1947.

POULTRY COUNCIL OF THE STATE COLLEGE OF WASHINGTON: LAYING CAGES FOR CHICKENS. Wash. Ext. Bul. 383. 1949.

POULTRY COUNCIL OF THE STATE COLLEGE OF WASHINGTON. LAYING HOUSE EQUIPMENT. Wash. Ext. Bul. 341. 1949.

PROMERSBERGER, W. J.: INSULATING FARM BUILDINGS. N. D. Sta. Bul. 325. 1943.

REED, F. D., AND HUBER, M. G.: A TWO-STORY LAYING HOUSE FOR MAINE. Me. Sta. Bul. 257. 1939.

SINNARD, H. R., GRIEBELER, W. L., AND BENNION, N. L.: TWO-STORY POULTRY HOUSE. Ore. Sta. Circ. 174. 1948.

SKELTON, R. R.: CEMENT-SAWDUST CONCRETE FOR POULTRY HOUSE AND DAIRY BARN FLOORS. N. H. Ext. Circ. 217. 1938.

THOMPSON, R. B.: OKLAHOMA HOUSES FOR LAYING HENS. Okla. Sta. Bul. B–253. 1942.

CHAPTER 9 |||||||||||||||||||||||||||||||||||||||||||||||||||||||||||||||||

Feeding Principles

▼

The primary purpose in keeping poultry is to transform farm feedstuffs into meat and eggs. The fowl may be compared to a factory. Feedstuffs, such as corn, meat scraps, grass, and oyster shells, are the raw materials. Meat and eggs are the manufactured products. The manager of the factory is the poultry feeder. The efficiency of the factory will depend upon (1) suitability for purpose, or type of bird; (2) quality of construction, or breeding of bird; (3) working conditions in factory, or health of bird; (4) raw materials, or the feedstuffs fed; and (5) management, or feeding and care provided by the feeder.

Nutrients

The body of the fowl, eggs, and feedstuffs are composed of various combinations of chemical compounds known as nutrients. They are classified according to physical, chemical, and biological properties into six general groups: water, carbohydrates, fats, proteins, minerals, and vitamins (Table 46). There is some similarity between the occurrence of nutrients in feedstuffs and their occurrence in the body of the fowl or in eggs. For instance, the vitamin D content of the egg depends on the vitamin D content of the ration. Most of the feedstuffs, however, are reduced to simpler substances in the body by processes of digestion and reassembled in different forms as body tissues and eggs.

Water. Water is the only one of the six nutrients that is a definite compound. It is composed of two atoms of hydrogen and one of oxygen (H_2O).

Water plays a highly important part in plant and animal life. It is a chemical constituent of feedstuffs, fowls, and eggs (Table 1, Appendix). Water constitutes from 55 to 78 per cent of the live weight of chickens. Young birds, like young plants, have higher moisture content than older ones. Water softens and hydrolizes feed in the processes of digestion. As an important constituent of blood and lymph, water carries digested food to all parts of the body and waste products to the points of elimination. Water controls body temperature by absorbing the heat of cell reactions and by vaporizing moisture for excretion by way of the air sacs and lungs. It also serves as a lubricant for joints, muscles, and other body tissues.

245

Table 46

Nutrients	Chief Functions for Poultry	Chief Sources for Poultry
Water	Digestion, carrier of food and waste products, and regulator of body temperature	Water, liquid milk, and young green grass
Carbohydrates	Heat, energy, and fat production	Cereal grains and grain by-products
Fats	Reserve supply of heat and energy	Cereal grains and grain by-products
Proteins	Growth and repair of body tissues, egg formation, and heat, energy, and fat production	Milk, meat scraps, fish meal, soybean meal, corn gluten meal, and cottonseed meal
Minerals	Skeleton formation, egg production, and regulation of body neutrality	Meat scraps, fish meal, milk, bone meal, oyster shells, limestone, and salt
Vitamin A	Growth; health of eye nerves, and respiratory epithelium; prevention of nutritional roup, and xerophthalmia	Green grass, dehydrated alfalfa meal, some fish oils, corn gluten meal, and yellow corn
Thiamin (B₁)	Appetite, digestion, health of nerves, and prevention of polyneuritis	Green grass, alfalfa meal, whole grains, wheat by-products, and milk by-products
Vitamin D	Mineral assimilation; egg production; hatchability; and prevention of rickets, cracked breastbones, and thin eggshells	Sunshine, fish oils, irradiated animal sterols and yeast, and ultraviolet light
Vitamin E	Health of reproductive organs and for fertility and hatchability	Green grass, alfalfa meal, whole grains, and wheat by-products
Riboflavin (B₂ or G)	Growth, hatchability, and prevention of curled toe paralysis	Green grass, alfalfa meal, milk by-products, some fish meals, distillers' solubles, and yeast
Pantothenic Acid	Growth, hatchability, health of skin, and prevention of chick dermatitis	Green grass, alfalfa meal, milk products, distillers' solubles, and yeast
Choline	Growth, bone development, egg production, and prevention of perosis	Grains, wheat by-products, soybean meal, milk products, meat scraps, and fish meal
Vitamin B₁₂	Growth and hatchability	Fish meal and solubles, meat scraps, milk, and used or built-up poultry litter and fermentation products.

* Also, see pages 247–56.

Water generally constitutes from 5 to 12 per cent of air-dried grains and other feedstuffs fed to poultry. It is also formed in the body as an end product of the oxidation or burning of digested food (Fig. 129). These two sources supply only a small fraction of the water needed by a bird for its body processes. Therefore, a liberal quantity of water or liquid milk, which is about 90 per cent water, should be kept before poultry at all times.

The water or moisture content of a feedstuff or other material is determined by drying a weighed sample of the product and calculating the loss in weight.

Carbohydrates. Carbohydrates are composed of carbon, hydrogen, and oxygen, with the latter two nearly always occurring in the same proportion as in water. They occur in very small amounts in animals and poultry products. Carbohydrates constitute about 75 per cent of the dry weight of plants and grains (Table 1, Appendix). Therefore, they make up a large part of poultry rations.

The plant manufactures carbohydrates in its leaves from water brought from its roots and carbon dioxide taken from the air. Simple carbohydrates, such as glucose ($C_6H_{12}O_6$), are formed into more complex ones, such as starch ($C_6H_{10}O_5$)X and cellulose. Energy from sunlight is stored up in the carbohydrates. It is liberated when carbohydrates are eaten, digested, and oxidized in body tissues.

Carbohydrates serve as a source of heat and energy in the animal body. A surplus taken into the body may be transformed into fat and stored as a reserve supply of heat and energy (Fig. 129).

Simple sugars consist of the hexoses, or six-carbon sugars ($C_6H_{12}O_6$), and the pentoses, or five-carbon sugars ($C_5H_{10}O_5$). *Glucose, fructose,* and *galactose* are the chief hexose sugars found in plants. Glucose is of special importance in animal nutrition, for it is the chief end product of the digestion of more complex carbohydrates and the sugar found in the blood. The pentoses are constituents of more complex carbohydrates.

Compound sugars consist of two or more molecules of simple sugars. *Sucrose* ($C_{12}H_{22}O_{11}$) is one of the most common of these sugars. It consists of a molecule of glucose and one of fructose. Sucrose is found in sugar cane and sugar beets. *Lactose* is composed of a molecule of galactose, and one of glucose. It is the sugar in the milk of all mammals. *Maltose* consists of two molecules of glucose. It is formed from starch in the germination of seeds and in digestion by animals.

Starch ($C_6H_{10}O_5$)$_x$ consists of many molecules of glucose. It is stored in the seeds and tubers of plants as a reserve food supply. Starch is, therefore, an important source of energy in the feed of farm animals. The starch grains in different plant products differ in size and shape. An examination of starch grains under the microscope can be used to determine their source. This is often a useful method of detecting adulteration in feeds. Starch is not found in the tissues of animals. *Glycogen,* a reserve supply of carbohydrates, somewhat resembling starch, is stored in the liver and muscles of the body.

Fiber, or cellulose, is the woody component of the cell walls of plants. It is more complex than starch. Fiber is poorly digested by animals. It is

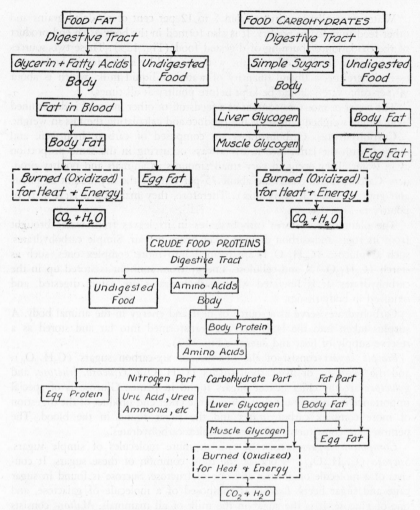

Fig. 129. The digestion and metabolism of nutrients by the fowl. (California Station Bulletin 417.)

determined by boiling a dry, fat-free sample in dilute acid, washing free of acid, boiling in dilute alkali, and washing. The dry solid residue remaining after all soluble material has been washed out is termed crude fiber.

Nitrogen-free extract consists of the digestible carbohydrate portion of a feed. It includes the sugars, starches, and soluble portion of the more complex carbohydrates. The total weight of the feedstuff minus the sum of the moisture, ash, crude protein, fiber, and fat is the nitrogen-free extract.

Fats. Fats are composed of the same elements as are found in carbohydrates, but in different proportions. There is much more carbon in proportion to oxygen in fats (stearin $C_{57}H_{110}O_6$) than in carbohydrates. When fats are oxidized or burned, the large amount of energy stored up with the carbon is released. Fats have about 2.25 times the heat-production value of carbohydrates. Fats serve as a reserve supply of heat and energy. Subcutaneous fat serves as a body insulator.

Fats constitute about 17 per cent of the live weight of the fowl and 10 per cent of the whole egg. The germs of grains and seeds are also rich in fat or oil content (Table 1, Appendix). Fats are composed of an alcohol (glycerin) and fatty acids. They are formed from carbohydrates in plants. Some fats (tallow, for instance) are quite firm and hard because of their high molecular weight and saturated fatty acids. Others, like chicken fat, are oily because of their lower molecular weight and unsaturated fatty acids.

Ether extract, or crude fat, includes not only the true fats, but all related plant or animal substances soluble in ether or other fat solvents. It is determined by extracting a dry sample with ether. The loss in weight of the product after extraction is the ether extract. It includes fats, sterols, carotenes, chlorophyll, phospholipids, waxes, and essential oils.

Sterols are complex alcohols found in very small amounts in plants and animals. *Ergosterol* is a plant sterol which assumes vitamin D properties when irradiated with ultraviolet light rays (p. 254). *Cholesterol* is an animal sterol found in the skin, nerves, fat, and blood. It probably aids in transporting digested fat from one part of the body to another. When irradiated, it assumes vitamin D properties (p. 254).

Carotene and related pigments are colored substances found in traces in plants and animals. Carotene is transformed into vitamin A in the body (p. 252). It is the yellow coloring found in yellow corn, carrots, sweet potatoes, and butter fat. Carotene is also supplied by green-colored parts of plants where its yellow color is hidden by the green chlorophyll.

Chlorophyll is the green-colored substance found in all green plants. It is necessary for the formation of carbohydrates in the leaves of plants.

Phospholipids are fats containing phosphoric acid and nitrogenous groups in their molecules. They are vital parts of living protoplasm. *Lecithin* is found in egg yolk, blood, and the liver. Other phospholipids are found in the brain and other nervous tissue.

Waxes form a coating or bloom on the surface of plants for protection against weather.

Essential oils give the plants their characteristic odors and tastes.

Proteins. Proteins are composed of carbon, hydrogen, oxygen, and nitrogen. Some of them also contain iron, phosphorus, and sulphur. Proteins are widely distributed in both plants and animals (Table 1, Appendix). They form a part of the protoplasm and nuclei of cells and are, therefore, essential to life. In plants the greater part of the proteins are concentrated in the seeds and leaves. Proteins constitute a large part of the muscles, internal organs, cartilages, skin, feathers, beak, scales, and toenails. They also occur in blood, nerve tissue, and bone. The chick contains about 15 per cent protein, the hen 25 per cent, and the whole egg 12 per cent.

Proteins are used for growth and repair of tissues. An excess protein eaten in the ration may be de-amized and the carbohydrate portion used for heat and energy or transformed into fat (Fig. 129).

Nitrates and other minerals entering the plant through the roots are combined with the carbohydrates formed in the leaves to produce nitrogenous products, including amids, amino acids, and proteins.

Animals manufacture the proteins characteristic of their own tissues, but in general they cannot build them up from simple inorganic substances such as suffice for plants. They must depend upon the digestion products obtained from the proteins of their feed.

Proteins are large complex molecules. They are insoluble in all fat solvents. Proteins differ in their solubilities in water, salt solutions, and alcohol. These differences play a considerable part in their classification.

Amids are simple nonprotein nitrogenous products found in growing plants. They are used in making amino acids. Amids cannot be substituted for proteins in the ration, but they may be used for heat and energy purposes.

Amino acids are the building stones for proteins. The twenty-three or more known amino acids may be combined in various ways to produce many proteins, as the letters of the alphabet may be used to form innumerable words. Most of the amino acids needed in the body can be made from nitrogen digestion products in the food.

Arginine, histidine, isoleucine, leucine, lysine, methionine, phenylalanine, threonine, tryptophan, and valene are essential amino acids. They must be supplied by proteins fed in the ration. Therefore, care is needed in the selection of feedstuffs to supply the proper kind and amounts of the essential amino acids. The occurrence of some of the amino acids in feedstuffs is shown in Table 47.

Enzymes are protein-like substances which aid in the digestion of foods. They occur in small amounts in plant products and are secreted in the digestive juices of animals. Amylase digests carbohydrates, lipase acts on fats, and pepsin and trypsin digest proteins.

Crude protein is the nitrogen content of a product × 6.25. This factor is used because proteins contain approximately 16 per cent nitrogen.

Minerals. Minerals, frequently referred to as ash, are essential constituents of both plants and animals. The ash content of plant products varies from less than 1 per cent in polished rice to more than 30 per cent in kelp. It constitutes 3 to 4 per cent of the live weight of the fowl and about 10 per cent of the egg.

Minerals are used for bone and egg formation, digestion, maintenance of body neutrality, respiration, and elasticity and irritability of muscles and nerves.

Calcium is needed for bone and eggshell formation, and for muscle action. *Phosphorus* is a constituent of bones, egg yolk, nerves, and other tissues. In the form of phosphates in the blood and other body tissues, it regulates body neutrality. *Iron* is needed for hemoglobin formation in the blood. In this combination, it aids in carrying oxygen from the lungs to the body tissues and cells and carbon dioxide from them to the lungs. *Sulphur* is a constituent of

Table 47

THE PRINCIPAL ESSENTIAL AMINO ACIDS REQUIRED BY CHICKS AND THEIR OCCURRENCE IN THE FEEDSTUFFS COMMONLY FED TO POULTRY

OBSERVATION	ESSENTIAL AMINO ACIDS					
	Arginine	Lysine	Methionine	Cystine	Trypto-phane	Glycine
Required * for chick growth (Per cent of total protein fed)............	4.5	4.5	2.5	1.5	1.0	4.0
Supplied † by the protein in:						
Fish meal.............	155 ‡	127	128	73	120	100
Fish solubles (cond.)....	96	109	75	39	35	
Meat scrap............	155	113	80	67	70	100
Skim milk.............	89	167	112	80	130	13
Soybean meal.........	129	149	84	100	120	100
Cottonseed meal.......	164	60	84	133	110	132
Peanut meal..........	220	67	68	107	90	140
Sesame meal..........	193	62	136	87	150	230
Sunflower seed meal....	182	85	156	107	130	100
Linseed meal..........	138	55	92	127	140	
Yeast.................	96	133	72	87	110	
Alfalfa...............	147	111	92	120	220	
Corn.................	89	56	92	73	60	100
Wheat...............	62	60	80	87	110	180
Wheat bran...........	133	74	52	73	100	
Oats.................	129	74	92	100	120	
Barley...............	107	40	84	120	80	

* Gran. Flour and Feed. 46:No. 2. 1945.
† Almquist. Flour and Feed. 46:No. 3. 1945.
‡ 100 is considered adequate. Numbers below 100 indicate deficiencies and those above 100 indicate amounts greater than required.

essential amino acids found in the egg. *Sodium* and *potassium* are constituents of phosphates in the blood, which prevent excess acidity or alkalinity. They are also constituents of the bile and other body fluids. *Chlorine* is a constituent of the hydrochloric acid, secreted in the gastric juice, for dissolving minerals and digesting proteins. *Iodine* is a constituent of the thyroid. *Magnesium* and *manganese* are constituents of bones. *Copper* acts as a catalyst for hemoglobin formation. Traces of boron, zinc, and other mineral elements may also have some function in plant and animal life.

The mineral or ash content of a product is determined by burning a weighed sample. The residue is the ash. It does not give needed information regarding the kind, quantity, or form of the mineral elements present. By long, laborious, and expensive methods it is possible to determine the kind and quantity of mineral elements present in an ash. The distribution of some mineral elements in poultry feedstuffs is given in Table 2, Appendix.

Vitamins. Vitamins constitute the newest group of nutrients discovered in plants and animals. They are organic substances, occurring in feedstuffs in very small quantities. Vitamins are essential for the health and well-being of animals. They must be stored in the egg along with other nutrients for embryo development.

Vitamins are determined by chemical or biological tests. The latter may be made by microbiological methods or by chick- or rat-feeding tests. The vitamin potency is determined by adding the product to be tested at different levels as a supplement to a bacteriological culture media or to an animal ration known to be devoid of the vitamin under consideration. The results are compared with those produced by a similar media or ration to which different levels of the known vitamin have been added.

Vitamins were discovered by observing nutritional diseases that occurred when certain foods were lacking in the ration. Since the chemical composition of the vitamins was not known at the time of their discovery, they were designated by letters. There are now seven vitamins—A, B, C, D, E, G, and K —that have been studied in detail (Table 3, Appendix). Some of these consist of several fractions. Other vitamins are now recognized and are being investigated.

Vitamin A. Vitamin A is a thick, pale yellow liquid at ordinary temperature. At very low temperature, it occurs in pure crystalline form. Vitamin A has the empirical formula $C_{20}H_{30}O$. It is associated with animal fats and is soluble in fat solvents. Vitamin A is formed in the animal body from carotene and cryptoxanthin eaten in the feed. True vitamin A and the carotenoid pigments from which it is formed are destroyed by prolonged heat and exposure to air.

A reserve supply of vitamin A and its precursors is stored in the liver and fat tissues of the body. Vitamin A is also stored in the egg, the amount depending upon the amount fed in the ration.

Vitamin A is necessary for growth, egg production, hatchability, resistance against respiratory and eye infections, and normal kidney function. Vitamin A deficiency diseases are nutritional roup (p. 343) and xerophthalmia.

True vitamin A is abundant in the livers of certain kinds of fish. The oils obtained from the livers of bass, eels, halibut, cod, and tuna are the richest natural sources (Table 3, Appendix).

Carotenes $(C_{40}H_{56})$ are plant sources of vitamin A. The carotenes are yellow, fat-soluble pigments found in green plants and yellow carrots. In fact, the green or yellow coloring is a rough indication of the richness of foods of plant origin in carotene—the more intense the coloring, the greater the carotene content. Young, tender, leafy green or dehydrated grasses, such as lawn grass or clippings, and alfalfa, are good sources of vitamin A.

Cryptoxanthin, a yellow pigment found in grasses, yellow corn, and the yolk of the egg, is another source of vitamin A. Additional sources are listed in Table 3, Appendix.

The relative amounts of vitamin A and vitamin A-active carotinoids in foods can be measured by controlled feeding experiments with rats. Diets free from vitamin A, but adequate in all other respects, are fed to normal young rats until their body stores of the vitamin have been depleted. The body weights of rats that have reached this stage cease to increase and signs of an abnormal eye condition are apparent.

The food being tested for its vitamin A content is then fed as weighed daily supplements in such quantities as will promote a rate of growth equal to that induced by a standard quantity of pure beta-carotene.

The International and U.S.P. (United States Pharmacopeia) unit of vitamin A is .0006 milligram (.6 gamma) of pure beta-carotene. The quantity of test food that must be fed daily to each rat in order to promote the same average rate of growth as is induced by feeding .0006 milligram of beta-carotene per rat per day is said to contain 1 International or U.S.P. unit of vitamin A.

Foods tested in this way may contain both vitamin A and vitamin A-active carotinoids. The animal feeding tests do not distinguish between the growth responses due to vitamin A and these carotinoids, and for this reason the results are usually expressed as total vitamin A value.

Animal feeding tests are expensive, time-consuming, and laborious. Efforts are being made to develop chemical and physical methods of testing the vitamin A value of foods and feedstuffs. One of these is to extract the sample with a fat solvent; remove the fat, vitamin A-free pigments, and other impurities; and compare a solution of the residue with a standard solution of beta-carotene by means of a spectrophotometer or colorimeter.

Thiamin (B_1). The water-soluble, growth-promoting substance formerly known as vitamin B is now known to consist of several vitamins. The principal ones from the standpoint of poultry nutrition are thiamin (B_1), riboflavin (B_2 or G), pantothenic acid, and vitamin B_{12}.

Thiamin (B_1), also known as the antineuritic vitamin, has been prepared synthetically in the laboratory. The empirical formula is $C_{12}H_{18}N_4Cl_2SO$. Vitamin B_1 is soluble in water and destroyed by heat in alkaline solution. It cannot be synthesized or readily stored in the animal body. Therefore, it must be supplied in the ration.

Vitamin B_1 is manufactured by plants and stored principally in the germs of the seeds.

Vitamin B_1 appears to play a role in the metabolism of every living cell in plants and animals. It is necessary for appetite, digestion, growth, egg production, hatchability, prevention of bacterial intestinal infection, and the prevention of nerve disorders. Polyneuritis is a specific nerve inflammation and paralysis of poultry resulting from a deficiency of vitamin B_1 in the ration.

Whole grains, wheat by-products, green grasses, alfalfa meal, milk by-products, glandular tissues, and yeast are good sources of vitamin B_1. Since this vitamin is so widely distributed in poultry feedstuffs, there is not much danger of a deficiency of it in poultry rations.

Vitamin B_1 values are expressed in International units. One unit is equivalent to 3 micrograms or 3 millionths of a gram of pure crystalline B_1 for growth of rats.

Vitamin C. Vitamin C is also known as ascorbic or cevitamic acid. It is needed by guinea pigs, monkeys, and human beings, and must be supplied in their rations. Poultry, swine, and cattle make their own vitamin C and do not need to have it supplied in their rations. Therefore, a discussion of vitamin C will be omitted here.

Vitamin D. The discovery of vitamin D and its use, in the form of cod liver oil, for the control of rickets in poultry has revolutionized the poultry industry during the past twenty-five years. It has made it possible to rear poultry indoors and at all seasons of the year.

Compounds of plant and animal origin may be made to possess vitamin D properties by irradiation with sunlight or ultraviolet light.

Cholesterol is a sterol found in the skin and other tissues of animals. Upon exposure to sunlight or ultraviolet light, this sterol is activated to form vitamin D. It is known as activated 7-dehydro-cholesterol or vitamin D_3. This is the form of vitamin D that predominates in animal and fish oils.

Ergosterol is a sterol found in plants, especially the fungus, ergot, and yeast. Upon irradiation by means of ultraviolet light, it assumes strong vitamin D properties. Concentrated products of irradiated ergosterol are sold under the name of viosterol, calciferol, or vitamin D_2. It is satisfactory for four-footed animals but not very good for poultry.

Vitamin D products are closely related to fats and are associated with them. They are soluble in fat solvents. Vitamin D is fairly resistant against destruction by heat or oxidation. Vitamin D eaten in the ration may be stored in the body and in the egg.

Vitamin D is necessary for normal mineral assimilation. It prevents rickets (p. 348) and crooked breastbones in growing chickens. These bone abnormalities are characterized by poor calcification (Fig. 141) and low ash content. Vitamin D is also necessary for egg production, normal shell texture, and hatchability. If the hen has not stored a sufficient amount of vitamin D in the egg, the embryo will develop normally during the first week or so and then die because of inability to assemble calcium and phosphorus for skeleton formation.

The vitamin D factor may be supplied by fish oils, irradiated yeast, and irradiated ergosterol (Table 3, Appendix). It may be produced in animals by exposure to sunlight or ultraviolet light.

Vitamin D is determined by biological feeding tests with rats and chickens.

The International unit is the calcifying activity of .025 micrograms of calciferol for the rat.

The U.S.P. unit is identical with the International unit; but as a standard of reference, a cod liver oil is used that has been carefully standardized against the international standard calciferol.

The A.O.A.C. (Association of Official Agricultural Chemists) chick unit of vitamin D is the calcium depositing efficiency for the chick of a U.S.P. unit of cod liver oil. Vitamin D products that are to be fed to chickens should be tested on chicks rather than with rats. These two species of animals do not respond alike to all vitamin D products. For instance, an International unit of cod liver oil is several times as potent as a unit of calciferol for the chick.

Vitamin E. Vitamin E is a solid alcohol known as tocopherol. It is soluble in fat solvents and found in the nonsaponifiable fraction of the fat extract. As it occurs naturally in feedstuffs, it is fairly resistant against heat and oxidation.

Vitamin E is necessary for reproduction and the prevention of muscle degeneration. Embryos die during the first day or so as a result of disintegration of the circulatory system when vitamin E is lacking in the ration and subsequently in the egg. There are also abnormal cell proliferation and hemorrhage in young embryos as a result of vitamin E deficiency. The testes in males undergo degeneration when the birds are deprived of vitamin E for several months. A deficiency of vitamin E or the presence of rancid fats, which destroys it, results in nutritional encephalomalacia (p. 348).

Vitamin E is widely distributed in poultry feedstuffs. Poultry rations will generally contain ample quantities of it. The oil from germs of grains, especially wheat germ oil, wheat by-products, grains, green grass, and alfalfa meal are good sources of vitamin E.

The presence of vitamin E in feedstuffs may be determined by feeding different amounts of them to rats on vitamin E-free rations and observing their ability to produce living young.

Riboflavin. Riboflavin has also been known as vitamin B_2, G, or the growth vitamin. It has been produced in pure, yellow orange, crystalline form from egg white, milk, and other plant and animal sources. In solution, riboflavin has a greenish-yellow fluorescence. Its empirical formula is $C_{17}H_{20}N_4O_6$. Riboflavin is stable at temperatures at which B_1 is destroyed. It is water soluble, gradually destroyed by light, and easily destroyed at high temperatures in the presence of alkali.

Riboflavin is stored in the white of the egg for the development of the chick embryo. It gives the albumen its slight greenish-yellow opalescence.

Riboflavin is essential for cellular oxidations. It is necessary for growth and hatchability. A deficiency of vitamin G in the egg results in early embryo mortality. It is also necessary for preservation of health of peripheral nerves and the prevention of the acute neuromalacia and the less acute "curled toe paralysis."

Sources of riboflavin for poultry are milk whey, yeast, liver meal, alfalfa meal, and green grass. Additional sources are given in Table 3, Appendix.

Riboflavin content of feedstuffs is determined biologically with rats and chickens, and chemically by measuring the fluorescence in concentrated extracts. It may also be determined by microbiological methods.

In the chick method, the chicks are placed on a vitamin G-free ration until they cease growing, then graduated amounts of the product under test are fed to different lots. The Cornell chick unit of vitamin G is the growth-promoting activity of .001 milligram of flavine.

Vitamin B$_{12}$ (APF factor). This is one of the B-complex vitamins which was first found in animal tissue and excreta. Hence, the name animal protein factor (APF). It is now known that vitamin B$_{12}$ and other as yet unidentified factors may be synthesized by a number of microörganisms. Vitamin B$_{12}$ is necessary for growth, normal feathering, and hatchability. Good sources are fish products, packing house by-products, animal feces, used poultry house litter, yeast, and microbiological fermentation products.

Vitamin K. Vitamin K is also known as the antihemorrhagic vitamin. It is a fat-soluble product which was first extracted from alfalfa. It has now been prepared synthetically. Vitamin K is a naphtho-quinone. It is destroyed by oxidation, sunlight, and strong alkalis or acids.

Vitamin K is necessary for the normal clotting of blood. A deficiency of the vitamin results in internal, subcutaneous and intramuscular hemorrhages and delayed clotting time of the blood. It also results in bleeding from the pinfeathers, internal hemorrhage, and greater loss of blood resulting from cannibalism.

Vitamin K is found in green grass, alfalfa meal, fish meal, and meat scraps.

Choline. This vitamin is a constituent of complex fats. It is used for growth, normal bone development, fat metabolism, egg production, and the prevention of perosis (p. 349). Liver meal, fish meal, yeast, wheat germ, soybean meal, tankage, meat scraps, and distillers' solubles are good sources of choline.

Pantothenic acid. This member of the B-complex vitamins is necessary for growth, good feathering, and hatchability. It prevents a chick dermatitis (p. 346) and maintains a normal condition of certain nerves. Good sources of pantothenic acid are yeast, liver, peanuts, milk products, alfalfa meal, green grass, and distillers' solubles. Some is present in all grains and seed products. A commercial source is calcium pantothenate.

Biotin. This vitamin is necessary for growth, hatchability, and the prevention of a type of perosis and dermatitis. Liver and gland meals, yeast, grains, cane molasses, grass, and alfalfa meal are good sources of biotin.

Pyridoxine (B$_6$). This member of the B-complex vitamins is necessary for appetite, growth, utilization of certain fats, and the prevention of convulsions. It is present in grains, milk, fish products, yeast, and distillers' solubles.

Niacin (nicotinic acid). This is one of the water-soluble vitamins. It is necessary for growth, good feathering, and maintaining a normal condition of the lining of the upper portion of the alimentary tract. It is synthesized by the chicken but possibly not rapidly enough from certain rations which promote rapid growth. Good sources are liver, yeast, bran, middlings, and milk.

Inositol. This water-soluble vitamin is found in nearly all plant and animal tissue, including the egg and chick. The chick may be able to synthesize this vitamin from the ration.

Folic acid (B$_c$). This vitamin is necessary for growth, the normal development of feathers, and prevention of a type of anemia in chicks. It is found in most of the feedstuffs commonly fed to poultry.

Other vitamins. Other vitamins that have been found necessary for the chick include the whey factor, an unknown fish meal factor, factors found in yeast, and microbiological fermentation products.

Metabolism

Metabolism is here used to designate all of the processes undergone by a food from the time it enters until it leaves the body.

Digestion

Digestion is the disintegration of feedstuffs into simple nutrients in the intestinal tract for absorption and use by the body tissues. It involves a series of mechanical and chemical processes and is influenced by many factors.

Feed intake and storage. Feed is picked up in the beak of the fowl, moistened by the thick saliva in the mouth, and swallowed without mastication, since the bird is not provided with teeth. It passes down the gullet to the crop (Fig. 28) where it is stored until it can be ground, mixed with digestive juices, and digested. While in the crop, the feed becomes softened by the saliva swallowed with it and by the liquid secretions from the lining of the inner crop wall. The enzymes, present in the feed, result in a little predigestion of the carbohydrates. The crop contents develop a slightly acid reaction due to the formation of lactic acid.

It has been observed that when a bird is hungry, the first feed eaten passes directly to the gizzard. It has also been observed that a crop filled with whole grains is emptied quicker than one filled with ground grains. This is to be expected, since the whole grains must be ground before they are ready for digestion.

Preparation of feed for digestion. The feed moves from the crop, a small quantity at a time, on down through the lower portion of the gullet and glandular stomach into the gizzard. Rythmic-like contractions of the walls of the intestinal tract force the feed along through the tube. As the feed passes through the glandular stomach (proventriculus), it stimulates the glandular cells in this region to secrete a gastric juice into the intestinal tract. This is a pepsin-hydrochloric acid mixture used for the digestion of proteins and for dissolving minerals.

The feed is thoroughly macerated and mixed with the gastric juice in the gizzard. Thorough grinding is necessary in order that the digestive juices may reach all parts of the material and digest as much of the nutrients as possible. The grinding is more thorough than in the case of most farm animals in spite of the fact that the bird does not have teeth.

The feed is ground and mixed by slow, rhythmic, rotary-like movements of the powerful muscles in the walls of the gizzard. The feed is squeezed between and rubbed over the rough washboard-like linings of the crop walls. Whole grains, having been previously softened in the crop, are easily macerated and pulverized in the process.

It is a common belief that hard insoluble grit is necessary, or at least desirable, in the gizzard for the grinding process. Experimental data are conflicting on this point. In fact, the presence of hard insoluble grit and foreign material in the gizzard may take up valuable space and interfere with the grinding process and the passage of the ground feed.

Digestion of carbohydrates. As the ground feed passes from the gizzard into the duodenal loop, pancreatic juice is secreted from the pancreas into this region of the intestinal tract. At the same time, alkaline bile salts, produced in the liver and stored in the gall bladder, are also secreted into the duodenal loop. The bile salts neutralize the acidity of the intestinal contents in this region of the intestine and produce an alkalinity. Three digestive enzymes are secreted in the pancreatic juice. One of these is amylase, which breaks starch down into disaccharides or complex sugars. As the food passes along into the small intestine, sucrase and other sugar-splitting enzymes, secreted in this region, further hydrolize or digest the compound sugars into simple sugars, chiefly glucose. Simple sugars are the end products of the digestion of carbohydrates.

Starches and sugars are easily digested by poultry, while the pentosans and crude fiber are poorly digested (Table 4, Appendix). The intestinal tract in the chicken is so short and the passage of food through it is so rapid, that bacteria have little time to work on the complex carbohydrates.

Digestion of fats. The bile salts from the liver emulsify the fats in the duodenal loop. They are then acted upon by an enzyme, lipase, a product of the pancreatic juice. The fats are digested or broken down into fatty acids and glycerol. These are the end products of fat digestion.

Fats are not very palatable or easily digested by poultry.

Digestion of proteins. While the feed is being ground and mixed in the gizzard, the pepsin-hydrochloric acid mixture breaks some of the proteins down into less complex fractions as proteoses and peptones.

While fats and carbohydrates are being digested in the duodenal loop, trypsin from the pancreatic juice breaks down some of the proteoses and peptones into still simpler products—amino acids. Erepsin, secreted in the small intestine, completes the digestion of protein split products into amino acids. These are the end products of protein digestion.

Digestion of minerals and vitamins. Minerals are dissolved rather than digested. Many of them change from the solid to the liquid form in the gizzard. Oyster shell and limestone grit, for example, are dissolved in this region.

The digestion and metabolism of vitamins in the body are not well understood. Carotene, the precursor of vitamin A, is transformed into true vitamin A in the liver, The bird manufactures vitamin C from digested feed fragments, in the body. Cholesterol in the skin is transformed into vitamin D by exposure to sunlight or ultraviolet light.

Rate of digestion. Digestion is rapid in the chicken. The time required for food to pass from the mouth to the cloaca is about two and one-half hours in a laying hen. The rate of passage is much slower (eight to twelve hours) in birds out of production.

Absorption and Assimilation

Absorption of nutrients. The digested nutrients pass through the intestinal wall into the blood stream. Most of the absorption takes place from the small intestine. The surface for absorption is greatly increased by the presence of innumerable villi or finger-like projections. These villi, which give the mucous membrane a velvety appearance, project toward the center of the lumen and thus come in intimate contact with the fluid contents.

Within each villus is a lacteal, or drainage tube of the lymphatic system, and a network of capillaries of the blood system.

Digested nutrients in the form of simple sugars, amino acids, and dissolved minerals pass through the wall surface into the blood capillaries. The method or methods by which the materials pass through the intestinal wall are not well understood.

Digested fats pass through the intestinal wall into the lacteals of the lymphatic system. Here again, they form neutral fats. The fats in the lymph are more like body fat than like that of the feed eaten. The fats pass along with the lymph and enter the venous blood stream near the heart.

Transfer of nutrients. The digested nutrients, entering the blood stream by way of the capillaries in the intestinal wall, are collected in the portal vein. It transports blood and the absorbed food nutrients to the liver, on their way to the heart.

As the digested nutrients pass through the capillaries of the liver, most of the glucose is transformed into glycogen (p. 247) for storage in the liver and muscles. Some amino acids and nitrogenous products of tissue metabolism are de-amized as they pass through the liver. The carbohydrate fractions are made available for heat and energy purposes and the nitrogenous fractions are transported to the kidneys for elimination. The liver also removes some of the fat from the blood stream for storage. This accounts for the pale yellow livers in fat birds and newly hatched chicks. Many impurities absorbed from the intestinal tract into the blood stream are retained by the liver cells as the blood passes through its capillaries. In case of absorbed poisons, a high concentration of them is usually found in the liver.

The blood, carrying the digested nutrients, passes from the liver by way of the hepatic and postcaval veins to the heart. It passes from the heart to the lungs, where carbon dioxide and water are given off and oxygen is taken in. The blood is returned from the lungs to the heart, and is then pumped out through the arteries to all of the tissues of the body.

The digested nutrients pass from the capillaries to the lymph which bathes the tissue cells. The lymph serves as a medium of exchange between the capillaries and the tissue cells. It carries digested food to the cells and waste products from them.

The assimilation of nutrients. *Glucose* is burned in the cells for heat and energy production, the end products being heat or energy, carbon dioxide, and water. The process may be represented by means of a chemical equation, thus:

$$C_6H_{12}O_6 \quad + \quad 6O_2 \quad = \quad \triangle \quad + \quad 6CO_2 \quad + \quad 6H_2O$$

| Glucose | Oxygen | Heat or energy | Carbon dioxide | Water |

An excess of digested carbohydrates, over and above that stored as glycogen, is transformed into body and egg fat.

Fats are gradually removed from the blood stream and stored as adipose tissue mainly, under the skin in the abdominal region, along the intestines, and in the egg. They serve as a reserve supply of heat and energy. In case of inadequate food supply, as soon as the glycogen is used up, the fats are burned with the same end products as formed by the burning of carbohydrates. As long as fats are present, the proteins are protected from consumption.

Amino acids, absorbed into the blood stream, are used to build new body tissues, rebuild worn-out tissue, and to form the white and much of the yolk of eggs. Excess amino acids may be used for heat and energy purposes or transformed into fats.

The carbohydrates and fats are preferable to proteins for the production of heat and energy because they are cheaper. Their digestion and metabolism, including the excretion of the resulting waste products, require less work on the part of the body than is required by protein food. Experiments show that carbohydrates are more efficient protein sparers than fats, even though the latter have a greater energy content.

Minerals absorbed into the blood stream are transformed into bone, put into the shell and yolk of the egg, and used in the blood. There is also some storage of excess minerals taken into the body.

Vitamins are stored in the liver and in the egg, and to a lesser extent in other tissues of the body. There appears to be greater storage of the fat-soluble than of the water-soluble vitamins.

Energy Production and Metabolism

Energy is required for all of the body processes, such as digestion, assimilation of food, elimination of waste products, the heart beat, respiration, body movements, and maintenance of body temperature. It is supplied by the feed eaten.

Gross energy. The gross energy value of any feedstuff for the animal depends on the amount of energy that it will furnish when burned. It is determined by burning a weighed sample in pure oxygen gas under pressure in an apparatus known as a calorimeter. The heat given off is taken up by water surrounding the combustion chamber and is measured with an exceedingly accurate thermometer.

The unit of measurement employed in measuring heat and energy is the calorie (C). It is the amount of heat required to raise a kilogram of water 1° C. A large calorie (C) is equivalent to 1000 small calories (c). A therm (T) is 1000 large calories.

The gross energy of one hundred pounds of various substances when burned is as follows:

	Therms
Corn meal	180.3
Linseed meal	210.3
Pure digestible protein	263.1
Pure digestible carbohydrates	186.0
Pure digestible fat	422.0

Digestible protein yields considerably more heat than a similar weight of carbohydrates. Fat yields more than twice as much energy as a similar weight of carbohydrates.

Available energy. The available energy of a feed is the gross energy minus the energy lost in the feces, urine, and combustible gases. It is determined by placing the animal in an apparatus known as a respiration calorimeter (Fig. 130), and keeping records of the feed eaten and of the feces, urine, and combustible gases given off. The gross energy of samples of the products are determined and from them the available energy is calculated.

Net energy. The net energy of a feed is the available energy minus the energy lost in the work of digestion. The work of digestion includes the energy required for grinding in the gizzard, intestinal contractions for moving the food, secretion of digestive juices, and increased work of the heart and lungs resulting from these processes.

All of the energy consumed in the processes takes the form of heat, and helps to warm the body. It cannot be used for other body purposes, because the body has no means of converting heat into other forms of energy.

In addition to the losses of energy due to the actual work of grinding, mixing, digestion, and assimilation of food, a further loss occurs through the speeding up of general metabolism in the body, which always follows the consumption of food. It has been found that the rate of metabolism is at once increased when nutrients are absorbed from the digestive tract following a meal. As a result, more heat is produced. This additional production of heat is sometimes called the "specific dynamic effect" of the food nutrients.

The net energy of a feed is used first of all to meet daily maintenance needs. These include the work of the heart, lungs, and other organs, as well as work done by the muscles in producing body movements. Any surplus of net energy may be used for growth, fattening, or egg production.

Basal heat production. The heat produced by an inactive fasting animal is known as the basal heat production. By measuring the oxygen consumption and the carbon dioxide elimination, it is possible to estimate the basal heat production and to determine the kind of tissue being oxidized.

The volume of carbon dioxide produced divided by the volume of oxygen consumed is known as the respiratory quotient (R.Q.). The respiratory

Fig. 130. An apparatus used to measure the oxygen consumption and carbon dioxide and heat production of a bird. The bird is confined in the chamber at the right. The air is drawn through chemical agents before and after it leaves the chamber in order to absorb various constituents. The volume of air is measured by the air meter at the left.

quotient of carbohydrates is 1 (p. 247), fats .7, and proteins between .7 and 1. The determination of the respiratory quotient and basal heat production are useful in studying nutritive requirements and in the diagnosis of disease.

The critical temperature. The critical temperature is the environmental temperature below which the heat produced by the normal body processes is no longer sufficient to maintain the normal body temperature. When the environmental temperature drops below the critical temperature of the bird, it must use food primarily for the production of body heat. In the absence of food, it must oxidize body tissues for this purpose. Experiments conducted at the Illinois Agricultural Experiment Station have shown that the critical temperature of the inactive fasting hen is 62° F. If the hen is in production, has access to feed at all times, and is free to move about, the critical temperature is lowered to 15° F.

Excretion

Excretory products include materials which have not been digested and waste products resulting from body metabolism.

The feces. The feces includes indigestible food, intestinal bacteria, digestive juices, bile, worn-out intestinal lining tissue, and mineral material resulting from body metabolism.

Some of the unabsorbed and undigested contents of the small intestine back up into the ceca. A little absorption may take place here. The ceca contract and force the material out into the large intestine about once a day. As the undigested food passes along through the large intestine, some of the water is reabsorbed into the body circulation. The undigested material is voided from the large intestine into the cloaca and from it to the outside of the body as feces.

The mixture of feces and urine voided by birds is known as manure. It contains about 1.44 per cent nitrogen, .99 per cent phosphoric acid, and .39 per cent potash. A hen will produce about forty-three pounds of manure a year. It is of considerable importance as a fertilizer.

The urine. The urine consists mainly of nitrogenous waste products and water resulting from body metabolism processes.

Liquid waste products pass out of the blood stream into the kidney tubules as the blood passes through the capillaries of the kidneys. The material passes from the kidney through the ureters to the cloaca, where it is excreted into the cloaca as urine. As the liquid urine passes along through the ureters, in the region of the large intestine, much of the water in it is reabsorbed into the body circulation. The urine is generally a white pasty material which is mixed with, and coats, the droppings.

About 65 per cent of the urinary nitrogen excreted by birds exists in the form of uric acid. Other constituents include purine nitrogen, 9.6 per cent; urea, 6.5; ammonia, 7.5; creatine, 4.5; and allantoin, 3.8.

A hen probably secretes 700 to 800 cc. of liquid urine from the kidneys every twenty-four hours. Much of the water is reabsorbed so that very little liquid urine is eliminated from the body.

Carbon dioxide and water elimination by respiration. A five-pound hen will exhale about fifty-two liters of carbon dioxide every twenty-four hours. This will vary greatly, depending upon the activity and egg production of the bird.

The water elimination of a hen per day is about .37 pounds by way of the excreta and .09 by way of the lungs. This also will vary within wide limits, depending upon the temperature, activity of the bird, kind of ration fed, and the rate of production.

Determination of the Value of Feeds

There are several methods used for judging the value of feeds. These include chemical and microscopic analysis, digestibility, energy value, and biological value for growth and reproduction.

Chemical analysis of feeds. Chemical analysis of feedstuffs and rations has been used for many years to measure their food value. It gives the amounts of the different groups of nutrients present. Chemical analysis of feeds aids in judging their food value. However, it is by no means the final answer.

The usual chemical analysis of feeds includes moisture, crude protein, ether extract (fat), crude fiber, and ash.

The *crude protein* analysis gives the amount of nitrogen present in a feed and indirectly the crude protein (p. 249). It does not show the source of the protein or the kinds and amounts of essential amino acids present. Just as a chain is no stronger than its weakest link, a protein feed is no better than the smallest amount of an essential amino acid which it contains. Therefore, crude protein content of a feed does not give much information regarding its protein value. The feeding value of protein feedstuffs is now determined by nitrogen retention or growth studies (p. 267).

The *ether extract* or crude fat analysis includes all of the substances soluble in fat solvents (p. 248). Most state laws require a statement of the minimum fat content. Some of the fatlike substances are unpalatable and poorly digested, while others become rancid and cause destruction of vitamins present in feed mixtures. It would probably be better for state laws to specify the maximum rather than the minimum fat content of feeds.

The *crude fiber* analysis is of value (p. 247). Crude fiber is poorly digested. Very little fiber is utilized by animals. The contents of coarse, stemmy materials, hulls, and other woody materials are determined by crude fiber analysis.

Ash or mineral analysis is of some value (p. 250). It gives the amount but not the kind of mineral elements present or the forms in which they exist. Mineral elements may be determined by chemical analysis. The procedures are often expensive and time-consuming. Spectrographic analysis, which is now being used on an extensive scale, will probably greatly shorten the time required to determine the kinds and amounts of mineral elements present in ash.

Chemical analysis is not a very satisfactory means of determining some of the vitamins present in a feed. Most of them are determined by feeding tests with rats or chicks.

Microscopic analysis of feeds. Microscopic analysis is of value in determining the presence of ingredients in mixtures. It may be used for checking claims made for the presence of ingredients in mixtures. It may also be used to detect adulterants and foreign substances in feedstuffs and mixtures.

Within certain limits, microscopic analysis may be used to estimate the quantities of ingredients in mixtures. It is of little value in determining the quality of ingredients or mixtures. Two substances may have the same chemical analysis and look alike under the microscope, yet vary greatly in feeding value.

Microscopic analysis is an aid and supplement to chemical analysis in determining the value of a feed. Other determinations need to be made. Chemical and microscopic analyses do not give the amino acid, mineral element, and vitamin content; the palatability; digestibility; or value of the feed for maintenance, growth, egg production, fattening, or reproduction (hatchability).

Biological analysis of feeds. Biological analysis of feeds involves feeding tests with animals. They may be made in the laboratory with small animals such as chicks or rats, or with larger animals and poultry flocks under practical farm conditions. Biological analyses include studies of palatability, digestion, balance experiments, energy metabolism, and effects of feeds on growth and reproduction.

Palatability of feeds. Palatability is the first factor determining the biological value of a feed. If a feed is not consumed readily, it cannot be expected to produce good growth or production. Unpalatable feeds do not stimulate normal intestinal movements and secretion of digestive juices. They have a tendency to remain in the crop longer than palatable ones.

A bird probably chooses food by sight and touch more than by smell and taste. Whole grains are more palatable than finely ground ones. Wheat is more palatable than the other cereal grains. Coarsely ground mash is preferred to finely ground material. Freshly ground grains are more palatable than stale ground grains. Moist mash is more palatable than dry mash. Animal protein feedstuffs, such as milk, meat scraps, and fish meal are eaten more readily than vegetable protein feedstuffs, such as soybean, cottonseed, and linseed meals.

Digestibility of feeds. Feeds must be digested before they can enter the blood stream and be transported to the tissues. Furthermore, the tissue cells can utilize nutrients only in the form of the simple end products of digestion (p. 258).

Methods of determining digestibility of feeds with chickens differ greatly. The difference between the amount of a nutrient eaten in a given time and the amount of it excreted in the feces is regarded as its digestibility. This is always subject to some error, more so in the case of some nutrients than others. In the case of crude protein, for instance, the feces contain, in addition to undigested protein from the feed eaten, some crude protein resulting from wear and tear of the intestinal lining, digestive enzymes, and intestinal bacteria. The crude protein should not be considered as indigestible. In the case of birds, a still greater source of error is encountered. The urine and feces are excreted together. The crude protein in the urine has been digested. It results from the breakdown of protein material in body processes. Troubles are encountered in separating the urine and feces in digestion trials with poultry.

One method of separating urine and feces for digestion studies has been to operate on the bird and divert the urine from the ureters out through cannulae before it reaches the cloaca and becomes mixed with the feces. This creates an abnormal metabolism.

Another method of separating urine and feces for digestion trials is the use of a solvent for the urinary constituents. This separation is subject to error because it is impossible to dissolve out all of the urinary constituents without dissolving part of the fecal material.

The *coefficient of digestibility* is the percentage of a feed or nutrient consumed that is digested. For example, if 100 grams of corn are consumed and 10 grams are excreted by way of the feces, the amount digested is $100 - 10$, or 90 grams. This amounts to $90 \div 100$, or .9 digested; or in terms of percentage, $.9 \times 100 = 90$, or 90 per cent is the coefficient of digestibility.

The digestibility of each nutrient is figured separately. They are then totaled in order to get the total digestibility of the feedstuff. To calculate the digestibility of a mash feed, determine the number of pounds of digestible nutrients in the quantity of each feedstuff used and then total the feedstuffs and their digestible nutrients.

The digestibility of nutrients in some poultry feedstuffs tested with chickens is given in Table 4, Appendix.

The nutritive ratio of a feedstuff or ration is the relationship between the digestible energy and tissue-building portions of the material. It may be expressed by the following formula:

$$\frac{\text{digestible carbohydrates} + \text{digestible fat} \times 2.25}{\text{digestible crude protein}}$$

The digestible fat is multiplied by 2.25 because it produces 2.25 times as much heat and energy as an equal weight of carbohydrates. The nutritive ratio of most poultry rations varies from about 1:3 to 1:5, which means that the energy part of the ration is three to five times that of the tissue-building part. The 1:3 ration would be called narrow, and the 1:5 would be wide.

Factors influencing digestibility of feeds are important. Young and healthy animals digest feed better than old or sick animals. A given quantity of feed fed in small amounts at a time is digested more efficiently than when fed at one time. Animal feedstuffs are generally digested better than plant feedstuffs because they do not contain fiber, which must be disintegrated so that the digestive juices can attack the nutrients. High temperature used in the processing and drying of certain feedstuffs generally reduces their digestibility. Combinations of feedstuffs fed in a mixture influence the digestibility of each of the ingredients. For instance, feeding a mixture of milk and corn results in better digestibility of the corn than when it is fed alone. It is believed that certain feedstuffs—milk, for instance—create a more favorable environment for useful intestinal bacteria. These, in turn, bring about more complete digestion of the feed.

Retention value of feeds. The value of feeds is sometimes measured by balance experiments. Records are kept of the intake and outgo of certain elements during a definite period of time. For instance, the biological value of proteins for growth of chickens has been measured by nitrogen balance experiments (Fig. 131). The test periods are generally of short duration. They do not measure the value of the feed for extended periods of growth or for reproduction and health.

Energy value of feeds. There are other losses that must be taken into consideration, in addition to feed that is not digested. These include the energy lost in grinding and mixing, digestion, and absorption. Various types of respiration apparatus and respiration calorimeters have been designed to measure these losses (Fig. 130). The more complete type of respiration apparatus is an air-tight chamber in which the animal is placed. This is so equipped that all of the air entering the chamber and leaving it can be accurately measured and analyzed. All food, feces, and urine are likewise carefully weighed and analyzed.

The amount of carbon and nitrogen stored or lost can be measured. From

COURTESY G. F. HEUSER

Fig. 131. Cage used in nitrogen-balance experiments with feeder specially designed to prevent wastage.

this information, the amounts of body protein and fat that have been stored or lost can be computed, and likewise the gain or loss in energy.

Limitations of net energy values are worthy of note. The net energy value of a feed does not measure its value for maintenance. For instance, roughages have low net energy values. They are much better for the production of body heat than for the production of fat.

Net energy values are far more expensive to determine than total digestible nutrients. The latter give a fair idea of the value of a feed for heat production.

The net energy values differ with different species of animals. For instance, studies at the University of Illinois have shown that the net energy value of corn grain for chickens is 128.5 therms per 100 pounds. This is 52 per cent higher than the net energy value of the same grain for fattening cattle.

The net energy values of feeds are higher when scantily fed than when fed liberally.

A deficiency of vitamins and certain amino acids in a ration reduces its net energy value.

Growth value of feeds. The value of a feed as determined by growth studies shows what a feed will do. This is often measured in the laboratory

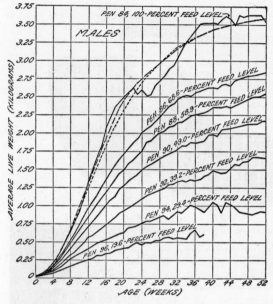

Fig. 132. Age of chickens, level of feed intake, and rate of growth. (Titus, Jull, and Hendricks, 1934.)

by feeding tests with rats and chicks. Tests made with rats give an indication of results that may be expected when the feed is fed to other animals. Final tests need to be made with the animals for which the feed is intended. Different species of animals do not always respond the same when fed the same ration. For instance, the chick and the rat do not need vitamin C, while some farm animals and man need it. Another ilustration is the difference between the U.S.P. and A.O.A.C. vitamin D units of some vitamin D products for chicks and rats. Fortunately, when feeds are tested on chicks, the results are of direct value.

The *number of chicks required* per lot to show growth differences in two feeds will depend on the differences to be shown. Where there is quite a noticeable difference in feeds, twenty or twenty-five chicks are sufficient. Where there is very little difference many more chicks are required.

The *length of the feeding trial* for growth studies of chicks is usually eight weeks. Almost all nutritional troubles will show up in this length of time. Tests have shown that differences in lots of chicks at four weeks of age will remain so at eight and sixteen weeks. Birds are more sensitive to growth factors in feeds early in life than later on.

The *age of the chick* influences the rate of growth. There is an early period of increasing rate of growth (the first eight to twelve weeks) and a later period of decreasing rate (Fig. 132). If early growth rate is inhibited by low protein levels or other causes, the later growth rate will be greater than normal.

The *amount of feed consumed* is another important factor governing the rate of growth. The older the bird during the growing period, the greater the proportion of feed eaten that is used for maintenance and the smaller the proportion used for growth (Fig. 133). Each succeeding 1000 grams of feed eaten by young chickens results in about 9 per cent decrease in the amount of gain secured. The amount of feed required under the conditions of the experiment to produce any given average live weight from 200 to

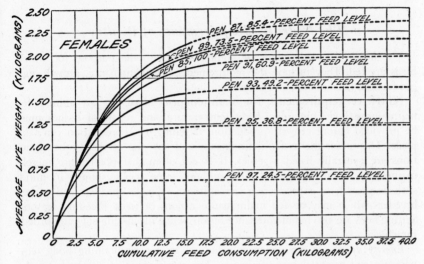

Fig. 133. Weight of chicks (Rock-Red cross) and feed consumption. Solid lines, the interval studied; broken lines are extrapolations. (Titus, Jull, and Hendricks, 1934.)

2200 grams, may also be read from the graph. Titus and Hendricks have shown that the rate of growth is more a function of food intake than time when birds are fed good rations. They could predict the live weight better than the age of chicks any time during the first six weeks by knowing the amount of feed consumed.

The *protein level* of the ration influences the rate of growth of chicks. Birds fed a high protein ration make faster earlier growth than those fed a low protein ration (Fig. 134). Those fed a low protein ration make faster growth later in life.

The *vitamin content* of the ration, especially riboflavin and B_{12} influence the rate of growth.

These and other factors will be discussed under nutritive requirements for maintenance, growth, and finishing poultry.

Reproduction value of feeds. The final test of the value of a feed is its efficiency for growth and reproduction through succeeding generations. If growth, health, and reproduction are normal through one generation, they will generally remain so during succeeding generations.

In the case of poultry, it takes a better feed to produce hatchable eggs than merely to produce eggs. This is to be expected since the hen must store all the nutrients for the development of the embryo in the egg. If an inadequate supply is stored, the embryo will develop for a time and then die.

Some feeds are satisfactory for maintenance but not for growth or egg production. Others are satisfactory for growth and egg production but not for hatchability. However, a feed that produces good hatchability is satisfactory for maintenance, growth, and egg production.

The Nutritive Requirements of Poultry

The nutritive requirements of poultry vary with the purpose for which birds are fed. They include the requirements for maintenance, growth, egg production, hatchability, and fattening.

Nutritive requirements for maintenance. Needs of an animal for maintaining body functions, body temperature, and repair of tissues must be provided before growth, production, fattening, or reproduction can take place. The requirements for maintenance and any one of these other functions are generally listed together. It is not often that poultry are merely maintained for any length of time without some specific object in mind, such as growth or reproduction. Exceptions are male chickens and turkey breeders which may be fed maintenance rations between breeding seasons. Setting hens are also fed maintenance rations while incubating eggs and brooding chicks.

Energy needs for maintenance include those for maintaining body temperature and essential body activities. The temperature of the body of the chicken must be maintained near 107° F. for normal functioning of the body activities. Heat resulting from the heart beat, respiration, digestion, and body movements is used for this purpose. When the heat from these sources is insufficient to maintain the normal body temperature, the animal will eat additional food for heat production. In the absence of food, the body will oxidize its own tissues for this purpose. The lower the environmental temperature and the greater the body surface in proportion to body mass, the greater the heat loss from the body and consequently the more food required to maintain the body temperature.

The energy from food required for maintaining body temperature and essential body activities amounts to about eight hundred calories per square meter of body surface per day. The basal heat production (p. 261) of males is a little greater than that of females, while that of capons is considerably lower. It will vary with the environmental temperature of the bird.

The critical temperature (p. 262) of the chick is 96° F. at hatching time. A seven-degree decrease from the critical temperature results in about 15 per cent increase in metabolism. The critical temperature of the inactive fasting hen is 62° F. The greater the activity of the bird and the greater the amount of food eaten, the lower the critical temperature. The energy needs of moderately active birds are approximately 50 per cent greater than for basal heat production.

The *protein needs for maintenance* are determined by measuring the amount of nitrogen in urine of animals fed a nitrogen-free diet so designed as to furnish all other nutrients in ample amounts. It is usually expressed in terms of milligrams per kilogram of body weight. The endogenous nitrogen (that required for maintenance) amounts to about two milligrams per calorie of heat production. Ackerson and his associates at the Nebraska Agricultural

Experiment Station have shown that the nitrogen requirement of young birds is greater per unit of weight than that of old birds. Males probably have a greater nitrogen requirement than females because of the greater basal heat production. Activity should not affect the nitrogen needs for maintenance as long as ample food energy is used to meet the needs for the activity.

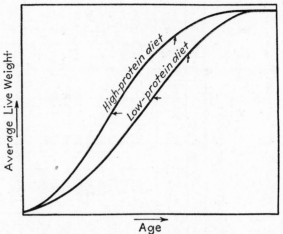

TITUS AND HAMMOND, 1935. REPRODUCED IN ''POULTRY HUSBANDRY'' BY M. A. JULL. BY PERMISSION OF MCGRAW-HILL BOOK CO., PUBLISHERS

Fig. 134. Protein level and growth rate. A high protein ration results in early rapid growth, while a low protein ration results in later growth. The horizontal arrows represent changes in growth rates while the vertical arrows represent the approximate age at which production begins.

The *mineral needs for maintenance* have not been studied so carefully as the energy and protein needs. The latter two are used up and the by-products excreted. Some of the minerals are used over again and small amounts are excreted when birds are kept on maintenance rations. When sufficient food is supplied to meet the energy and protein needs, it will generally contain sufficient mineral elements to meet the mineral needs for maintenance.

The *vitamin needs for maintenance* have not been carefully investigated. They are lower than for growth or production. Vitamins of the B complex (p. 253) are probably the most essential ones for maintenance.

Nutritive requirements for growth. Growth is the elaboration of new tissues that make up the changes in weight, form, or composition of the animal. The rate of growth is determined by the inherent capacity for growth, the kind and amount of feed consumed, and the environment of the birds. The chicken grows more rapidly than other domestic animals, doubling its weight in about two weeks and increasing it by ten times in six weeks (Table 48). The absorbed yolk furnishes the first nutrients required by the newly hatched chick. It supplies the energy and other needs until the chick can move about and locate food.

The *energy needs for growth* include the energy required for maintenance, that required for activity, and the energy of the new tissue formed. On the basis of per unit of body weight, the energy represented by the growth of tissue decreases with age; but the amount of energy stored per unit of increase in body weight increases with age (Table 49). The average daily expenditure in muscular activity has been estimated to be 50 per cent of that

Table 48

GROWTH AND FEED CONSUMPTION OF CHICKENS, TURKEYS, AND DUCKS (LBS.)

Age Wks.	S. C. White Leghorns [a]				American Breeds [b]				W. Rock Capons [c]		Bronze Turkey [d]			W. Pekin Ducks	
	Av. Wt. Cockerels	Av. Wt. Pullets	Av. Total Feed Pullets	Av. Total Feed Cockerels	Av. Wt. Cockerels	Av. Wt. Pullets	Av. Total Feed Pullets	Av. Total Feed Cockerels	Av. Wt. of Capons	Av. Total Feed	Av. Wt. Males	Av. Wt. Females	Av. Total Feed	Av. Wt. of Ducks	Av. Total Feed
Day old	.09	.09	0	0	.09	.09	0	0	.08	0	.11	.12	0	.10	0.00
2 wk	.22	.19	.36	.36	.19	.18	.29	.29	...	...	.31	.29	.55	.64	1.19
4	.48	.39	1.03	1.03	.46	.43	.98	.98	.44	.95	.72	.63	1.57	2.26	5.08
6	.82	.68	2.10	2.10	.96	.83	2.28	2.28	...	...	1.38	1.15	3.00	4.05	12.59
8	1.33	1.09	3.46	3.72	1.55	1.29	4.13	4.13	1.45	4.53	2.40	1.90	5.38	5.16	22.80
10	1.89	1.46	5.28	6.09	2.09	1.59	6.47	6.47	...	...	3.80	3.20	8.60	6.00	34.57
12	2.35	1.71	7.20	8.67	2.81	2.13	9.22	9.22	2.55	9.69	5.80	4.80	13.55	...	...
14	2.79	2.08	9.37	11.30	3.58	2.60	11.90	11.90	...	...	8.10	6.50	19.80	...	...
16	3.18	2.39	11.66	13.61	4.02	3.04	14.57	15.68	3.79	15.72	10.06	7.70	27.10	...	...
18	3.45	2.69	13.99	16.48	4.63	3.47	17.39	19.31	...	...	...	...	...	...	...
20	3.75	2.99	16.12	19.38	5.01	3.73	19.99	22.77	4.85	22.03	15.02	10.60	45.90	...	...
22	3.98	3.19	18.56	22.28	5.44	3.96	22.87	26.51	...	...	...	...	...	...	...
24	4.19	3.36	21.07	25.60	5.55	4.27	25.89	29.94	5.84	28.97	19.00	12.50	67.90	...	...
26	4.58	3.47	23.78	29.20	5.65	4.49	28.82	33.30	...	...	...	...	...	...	...
28	4.75	...	...	32.45	6.07	...	...	36.48	6.47	35.86	...	...	...	...	...
30	4.86	...	...	36.52	6.63	...	...	40.77	...	...	...	...	...	...	...
32	...	...	...	...	6.72	...	...	45.81	7.07	43.03	...	...	...	...	...

[a] Cornell Ext. Bul. 240. Feed consumption of pullets and cockerels not determined separately until after 6 wks.
[b] Cornell Ext. Bul. 240. Feed consumption of pullets and cockerels not determined separately until after 14 wks.
[c] Kan. Sta. Bul. 274. Cockerels were caponized when 12 weeks old.
[d] Pa. Sta. Bul. 250.

Table 49

NET-ENERGY REQUIREMENTS OF GROWING WHITE LEGHORN COCKERELS [1]

Body Weight (Pounds)	Net Energy (Calories)				Equivalent Weight of Corn (Grams)
	Maintenance	Activity	Growth	Total	
0.5	37	18	15	70	25
1.0	55	27	19	101	36
1.5	59	29	21	109	39
2.0	72	36	21	129	46
3.0	94	47	19	160	57
4.0	114	57	14	185	66
5.0	133	66	10	210	75

required for maintenance. The equivalent weight of corn in Table 49 refers to the amount of corn required to meet the net energy requirements, assuming that the net energy value of corn is 280 calories per 100 grams.

If the ration is composed of ingredients to supply adequate and economical sources of proteins, minerals, and vitamins, there will be no shortage of energy.

The *protein needs for growth* are high, since the increase in weight of a growing animal is largely due to the increase in protein and water. The level of protein intake influences the amount of feed consumed, the efficiency of utilization of feed, the rate of growth, the maximum weight attained, and the time required to attain maximum weight (Table 50). As the protein of the diet increases from 13 to 21 per cent, there is a definite increase in the average

Table 50

RELATIVE EFFECTS OF DIFFERENT LEVELS OF PROTEIN INTAKE ON THE GROWTH AND UTILIZATION OF FEED BY MALE CHICKENS [2]

Level of Protein Intake	Efficiency of Feed Utilization	Maximum Live Weight Attained	Quantity of Feed Required for Attaining Maximum Weight	Length of Time Required to Attain Maximum Weight
Per Cent	Per Cent	Per Cent	Per Cent	Per Cent
13	67.7	97.6	144.1	119.9
14	80.6	97.9	121.3	111.7
15	87.3	98.2	112.5	107.8
16	91.5	98.6	107.7	104.6
17	94.6	98.9	104.6	102.6
18	97.2	99.2	102.1	101.5
19	98.7	99.5	100.7	101.0
20	99.7	99.8	100.1	100.5
21	100.0	100.0	100.0	100.0
22	97.9	100.2	102.3	99.7
23	94.3	100.4	106.4	99.5
24	90.2	100.5	111.4	99.4
25	85.6	100.6	117.5	99.2

[1] Mitchell, Card, and Hamilton, 1931.
[2] Titus, U. S. D. A. Yearbook, 1939, p. 813.

efficiency of the utilization of feed for growth; but as the protein increases from 21 to 25 per cent, there is a rather sharp decrease in efficiency. The data indicate that the optimum level is probably between 20 and 21 per cent. The optimum level will vary with the quality of the protein, being somewhat less for protein of high biological value. Protein levels above 13 per cent have little influence on the maximum weight attained. The time required to reach maximum weight is increased noticeably, as the protein level is decreased from 21 to 13 per cent.

While the optimum level of protein intake from the physiological standpoint is about 21 per cent, the most economical level for most purposes is around 18 or 19 per cent. The efficiency of feed utilization at this level is only slightly lower than at the higher level, while the cost of the lower protein feed is generally noticeably lower.

Since a larger proportion of the feed eaten is needed for energy purposes and a smaller proportion for growth of tissue, as a bird increases in weight, the protein level may be reduced when the period of rapid growth has been passed. This is generally between eight and twelve weeks of age. The protein level may be reduced from the 18- to 20-per cent of the starting and growing ration to 15 or 16 per cent, which is the amount recommended in the laying ration (p. 275).

The *mineral needs* for growth are principally needs for calcium and phosphorus for bone formation. The deposit of the mineral elements depends on the amounts present, the ratio between them, and the presence of vitamin D. Studies made at several of the experiment stations indicate that the chick ration should contain 1 per cent calcium and 0.6 per cent phosphorus. The ratio of calcium to phosphorus should be between 1:1 and 2:1.

The sodium chloride or salt requirement for growth is met by the salt content of animal protein feedstuffs (p. 289), when these are used as the only protein feedstuffs. When vegetable protein feedstuffs are used, it is advisable to add 0.5 per cent salt to the ration. Amounts up to 2 per cent of chick rations appear to make no difference in growth and health of birds. The more salt consumed, the more water consumed and consequently the more fluid the droppings become and the damper the litter.

The chick needs little more than traces of iron in the ration. This is supplied in adequate amounts by animal protein feedstuffs and by the traces found in alfalfa, middlings, and other vegetable substances making up the ration (Table 2, Appendix).

The chick needs thirty to fifty parts of manganese per million parts of the ration for normal growth of bone.

The *vitamin needs for growth* have been more thoroughly investigated than those required for egg production and hatchability. Vitamins A, D, G, and B_{12} are the ones that are most likely to be deficient in poultry rations. Even these are supplied in adequate amounts when birds are grown on green grass range.

The starting and growing chick needs 1500 to 2000 International units of vitamin A, 180 A.O.A.C. chick units of vitamin D, 0.014 mg. of vitamin B_{12}, and 1.6 milligrams of riboflavin (G) for starting and 0.9 for growing chicks, per pound of feed. Daily exposure to sunlight varying from two and one-half minutes in the summer to twenty-five minutes in the winter may be used in place of vitamin D for the prevention of rickets among growing chicks. Ultraviolet lights may be used in place of sunlight. The length of exposure of chicks under these lamps will vary with the kind of light, its intensity, and its distance from the chicks.

The nutritive requirements for egg production. The nutritive needs for egg production include those for maintenance, growth of pullet layers, and the nutrients in the eggs produced. The nutritive requirements will be greater for birds with an inherited capacity for high egg production than for birds that will lay only a few eggs. The standard-weight egg contains about 95 calories of gross energy, 7.5 grams of crude protein, and 2 grams of calcium.

The energy needs of a four- to five-and-one-half-pound hen include .145 to .227 pounds of feed daily for maintenance, and .078 to .1 pound for the production of an egg, or a total of .223 to .327 pounds. Naturally, the larger the bird and the larger the egg, the greater the energy needs for egg production.

The *protein needs* for egg production include about 6.5 grams daily for maintenance, and 7.5 grams for the egg. An additional amount is needed the first few months of production to meet the growth requirements. A protein content of 15 per cent in most laying rations will generally take care of the protein requirements. Pullets may need as high as 18 per cent protein the first few months of production to take care of the intensity of egg production and body growth. Old hens, on the other hand, may produce as well on 13 to 15 per cent protein as on higher levels.

Molting birds need proteins of high cystine content for renewal of feathers. Tests conducted at the Nebraska Agricultural Experiment Station have shown that the endogenous nitrogen loss among nonmolting hens amounts to about 144 milligrams per kilogram of body weight, and among molting hens, 219 milligrams. Evidently the molting hen breaks down tissue protein to supply the amino acid cystine for feather growth. When 145 milligrams of cystine were added to the diet of the molting hen, the endogenous nitrogen loss was reduced to 137 milligrams. The feeding of cystine exerted a protein sparing out of proportion to its nitrogen content, thus indicating its value for feather growth.

The mineral needs for egg production are mostly needs for calcium and phosphorus. The shell of the egg constitutes about 11 per cent of its total weight. It consists largely of calcium carbonate. The yolk of the egg contains about 80 milligrams of phosphorus. The laying ration should contain about 2.3 per cent calcium and .8 per cent phosphorus. The requirements will vary within wide limits, depending on the rate of production. Oyster shells or some other source of calcium should be kept available to supply additional calcium for high-producing hens. These hens will eat more mash feed, and therefore will secure additional phosphorus from this source.

The egg contains 1.5 milligrams of iron. Studies made at Ohio State University and elsewhere have shown that the traces of iron found in poultry feedstuffs meet the iron requirements for egg production. The traces of iodine found in oyster shell, fish meal, and other marine products meet the iodine needs of laying and breeding stock.

The salt needs are met by the use of animal protein feedstuffs. When vegetable protein feedstuffs are used, it is advisable to add 0.5 per cent sodium chloride to the ration. It may also be added to rations containing animal protein feedstuffs.

The laying and breeding ration should contain fifty parts of manganese per million for the production of normal shell texture and hatchability.

The *vitamin needs* for egg production should include about 3150 International units of vitamin A, 360 A.O.A.C. chick units of vitamin D, and .9 milligrams of riboflavin (G) per pound of feed.

Nutritive requirements for hatchability. It requires a better ration for the production of hatchable eggs than for the production of market eggs. The hen must store in the egg all of the vitamins and other nutrients required for chick embryo development. The ration has little influence on the production of sperm cells by males as long as the birds remain healthy.

Energy needs for the production of hatchable eggs are the same as for the production of market eggs.

Protein needs for the production of hatching eggs are the same in quantity as for the production of market eggs. Proteins of higher biological value are required for the production of hatching eggs than for the production of market eggs. Animal protein feedstuffs such as milk, fish meal, and meat scraps produce better hatchability than blood meal and "stick" (cooking water residue from the steam rendering of animal products). This may be due to their vitamin B_{12} content.

Mineral needs for the production of hatchable eggs are the same as for the production of market eggs (p. 275).

Vitamin needs for the production of hatching eggs are higher than for the production of market eggs. The breeding ration should contain about 3300 International units of vitamin A, 0.004 mg. of vitamin B_{12}, 450 A.O.A.C. chick units of vitamin D, and 1.3 milligrams of riboflavin per pound of feed. Vitamin E is also necessary for hatchability. It is widely distributed in poultry feedstuffs (Table 3, Appendix), and there is little chance of a deficiency in breeding rations.

It is desirable to feed rations suitable for the production of hatchable eggs to flocks kept for the production of market eggs. The eggs produced will have greater vitamin content and consequently greater food value. The vitamin D content of egg yolks has been increased tenfold by increasing the vitamin D content of the ration. When birds are fed a ration sufficiently high for the production of hatchable eggs, there is less depletion of the vitamin content of the body. The layers have better health and are better able to resist or withstand attacks of poultry disease.

Nutritive requirements for fattening. Birds that are fairly well matured, such as fryers, roasters, and capons and mature birds, may be fattened. The fattening of birds increases the palatability of the meat and makes it more tender. Another purpose of fattening is to add body weight.

Energy needs for fattening are high because the deposit of fat means the deposit of a rich source of energy. Carbohydrate feedstuffs make up a large proportion of the fattening ration because they are cheap and are readily transformed into fat by the animal. The addition of 2 to 4 per cent of corn or peanut oil to the ration will increase its fat-producing value.

Protein needs for fattening are low because animals that fatten well are nearly or completely finished growing. There is, therefore, little demand for protein for the growth of tissues. Animal proteins, such as milk, do improve the palatability of poultry, increase feed consumption, and consequently increase body weight. Rations containing 14 or 15 per cent protein are generally used for fattening poultry.

Mineral needs for fattening poultry are the same as for growth (p. 274). If vitamin D is omitted from the ration, the ratio of calcium to phosphorus may be increased to 2.3 to 1 to prevent the development of brittle wing and leg bones.

The *vitamin needs* for fattening are approximately one-half the needs for growth (p. 271).

Estrogens (female sex hormones) injected, implanted, or fed in the ration stimulate fat production and alter the requirements for fattening.

Summary of the nutritive requirements of poultry. Table 51 gives a summary of the nutrient allowances for chickens recommended by the Committee on Animal Nutrition of the National Research Council in 1946. The allowances take into consideration reasonable margins of safety to cover differences in composition, manufacture, and storage losses.

REVIEW QUESTIONS

1. Poultry products and poultry feedstuffs are composed of what nutrients?
2. What are the functions of minerals in the animal body?
3. What determines the value of a protein in a ration?
4. Differentiate between fat and ether extract.
5. What vitamin is most likely to be deficient in poultry rations? Why?
6. What are the most practical and economical sources of vitamin A for poultry?
7. What are the chief functions of vitamin G?
8. Differentiate between the U.S.P. and A.O.A.C. units of vitamin D.
9. Is there likely to be a shortage of vitamin E in poultry rations? Why?
10. Define metabolism.
11. Why are digestion trials with chickens subject to greater error than digestion trials with other domestic animals?
12. Why does the biological analysis of a feed give more information regarding the feeding value of a feed than is given by the chemical analysis?
13. Of what value is microscopic analysis of feeds?

Table 51

RECOMMENDED NUTRIENT ALLOWANCES FOR POULTRY
NATIONAL RESEARCH COUNCIL
June 1944 (Revised November 1, 1946)

	AMOUNT PER POUND OF FEED						
	Chickens				Turkeys		
NUTRIENTS	Starting 0–8 Wks.	Growing 8–18 Wks.	Laying Hens	Breeding Hens	Starting 0–8 Wks.	Growing 8–16 Wks.	Breeding Hens
Total protein, per cent.....	20	16	15	15	24	20 §	15
Vitamins							
A, International units....	2,000	2,000	3,300	3,300	4,000	4,000	4,000
D, (A.O.A.C. units)......	180	180	450	450	800	800	800
Thiamin, mg...........	.9	?	?	?	?	?	?
Riboflavin, mg.........	1.6	0.9	0.9	1.3	2.0	?	1.6
Pantothenic acid, mg.....	5.0	?	2.5	5.0	?	?	?
Nicotinic acid, mg........	8.0	?	?	?	?	?	?
Pyridoxine, mg.........	1.6	?	1.6	1.6	?	?	?
Biotin, mg.............	.045	?	?	.07	?	?	?
Choline, mg............	700.0	?	?	?	900	?	?
Minerals							
Calcium, per cent........	1.0	1.0	2.25 *	2.25 *	2.0	2.0	2.25
Phosphorus, per cent †....	.6	.6	.75	.75	1.0	1.0	.75
Salt, per cent ‡..........	.5	.5	.5	.5	.5	.5	.5
Manganese, mg.........	25.0	?	?	15.0	25.0	?	15.0
Iodine, mg.............	.5	.5	.5	.5			
Amino acids							
Glycine, per cent........	1.0						
Arginine, per cent........	1.0						
Methionine, per cent.....	.9						
or Methionine, per cent.	.5						
and Cystine, per cent...	.4						
Lysine, per cent.........	.9						
Tryptophane, per cent....	.25						

* Part of the calcium may be supplied free choice as oyster shell or limestone grit.
† Inorganic phosphorus should constitute 0.2 per cent of the total feed.
‡ Represents added salt or sodium chloride.
§ The protein content may be reduced to 16 per cent after the 16th week.

14. List factors which contribute to the palatability of a ration.
15. What are some of the factors which influence the digestibility of a ration?
16. What are some of the factors which influence the results obtained when the growth value of a feed is being determined?
17. What is the final or most reliable test of all in measuring the biological value of a feed?
18. Approximately what per cent of the feed eaten by laying hens is used for maintenance?
19. For what purposes may maintenance rations be fed on the farm?
20. Compare the protein and energy needs of a growing bird as it increases in body size.
21. What are the two principal mineral elements needed for growth?
22. Why is manganese needed in poultry rations?
23. What are the four vitamins that are most likely to be deficient in chick rations?

24. Compare the protein requirements for growth and egg production.
25. Why are the nutritive requirements higher for the production of hatching eggs than for the production of market eggs?
26. Why is it advisable to feed for the production of hatchable eggs even though they are to be sold as market eggs?
27. Compare the nutritive requirements for growth and fattening.

REFERENCES

ACKERSON, C. W., AND BLISH, M. J.: THE EFFECT OF CYSTINE ON THE ENDOGENOUS METABOLISM OF MOLTING HENS. Poultry Sci., 5: 162–165. 1926.

ALMQUIST, H. J.: PROTEINS AND AMINO ACIDS. Flour and Feed, 46, No. 3: 10–12. 1945.

BARLOW, J. S., SLINGER, S. J., AND ZIMMER, R. P.: THE REACTION OF GROWING CHICKS TO DIETS VARYING IN SODIUM CHLORIDE CONTENT. Poultry Sci., 27: 542–552. 1948.

BERRY, E. P., CARRICK, C. W., ROBERTS, R. E., AND HAUGE, S. M.: SUPPLEMENTARY EFFECT OF CORN GLUTEN MEAL WITH SOYBEAN OIL MEAL. Poultry Sci., 25: 498–500. 1946.

BETHKE, R. M., AND RECORD, P. R.: THE RELATION OF RIBOFLAVIN TO GROWTH AND CURLED TOE PARALYSIS IN CHICKS. Poultry Sci., 21: 147–154. 1942.

BIRD, H. R.: THE VITAMIN REQUIREMENTS OF CHICKS. Vitamins and Hormones, 5: 163–173. 1947.

BIRD, S., AND SINCLAIR, J. W.: A STUDY OF THE ENERGY REQUIRED FOR MAINTENANCE, EGG PRODUCTION, AND CHANGES IN BODY WEIGHT IN THE DOMESTIC HEN. Sci. Agr., 19: 542–550. 1939.

CARVER J. S., HEIMAN, V., COOK, J. W., AND ST. JOHN, J. L.: THE PROTEIN REQUIREMENTS OF WHITE LEGHORN PULLETS. Wash. Sta. Bul. 383: 30. 1939.

CLARK, T. B., RUNNELS, T. D., RIETZ, J. H., AND WEAKLEY, C. E.: EFFECT OF CERTAIN PROTEIN LEVELS ON EGG PRODUCTION AND MORTALITY IN WHITE LEGHORNS. W. Va. Sta. Bul. 331. 1948.

COMBS, G. F., NORRIS, L. C., AND HEUSER, G. F.: THE INTERRELATIONSHIP OF MANGANESE, PHOSPHATASE, AND VITAMIN D IN BONE DEVELOPMENT. Jour. Nutrition, 23: 131–140. 1942.

COUCH, J. R., JAMES, L. E., AND SHERWOOD, R. M.: THE EFFECT OF DIFFERENT AMOUNTS OF VITAMIN D IN THE DIET OF HENS AND PULLETS. Poultry Sci., 26: 30–37. 1947.

COUCH, J. R., CRAVENS, W. W., ELVEHIEM, C. A., AND HALPIN, J. G.: RELATION OF CARBOHYDRATE TO INTESTINAL SYNTHESIS OF BIOTIN AND HATCHABILITY IN MATURE FOWL. Jour. Nutrition, 35: 57. 1948.

CRAVENS, W. W., SEBESTA, E. E., HALPIN, J. G., AND HART, E. B.: STUDIES ON THE PYRIDOXINE REQUIREMENTS OF LAYING AND BREEDING HENS. Poultry Sci., 25: 80–82. 1946.

CRAVENS, W. W., AND HALPIN, J. G.: THE EFFECT OF PTEROYLGLUTAMIC ACID AND AN UNIDENITIFIED FACTOR ON EGG PRODUCTION AND HATCHABILITY. Jour. Nutrition, 37: 127. 1949.

DUKES, H. H.: STUDIES ON THE ENERGY METABOLISM OF THE HEN. Jour. Nutrition, 14: 341–354. 1937.

EWING, W. R.: Handbook of Poultry Nutrition. W. R. Ewing, Publisher, South Pasadena, Calif. Revised, 1947.

FRAPS, G. S.: DIGESTIBILITY AND PRODUCTION COEFFICIENTS OF POULTRY FEEDS. Tex. Sta. Bul. 372. 1928.

FRAPS, G. S.: COMPOSITION AND PRODUCTIVE ENERGY OF POULTRY FEEDS AND RATIONS. Tex. Sta. Bul. 678. 1946.

FRITZ, J. C.: THE EFFECT OF FEEDING GRIT ON DIGESTIBILITY IN THE DOMESTIC FOWL. Poultry Sci., 16: 75–79. 1937.

GERICKE, A. M.: THE NUTRITION OF POULTRY. Union of South Africa, Dept. of Agri. Bul. 260. 1945.

GILLIS, M. B.: PANTOTHENIC ACID IN THE NUTRITION OF THE HEN. Jour. Nutrition, 35: 351. 1948.

GILLIS, M. B., NORRIS, L. C., AND HEUSER, G. F.: THE EFFECT OF PHYTIN ON THE PHOSPHOROUS REQUIREMENT OF THE CHICK. Poultry Sci., 28: 283–288. 1949.

GRAU, C. R.: AMINO ACID NEEDS OF POULTRY. Flour and Feed, 46, No. 2: 36–38. 1945.

GRAU, C. R.: EFFECT OF PROTEIN LEVEL ON THE LYSINE REQUIREMENTS OF THE CHICK. Jour. Nutrition, 36: 99. 1948.

GRAU, C. R.: THE TREONINE REQUIREMENT OF THE CHICK. Jour. Nutrition, 37: 105. 1949.

HALNAN, E. T.: DIGESTIBILITY TRIALS WITH POULTRY, IX–XI. Jour. Agri. Sci. (Eng.), 33: 113–115. 1943; 34: 133–138, 139–154. 1944.

HALPERN, G. R., MARCH, B., AND BIELY, J.: STABILITY AND UTILIZATION OF VITAMIN A EMULSIONS IN MIXED FEEDS. Poultry Sci., 28: 168–172. 1929.

HEITMAN, H., AND HOGAN, A. G.: VITAMIN DEFICIENCIES IN RATIONS OF NATURAL FEEDSTUFFS. Mo. Sta. Res. Bul. 432. 1949.

HESS, C. W., AND JULL, M. A.: A STUDY OF THE INHERITANCE OF FEED UTILIZATION EFFICIENCY IN THE GROWING DOMESTIC FOWL. Poultry Sci., 27: 24–39. 1949.

HEUSER, G. F.: PROTEIN IN POULTRY NUTRITION—A REVIEW. Poultry Sci., 20: 362–368. 1941.

HEUSER, G. F.: THE RATE OF THE PASSAGE OF FOOD FROM THE CROP OF THE HEN. Poultry Sci., 24: 20–24. 1945.

HEUSER, G. F.: FEEDING POULTRY. John Wiley & Sons, Inc., New York. 1946.

HEYWANG, B. W., DENTON, C. A., AND BIRD, H. R.: THE EFFECT OF THE DIETARY LEVEL OF COTTONSEED MEAL ON HATCHABILITY. Poultry Sci., 28: 610–617. 1949.

HILL, D. C.: PROTEIN IN POULTRY NUTRITION. Sci. Agr., 24: 551–590. 1944.

HILL, F. W.: THE MULTIPLE NATURE OF THE DEFICIENCY OF UNIDENTIFIED NUTRIENTS IN CRUDE ALL-VEGETABLE PROTEIN CHICK STARTER RATIONS. Poultry Sci., 27: 536–541. 1948.

JOHNSON, E. L., CARRICK, C. W., AND HAUGE, S. M.: THE VITAMIN A REQUIREMENTS OF YOUNG CHICKENS. Poultry Sci., 27: 308–314. 1949.

JUKES, T. H.: THE RELATIONSHIP OF CHOLINE, METHIONINE, AND BETAINE IN THE NUTRITION OF CHICKENS. Flour and Feed, 50: 50. July, 1949.

KEITH, H., CARD, L. E., AND MITCHELL, H. H.: THE RATE OF PASSAGE OF FOOD THROUGH THE DIGESTIVE TRACT OF THE HEN. Jour. Agr. Res., 34: 759–770. 1927.

KRATZER, F. H., BIRD, F. H., ASMUNDSON, V. S., AND LEPKOVSKY, S.: THE

COMPARATIVE PYRIDOXINE REQUIREMENTS OF CHICKS AND TURKEY POULTS. Poultry Sci., 26: 453–456. 1947.

LAMON, H. M., AND LEE, A. R.: Poultry Feeds and Feeding. Orange Judd Co., New York. 1922.

LAMOREUX, W. F., AND HUTT, F. B.: GENETIC RESISTANCE TO DEFICIENCY OF RIBOFLAVIN IN THE CHICK. Poultry Sci., 27: 334–341. 1948.

LEPKOVSKY, S., BIRD, F. H., KRATZER, F. H., AND ASMUNDSON, V. S.: THE COMPARATIVE REQUIREMENTS OF CHICKS AND TURKEY POULTS FOR PANTOTHENIC ACID. Poultry Sci., 24: 335–339. 1945.

LILLIE, R. J., MARSDEN, S. J., GROSCHKE, A. C., AND BIRD, H. R.: RELATIVE REQUIREMENTS AND SOURCE OF B$_{12}$ FOR TURKEYS AND CHICKENS DURING THE LATER STAGES OF GROWTH. Poultry Sci., 28: 541–548. 1949.

LYMAN, C. M., KUIKEN, K., AND HALE, F.: THE ESSENTIAL AMINO ACID CONTENT OF COTTONSEED, PEANUT, AND SOYBEAN PRODUCTS. Tex. Sta. Bul. 692. 1947.

MACDONALD, A. J., AND BOSE, S.: STUDIES ON THE DIGESTIBILITY COEFFICIENTS AND BIOLOGICAL VALUES OF THE PROTEINS IN POULTRY FEEDS. Poultry Sci., 23: 135–141. 1944.

MAYNARD, L. A.: ANIMAL NUTRITION, 2nd ed. McGraw-Hill Book Co., New York. 1947.

MCCLYMONT, G. L., AND HART, L.: STUDIES ON NUTRITION OF POULTRY, 2. INVESTIGATIONS ON THE EFFECT OF VITAMIN A DEFICIENCY ON HATCHABILITY AND EGG PRODUCTION. Australian Vet. Jour. 24; 5–12. 1948.

MCKETTRICK, D. S.: THE INTERRELATIONS OF CHOLINE AND GLYCINE BETAINE IN THE GROWTH OF THE CHICK. Arch. Biochem. 18: 437. 1948.

MILBY, T. T., AND THOMPSON, R. B.: THE STABILITY OF D-ACTIVATED ANIMAL STEROL WHEN PREMIXED WITH COMMON POULTRY FEED INGREDIENTS. Poultry Sci., 23: 405–407. 1944.

MISHLER, D. H., CARRICK, C. W., AND HAGUE, S. M.: METHIONINE, CHOLINE, BETAINE, AND FISH PRODUCTS IN A SIMPLIFIED RATION. Poultry Sci., 28: 24–30. 1949.

MITCHELL, H. H., AND HAINES, W. T.: THE BASAL METABOLISM OF MATURE CHICKENS AND THE NET ENERGY VALUE OF CORN. Jour. Agr. Res., 34: 929–948. 1927.

MITCHELL, H. H., CARD, L. E., AND HAMILTON, T. S.: A TECHNICAL STUDY OF THE GROWTH OF WHITE LEGHORN CHICKENS. Ill. Sta. Bul. 367. 1931.

MOREHOUSE, N. F.: ACCELERATED GROWTH IN CHICKENS AND TURKEYS PRODUCED BY 3-NITRO-4-HYDROXYHENYLARSONIC ACID. Poultry Sci., 28: 375–384. 1949.

MORRISON, F. B.: FEEDS AND FEEDING, 21st ed. The Morrison Co., Ithaca, N. Y. 1948.

NATIONAL RESEARCH COUNCIL: RECOMMENDED NUTRIENT ALLOWANCES POULTRY, Washington, D. C. Revised, 1946.

NICHOL, C. A., ROBBLEE, A. R., CRAVENS, W. W., AND ELVEHIEM, C. A.: THE GROWTH RESPONSE OF CHICKS TO ANTIPERNICIOUS ANEMIA PREPARATIONS. Jour. Biol. Chem. 177: 631. 1949.

OLSSON, N.: INVESTIGATION OF THE VITAMIN D REQUIREMENTS OF CHICKS, POULTS, DUCKLINGS, AND GOSLINGS. Annals of the Royal Agricultural College of Sweden, 16: 1–38. 1948.

PATRICK, H., AND MORGAN, C. L.: STUDIES ON THE ROLE OF VITAMIN E IN CHICK NUTRITION. Poultry Sci., 23: 525–528. 1949.

ROBERTSON, E. I.: THE FOLIC ACID REQUIREMENT OF CHICKS FOR GROWTH, FEATHERING, AND HEMOGLOBIN FORMATION. Soc. Exp. Biol. and Med. Proc. 62: 97–101. 1946.

ROBERTSON, E. I., MILLER, R. F., AND HEUSER, G. F.: THE RELATION OF ENERGY TO FIBER IN CHICK RATIONS. Poultry Sci., 27: 736–741. 1948.

ROSENBERG, H. R.: Chemistry and Physiology of the Vitamins. Interscience Publishers, New York. 1942.

SCHAIBLE, P. J.: THE MINERALS IN POULTRY NUTRITION—A REVIEW. Poultry Sci., 20: 278–287. 1941.

SCHWEIGERT, B. S.: THE VALUE OF VARIOUS FEEDS AS SOURCES OF ARGININE, HISTIDINE, LYSINE, AND THREONINE FOR POULTRY. Poultry Sci., 27: 223–227. 1948.

SHERWOOD, R. M., COUCH, J. R., JAMES, L., AND CARTER, C. W.: EFFECT OF SULPHUR ON CHICK NUTRITION. Tex. Sta. Bul. 633. 1943.

SINGSEN, E. P.: THE PHOSPHORUS REQUIREMENTS OF THE CHICKEN. Conn. Sta. Bul. 260. 1948.

SINGSEN, E. P.: THE EFFECT OF PROTEIN LEVEL ON GROWTH AND EFFICIENCY OF FEED UTILIZATION. Poultry Sci., 28: 713–717. 1949.

SLOAN, H. J.: THE SEASONAL VARIATION IN THE ANTIRACHITIC EFFECTIVENESS OF SUNSHINE. Jour. Nutrition, 8: 731–749. 1935.

TAYLOR, L. W.: THE EFFECT OF FOLIC ACID ON EGG PRODUCTION AND HATCHABILITY. Poultry Sci., 26: 372–376. 1947.

TEMPERTON, H., AND DUDLEY, F. J.: THE EFFECTS OF USING PREFORMED VITAMIN A AS THE SOLE DIETARY SOURCE OF VITAMIN A FOR GROWING CHICKENS AND ADULT FOWLS. Harper Adams Utility Poultry Jour. 32: 83–110. 1947.

TITUS, H. W., JULL, M. A., AND HENDRICKS, W. A.: GROWTH OF CHICKENS AS A FUNCTION OF FEED CONSUMPTION. Jour. Agr. Res., 48: 817–835. 1934.

TITUS, H. W.: PRACTICAL NUTRITIVE REQUIREMENTS OF POULTRY. U. S. D. A. Yearbook: 787–843. 1939.

TITUS, H. W.: The Scientific Feeding of Chickens, 2nd ed. The Interstate, Danville, Ill. 1949.

WEIS, A. E., AND BISEBEY, B.: THE RELATION OF THE CAROTENOID PIGMENTS OF THE DIET TO THE GROWTH OF YOUNG CHICKS AND TO THE STORAGE IN THEIR TISSUES. Mo. Sta. Res. Bul. 405. 1947.

WHITSON, D., CARRICK, C. W., ROBERTS, R. E., AND HAUGE, S. M.: UTILIZATION OF FAT BY CHICKENS. Poultry Sci., 22: 137–141. 1943.

WILGUS, H. S., NORRIS, L. C., AND HEUSER, G. F.: THE RELATIVE PROTEIN EFFICIENCY AND THE RELATIVE VITAMIN G CONTENT OF COMMON PROTEIN SUPPLEMENTS USED IN POULTRY RATIONS. Jour. Agr. Res., 51: 383–399. 1935.

WILSON, W. O.: HIGH ENVIRONMENTAL TEMPERATURES AS AFFECTING THE REACTION OF LAYING HENS TO IODIZED CASEIN. Poultry Sci., 27: 581–592. 1949.

CHAPTER 10 ||||||||||||||||||||||||||||||||||||||||||||||||||||||||

Feeding Practices

▼

The feed cost amounts to about 60 per cent of the total cost of poultry production. The results obtained are largely dependent upon the rations and how they are fed. The value of a ration is determined by the kind, quality, and amounts of feedstuffs used.

Poultry Feedstuffs

Poultry derive part of their feed directly from plant sources and part indirectly through animal sources.

Feedstuffs may be classified into four principal groups, depending upon the primary purposes for which they are fed. These groups are carbohydrate, protein, mineral, and vitamin feedstuffs.

Carbohydrate Feedstuffs

Carbohydrate feedstuffs constitute about 75 to 90 per cent of poultry rations. They are used primarily for heat, energy, and fat production. The carbohydrate feedstuffs are produced easily, are readily available, and are cheap. They contain other nutrients in addition to carbohydrates or nitrogen-free extract (Tables 1–3, Appendix). They are deficient in certain essential amino acids, minerals, and vitamins.

The cereal grains are the chief carbohydrate feedstuffs. They are much alike in composition and feeding value. The amounts of different grains in rations may be varied within wide limits, depending upon price and availability. Grains are graded according to moisture content, weight per bushel, soundness of kernels, and freedom from foreign seeds and dirt (Table 52).

Corn. Indian corn, or maize, is the chief cereal grain produced in the United States. It produces better yields than the other grains, is easily grown, and is well liked by domestic animals. Corn is high in nitrogen-free extract, chiefly starch, and relatively high among the cereal grains in fat. It is low in protein and mineral content. The two chief types of corn fed to livestock are dent and flint. They have about the same feeding value. Flint corn is harder than dent corn. Hybrid corn is rapidly replacing open-pollinated corn because of greater yield. However, its protein content is lower.

283

Table 52

GRAIN STANDARDS [1]

Grain	Grade	Minimum Test Weight per Bushel	Moisture	Damaged Kernels		Foreign Material	
				Total	Heat Damaged	Total	Matter Except Other Grains
		Pounds	*Per Cent*				
Corn (Yellow, white and mixed)	1	54	14.0	3	0.1	2	
	2	53	15.5	5	.2	3	
	3	51	17.5	7	.5	4	
	4	48	20.0	10	1.0	5	
	5	44	23.0	15	3.0	7	
Wheat (Hard, red winter)	1	60		2	0.1	1	0.5
	2	58		4	.2	2	1.0
	3	56		7	.5	3	2.0
	4	54		10	1.0	5	3.0
	5	51		15	3.0	7	5.0
Oats	1	32		0.1		2	
	2	30		.3		3	
	3	27		1.0		4	
	4	24		3.0		5	
Barley	1	47		0.1		1	
	2	46		.2		2	
	3	43		.5		3	
	4	40		1.0		4	
	5	35		3.0		6	
Rye	1	56		2	0.1	3	1
	2	54		4	.2	6	2
	3	52		7	.5	10	4
	4	49		15	3.0	10	6

[1] Condensed from U. S. D. A. Handbook of Official Grain Standards, Revised, 1949.

New corn that is well matured at husking time, should not contain more than 20 or 25 per cent moisture. It is satisfactory for poultry-feeding purposes as soon as it is dry enough to shell. The feeding value of new corn per pound as purchased becomes greater as it becomes drier.

Shelled corn may spoil, when stored, if it contains more than 14 to 15 per cent water. It pays to shell corn and feed it to poultry in hoppers rather than to feed it as ear corn in the litter.

Ground corn generally has about the same feeding value as whole corn. Some of the whole corn is used by the animal for energy for grinding, thereby lowering its net feeding value. In ground corn there is a tendency to dry out and become unpalatable. The fat in the germ becomes rancid and there is loss of vitamin A. These factors reduce the net value of ground corn. Coarsely ground corn is more palatable and gives better results than finely ground material. The feeding value of ground corn is also higher when it is ground only a few days before it is to be fed.

Cracked corn has no greater feeding value than coarsely ground corn, if as great. Sifting out the fine material from cracked corn adds to the expense of this material over that of whole or ground corn. The fine material sifted out contains corn bran and part of the corn germ. These materials have higher nutritive value than the more starchy cracked corn.

Corn feed meal is the fine siftings obtained in the manufacture of cracked corn, with or without aspiration products added to the siftings. It is, therefore, not a standard product. It varies in composition and feeding value, depending upon the amount of germ and bran it contains.

Hominy meal is a by-product of the manufacture of hominy, hominy grits, and corn meal by the degermination process. It contains the corn bran, germ, and part of the starchy portion of the grain. It varies in composition, depending on the amount of germ and bran it contains. Hominy contains 5 to 7 per cent fat, and about 11 per cent protein. Hominy meal is probably slightly better than ground corn in fattening rations because of its greater fat content. In growing and laying rations, hominy meal is no better than ground corn, if it is as good.

Wheat. Wheat is second only to corn as a cereal in the United States. It is raised primarily for the manufacture of flour and other human foods. It is generally more expensive than corn and other cereal grains, and is therefore less used in livestock rations. Wheat by-products, bran and middlings, resulting from the manufacture of flour, are widely used in live stock and poultry rations. Wheat from the western plains contains about 13.5 per cent protein, while that from the Pacific Coast has only 9.9 per cent. Spring wheat is slightly higher in protein and fiber than winter wheat. Wheat is low in calcium, but is a fairly good source of phosphorus. It is a good source of vitamins B_1 and E. Winter and spring wheat have about the same feeding value.

Whole wheat is the most palatable of all the grains for poultry. Young chicks are able to eat and utilize it after they are two or three weeks old. Good, sound, and clean whole wheat is usually worth more for flour milling purposes than for livestock feeding. Shriveled wheat that is unsatisfactory for milling purposes is satisfactory for poultry feeding. The same is true of wheat that contains other grains and possibly some weed seeds. Wheat gives better results when fed as the whole grain in feeders than when ground and mixed in the mash.

Ground wheat may be used as a substitute for bran and middlings in poultry mashes when it is cheaper. The wheat should be coarsely ground. Large amounts of ground wheat in poultry rations cause them to have a tendency to pack and to cause sticky masses in the mouth when eaten. This is due to the large amount of flour material and to the wheat gluten present. When ground wheat is used in poultry mash feeds, it is desirable to use ground oats, alfalfa, and possibly wheat bran to add bulk and prevent packing. The use of 25 per cent ground wheat and 5 per cent wheat bran makes a satisfactory substitute for a similar amount of middlings and bran. Ground wheat is lower in protein, minerals, and vitamins than bran and middlings, and consequently is not quite so valuable a feedstuff.

Wheat bran is a by-product obtained in the milling of wheat for flour. It is the outer coating of the wheat grain. As the wheat passes through successive pairs of rollers, it is broken and crushed, the bran flattened out, and the flour sifted out. In the milling of wheat, the yield of flour amounts to about 72 to 75 per cent of the whole wheat, and the by-products are composed of about 11 per cent bran and 11 per cent middlings. Bran contains about 16 per cent protein, 5 per cent fat, and 10 per cent fiber. It is low in calcium, but contains more phosphorus than any of the other grain products. Bran should not constitute more than 10 to 15 per cent of the chick ration because of its bulkiness, high fiber content, phosphorus content, and laxative effect. The best grades of bran have large clean flakes and contain no screenings. Fine, reground bran or standard bran often contains screenings. These screenings are chiefly weed seeds. They may interfere with palatability, depending upon the kind and amount of seeds present. Bran is used in rations primarily to add bulk and for its mild laxative effect.

Wheat standard middlings consist of fine particles of bran and germ and red dog flour obtained as a by-product in the milling of wheat for flour. This feedstuff consists of 17.4 per cent protein, 6.8 per cent fiber, and 5.5 per cent fat. It supplies about 12 per cent more digestible nutrients than bran and is a better feedstuff. Middlings generally constitute from 15 to 30 per cent of poultry mashfeeds. It adds to the palatability of the mash, supplies B_1, E, and other vitamins through its germ content, and helps to prevent perosis because of its manganese content. The protein in middlings, like that of other cereal grains, is low in biological value and needs to be supplemented with animal protein feedstuffs.

Wheat flour middlings, also known as wheat gray shorts, contains more flour and less bran and germ than found in standard middlings. This feedstuff should not contain more than 6 per cent fiber. It has about the same or a little less feeding value than standard middlings.

Wheat red dog flour, also known as white shorts, contains more flour and less fiber than found in flour middlings. While it is higher in digestible nutrients than standard middlings, it is lower in feeding value because it contains less germ and bran, and consequently less of the valuable vitamins and minerals.

Wheat mixed feed, also known as "mill run," consists of the bran and middlings obtained in the milling of wheat. It has about the same feeding value as equal parts of bran and middlings and may be used in place of them in poultry rations.

Wheat germ in some of the larger mills is separated more or less completely from the middlings and sold as wheat germ meal. It is rich in vitamins B_1 and E, and contains about 25 to 30 per cent protein.

Oats. Oats rank third in acreage among the cereals in the United States. They contain about 12 per cent protein, 10.6 per cent fiber, and 4.7 per cent fat. Oats vary all the way from 30 per cent hulls or less and thirty-two pounds or more per bushel to more than 50 per cent hulls and less than twenty-five pounds per bushel. Good, heavy oats weighing thirty-two pounds per bushel are a valuable feedstuff for poultry. This feedstuff supplies factors which aid in preventing cannibalism and in the prevention of perosis (p. 349). Since these factors are found in the hull and outer coating of the oat kernel, the entire oat grain should be fed. Oats generally constitute from 10 to 30 per cent of poultry rations.

Whole oats are a satisfactory feedstuff for poultry. They can be utilized satisfactorily by chickens and turkeys which are at least six weeks old. The consumption will vary with the environment and other constituents in the ration. Chickens kept in confinement and on wire will consume more oats than birds kept on straw litter and given green grass range. Oats may be kept before the birds in hoppers or mixed with other grains or the mash.

Ground oats are used satisfactorily in mash feeds. They should be finely ground with a hammer mill.

Clipped oats have been run through an oat clipper, which clips off the pointed end of the hulls. This process is unnecessary.

Hulled oats, also known as oat groats, and rolled oats are of less value than whole or ground oats for poultry. While hulled oats contain less fiber and more digestible nutrients than ground whole oats, they contain less of the factors which prevent cannibalism and perosis. It is not economical to feed hulled oats to poultry.

Sprouted oats have no greater feeding value than unsprouted whole oats (Table 53). They were once used as a substitute for green grass and succulent feed during the winter months. Alfalfa meal is now used in place of sprouted oats. It furnishes the material supplied by sprouted oats and additional protein, mineral, and vitamin nutrients.

Barley. Barley ranks fourth in importance as a grain crop in the United States. It is the most widely cultivated of the cereals throughout the world, as it is adapted to a wide range of climatic conditions. Barley production is gradually replacing oat production. The two grains are much alike in composition and feeding value. Heavy barley, weighing forty-eight pounds

Table 53

THE FEEDING VALUE OF DIFFERENT FORMS OF OATS
FOR EGG PRODUCTION [2]

Kind of Oats Constituting 20 Per Cent of the Ration	Egg Production Per Bird (50 Weeks)
Basal ration—no oats....................	116
Ground oats..........................	140
Whole oats...........................	133
Germinated oats.......................	135
Hulled oats...........................	131

or more per bushel, is more satisfactory for poultry feeding than lighter barley weighing only about forty-five pounds per bushel. Barley may be used in the same manner as oats in poultry rations. It may be used to replace oats or a part of the corn and wheat products commonly used in poultry rations.

Rye. Rye, although resembling wheat closely in composition, is an unsatisfactory feedstuff for poultry. The whole grain is hard and unpalatable. The use of 20 per cent or more of ground rye in chick rations causes digestive disturbances and the droppings have a tendency to adhere to the feet. A small amount of rye, not exceeding about 15 per cent, may be used in growing and laying rations. It should be ground and used in the mash feed.

Buckwheat. Buckwheat is unpalatable because of its dark, unattractive appearance and high fiber content. It is unsatisfactory as a whole grain feed. Ground buckwheat or buckwheat middlings may be used to replace 10 to 20 per cent of other grains or their by-products in poultry mash feeds.

Sorghum grains. Sorghum grains are grown in the southwestern part of the United States where there is a scarcity of rainfall. The chief kinds are milo, kafir, feterita, kaoliang, hegari, durra, and shallu. The sorghums resemble corn in composition (Table 1, Appendix). Unlike yellow corn, they are deficient in vitamin A. There are no advantages in including sorghum grains in poultry rations unless they are cheaper than corn, wheat, and oats. In fact, the sorghum grains do not give quite so satisfactory results.

Rice. Rice is one of the most important cereal crops of the world. However, the production in the United States is of minor importance. Rice is grown in the coastal section of Louisiana, and in Arkansas, Texas, and California. Rice products, such as rice bran, rice polish, and brewers' rice, can be used to replace part of the other grains in the ration. Rice is a good feedstuff and well liked by poultry. It is seldom economical for use in rations except in regions where it is produced.

Screenings. Screenings consist of small, broken, or shrunken kernels of grain, wild oats, and wild buckwheat, smaller weed seeds, chaff, and broken stems. This material is removed as completely as possible from wheat and other grains before they are milled for human consumption. Screenings vary so greatly in composition and feeding value that no definite statements can

---

[2] Kennard and Chamberlain, 1936.

be made regarding them. Bulky screenings are unsatisfactory for poultry and are of low food value. The presence of many weed seeds such as lamb's-quarter, pigweed, and mustard, will interfere with palatability. It is a safe plan to avoid the use of screenings or feedstuffs containing much of them in poultry rations.

Cane molasses. Cane molasses, also known as blackstrap, is a by-product of the manufacture of cane sugar from sugar cane. Some cane molasses is produced in the Gulf Coast states, but most of the material used in the United States is imported from Cuba and Hawaii. This feedstuff consists mostly of sugars and water. It also contains some minerals and vitamins (Tables 1–2, Appendix). Cane molasses may be used to replace cereal grains, pound for pound, up to 10 per cent of the ration. It should be incorporated in the mash feed with a power mixer. Cane molasses used in rations containing little or no milk will increase palatability, increase water consumption, and serve as a mild laxative. It appears to keep poultry in a more healthy condition.

Beet molasses is not so satisfactory as cane molasses as a poultry feedstuff because of its higher alkaline salt content and greater laxative effect.

Bread. Bread and other stale bakery products are sometimes fed to poultry. The analysis of bread is quite similar to that of grains (Table 1, Appendix). Bakery products may be used to replace a part of the grains fed to poultry.

Potatoes. Potatoes which are too small for sale may be cooked and fed to poultry. A gallon of cooked potatoes may be fed to one hundred hens daily to take the place of about a quart of grain.

Protein Feedstuffs

The protein feedstuffs are the most costly group of feedstuffs used in poultry rations. They generally constitute from 10 to 30 per cent of the ration. Protein feedstuffs are derived from both plant and animal sources. Care is needed in the selection of protein feedstuffs for poultry rations in order to secure a sufficient quantity of the essential amino acids for growth and egg production.

Animal protein feedstuffs include milk, meat scraps, tankage, fish meal, and hatchery residue. They are more palatable, higher in mineral, vitamin B_{12} and riboflavin content, and higher in biological value (Table 54) than vegetable proteins. Most animal protein feedstuffs are more variable in composition than vegetable protein feedstuffs because they are blends of various packing house and cannery by-products. The use of high temperatures in the preparation of animal protein feedstuffs reduces their digestibility, vitamin content, and biological value.

Vegetable protein feedstuffs include soybean oil meal, corn-gluten meal, cottonseed meal, peanut oil meal, and linseed meal. They are not so palatable or digestible, or of so high a biological value as the animal protein feedstuffs. Vegetable protein feedstuffs are low in mineral and vitamin G content. Cooking, in the process of removing oil, increases their feeding value.

Table 54

RELATIVE EFFICIENCY OF PROTEIN FEED-
STUFFS AS MEASURED BY NITROGEN
RETENTION BY GROWING BIRDS [3]

Protein Feedstuffs	Relative Protein Efficiency
Casein (standard control)............	100
Dried skim milk.....................	100
White fish meal	
Vacuum dried.....................	104
Steam dried.....................	104
Flame dried.....................	94
Sardine fish meal	
Domestic.......................	98
Asiatic........................	91
Menhaden fish meal	
Steam dried.....................	91
Flame dried.....................	80
Soybean meal	
Expeller process..................	89
Hydraulic process.................	85
Meat scrap	
75% protein......................	69
60% protein......................	75
55% protein......................	82
50% protein......................	73
45% protein......................	72
Whale meat meal	
70–75% protein...................	73
55–60% protein...................	53
Corn gluten meal..................	61
Ground soybeans...................	58

Milk. Milk is one of the most valuable poultry feedstuffs. It is recommended for use in nearly all poultry rations because of its high-quality proteins, good assortment of minerals, and vitamin content. Milk adds to palatability of poultry rations, is easily digested and assimilated, acts as an antidote for most toxins, and has a mild laxative effect.

Whole milk is generally too expensive for feeding poultry. Skim milk or buttermilk is just as valuable and much cheaper. The vitamin A removed with the cream from skim milk is supplied by other feedstuffs in poultry rations.

Sweet and sour milk are of equal value for poultry. Sometimes it requires a few days for birds to become accustomed to the change from one form to the other. The lactic acid content of milk at the time of feeding has little in-

---

[3] Wilqus, Norris, and Heuser, 1935.

fluence on its value after consumption. Acids and alkalis in the digestive processes quickly change the characteristics of milk.

Skim milk is whole milk from which the cream has been removed. It is available on farms where cream is sold. Skim milk may be used in place of water as a drink for poultry. The consumption will vary all the way from .5 to 6 gallons per day per hundred birds, depending on size of birds, temperature, the type of ration fed, and the rate of production. Milk that sours during the day and turns to a semisolid form (clabber) is still satisfactory for supplying the moisture needs of poultry. Giving chickens nothing but milk as a drink is equivalent to the use of about thirteen pounds of dried milk in each hundred pounds of feed. This practice will reduce the other feed consumption by about 13 per cent. It also will supply all of the protein feedstuff needed for the laying, breeding, or fattening ration.

Liquid skim milk and buttermilk are generally cheaper than the condensed and dried forms when compared on the basis of the same solid content, because the evaporation of water from milk is an expensive process.

Buttermilk is the by-product remaining after the fat has been removed as butter from a mixture of cream and milk. It is more variable in composition than skim milk because it may contain neutralizers and washwater from the churn. During the summer months, cream may become too sour to churn properly. Neutralizers, chiefly calcium oxide and magnesium oxide, are added to the cream to reduce the acidity. These minerals remain in the buttermilk. One researcher has analyzed samples of dried buttermilk which varied in ash content from 8 to 14 per cent. Figure 135 shows two groups of chicks fed the same ration and the same amounts of dried buttermilk. The two samples of milk came from different plants and differed widely in ash content. Buttermilk and skim milk containing the same water and ash content have about the same feeding value.

Condensed milk, also known as semisolid, is milk in which part of the water has been removed. It exists in a semisolid or paste form. Condensed milk varies greatly in moisture content. The products on the market generally contain 26 to 30 per cent solids, the remaining 70 to 74 per cent being water. The solids in condensed milk have about the same nutritive value as those in liquid or dried milk. A gallon of liquid skim milk or buttermilk is equal to about 3 pounds of the semisolid, or .9 pounds of the dried form in feeding value. Condensed milk is generally more expensive than the dried form when compared on the same solid basis, because of the greater amount of water that must be handled in transporting it.

Dried milk contains about 35 per cent protein, 8 per cent ash, and 50 per cent lactose, or milk sugar. Dried skim milk and dried buttermilk are both sold for animal feeding purposes. More skim milk than buttermilk is used. Some of the dried skim milk produced is used for human consumption. Sweet cream buttermilk is preferable to the sour cream product because of its more uniform ash and higher vitamin G content. Dried skim milk is more constant in composition than dried buttermilk. The vitamin G content of both kinds of milk will vary within rather wide limits, depending upon the rations fed

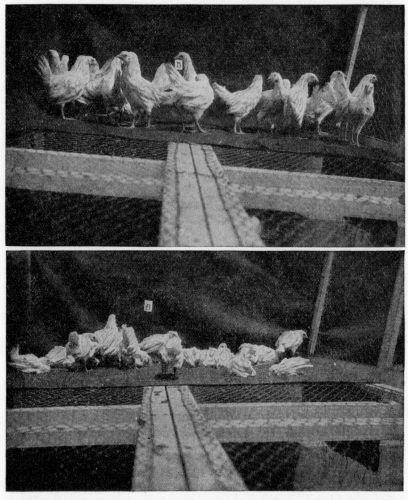

Fig. 135. Influence of the quality of dried buttermilk on the growth of chicks. The two lots received the same ration but different brands of dried buttermilk.

to the cows and the temperature used in drying the milk. Dried milk should be white or creamy white in appearance and free from brown or charred particles. The use of about 5 per cent dried milk in poultry rations will supply sufficient milk proteins to supplement other proteins in the ration and to supply the needs for vitamin G and B_{12}.

Meat scraps. Meat scraps are composed of the ground, dry-rendered residue from animal tissues exclusive of hoof, horn, manure, and stomach contents, except in such traces as might occur unavoidably in good factory practice. It varies widely in composition and feeding value, depending on the amount of bone, cracklings, glandular tissue, and meat present. The more bone present, the higher the mineral content and the lower the protein content. The vitamin content is largely determined by the amount of glandular tissues present, such as livers and kidneys, and the temperature used in the process of preparation. Meat scraps are widely used in poultry rations to supply protein and minerals. The amount used is generally between 5 and 15 per cent. Milk and fish meal are sometimes used in place of all or a part of the meat scraps in poultry rations.

Tankage. Tankage is a packing house by-product somewhat similar to meat scraps. It generally contains 60 per cent protein, while meat scraps generally contain 50 per cent. Tankage may be prepared by cooking under live steam or by the dry-rendering process. The latter process produces a product of higher nutritive value. "Stick," or the cooking water residue, and blood meal are often added to raise the protein content to 60 per cent. Both of these products are of low biological value. Therefore, tankage may be of lower nutritive value than meat scraps.

Fish meal. Fish meal is the clean, dried, ground tissue of undecomposed whole fish or fish cuttings, either or both, with or without the extraction of part of the oil, and containing not more than 3 per cent salt. Fish meals vary in composition and feeding value. Those made from white fish are superior to those made from dark, inedible fish. Fish meals made at low temperatures are superior to those processed at high temperatures. Fish meals containing much of the viscera, as are obtainable from some fish canneries, are superior to meals made from whole fish. The average fish meal has about the same composition and feeding value as meat scraps. In coastal regions, fish meal is as cheap or cheaper than meat scraps. Inland it is more expensive. White fish meal made by a low temperature or vacuum process contains protein of high biological value and is a good source of vitamin G. It compares favorably with milk as an animal protein feedstuff.

Hatchery residue. Hatchery residue, also known as chicken tankage, consists of infertile eggs, dead embryos, cull chicks, and eggshells obtained in hatchery operation. Most of the material is a total loss at the present time. It may be processed like meat scraps. Chicken tankage is a satisfactory animal protein feedstuff for poultry. It may be used in the place of meat scraps in laying rations.

Blood meal. Blood meal is a poor protein feedstuff for poultry. It is unpalatable and its protein is of low biological value.

Soybean oil meal. Soybean oil meal is the most widely used of all the vegetable protein feedstuffs. It is prepared from soybeans by removing the oil and grinding the resulting presscake. Soybeans are unpalatable and unsatisfactory as a feedstuff. Soybean oil meal is palatable and a good protein feedstuff when supplemented with minerals and vitamins B_{12} and G. Soybean oil is used in industry. A ton of beans will yield about 1600 pounds of soybean oil meal and 400 pounds of oil. The beans may be processed by the expeller, hydraulic, or solvent methods. In the expeller method, the crushed beans are subjected to great pressure in "expellers" to remove the oil. Some heat is generated in the process. In the hydraulic or old process, the beans are cooked and most of the oil pressed out in hydraulic presses. This method is the one generally used in processing cottonseed and flaxseed. In the solvent process, the ground beans are extracted with low-boiling-point gasoline. The solvent is later removed by treatment with steam, which also cooks the feed. Soybean oil meal made by this process contains about 44 per cent protein and 1 per cent fat, while that made by the hydraulic process contains about 41 per cent protein and 5 or 6 per cent fat.

Soybean oil meal for poultry rations should have been thoroughly cooked while being processed. This is indicated by a pleasant nutlike taste and a light brownish or tan color. If the soybean oil meal has a raw "beany" taste, it has not been heated sufficiently. Soybean oil meal needs to be fed with some animal protein feedstuff for best results. It may constitute 75 per cent of the protein feedstuffs used in chick and breeding rations, and as much as 90 per cent of the protein feedstuffs used in rations for finishing pullets and turkeys, and for market egg production. When soybean meal replaces most of the meat scraps or fish meal in poultry rations, an additional quantity of minerals and vitamins B_{12} and G need to be included in the ration. Milk is an excellent feedstuff for feeding with soybean meal. It supplements the soybean protein, provides some of the needed minerals, and supplies necessary vitamins. A pound of mineral mixture (p. 297) is generally added to the ration for each 5 or 6 pounds of soybean oil meal used when animal protein feedstuffs constitute less than 50 per cent of the total protein feedstuffs used.

Corn gluten meal. Corn gluten meal is that part of shelled corn that remains after the separation of the larger part of the starch, the germ, and the bran, by the process employed in the manufacture of corn starch and glucose. It is a good protein feedstuff, but like other grain proteins is deficient in essential amino acids. Like soybean oil meal, it should be fed with animal protein feedstuffs and minerals. Corn gluten meal made from yellow corn contains about twice as much vitamin A as yellow corn.

Cottonseed meal. Cottonseed meal is a cheap and satisfactory protein feedstuff for poultry rations in the cotton-producing states. It needs to be supplemented with animal protein, minerals, and vitamins B_{12} and G, as in the case of soybean meal (p. 293). The use of more than 5 or 6 per cent cottonseed meal in laying rations results in the production of eggs which develop green and brown spots on the yolks, when the eggs are held more than a few weeks in storage.

Distillers' dried grains. Distillers' dried grains are of variable composition because of the variation in grain mixtures used by different distilleries. The protein content varies from 15 to 30 per cent, and the fiber from 10 to 15 per cent. This feedstuff is little used in poultry rations.

Linseed oil meal. Linseed oil meal is made from flaxseed. The production in the United States is small. Linseed oil meal is not so palatable as soybean oil meal or corn gluten meal. There is no advantage in including it in poultry rations when the more palatable protein feedstuffs are available.

Peanut oil meal. Peanut oil meal is a good vegetable protein feedstuff. The quantity produced is small. It may be used economically in poultry rations in the few southern states where peanuts are produced.

Mineral Feedstuffs

Growing birds need minerals for growth of skeleton and the laying hens need minerals for the formation of the egg yolks and eggshells. Most of the feedstuffs used in poultry rations are low in mineral content. This is true of the grains and vegetable protein feedstuffs. Animal protein feedstuffs are good sources of minerals. When little or no animal protein feedstuffs are included in poultry rations, additional minerals need to be added. Calcium, phosphorus, manganese, sodium, and chlorine are the mineral elements most likely to be deficient in feedstuffs comprising poultry rations. The laying hen has an exceptionally high requirement for calcium for making eggshells.

Bone meal. Bone meal consists mainly of calcium phosphate $(Ca_3PO_4)_2$. It varies in composition, depending on method of manufacture.

Poultry bone meal, sometimes called raw bone meal or steamed bone meal, consists of bones which have been thoroughly cooked, dried, and ground. This product contains 20 to 25 per cent protein. *Special steamed bone meal* is a by-product of gelatin or glue manufacture. It is cheaper than poultry or steamed bone meal and is as satisfactory as a mineral feedstuff. It contains more calcium and phosphorus and much less protein than poultry bone meal. *Fertilizer bone meal* is unpalatable, has a disagreeable odor, and is unsuitable for a poultry feedstuff.

Bone meal is added to poultry starting and growing rations which contain less than about 10 per cent animal protein feedstuffs. It is an important ingredient of mineral mixtures (p. 297).

Limestone. Limestone consists mainly of calcium carbonate $(CaCO_3)$. Good grades of limestone for poultry feeding purposes contain 95 per cent or more calcium carbonate and a low percentage of magnesium. The presence of magnesium appears to be antagonistic to calcium assimilation. Ground limestone is sometimes added to mash feed to balance the calcium deficiency of the grains. The amount used is usually about 2 per cent. This will make a satisfactory ratio of calcium to phosphorus. Limestone is one of the principal ingredients of mineral mixtures (p. 297).

Limestone grit is often used as a substitute for or in addition to oyster shells for laying hens. It is not quite so palatable as oyster shells and generally does not give quite so satisfactory an egg production. Bright, shiny limestone grit is eaten more readily than dull gray dolomitic limestone grit. Many poultrymen keep both oyster shells and limestone grit before the laying hens in separate shell hoppers. It is better to allow laying hens free access to these sources of calcium than to incorporate all that is needed in the mash feed. A hen that lays 250 eggs in a year will need much more than one that lays 125 eggs. If enough calcium is added to meet the needs of high-producing birds, much of it will have to be excreted by low-producing birds.

Oyster shells. Oyster shells contain 96 per cent or more calcium carbonate. They are used extensively as a source of calcium for eggshell formation. Crushed hen-size oyster shell grit is usually kept before the laying hens in separate shell hoppers. A hen will eat two to four pounds of oyster shell or limestone grit in a year, depending on the number of eggs produced and the amount of calcium in the mash feed. When given free access to oyster shell and limestone grit, the hens consume much more oyster shell than limestone. Apparently the small amount of muscle adhering to the oyster shell adds to its palatability. Ground oyster shells are sometimes added to the mash feed and used in mineral mixtures in place of limestone.

Clam shells may be used as a substitute for oyster shells, although they are not quite so satisfactory.

Defluorinated rock phosphate. Rock phosphate that has been ground and heated to remove most of the fluorine may be used as a substitute for bone meal in poultry rations. Untreated raw rock phosphate is objectionable as a mineral feedstuff because it contains fluorine, which interferes with normal mineral assimilation.

Phosphatic limestone is a natural mineral consisting of a mixture of limestone and rock phosphate in which the former predominates. It may be substituted for mixtures of limestone and bone meal in mash feeds and mineral mixtures. It is a fair substitute for oyster shells for eggshell formation.

Salt. Salt, or sodium chloride (NaCl), is needed in poultry rations for palatability and digestion. It is deficient in plant feedstuffs, such as grains and vegetable protein feedstuffs. Meat scraps and milk contain salt because the mineral is fed to animals from which they are obtained. Fish meal is also a good source. Salt is generally added to poultry rations at the rate of 0.5 per cent.

Kelp. Kelp is a giant seaweed obtained from the seacoast of southern California. It contains about 30 per cent ash. This ash is composed largely of sodium chloride and a wide variety of other sea minerals. Kelp is incorporated with fish meal and sold under the trade name of *Manamar*.

Manganese. It has recently been shown that manganese is an essential mineral element for bone formation and hatchability. Only about fifty parts per million are needed in the ration. It may be supplied by the proper selection of feedstuffs (Table 2, Appendix). Manganese may be added to mash feeds or mineral mixtures in the form of manganese sulphate.

Iron. Only a very small amount of iron is needed in poultry rations. It is supplied by a number of feedstuffs used in poultry rations, such as meat scraps, fish meal, alfalfa, and grass. A small amount of iron is usually added to mineral mixtures in the form of iron oxide, chloride, or sulphate (p. 297).

Iodine. A very small quantity of iodine is needed in poultry rations. Ample amounts are provided by the use of marine products, such as fish meal, oyster shells, or fish oil. Iodized salt is sometimes used in poultry rations. Iodine is generally added to mineral mixtures in the form of potassium iodide (KI).

Mineral mixtures. Mineral additions are necessary in rations that contain little or no animal protein feedstuffs. It is often desirable to mix the minerals

Fig. 136. Colony houses on grass range. All the vitamin requirements are taken care of when birds have a good green, young, and tender grass range. (Ohio Extension Bulletin 126.)

together and incorporate the mixture in the mash feed. It is difficult or impossible to mix thoroughly a minute quantity of a mineral in a big pile of feed.

Two simple yet satisfactory mineral mixtures are listed below:

No. 1—Bone meal, 40; limestone, 40; salt, 19; and manganese sulphate, 1 per cent.

No. 2—Bone meal, 26.97; limestone, 50; salt, 20; ferrous sulphate, 2; potassium iodide, .02; copper sulphate, .01; and manganese sulphate, 1 per cent.

Vitamin Feedstuffs

Many of the feedstuffs used in poultry rations are good sources of more than one group of nutrients. In this chapter the feedstuffs have been classified according to the primary purpose for which they are fed. Some of the following feedstuffs classed as vitamin feedstuffs are also good sources of proteins and minerals.

Green grass. Young, tender, green grass supplies all of the vitamins needed by chickens except vitamin D (Fig. 136). When the birds are on range they will secure this vitamin from sunlight. Grass also supplies protein, minerals, and carbohydrates needed by poultry. Less expensive feed and a smaller amount are needed by poultry when they are kept on young, tender, green grass range (Table 55). Unfortunately, suitable range is generally available only during the spring and early summer months. As the season advances and the grass becomes older, the protein, mineral, and vitamin content declines rapidly and the fiber content increases. By pasturing the range closely or by making frequent cuttings of the grass, and by irrigation, it is possible to maintain suitable pasture for poultry. Alfalfa or ladino clover range may be used to supply green feed throughout the summer and fall.

Layers given green grass range produce eggs of lower market quality than birds kept in confinement. The yolks have a darker yellow color and the

Table 55

INFLUENCE OF RANGE VS. CONFINEMENT
ON POULTRY PRODUCTION [4]

Observations made	Confinement (Bare Lot)	Range (Grass)
Growth of Barred Rocks to 28 weeks		
Av. weight (pounds)................	5.2	5.5
Pounds feed per pound gain..........	6.1	5.7
Per cent mash of total feed..........	72.9	66.3
Mortality (per cent)................	13.0	6.4
Per cent of pullets culled............	29.9	5.8
Layers (Data for 1 or 2 years)		
Egg production (per cent)............	30.4	41.1
Feed per dozen eggs (pounds)........	9.5	7.9
Mortality (per cent)................	26.3	29.3
Hatchability (per cent)..............	50.1	77.7

whites are more watery. While such eggs are of lower value from the stand-point of market grade, they are of greater food value because of the higher vitamin A, D, and G content.

Alfalfa. Alfalfa meal or hay is used as a substitute for green grass for birds kept in confinement and during the winter months. It is fed primarily to supply vitamins A and G, but it also supplies other vitamins, proteins, and minerals.

Alfalfa hay may be fed on the litter. Shatterings from the haymow may be fed in a similar manner. The leaves contain most of the nutrients found in the hay. The birds are able to pick out the leaves and leave the unpalatable stems and blossoms.

Clover and soybean hay may be used as substitutes for alfalfa hay. They do not make satisfactory meals because of the large amount of stems. Soybean hay leaves are even more palatable than alfalfa leaves. Third-cutting alfalfa hay is more satisfactory for poultry than first or second cutting because it is more leafy and freer from stems, other grasses, and weeds. A hundred hens will eat about two pounds of alfalfa hay daily when kept in confinement.

Dehydrated alfalfa hay has higher nutritive value than sun-cured hay. The carotene (provitamin A) content is two to ten times as great and the vitamin G content may be double that of the sun-cured product. The alfalfa is cut and brought directly from the field to the dryer. It is run through a cutter, passed through a dryer, separated into fine and coarse material, ground in a hammer mill, and sacked. The time required for the green hay to be changed

[4] Tenn. Sta. Bul. 185, 1943, and 188, 1944.

into alfalfa meal is three to ten minutes. If hay is rained on during the drying process, some of the protein and minerals and much of the vitamin G are washed out. Therefore, the use of dehydrated alfalfa meal insures the presence of a normal vitamin G content.

Alfalfa meal. Alfalfa meal is ground alfalfa hay. It varies widely in protein, fiber, and vitamin content, depending upon the time of cutting, soil upon which it is grown, and method of curing. Alfalfa meals vary all the way from about 13 per cent protein and 35 per cent fiber to 17 per cent protein and 26 per cent fiber. Alfalfa meals containing more than 17 per cent protein are generally classed as leaf meals, and those with less than 13 per cent as stem meals. The higher the protein content and the lower the fiber content of an alfalfa meal, other things being equal, the more satisfactory it is as an ingredient of poultry mash feeds.

It is difficult to judge the vitamin A and G content of an alfalfa meal by its protein content and appearance. A high-protein meal having a good green color and alfalfa fragrance is more likely to have a good vitamin content than a low-protein meal with a pale green color.

Silage. Grass, legume, and cereal grass silage production is increasing. These products retain their original vitamin content better than sun-cured and even better than the dehydrated products. They are palatable and serve as excellent substitutes for green grass range during the late summer, fall, and winter months. Silage-fed birds produce eggs that are quite similar to those produced by birds on range. Naturally the more leafy the silage, the better it is for poultry. A hundred layers may be fed about three pounds of silage per day to take the place of green grass range or as a substitute for alfalfa meal in the ration.

Fish oils. The principal fish oils used as sources of vitamins for poultry are cod, sardine, pilchard, salmon, tuna, menhaden, and herring. They are used as sources of Vitamins A and D. The vitamin content varies within wide limits, depending on the kind of fish, the time of year they are caught, and the method used in removing the oil (Table 56). Much of the oil sold to the poultry trade is a blend of two or more oils and vitamin concentrates to produce a given vitamin potency. A satisfactory oil for poultry-feeding purposes should contain not less than 600 U.S.P. units of vitamin A, and 85 A.O.A.C. units of vitamin D per gram (p. 254). To calculate potency per pound, multiply the units per gram by 454. Fortified oils are generally about four times as potent as unfortified oils.

Fish oils or other sources of vitamins A and D are necessary in poultry rations only when birds are kept in confinement and in breeding rations during the winter months. The amount of oil used in poultry rations varies from about .25 to 2 per cent, depending on the system of feeding, the purpose of feeding, and the type of oil. Fortified oils are preferable to unfortified oils for use in high protein mash feeds (24 per cent and above). It is desirable to eliminate fish oils from chicken rations during the last two weeks, and from turkey rations during the last four weeks before the birds are sold for poultry meat.

Table 56

RELATIVE EFFICIENCY OF FISH OILS AND STEROLS
WHEN COMPARED ON THE SAME RATE UNIT BASIS AS
A SOURCE OF VITAMIN D FOR CHICKS [5]

Source of Oil	Relative Efficiency Compared with Cod Liver Oil
Cod liver oil (control)	100
Halibut	86
Tuna, blue fin (Calif.)	16
Tuna (New England)	81
Tuna (Oriental)	65
Albacore	61
California bonito	28
California mackerel	120
Swordfish	151
Black sea bass	109
White sea bass	314
Sable fish	162
Basking shark	162
Dogfish	230
Sardine	109
Irradiated ergosterol	3
Irradiated cholesterol	103

Green grass, alfalfa meal, yellow corn, and corn gluten meal may be used to supply sources of vitamin A in the place of fish oils. Sunshine, D-activated animal sterol, or ultraviolet lights may be used as substitutes for fish oils to supply vitamin D.

Fish oils should be purchased on the basis of vitamin content and not on the price per pound or per gallon. Reliable companies guarantee the vitamin content of their oils. The potency of the oils is given on the containers.

D-activated animal sterol. This is a product with strong vitamin D properties obtained by activation of a sterol fraction of animal origin with ultraviolet light or other means. It may be used to increase the vitamin D potency of oils or may be mixed with flour or some other feedstuff as a carrier and sold as a dry form of vitamin D. This dry form of vitamin D is largely replacing fish oil because it is cheaper per unit of vitamin and does not have a fishy odor.

Whey. Dried whey, a by-product of the manufacture of cheese, is a good source of vitamin G. It contains about 1.5 times the amount found in milk. It may be used as a substitute for dried milk in poultry rations, using two-thirds as much whey as milk and making up the difference with soybean oil meal or some other protein feedstuff. The vitamin G content of whey is further concentrated in some products by removing the lactose and some of the

[5] Bills, 1937.

minerals. The concentrated product is mixed with soybean meal and other products and sold as a vitamin concentrate under various trade names.

Liver meal. Pork liver is an excellent source of vitamin G and other vitamins of the B-G complex. Liver meal from other sources is of lower vitamin potency. The method of production of liver meal also affects its vitamin potency. There is a very limited amount of high-quality liver meal available for use in poultry rations.

Fish solubles. Condensed fish solubles is the product obtained by condensing the water resulting from the hydraulic extraction of oil from fish. It is a good source of B-complex vitamins including B_{12}.

Yeast. Yeast is an excellent source of vitamins B_1 and G, and irradiated yeast is also a good source of vitamin D_2. It is usually more economical to supply the vitamin needs of poultry by the proper selection of feedstuffs for the ration than to add yeast. The vitamin content of yeast varies within wide limits, depending on the kind of yeast, the method of production, and the purity of the product.

Distillers' solubles. Distillers' solubles and distillers' grains with solubles are good sources of riboflavin and other B-complex vitamins. They also contain 25 per cent or more protein, some minerals, and other nutrients. They may be used to replace milk products, liver meal, alfalfa, or yeast as a source of riboflavin and other B-complex vitamins. Distillery by-products may be fed in amounts up to 10 per cent of the ration.

Miscellaneous Feedstuffs

There are some substances used in poultry rations that are either hard to classify or are of questionable nutritive value. These include succulent feeds, grit, charcoal, and tonics. Things having an influence on the vitamin D needs of poultry rations include sunlight, glass substitutes, and ultraviolet light.

Succulent feeds. Succulent feeds are palatable but are high in water content and low in nutritive value. Laying hens should be limited to about two to four pounds of succulent feed per hundred birds daily. The use of larger amounts may result in the production of poor-quality eggs with watery whites.

Yellow carrots are a good source of vitamin A. The yellow color of carrots is due to carotene (provitamin A). It does not influence shank, fat, or egg yolk color.

Kale is used as a succulent feed in the Pacific Coast states. While it belongs to the cabbage group of plants, it forms no head and all its leaves are green. Kale is a good source of vitamins A, B_1, and E.

Lettuce is a good source of vitamin A. It should be fed while still retaining its crispness, as badly wilted lettuce may cause harmful results.

Lawn clippings are an excellent source of all the known vitamins except vitamin D. If the lawn is irrigated, fertilized, and mowed frequently, the yield of clippings will equal or exceed that of other green feeds and at the same time furnish more vitamins.

Rape is a good source of vitamin A, but not so palatable to poultry as kale. If it is cut below the crown, it may be harvested several times during the summer.

Sprouted grains are sometimes used to supply green feed during the winter months. Sprouting grains does not increase their nutritive value. Alfalfa meal has largely replaced sprouted grains in poultry rations in recent years.

Beets, mangel worzels, and other closely related vegetables have been grown for feeding poultry during the winter months. They are low in food value and of little importance in the ration.

Cabbage is sometimes fed to poultry during the winter months. It supplies vitamin B_1, and the outer leaves are a source of vitamin A. Cabbage, like beets, contains much water and only a small amount of nutrients. These are supplied in adequate amounts by other feedstuffs in the ration.

Grit. The term "grit" is usually intended to refer to hard, insoluble minerals, such as mica. Limestone and oyster shells are also referred to as grit. There are those who hold that hard, insoluble grit is necessary or desirable for aiding the gizzard in grinding feed. Others believe that hard grit is unnecessary in the ration of poultry, maintaining that oyster shell and limestone grit will serve for grinding purposes and at the same time provide needed calcium. It is the opinion of the authors that hard, insoluble grit is not necessary in poultry rations. There is no objection to putting out mica or other hard, insoluble grit along with limestone or oyster shell grit in separate containers. Birds should not be forced to eat grit by placing it on top of the feed. A sack of hard, insoluble grit will last a flock of birds a long time if limestone and oyster shells are kept available.

Charcoal. Charcoal has very little more value than sawdust. There is no conclusive experimental evidence for justifying its use in poultry rations.

Tonics. Poultry tonics are of questionable value. They are supposed to stimulate appetite and by increased feed consumption result in better growth, production, or hatchability. Some of the tonics sold on the market are unpalatable and do more harm than good. Many of them are based on theory and their value has not been proven by carefully controlled feeding tests with poultry. In most cases at least, a good ration is the best tonic and milk or fish meal is the best ingredient.

Sunlight. Sunlight supplies the vitamin D factor needed by poultry by its effect on cholesterol in the skin of the bird. Exposure of the skin to ultraviolet rays of sunlight gives its cholesterol vitamin D properties. Summer sunlight is more powerful than winter sunlight. The chicken receives the beneficial rays of sunlight through the skin of the face and comb. Feathers shut out the ultraviolet rays. The amount of exposure to sunlight needed will depend on the kind of poultry, the purpose for which they are kept, the season of the year, the ration fed, and the locality in which the birds are kept. The amount of sunlight needed daily will vary from about five minutes to about five hours. Breeding hens will need more sunlight than chicks. Clouds, smoke, and fog shut out some of the ultraviolet rays of sunlight and reduce its efficiency.

Glass substitutes. Glass substitutes are available which will permit the passage of some ultraviolet rays of sunlight, which ordinary window glass shuts out. The amount of ultraviolet light which will pass through the glass substitutes is influenced by the mesh or porosity of the materials. Products with a wire base, resembling fly screen, will permit the passage of more beneficial rays than products having a fine mesh, such as cloth materials. The products are not very durable. They collect dust easily, and this inhibits the passage of ultraviolet light. Furthermore, the window space and arrangement are generally inadequate for the entrance of sufficient sunlight to supply all of the vitamin D needs of birds kept in confinement.

Ultraviolet light. Ultraviolet lights are available which produce biologically effective ultraviolet light. The efficiency of these lights will depend on construction, size, distance from birds, and length of time they are used. Ultraviolet lights have not been very practical for poultry raisers to date. The original cost is high, the life of the light is relatively short, and the current consumption is usually high. The lights must be burned several hours during the day if hung over the feeders and waterers. This is necessary to make sure that all the birds have come under the lights to eat and drink and have been there long enough to absorb a sufficient quantity of the ultraviolet rays.

Electric light bulbs are available on the market which transmit some ultraviolet light. They may be used in battery brooders to supply light, heat, and ultraviolet light. The chicks are close to the lights at all times in the brooding compartments of the battery brooders.

Formulating Rations

When the nutritive requirements of poultry and the nutritive value of feedstuffs are known, it is a comparatively simple task to formulate poultry rations. Since there are a great many poultry feedstuffs, an unlimited number of satisfactory rations may be formulated. In choosing a ration for a given purpose, one needs to keep in mind the nutritive requirements, the available feedstuffs, their supplementary value when fed in combinations, the price, and the system of feeding to be used. Nearly every feeder has a different set of conditions. A suitable and economical ration for one farmer may not be the most economical for his neighbor. The feedstuffs available on the farm or in the community are important in determining the ration and system of feeding that should be used on any given farm.

Price and availability of ingredients. The price and availability of ingredients will have a marked influence on the choice of feedstuffs.

The *carbohydrate feedstuffs* are abundant and cheap. The price is generally lowest about harvest time and increases slightly during the year. In the Corn Belt, more corn is used than any of the other cereals in poultry rations. In the Northwest, wheat and its by-products are plentiful and are used in larger amounts than in other parts of the country. In the Southwest, the sorghum grains grow well and are used to replace part of the cereal grains generally used in poultry rations. In some of the northern states barley is used in place of most of the corn because it grows well and because the season is too short for corn. These and other available facts illustrate that the carbohydrate feedstuffs may be varied within wide limits, depending on price and availability.

The *protein feedstuffs,* especially the animal protein feedstuffs, are expensive. Dried milk is the most expensive of the group. Soybean oil meal is the cheapest. There is a supplementary effect among the animal and vegetable protein feedstuffs. The economical procedure is to use as much vegetable protein feedstuffs and as little animal protein feedstuffs as possible without lowering the value of the ration. There is often a tendency to feed too little protein and too much grain because of difference in price and availability.

The *mineral feedstuffs* are cheap and readily available. The fowl can use only a limited amount of minerals. There is often a tendency to use too much minerals, especially limestone, in poultry rations because they are cheap.

The *vitamin feedstuffs* are generally expensive. Fortunately only small amounts are used. Fish oil, milk, and dehydrated alfalfa leaf meal are the chief products used. Single vitamins such as carotene, irradiated animal sterol, riboflavin, and vitamin B_{12} are now being added to replace these feedstuffs. They are used in rations for confined birds to take the place of green grass range and sunlight. Rations may be cheapened by providing birds with green grass range and replacing the oil and alfalfa by one of the cereal grains and part of the milk by one of the cheaper protein feedstuffs.

Selection and balance of ingredients. The number of ingredients used in a ration is not a true measure of the value of the ration. Simple rations, consisting of six or eight ingredients, are often as valuable or even more so than complex rations consisting of a dozen or more ingredients. It is true that variety adds to palatability and increases the chances of making good the deficiencies found in certain feedstuffs, provided the materials chosen are palatable and have a supplementary effect. For instance, a grain mixture of corn, wheat, and oats is not improved by adding barley, buckwheat, and rye to it. These latter grains are not so palatable and do not supply anything not supplied by corn, wheat, and oats.

The *carbohydrate feedstuffs* generally constitute 75 to 90 per cent of the poultry ration. It is advisable to use at least three cereal grains and by-products (p. 283) in the ration. Corn, oats, and wheat or wheat by-products are the ones generally used.

The *protein feedstuffs* generally constitute from 10 to 20 per cent of the ration, depending on the age of the bird. Meat scraps or fish meal, milk, and soybean oil meal are the ones most generally used. The animal protein feedstuffs (p. 289) should constitute about 25 per cent of the total protein feedstuffs fed.

The *mineral feedstuffs* are supplied by the use of animal protein feedstuffs, such as meat scraps and milk. Salt is generally added to the ration at a 0.5 per cent level. Oyster shells are kept available for laying birds. A simple mineral mixture (p. 295) is generally added at the rate of a pound for every five or six pounds of vegetable protein used.

Vitamin feedstuffs are fed to birds in confinement to supply vitamins obtained by birds on green grass range. Alfalfa and milk or distillers' solubles are used at about 5 per cent levels to supply the vitamins A, B, E, G and the less well known ones found in grass. Fish oil or D-activated animal sterol is generally fed as a substitute for sunshine.

The National Research Council has suggested poultry ration formulas by ingredient percentage for various purposes and manners of feeding. These recommendations are summarized in Table 57.

Table 57

RECOMMENDED FORMULAS FOR POULTRY FEEDS [6]

Ingredients	Chick Starting Mash	Chick Growing Mash (to Be Fed with Grain)	Hen Laying Mash (to Be Fed with Grain)	Hen Breeding Mash (to Be Fed with Grain)	Turkey Starting Mash	Turkey Growing Mash (to Be Fed with Grain)	Turkey Breeding Mash (to Be Fed with Grain)
	Per Cent	*Per Cent*	*Per Cent*	*Per Cent*	*Per Cent*	*Per Cent*	*Per Cent*
Ground grains and grain by-products..........	62.5–72.5	68.5–78.5	62.5–77.5	56–68	50.5–60.5	62.5–72.5	52–66
Minimum animal protein supplements *........	3–4	3.5–4.5	3.5–4.5	7–9	4–5	3.5–4.5	7–9
Vegetable protein supplements...............	15–18	12–15	15–19	12–14	24–27	16–17	7–10
Riboflavin supplements †..	5–8			5–7	7–10	3–4	12–15
Alfalfa meal dehydrated ‡ .	2–5	4–10	4–10	4–10	2–5	4–10	4–10
Bone meal or defluor. rock phosphate............	1	1	2	2	1	1	2
Limestone..............	1.5	1	2	2	1.5	1	2
Vitamin D when necessary.	?	?	?	?	?	?	?

* When vitamin B_{12} concentrates are added, the animal protein feedstuffs may be further or completely replaced by the vegetable protein feedstuffs.
† Potency of 20 micrograms per gram or 9 milligrams per pound.
‡ When not on good, green grass range.

We have calculated the vitamin A, D, riboflavin, and the calcium and phosphorus requirements for mash feeds fed for different purposes and by different systems of feeding (Table 58). The calculations are based on the National Research Council recommendations (Table 51) and the use of a grain mixture, consisting of yellow corn 50 per cent, wheat 25 per cent, and oats 25 per cent, whenever required.

Methods of Feeding

Having selected the feedstuffs and amounts to be used, there are several satisfactory ways of feeding them. These include free choice of ingredients, free choice of mash concentrate and grains, mash and limited grains, and all-mash.

[6] National Research Council, 1944. Slightly modified by the authors.

Table 58

MINERAL-VITAMIN REQUIREMENTS * PER 100 POUNDS OF POULTRY MASH

Mash Protein Per Cent	Purpose	Minerals		Vitamins		
		Lbs. or Ca.	Per Cent Phos.	A U.S.P. Units	D A.O.A.C. Units	Riboflavin Milligrams
18...............	Starter	1.0	.6	200,000	18,000	160
18...............	Breeder	3.7 *	1.0	440,300	75,000	188
20...............	Starter	1.0	.6	200,000	18,000	160
20...............	Breeder	4.7 *	1.2	516,600	91,500	229
22...............	Breeder	5.7 *	1.4	588,900	115,400	267
24...............	Turkey	2.0	1.0	400,000	80,000	200
24...............	Breeder	6.7 *	1.6	666,000	136,400	308
26...............	Breeder	7.7 *	1.8	735,200	155,200	344
28...............	Breeder	8.5 *	1.9	801,000	173,100	379
30...............	Breeder	9.7 *	2.2	884,100	195,700	423
32...............	Breeder	10.6 *	2.3	952,600	214,300	459

* Most of the calcium should be supplied by keeping either oyster shell or limestone grit available for the hens.

Free choice of ingredients. Feedstuffs commonly used in mixed poultry rations may be fed free choice to poultry. This system permits birds to balance their ration according to individual needs, eliminates mixing, and results in a cheaper ration. The chief disadvantage is the extra labor in feeding the separate ingredients.

Chickens, like people, differ in individual nutritive requirements. The needs vary with the rate of growth and egg production. It is wasteful to feed a hen a ration that is suitable for a bird that will lay 250 eggs in a year when the bird will only lay 100 eggs. The shell requirements have long been taken care of by permitting birds free access to shells in hoppers. The protein and vitamin needs vary in much the same manner as the mineral needs.

Chicks given free access to many feedstuffs will balance their ration according to individual needs (Table 59). The same is true of laying hens. Excellent production has been obtained with birds receiving grains and milk to drink or free access to feedstuffs (Table 60).

The free choice system of feeding is suitable for general farmers who raise grain, sell cream, and have range for the flock.

Free choice of mash concentrate and grains. Mash protein concentrates varying from about 24 to 32 per cent protein content are available for feeding free choice with grains or for mixing with grains to make a mash feed to be fed with limited grains or to be used as an all-mash feed. If the mash feed is palatable, it gives very good results when fed free choice with grains (Table 61). The birds have an opportunity to balance the protein, and, to a certain extent, their vitamin needs in accordance with the rate of production. Birds in high production and pullet layers will eat more mash and less grain than old hens or birds in low production.

The free choice of mash concentrate and grain system of feeding eliminates the grinding and mixing of about 67 to 79 per cent of the ration. The

Table 59

SELECTION OF FEEDSTUFFS BY CHICKS WHEN GIVEN FREE CHOICE [7]

Ingredients	PERCENTAGE CONSUMED, FIRST FIVE WEEKS				
	1st	2nd	3rd	4th	5th
Ground corn............	13.31	16.16	16.39	15.24	23.22
Corn feed..............	6.5	8.15	12.07	7.09	7.18
Hominy................	13.1	11.6	7.80	12.20	13.97
Gluten feed....:........	0	0	0	0	0.28
Rolled wheat..........	3.68	4.19	9.41	14.64	11.17
Ground wheat.........	8.5	8.41	2.69	3.61	4.92
Wheat germ...........	0	0	4.92	8.92	9.49
Bran.................	0.9	4.01	2.49	1.05	1.01
Shorts...............	4.2	3.81	0.62	0.69	0.04
Crushed oats..........	10.0	6.5	17.26	7.06	6.16
Ground oats...........	0	0	0.32	0	0.05
Breakfast oat meal......	2.2	4.04	2.42	2.41	2.08
Pinhead oat meal......	1.7	.98	2.22	0.66	0
Rolled groats..........	2.26	2.39	0	0	3.56
Banner oat feed........	0	0	0	0	Trace
Oat dust..............	0	0	0	0	Trace
Rolled barley..........	0.87	3.11	0.81	1.37	0.38
Ground barley.........	0.78	1.21	0.33	0.59	0.08
Pea meal.............	2.16	1.97	0.99	1.03	0.99
Soybean oil meal.......	0	0	0	0	0.66
Ground rice...........	0.56	0.45	0.41	7.98	0.07
Liquid milk...........	0	0	0	0	0.87
Semisolid milk.........	7.66	4.41	7.89	5.26	0
Skim milk, powder......	1.73	1.36	0.38	0.70	1.50
Buttermilk, powder......	1.6	2.3	0.15	0.37	0.44
Beef scrap.............	3.3	3.74	5.58	4.77	3.13
Cod liver meal.........	0.7	0.65	0.15	0.18	0.08
Fish meal.............	0.7	1.64	0.89	1.06	1.45
Oyster shell...........	0.91	0.58	0.47	0.30	0.22
Granite grit...........	1.00	0.13	0.47	0.35	0.12
Bone meal.............	0.61	0.20	0.14	0.24	0.01
Chick starter..........	10.40	8.15	3.85	1.80	6.63
Alfalfa meal...........	0.37	0.14	0.11	0.17	0.02
Salt..................	0	0	0.05	0	0.05
Cod liver oil (pints per 100 lbs. feed).........	2.25	2.1	.25	.25	.04

mash may be used as an all-mash turkey starter or mixed with about an equal amount of corn meal to make an all-mash chick starting and growing ration. This mash may serve as an all-purpose poultry mash feed.

The free choice of mash concentrate and grain system of feeding is increasing in popularity. It permits the birds to balance their own ration and therefore simplifies the poultry feeding problems. It is economical and adaptable to the feeding of all kinds of poultry.

[7] Graham, 1932.

Table 60

A COMPARISON OF THE ALL-MASH AND FREE CHOICE SYSTEMS OF FEEDING
FOR PULLET EGG PRODUCTION [8]

Eggs and Feeds	100 Leghorn Pullets (46 weeks)		46 Red Pullets (34 weeks)	
	All-Mash	Free Choice	All-Mash	Free Choice
Eggs per bird.............	131	139	112	105
Feed per bird (lbs.) *....	60	61	59	56
Corn (per cent)........	52	19	52.5	27.4
Wheat................	0	60	0.0	39.1
Bran.................	5	0	5.0	0.0
Middlings............	20	0	20.0	0.0
Oats.................	10	9	10.0	23.1
Meat scraps..........	10	7	8.0	6.4
Dried milk...........	2	5	4.0	4.0
Salt.................	1	0	.5	0.0

* Birds were confined to small yards and fed chopped alfalfa hay and oyster shells ad libitum.

Table 61

THE INFLUENCE OF METHODS OF FEEDING ON EGG PRODUCTION, POUNDS
OF FEED AND FEED COST PER DOZEN EGGS [9]

Method of Feeding	Eggs per Bird	Pounds of Feed per Dozen Eggs	Feed Cost per Dozen Eggs (Cents)
All-mash..................	118	6.3	11.5
Mash and limited grain in litter..................	113	5.4	9.4
Mash and limited grain in hoppers................	136	5.3	9.2
Mash, pellets at noon, and limited grain in the litter..	141	5.4	9.5
Mash concentrate and grains free choice.......	150	4.9	8.6

Mash and limited grains. One of the most widely used systems of feeding layers during the past several years has been the feeding of about an 18 to 20 per cent protein mash feed and limited grain. The mash feed is kept before the birds all the time and about an equal amount of grain is fed. The birds are given about as much grain as they will clean up, late in the afternoon. The grain mixture generally consists of corn, wheat, and oats.

The mash feed may be used as an all-mash chick starter. As the birds reach maturity, grain is fed to reduce the protein level and make a suitable laying ration.

The mash and limited grain ration requires the grinding and mixing of

[8] Ohio State University, unpublished data.
[9] Robertson, Carver, and Cook, 1939.

Table 62

MASH AND GRAIN FEEDING TO MEET THE PROTEIN REQUIREMENTS
(15 per cent) for Egg Production

Protein Content of Mash (Per Cent)	Grain * Per Cent	Mash Per Cent	Protein Content of Mash (Per Cent)	Grain * Per Cent	Mash Per Cent
18....................	40	60	26....................	71	29
20....................	53	47	28....................	74	26
22....................	61	39	30....................	77	23
24....................	67	33	32....................	79	21

* Based on a grain mixture of yellow corn 50 per cent, wheat 25 per cent, and oats 25 per cent.

about 50 per cent of the ration (Table 62). It requires a good knowledge of poultry feeding. Otherwise, the feeder may feed too much grain for satisfactory growth or egg production.

All-mash. In the all-mash system of feeding, all of the feedstuffs eaten are ground, mixed, and fed as a single mixture. The ration is based on the requirements of the birds that need the most nutrients. There is no chance for the birds to vary their diet according to likes or needs. This system of feeding requires the grinding and mixing of all the ration. Ground feeds are not so palatable and do not retain their nutritive value so well as unground feeds.

The all-mash system of feeding is desirable for starting and growing chicks because it involves less labor. When the birds become older, the feed consumption much greater, and the individual needs more pronounced, one of the grain-and-mash systems of feeding is more economical.

The all-mash system of feeding is desirable in nutritional experimental work where the consumption of ingredients should be kept in constant ratio. It is also satisfactory in battery feeding of birds, where feeding space is at a premium. The all-mash system of feeding results in the production of eggs of more uniform yolk color and white consistency. However, even on the same ration the eggs from different individuals vary within wide limits as regards internal appearance.

Wet mash. Wet mash is sometimes fed as a supplement to the dry mash feed to increase palatability and stimulate feed consumption. Chickens pick over mash feed and it dries out in the hopper and becomes unpalatable. If the top dry mash in the hopper is scraped off, mixed to a crumbly mass with water or milk, and fed in small amounts, it is relished by birds. Wet mash is more palatable and of greater nutritive value when mixed with milk than when mixed with water. Layers may be fed as much wet mash as they will clean up in about ten minutes. An excess of wet mash should be avoided. It may become sour, moldy, caked, or unpalatable. Wet mash is usually fed to layers about the noon hour or about ten o'clock in the morning and about three o'clock in the afternoon. It is sometimes fed to broilers in addition to the dry mash.

The feeding of all of the mash feed in the form of a wet mash involves too much labor in feeding chicks and hens. However, it is the system generally used in fattening poultry (p. 324).

Pellets. Mash feed is now on the market in the form of pellets. It is forced through a press under high pressure and formed into pellets of varying size. Pellets may be more palatable than some finely ground mash feeds. There may be some advantage in feeding pellets in range feeders, where the wind may blow away part of the ground mash feed. The keeping quality of nutrients in the form of pellets may be better than in the form of finely ground mash feed.

Preparation of mash feed in the form of pellets adds to the cost of preparation. There is insufficient evidence at present to justify the use of pellet poultry feeds.

Artificial lights. Feeding for early rapid growth and fall egg production of hens is closely connected with the use of artificial light. It is used to lengthen the day to at least thirteen or fourteen hours, or even to a period of continuous lighting.

Chicks make faster early growth when all-night light is used. It therefore has a place in broiler production. The presence of light at night in the brooder house or battery room results in more comfort of the birds and less danger of piling. The birds can see to move about and secure feed when needed. A twenty-watt bulb is satisfactory in the ordinary colony brooder house.

Hens may be made to lay more eggs in the late summer, fall, and early winter by the use of artificial light. If lights are used in the fall, spring egg production will be less. Lights have little influence on total yearly egg production. A time switch may be used to turn the lights on about three o'clock in the morning. All-night lights may also be used. A forty-watt bulb is sufficient for a pen that will accommodate about one hundred hens. The light may be suspended over the feeders and water vessel or over the perches.

Artificial lights may be used to help hold up late summer and fall production of yearling hens, shorten the molting period of hens, bring hens into production for winter-hatching eggs, check the neck molt and slump in fall egg production of early-hatched pullets, and hasten the sexual maturity of late-hatched and slow-maturing pullets.

It was formerly believed that the chief benefit derived from the use of artificial lights on layers was to increase the length of day. It was believed that this would result in greater feed and water consumption and consequently greater egg production. Tests conducted at Ohio State University have shown that this is not the principal value of the use of lights. Birds exposed to light at night but deprived of feed and water produced nearly as many eggs on a twelve-hour eating day as birds which had lights and feed and water at night (Table 63). It is believed that the chief benefit of artificial light in the laying house is to stimulate hormone activity. The pituitary gland is stimulated to secrete a hormone into the blood stream. This is carried to the ovary and stimulates egg production.

Table 63

THE INFLUENCE OF LIGHT ON EGG PRODUCTION [10]

Light and Management	Eggs per Bird
No light at night....................	57
Low light intensity at night..........	66
Lights but no feed at night...........	85
Lights and feed at night.............	88

Feeding for Growth of Chickens

Feeding for growth includes rations and feeding practices for starting chicks, starting and growing broilers, growing and finishing pullets, cockerels, and growing capons.

Starting rations. All-mash feed is generally used for starting chicks. The protein content of the mash is usually about 20 per cent. Some chick starting mashes advocated for use in different parts of the country are listed in Table 64.

The United States Department of Agriculture starting mash is only one of several recommended. Bird recommends a riboflavin supplement containing 20 micrograms of riboflavin per gram (9 milligrams per pound); alfalfa leaf meal; either bone meal or low fluorine rock phosphate; manganized salt (a mixture of iodized salt 100 pounds and manganese sulphate 3 to 5 pounds); and vitamin A and D feeding oil (400 A.O.A.C. units of vitamin D and 2000 International Units of vitamin A per gram).

The Southern States Co-operative open formula mash feed is based on the recommendations of a college conference feed board composed of the agricultural college and experiment station workers in the territory. Sufficient quantities of vitamin supplements of known potencies are added to meet the requirements recommended by the National Research Council (Table 51).

The New England College Conference mash is based on the recommendations of the agricultural college and experiment station investigators in the New England territory. The board recommends either ground oats or barley; ground wheat or middlings; and meat scrap or fish meal. The whey may be replaced by fermentation product or yeast in sufficient quantity to provide the same riboflavin content. The A and D feeding oil recommended should contain 400 A.O.A.C. units of D and 2000 International Units of A per gram. If alfalfa meal containing 100,000 International Units of A per pound is available, the feeding oil may be replaced by 0.02 lb. of dry vitamin D (D-activated animal sterol containing 2000 A.O.A.C. units per gram).

The Quebec Provincial Feed Board mash is formulated from their recommendations that it should contain 55 per cent cereal grains, composed of at least three and with not more than 10 per cent oats. The board recommends about 24 per cent wheat mill feeds and alfalfa meal with not more

---

[10] Dakan, 1938.

Table 64

ALL-MASH STARTING RATIONS FOR GENERAL FARM CHICKS

Ingredients	U. S. Dept. Agr. (1)	Southern States Coop. (2)	New England College Conf. (3)	Quebec Provincial Feed Board (4)	Wisconsin (5)	California (6)
Ground yellow corn	42.9	34.7	36.4	24.7	45.5	35.0
Wheat middlings		5.0	20.0	16.0	15.0	8.0
Wheat bran		10.0		3.0	15.0	8.0
Ground oats	10.0	10.0	10.0	10.0		10.0
Cane molasses		2.0				
Ground wheat				20.0		20.0
Soybean oil meal	30.0	22.5	15.0	8.5	5.0	1.5
Linseed oil meal				1.5		
Meat scrap		3.8	10.0	4.5	5.0	
Fish meal	4.0	2.5			5.0	10.0
Dried milk				2.0		
Bone meal	1.5					
Low fluorine rock phosphate		1.5				
Ground limestone	1.0	1.5	1.0	1.0	2.0	2.0
Salt—iodized and manganized	0.5	.5	0.5	1.0	0.5	0.5
Flint grit					2.0	
Alfalfa leaf or special alfalfa meal	5.0	5.0	5.0	5.0	5.0	5.0
Dried whey		1.0	2.0			
Riboflavin supplement *	5.0	+		+		+
Vitamin A and D feeding oil *	0.1		0.1	0.3		
D-activated animal sterol *		+			+	+
Animal protein factor (B_{12}) supplement*		+				
Total	100.0	100.0	100.0	100.0	100.0	100.0

* + Amount added will vary with the potency of the product used.
(1) U. S. D. A. Circ. 788. 1948.
(2) Southern States Cooperative, Baltimore, Md. 1949–1950 Rations.
(3) New England College Conference. 1949–1950 Rations.
(4) The Quebec Provincial Feed Board, Macdonald College, Quebec. 1949–1950 Rations.
(5) Wisconsin Sta. Circ. 382. 1949.
(6) Calif. Ext. Circ. 159. 1949.

than 8 per cent bran and/or alfalfa. It also recommends 11.5 per cent vegetable protein supplements consisting of at least three different ones and including at least 1.5 per cent soybean oil meal. The recommendations call for 6.5 per cent animal protein feedstuffs including 2 per cent dried milk and/or fish meal. The riboflavin supplement may consist of 0.1 gram of crystalline riboflavin or a commercial source containing an equivalent amount. The feeding oil should be of the same potency as recommended in the U. S. D. A. and New England formulas.

The Wisconsin mash is one of several starting mashes recommended. Slightly different rations are recommended for starting light and heavy breeds. The recommendations include the use of either ground oats or barley, wheat bran and middlings, or ground wheat, alfalfa leaf meal, and either fish oil or a dry form of vitamin D.

The California starting mash is one of those recommended. The recommendations include ground grains, wheat bran, or mill run, alfalfa meal containing at least 67,000 International Units of vitamin A per pound, and fish meal containing 65 per cent crude protein. When soybean oil meal is used to replace much of the fish meal, iodized salt, containing 0.007 per cent iodine, is recommended.

Feeding young chicks. Chicks should be provided with feed as soon as they are placed under the brooder. The first feed is often placed on paper or egg case flats in order that the chicks may find it easily. Or, the chick feeders (p. 234) may be filled full for two or three days to accomplish the same purpose. Part of the feeder and waterer should be under the hover for the first few days, especially if the brooder room temperature is much below 80°F. Sufficient feeders should be provided so that at least half of the chicks can eat at one time. After the chicks have become accustomed to the location of the feed, the feeders should not be filled more than about one-half full, in order to prevent feed wastage. Feed and water should be kept before the birds all the time. The addition of a little fresh mash two or three times daily will result in a little better feed consumption and growth than when fresh feed is added only once daily.

Chick feed consumption will vary with the rate of growth (p. 268). One hundred average chicks eat about 10 pounds of feed the first week and 10 additional pounds each week during the first 10 weeks. From 10 to 20 weeks they eat about 5 pounds additional feed each week. For instance, 100 chicks will eat about 50 pounds of feed during the fifth week, and about 125 pounds during the fifteenth week. Rapidly growing broiler chicks will eat more than the above amounts.

The method of feeding may be varied according to the feedstuffs used, labor costs, and likes of the feeder. Chicks will balance their ration and make satisfactory growth when given free choice of feedstuffs (Table 65). However, chicks are generally started on all-mash feed to save labor. After the chicks are six to eight weeks old, they are generally fed mash and whole grains free choice. Some poultrymen continue to feed the same all-mash feed or one of about 16 per cent protein.

Whole grains fed with mash feeds generally consist of various combinations of two or more of the following: corn, wheat, oats, barley, and sorghum grains (Table 66). Price and availability are determining factors in the choice of grains.

Broiler rations. Broiler rations generally contain higher protein and energy and less fiber than regular starting and growing rations. Some typical broiler mashes are listed in Table 67.

The Southern States Co-operative regular broiler mash is fed free choice with grains after the birds are six to eight weeks old, while no grain is fed with the high-energy mash. The amount of vitamin concentrate additions vary with their potencies, but in no case does the total amount added exceed 0.2 pound per 100 pounds of mash.

The Connecticut regular broiler mash is the same as that recommended by the New England College Conference. The high-energy mash is one that produces more rapid growth and efficient feed utilization. The vitamin ad-

Table 65

GROWTH AND FEED CONSUMPTION OF CHICKS ON AN ALL-MASH AND
FREE CHOICE SYSTEM OF FEEDING [11]

	All-Mash Ration	Free Choice Ration
Weights of Birds		
Weight of pullets at four weeks.........	166 grams	144 grams
Weight of cockerels at four weeks.......	178	164
Weight of pullets at eight weeks........	418	379
Weight of cockerels at eight weeks.......	464	461
Composition of Feed		
Corn meal...........................	50	39.4
Wheat bran..........................	15	11.1
Wheat shorts........................	15	29.3
Dried buttermilk.....................	15	6.1
Dried skim milk.....................	00	4.8
Meat scraps.........................	00	5.4
Alfalfa leaf meal....................	00	.9
Bone meal...........................	4	3.0
Salt................................	1	.2
Total Pounds	100	100.2

Table 66

SUGGESTED WHOLE GRAIN MIXTURES FOR FEEDING WITH MASH FEEDS [12]

Ingredients	Mixtures					
	1	2	3	4	5	6
Yellow corn.....................	50	33.4	33.4	25.0	50.0	
Wheat..........................	50	33.3	33.3	25.0		50.0
Oats...........................		33.3		25.0	25.0	25.0
Barley.........................			33.3	25.0	25.0	25.0

ditions are greater because of the more rapid growth and the absence of oat and wheat products. The vitamin additions recommended per 100 pounds of mash are: 0.023 grams of riboflavin concentrate (8000 micrograms per gram); 128 grams of choline chloride; 0.1 pound of vitamin A and D feeding oil (2000 A and 400 D); and 900 milligrams niacin or nicotinic acid.

The Iowa broiler mash is a high-energy low fiber feed which gives results quite comparable to the more complex Connecticut high-energy broiler mash. This and other high-energy broiler mashes are well suited for the midwestern Corn Belt, because of their high content of corn. The vitamin additions rec-

[11] Funk, 1932.
[12] U. S. D. A. Circ. 788. 1948.

Table 67

BROILER MASHES

INGREDIENTS	SOUTHERN STATES (1)		CONNECTICUT (2)		IOWA (3)	GEORGIA (4)
	Regular	High Energy	Regular	High Energy		
Ground yellow corn	35.8 Lbs.	44.4	40.8	69.5	59.6	30.2
Wheat middlings	15.0	10.0	20.0			20.0
Wheat bran	5.0					5.0
Ground oats	7.5	5.0	10.0			5.0
Cane molasses	2.0	2.0				
Soybean oil meal	21.2	22.2	15.0	8.0	23.8	12.5
Corn gluten meal		3.0		2.5		3.0
Meat scrap	5.0	3.7	5.0	8.0	8.0	7.0
Fish meal		3.7		8.0	3.0	3.0
Liver meal				1.0		
Bone meal or low fluorine rock phosphate	0.5					1.0
Ground limestone	1.5	1.0	1.2			1.5
Salt—iodized and manganized	0.5	0.3	0.5	0.5	0.5	0.5
Distillers' solubles			2.5			3.8
Alfalfa leaf or special alfalfa meal	5.0	3.7	5.0	2.5	5.0	5.0
Dried whey	1.0	1.0				2.5
Riboflavin supplement *	+	+		+	+	+
A and D feeding oil *		+	+	+		+
Dry form of vitamin D *	+	+	+	+	0.1	
Animal protein factor (B₁₂) sup.*	+	+				+
Choline *				+	+	
Niacin *				+	+	
Pantothenic acid *					+	
Total	100.0	100.0	100.0	100.0	100.0	100.0

* + The amount of vitamin supplements to be added will vary with the potencies of the products used.
(1) Southern States Cooperative, Baltimore, Md. 1949–50 Rations.
(2) Connecticut INF—5. 1949.
(3) Iowa. 1949–1950 Rations.
(4) Georgia. 1949–1950 Rations.

ommended per 100 pounds of mash are: 0.1 pound of dry D (2000 A.O.A.C. units per gram); 1.5 pounds of riboflavin concentrate (500 micrograms per gram); nicotinic acid or niacin 1 gram; pantothenic acid 1 gram; and choline chloride 0.03 pound.

Feeding broilers. Broiler chicks are started the same as those used to produce pullets and cockerels for laying and breeding purposes (p. 313). However, more rapid early growth is desired. To accomplish this goal, the starting mash is usually fed until the birds are marketed and without the feeding of any grain. If the birds are to be marketed as large fryers or small roasters, grain is sometimes fed free choice with the mash during the last two weeks. In some instances, all night lights of low intensity are used. Commercial broiler chicks are raised with big numbers in a given pen. Automatic feeders (Fig. 124) are increasing in popularity for use in broiler plants.

Growing rations. Rations for growing chickens, from about the sixth or eighth week until about the sixteenth week, are generally lower in protein than that used for starting them. Two general types or rations are fed, all-mash or free choice of mash and whole grains. The two types of mash feeds vary in composition. Some typical growing mash formulas are listed in Table 68.

Table 68

GROWING MASHES TO BE FED WITH AND WITHOUT GRAIN

INGREDIENTS	U. S. D. A. (1)		SOUTHERN STATES COOP. (2)	NEW ENG. CONF. (3)		COLORADO (4)
	With Grain	All-Mash	With Grain	With Grain	All-Mash	With Grain
Ground yellow corn............	25.0	57.9	39.9	33.5	38.5	24.5
Wheat middlings...............	9.3		5.0	20.0	25.0	10.0
Wheat bran...................			10.0			
Ground oats or barley.........	10.0	10.0	12.5	15.0	20.0	20.0
Cane molasses................			3.0			
Soybean meal.................	37.0	21.0	18.7	15.0	5.0	20.0
Meat scrap or fish meal........			3.7	5.0	5.0	10.0
Dried milk..................						
Dried whey...................				2.0	1.0	
Bone meal or low flourine rock phosphate..................	4.5	2.5	1.0	2.5	1.0	2.5
Ground limestone.............	2.0	1.0	2.0	2.0	1.5	2.0
Salt—iodized and manganized....	1.0	0.5	0.5		0.5	1.0
Alfalfa leaf or special alfalfa meal.	5.0	5.0	3.7	5.0	2.5	10.0
Vitamin A and D feeding oil *...	0.2	0.1		+	+	+
Dry form of vitamin D *........			+			+
Riboflavin supplement *........	6.0	2.0	+			+
Total...................	100.0	100.0	100.0	100.0	100.0	100.0

* + The amount of vitamin supplement to be added will vary with its potency and the method of feeding the mash.
(1) U. S. D. A. Circ. 788. 1948.
(2) Southern States Cooperative, Baltimore, Md. 1949–1950 Rations.
(3) New England College Conference. 1949–1950 Rations.
(4) Colorado A. and M. College. 1949.

The United States Department of Agriculture suggests several growing mash formulas to be fed as all-mash and a like number to be fed free choice with grain after about the sixth to eighth week. Mash feeds to be fed with grain carry higher protein, mineral, and vitamin content than all-mash feeds. This is due to the fact that the grains are deficient in these nutrients.

The Southern States mash feed is intended for feeding free choice with grain after about the sixth week. The mash and system of feeding is recommended for growing pullets and cockerels for later use on egg and breeding farms.

The New England mash to be fed with grain is fed in the proportion of about two parts mash to one of grain. In the beginning, the grain and mash may be fed free choice. If the birds reach a point where they are eating too much grain in proportion to mash, the grain feeding is then limited.

The Colorado growing mash is intended to be fed free choice with whole grains from about the ninth to the sixteenth or eighteenth week, at which time the birds are changed to the laying ration.

Feeding growing pullets. After the pullets are six to eight weeks old, they may be changed to a growing mash. This may be an all-mash or one to be fed with grain (Table 68). The latter system is the more popular. It avoids the necessity of grinding and mixing all the feed. The mash and whole grains are kept before the birds at all times, until they reach sexual maturity. Then, they should be changed to a laying ration. Oyster shell or limestone grit should be kept available during the latter part of the growing period.

When good green grass range is available, the pullets may be fed a cheap low protein and vitamin ration. A grain-mash mixture recommended by the Ohio Experiment Station consists of whole corn or wheat 60, whole oats 10, ground corn 15, wheat bran 6, meat scrap 3, soybean oil meal 4, salt 1, and limestone or oyster shell 1. The birds obtain the additional protein needed from the green grass range. They also obtain the necessary vitamins from the range and sunlight.

Feeding breeding cockerels. The cockerels should be separated from the pullets when four to eight weeks old. If the cockerels are to be sold for meat, they may be fed and managed the same as broiler chicks. If they are to be kept for breeding purposes, they may be fed a growing mash and grain free choice. The nearer they reach maturity, the more grain and the less mash they will consume.

Feeding roasters. Chickens to be raised and sold as roasters, about four to seven pounds live weight, may be fed a growing mash and grain free choice after they are six to eight weeks old. They are generally marketed when 3.5 to 5 months old. The larger they become, the greater the per cent of grain and the less the per cent of mash consumed. Since they are kept beyond the age of most rapid growth, more pounds of feed are required to produce a pound of roaster than to produce a pound of broiler or fryer.

Feeding capons. Birds marketed as capons are usually five to seven months old. Since they are kept beyond the period of rapid growth, they may be fed free choice of a growing mash and whole grains. The pounds of feed required to produce a pound of capon is greater than for the production of a pound of broiler, fryer, small roaster, duck, or turkey (Table 48). However, if the birds are grown on good grass range and fed a ration consisting largely of grains, such as recommended by the Ohio Experiment Station, the feed cost of capon production is not great.

Feeding for Egg Production

Feeding for egg production involves feeding for numbers of eggs, egg quality, hatchability, and control of molt and broodiness. The same type of ration may be used for all of the above purposes. However, the system of management is varied somewhat. It requires a better ration for the production of hatching eggs than for the production of market eggs. The differences are mainly in vitamin requirements. Since the necessary vitamin supplements are now becoming generally available and cheap, it is advisable to feed a ration that will produce hatchable eggs even though they may be sold as market eggs. The eggs will have greater nutritive value and the layers will have greater vitamin reserves. This will probably result in healthier laying flocks.

Laying and breeding mashes. Some typical laying and breeding mashes recommended for use in various parts of the country are listed in Tables 69, 70, and 71.

Table 69

LAYING MASH FORMULAS

INGREDIENTS	U. S. D. A. (1) All-Mash	U. S. D. A. (1) Limited Grain	NEW ENG. CONF. (2) All-Mash	NEW ENG. CONF. (2) Limited Grain	TEXAS (3) Limited Grain	WASH. (4) Limited Grain
Ground yellow corn	56.2	30.0	40.2	28.7		10.0
Wheat middlings			20.0	15.0	20.0	20.0
Wheat bran					20.0	
Ground oats or barley	10.0	10.0	20.0	15.0	16.0	15.0
Kafir or milo					20.0	
Ground wheat						19.1
Soybean oil meal	20.0	40.0	10.0	22.5		18.8
Meat scrap			2.5	5.0	18.0	
Fish meal						3.5
Dried milk						
Bone meal or low fluorine rock phosphate	3.0	6.0	1.5	3.5		3.8
Ground limestone	3.0	2.5	1.5	1.8		2.8
Salt—iodized and manganized	0.5	1.0	0.5	1.0	1.0	1.0
Dried whey			1.0	2.0		
Alfalfa leaf meal or special alfalfa meal	5.0	5.0	2.5	5.0	5.0	6.0
Vitamin A and D feeding oil *	0.3	0.5	.3	.5	+	+
Dry form of vitamin D *						
Riboflavin supplement *	2.0	5.0		+		
Total	100.0	100.0	100.0	100.0	100.0	100.0

* + The amount added will vary with the potency of the product.
(1) U. S. D. A. Circ. 788. 1948.
(2) New England College Conference. 1949–50. Rations.
(3) Tex. Sta. Ext. Circ. 243. 1948.
(4) Wash. Sta. Ext. Bul. 349. 1949.

The Illinois mash (Table 71) is a 26 per cent protein mash feed recommended for feeding free choice with two or more whole grains to laying hens. The Illinois reference lists several other formulas and information on feeding and management practices.

The Minnesota mash concentrate (Table 71) contains 26 per cent protein and is recommended for feeding free choice with whole grains for the production of both market and hatching eggs.

The New England mashes include two for commercial egg production

Table 70

BREEDING MASH FORMULAS

INGREDIENTS	U. S. D. A. (1)		New Eng. Conf. (2)		New Jersey (3)	Okla. (4)
	All-Mash	Limited Grain	All-Mash	Limited Grain	Limited Grain	Limited Grain
Ground yellow corn	55.7	28.5	37.2	27.0	30.5	15.0
Wheat middlings			25.0	17.5	10	15.0
Wheat bran					10	27.0
Ground oats or barley	10.0	10.0	20.0	15.0	10	15.0
Cane molasses						
Soybean oil meal	14.0	28.0	5.0	15.0	15.0	
Cottonseed meal						5.0
Meat scraps			2.5	5.0	7.5	10.0
Fish meal	4.0	8.0	2.5	5.0	3.5	
Dried milk						5.0
Bone meal or low fluorine rock phosphate	2.5	5.0	1.0	3.0	1.5	
Ground limestone or oyster shell	3.0	2.0	1.5	2.0	2.0	1.0
Salt—iodized and manganized	0.5	1.0	0.5	1.0	0.5	1.0
Dried whey			2.0	4.0	2.5	
Alfalfa leaf or special alfalfa meal	5.0	5.0	2.5	5.0	6.5	6.0
Vitamin A and D feeding oil *	0.3	0.5	0.3	0.5	0.5	+
Dry form of vitamin D						
Riboflavin supplement	5.0	12.0				
Total	100.0	100.0	100.0	100.0	100.0	100.0

* 2,000 I. U. of vitamin A and 400 A. O. A. C. chick units vitamin D per gram.
(1) U. S. D. A. Circ. 788. 1948.
(2) New England College Conference. 1949–50 Rations.
(3) N. J. Sta. Circ. 528. 1949.
(4) Okla. Sta. Circ. C—133. 1949.

(Table 69) and two for the production of hatching eggs (Table 70). One of the mashes for each purpose is to be fed as all-mash with no additional grain, while the other one is to be fed with a limited amount of grain. The mash feed is kept before the birds, and grain is fed in about the proportion of mash consumed.

The New Jersey mash (Table 70) is recommended for feeding with about an equal amount of grain. It is satisfactory for both commercial and hatching-egg production.

The New York mash (Table 71) is a 32 per cent protein mash concentrate recommended for mixing with home grown grains to produce mash feeds of lower protein content. For instance, it is recommended that 800 pounds of the concentrate be mixed with 1200 pounds of grain to produce a breeding mash for feeding with about an equal amount of grain. The New York reference lists other mash formulas and feeding practices.

The Ohio mash (Table 71) is an all-purpose 26 per cent protein mash concentrate recommended for feeding free choice to laying or breeding hens. With slight modification in vitamin content, it may be used for starting poults.

The Oklahoma mash (Table 70) is recommended for feeding for the pro-

Table 71

LAYING AND BREEDING MASH CONCENTRATES

Ingredients	Southern States Coop. (1)	Ohio (2)	Illinois (3)	Minnesota (4)	New York (5)
Ground yellow corn..........		29.5			
Wheat middlings.............	8.5	10.0		20.0	4.5
Wheat bran..................			24.0	20.0	
Ground oats.................					
Cane molasses...............	5.0				
Soybean oil meal.............	57.5	35.0	20.0	25.5	32.0
Meat scrap..................	7.5	10.0	15.0	15.0	12.5
Fish meal...................	2.5				12.5
Dried milk..................			10.0		
Bone meal or low fluorine rock phosphate.................	5.0	1.0	5.0	6.0	8.5
Ground limestone or oyster shell	4.0	1.0	4.0	1.5	
Salt—iodized and manganized..	1.5	.5	2.0	2.0	2.5
Dried whey.................	1.0	3.0			15.0
Alfalfa leaf or special alfalfa meal.....................	7.5	10.0	20.0	10.0	12.5
Vitamin A and D feeding oil *..	+	+		+	
Dry form of vitamin D *......	+		+		+
Riboflavin supplement *.......	+			+	+
Animal protein factor (B₁₂) sup.*	+				
Total..................	100.0	100.0	100.0	100.0	100.0

* + Amount added will vary with the potency of the product, the protein content of the mash, and the purpose for which it is fed.
(1) Southern States Cooperative. 1949–50 Rations.
(2) Ohio Poultry Pointer 103. 1950.
(3) Ill. Sta. Circ. 606. 1946.
(4) Minn. Poultry Rations. 103. 1950.
(5) New York Ext. Stencil 193. 1948.

duction of both market and hatching eggs. It is fed with about an equal amount of grain.

The Southern States Co-operative mash (Table 71) is a 32 per cent protein concentrate recommended for feeding free choice with whole grains for commercial egg production. Ground grains may also be mixed with it to produce starting and growing mash feeds. The vitamin addition may need to be changed slightly depending on the purpose for which the mash is used.

The Texas mash (Table 69) is to be fed with an equal amount of a mixture of several grains including heavy oats. It may be used for both commercial and hatching-egg production.

The United States Department of Agriculture mash formulas may be used for commercial egg production (Table 69) and for the production of hatching eggs (Table 70). Part of them may be fed as all-mash, others may be fed with a limited amount of grain,—about equal parts grain and mash. The whole grains may consist of various proportions of corn and wheat alone or with the addition of oats or barley or both (Table 66).

The Washington mash (Table 69) is typical of several recommended for feeding with a limited amount of grain.

Feeding for control of molt. Birds do not molt and lay well at the same time. Early-hatched pullets generally lay well for a period of two or three months. Then they show a neck molt which may become general unless precautions are taken to check it. The practice used on some farms is to use artificial lights at night. This will check the molt and hold up production for about a month or six weeks. Then when production starts down again, wet mash is fed once or twice daily.

The molting of laying hens in the fall of the year, when egg prices are the highest, is another problem faced by poultrymen. To avoid a molt or to hasten birds through it, the consumption of mash feed should be encouraged. The use of lights and wet mash will also be beneficial. Feathers are largely protein, and mash feed contains the nutrients for feather growth. Moistening the wet mash feed with milk is desirable because milk is a good source of amino acids that are essential for feather growth. Some poultrymen prefer feeding pelleted mash in place of wet mash in order to stimulate feed consumption.

Some poultrymen force the hens to molt in the early summer when egg prices are low. The idea is to have the birds over the molt and back in production in late summer or early fall when egg prices are high. The mash feed is taken away and the birds are given water and grains for several days. The birds go out of production, but it is difficult to get all of them to go through a complete molt. The results obtained have been variable in different parts of the country. The forced molting of birds is a questionable practice. A better program is to feed the birds to produce all the eggs they will produce all the time.

Feeding for fall and winter egg production. The old saying that "a dozen eggs in the fall is worth two dozen in the spring" is still true. Toward the end of the first laying year or late in the summer or early fall many hens go out of production. Such birds may be kept in production until late fall or early winter by the use of artificial lights, and the feeding of wet mash. Slow-maturing pullets may be brought into production by the same practice. It also may be desirable to restrict the grain feeding in order to secure sufficient mash consumption for satisfactory egg production.

It should be remembered that hens which lay well in the fall will not lay so well in the spring. Flock owners who expect a high rate of production for hatching eggs in the late winter and spring should not force the flocks for high production in the fall.

Feeding for egg quality. The rations fed to laying hens influence both the market grade of eggs produced and their nutritive value.

Egg size is not influenced much by the ration. A good supply of oyster shells or limestone grit and vitamin D results in thicker eggshells and consequently slightly heavier eggs. Age and size of bird, rate and time of production, and breeding are the chief factors influencing egg size.

Shell quality is influenced by the calcium and manganese content of the ration and by the amount of the vitamin D factor supplied. Good quality oyster shells or limestone grit, or both, should be readily available for layers at all times. A special compartment at one or both ends of the feed hopper should be reserved for the shell or limestone. In case the eggshells become thin and crack easily, mineral consumption may be increased by sprinkling a handful of oyster shells over the mash feed in the hopper every day or so.

An ample supply of vitamin D should be provided by allowing the birds on range or by the use of feeding oil or a dry form of vitamin D when they are confined.

The *albumen quality* of eggs is influenced by the amount of succulent feed, such as cabbage, green grass, and lettuce that is fed. Birds should not be given more than about four pounds of succulent feed per hundred hens per day. If birds eat certain kinds of weeds, the albumen of the eggs produced may have a green or pink color, especially after being held in storage. Feeding cottonseed meal may also produce egg whites with a pinkish color. Rations high in protein produce a tougher white, which has a greater tendency to stick to the shell.

Yolk color is due to the amount of a carotinoid pigment, xanthophyll, fed in the ration. It is found in yellow corn, green grass, and alfalfa meal. Birds given green grass range and fed an abundance of yellow corn will produce eggs with dark yellow yolks. Eggs with pale yolks may be produced by keeping birds in confinement and feeding not more than 30 per cent yellow corn and 5 per cent alfalfa meal in the ration.

The use of more than 5 per cent cottonseed meal in the ration results in eggs with mottled yellow, salmon green, and nearly black yolks after they have been held in storage for a month or longer.

Weeds of the mustard family, such as shepherd's-purse and penny cress, impart a very undesirable olive color to the egg yolks of hens which pasture on them.

Keeping birds in confinement and feeding an all-mash ration results in the production of eggs with more uniform yolk color than when birds are given grass range or fed a grain and mash ration.

The *vitamin content* of the egg is influenced greatly by the ration fed. The more vitamins A, D, and G fed in the ration, the greater will be the content of these vitamins in the egg. The average run of eggs contains about 20 International units of vitamin A per gram of yolk (300 units per egg). The potency may be doubled when birds are fed good vitamin A rations, containing green grass, alfalfa, or good fish oil. When the vitamin A content of the ration is low, the vitamin A content may drop to 5 or 6 units per gram.

The average egg contains 10 to 12 U.S.P. units of vitamin D per yolk. When good vitamin D rations (with good fish oil or sunshine) are fed, the vitamin D content of the egg is increased to 60 to 80 units.

Both the white and yolk of the egg contain vitamin G. The average egg contains about .27 milligram or 270 gammas of riboflavin. The amount may be increased greatly by increasing the vitamin G content of the ration. The vitamin B_{12} content is also influenced by the ration fed.

Feeding for hatchability. It requires a better ration for the production of hatching eggs than for the production of market eggs. The hen must store all the nutrients in the egg that are needed for the development of the embryo. Since much mineral material needs to be assimilated in the embryo, the vitamin D content of the egg must be high for hatchability. The riboflavin and B_{12} content of the egg must also be high in order to meet the growth requirements of the embryo.

Special care in feeding is necessary when the breeding flock is kept in confinement. The birds should be fed fish oil or other sources of vitamin D to take the place of sunlight, and high-quality alfalfa or other legume hay to take the place of green grass. The breeding ration should also contain natural feedstuffs rich in B-complex vitamins such as liver meal, fish solubles, fish meal, milk, whey, brewers' yeast or distillers' solubles. Pure riboflavin, vitamin B_{12}, niacin, pantothenic acid or concentrates rich in these factors are now being used to replace most of the above feedstuffs.

The laying rations listed for use in feeding for egg production (Tables 69—71) are also satisfactory for the breeding flock, if the birds are kept on old used litter (see Table 72). Most poultrymen believe that it pays to feed for the production of hatching eggs even though they are to be sold for market. The eggs will be of higher nutritive value. The birds will have higher vitamin reserves and better health.

Table 72

HATCHABILITY OF CHICKEN EGGS AS AFFECTED BY BUILT-UP VERSUS FRESH FLOOR LITTER [13]

Ration	Litter	Trial	Eggs Set	Hatchability of Fertile Eggs
Basal *	New	1	797	45 *per cent*
		2	585	20
	Built-up	1	797	76
		2	585	81
Basal plus 2.5 per cent dried whey and 4 per cent meat scraps	New	1	792	82
		2	534	76
	Built-up	1	792	80
		2	534	81

* Corn 28.75, oats 20, bran 10, middlings 15, dehydrated alfalfa meal 5, soybean meal 16, bone meal 2.5, oyster shell 2.0, manganized salt 0.5, and feeding oil (2,000 A—400 D) 0.25 per cent.

No special care is needed in feeding the male birds in the breeding flock. They will do well on the ration fed the hens.

Feed consumption of laying hens. Feed consumption will vary with the size of the bird, rate of production, weather conditions, and quality of the ration. The average hen will eat from seventy to ninety pounds of feed in a year. About fifty-five pounds of this amount is used for maintenance. It has been observed at Cornell University that one hundred Leghorn hens of av-

[13] Kennard, Bethke, and Chamberlain, 1948.

erage size will eat the following amounts of feed per day, depending on the rate of production:

Per Cent Production	Total Feed Intake
0	18–19 lbs.
10	19–20
20	20–21
30	21–22
40	22–23
50	23–24
60	24–25
70	25–26

The following formula may be used to figure the feed consumption of any breed of fowls at various levels of production.

Total daily feed per 100 birds = 8.3 + 2.2 times the weight of the bird + one-tenth (0.1) of the egg production.

Fattening Poultry

Poultry is fattened to improve the quality of the meat and to increase the weight. Birds that are mature, or nearly so, may be fattened more easily than growing stock. The rations fed and the length of the finishing or fattening period influence the gains and the quality of the product produced.

The fattening or finishing period is short, varying from about one week in the case of hens to about two weeks for fryers.

The birds should be confined to pens or fattening batteries. Birds that are unusually active, easily frightened, or restless do not gain well.

Since the feeding period is short, no special provision need be made for vitamins A and D in the ration. Fish oils and alfalfa that are usually fed to supply these vitamins may be replaced by corn in the fattening ration.

The feed should consist mainly of ground grains. All of the ration and liquid consumed is given in the form of a wet mash. The birds eat more of the mash than they otherwise would, in order to satisfy their needs for water.

The mash is generally mixed with milk to make a batter that pours easily. Milk adds to palatability of the fattening ration and results in better gains.

The fattening mash and milk or water are generally mixed in the proportion of forty parts by weight of mash and sixty parts of liquid to make a mash of the proper consistency for pouring.

Fattening rations. Some typical fattening rations and systems of feeding advocated in different sections of the country are listed in Table 73.

The United States Department of Agriculture fattening mash feed, No. 1 (Table 73), is intended for broilers while No. 2 is recommended for roasters, capons, and fowls.

The Southern States Co-operative fattening mash probably contains more ingredients than justified by experimental data. This mash should be mixed with liquid milk to give best results.

Table 73

FATTENING MASH FORMULAS

INGREDIENTS	U. S. D. A. (1) No. 1	U. S. D. A. (1) No. 2	SOUTHERN STATES COOP. (2)	MACDONALD COLLEGE (3)	SOUTH DAKOTA (4)
Ground corn	40.0	45.0	60.0	24.0	61.0
Finely ground oats	30.0	34.0	5.0	23.0	10.0
Ground wheat				23.0	
Ground barley				23.0	
Middlings					10.0
Ground milo					
Cane molasses			3.0		
Meat scrap or meal	5.0	3.0		3.5	5.0
Dried milk	6.0	6.0		2.5	13.0
Soybean or corn gluten meal	14.0	10.0	25.0		
Bone meal or low fluorine rock phosphate			3.0		
Ground limestone	1.5	1.5	1.0		
Salt—plain or iodized and manganized	0.5	0.5	0.5	1.0	1.0
Alfalfa leaf or special alfalfa meal	3.0		2.5		
Riboflavin supplement			+		
Animal protein factor (B_{12}) supplement			+		
Total	100.0	100.0	100.0	100.0	100.0

(1) U. S. D. A. Circ. 788. 1948.
(2) Southern States Cooperative. Baltimore, Md. 1949 Rations.
(3) W. A. Maw. Macdonald College, Quebec.
(4) S. D. Bul. 335. 1940.

The Macdonald College fattening mash is intended primarily for roasters and capons. If the mash is mixed with liquid milk, the meat meal and dried milk may be replaced by corn or middlings.

The South Dakota fattening mash is recommended for fattening fryers, roasters, and broilers. If the mash is mixed with liquid milk, instead of water, the dried milk may be replaced by one of the cereal grains.

Feeding practice. It is customary to fatten or finish fryers, roasters, capons, and old hens, unless they are already in good flesh.

The birds are generally confined to pens, coops, or batteries. Very little feed is given the first day of confinement in order to develop a keen appetite. The birds are given about as much feed as they will clean up in about five minutes in the morning of the second day, and as much as they will clean up in ten minutes in the evening. On the third day, the birds may be fed as much as they will clean up morning, noon, and night in fifteen- to thirty-minute feeding periods.

In large fattening stations, birds are fed by what is sometimes termed the "continuous pouring" method. They are given as much feed as they will clean up in a few minutes several times a day.

Hens are generally fattened for about a week if in poor flesh, but not at all if in good condition. The gains are usually small, generally not more than about 7 per cent. However, the quality of the meat is improved.

Roasters, including capons, are generally fattened about ten days. Gains of 5 to 15 per cent may be expected.

Fryers, including large broilers, may be fattened for about two weeks, or as long as rapid gains and good feed consumption are maintained. Gains of 10 to 30 per cent may be expected.

Quality of poultry meat. The fattening ration influences the skin color, tenderness of the meat, flavor, firmness of the fat, and vitamin content of the edible tissues.

Skin color, in yellow-skinned varieties, is influenced by the fattening ration. White corn and milk in the fattening ration results in birds with pale skin color. Birds fattened on range and fed an abundance of yellow corn have a rich yellow skin color.

Tenderness of meat is influenced some by the ration fed as well as by age and the method of cooking. Rapidly growing and well-fattened birds are more tender than slow-growing and poorly fattened ones. Range-fattened birds are tougher than those fattened in pens or batteries.

Flavor of poultry meat is influenced by the ration fed. The use of oily fish meal or fish oil in the fattening or finishing ration should be discontinued at least two weeks before the birds are marketed. Otherwise, the cooked meat may have a fishy odor and taste.

Birds fattened largely on corn have a meat that is more palatable and juicy than birds fattened largely on wheat.

Fat may be increased in the muscles and elsewhere by administration of estrogen just before and during the fattening period. Mutton fat added to the ration produces a firm fat while vegetable oils produce a soft fat.

REVIEW QUESTIONS

1. Why are the cereal grains often varied within wide limits in poultry rations?
2. Which one of the cereal grains is most palatable?
3. Compare the feeding value of wheat and its by-products, middlings, and bran.
4. What is the most economical form in which to feed oats?
5. Why is yellow corn superior to white corn?
6. A hundred pounds of dried milk is equivalent to how many gallons of liquid milk and how many pounds of condensed milk in feeding value?
7. Which is more uniform in composition, dried buttermilk or dried skim milk? Why?
8. What are the differences between meat scraps and tankage?
9. What is one of the best kinds of fish meal?
10. What is the most widely used vegetable protein feedstuff in poultry rations?
11. Name a nutrient deficiency in vegetable protein feedstuffs that is not present in most animal protein feedstuffs.
12. Why is it undesirable to replace all animal protein feedstuffs in poultry rations by vegetable protein feedstuffs?
13. What mineral elements are most likely to be deficient in poultry rations?

14. Give the formula of a simple mineral mixture and directions for its use in poultry rations.
15. Why include a trace of manganese in poultry rations?
16. What groups of nutrients need to be considered in formulating poultry rations?
17. The carbohydrate feedstuffs constitute about what per cent of the ration?
18. What are the chief differences in formulating an economical ration for birds on range and in confinement?
19. Name the four principal methods of feeding poultry and give the advantages of each.
20. What is the principal way in which the use of artificial lights results in increased egg production?
21. Why do the producers of small broilers often feed a higher protein ration than farmers who raise poultry to replenish the flock?
22. What are the advantages of finishing pullets on a 15 or 16 per cent protein ration rather than on one of lower protein content?
23. Why is more feed required to produce a pound of capon than a pound of broiler, duck, or turkey?
24. Give the formula for an all-mash chick starting and growing ration for January-hatched chicks.
25. What feeding and management practices may be employed to prevent a slump in fall egg production of winter-hatched pullets?

REFERENCES

ACKERSON, C. W., HAM, W. E., AND MUSSEHL, F. E.: A COMPARISON OF OPEN POLLINATED AND HYBRID CORN IN A RATION FOR GROWING CHICKS. Neb. Res. Bul. 144. 1946.

ACKERSON, C. W., HAM, W. E., AND MUSSEHL, F. E.: A COMPARISON OF GROUND WHEAT AND GROUND RYE IN RATIONS FOR GROWING CHICKS. Neb. Sta. Res. Bul. 146. 1946.

ANDREWS, F. N., AND BOHREN, B. B.: INFLUENCE OF THIOURACIL AND STILBESTROL ON GROWTH, FATTENING, AND FEED EFFICIENCY IN BROILERS. Poultry Sci., 26: 447–452. 1947.

ANNIN, G. E., AND CRAVENS, W. W.: CHICKS, BROODING, FEEDING, REARING. Wis. Ext. Circ. 382. 1949.

ASSOCIATION OF AMERICAN FEED CONTROL OFFICIALS. Official Publication. 1946.

BERRY, L. N.: FEEDING AND MANAGEMENT OF BIRDS IN LAYING CAGES. N. M. Sta. Bul. 328. 1946.

BIRD, H. R., AND BURKHARDT, G. J.: FACTORS AFFECTING THE NUTRITIVE VALUE OF SOYBEAN OIL MEALS AND SOYBEANS FOR CHICKENS. Md. Sta. Bul. A, 27. 1943.

BIRD, H. R.: NUTRITIVE REQUIREMENTS AND FEED FORMULAS FOR CHICKENS. U. S. D. A. Circ. 788. 1948.

CARD, L. E.: PRACTICAL FEEDING OF POULTRY. Ill. Sta. Circ. 606. 1946.

CLARK, T. B., VAN LANDINGHAM, A. H., AND WEAKLY, C. E.: YOUNG GRASS LEGUME SILAGE IN THE POULTRY RATION. W. Va. Sta. Bul. 340. 1949.

DAKAN, E. L.: POULTRY HOUSE LIGHTING AND ITS INFLUENCE ON EGG PRODUCTION AND CHICKEN GROWTH. Rural Electrif. Exch., New Ser. 1, No. 1, pp. 13–15. 1938.

DRAPER, C. I.: THE NUTRITIVE VALUE OF CORN OIL MEAL AND FEATHER PROTEIN. Iowa Sta. Res. Bul. 326. 1944.

EVANS, E. V., SLINGER, S. J., AND MARCELLUS, F. N.: USE OF CRYSTALLINE RIBOFLAVIN IN PRACTICAL POULTRY RATIONS. Poultry Sci., 22: 433–437. 1943.

FUNK, E. M.: CAN THE CHICK BALANCE ITS RATION? Poultry Sci., 11: 94–97. 1932.

GERRY, R. W., CARRICK, C. W., ROBERTS, R. E., AND HAUGE, S. M.: RAW ROCK PHOSPHATE IN LAYING RATIONS. Poultry Sci., 28: 19–23. 1949.

GODFREY, G. F.: THE EFFECT OF FEEDING THYROPROTEIN ON EGG SHELL QUALITY AND HATCHABILITY. Poultry Sci., 28: 867–873. 1949.

GOODEARL, G. P.: COMPARISON OF PROSO, MILLET, AND YELLOW CORN FOR FEEDING LAYING HENS. N. D. Sta. Bul. 329. 1943.

GRAU, C. R., DRATZER, F. H., AND NEWLON, W. E.: FEED FOR CHICKENS. Calif. Ext. Circ. 159. 1949.

GUTTERIDGE, H. S., AND O'NEIL, J. B.: METHODS AND RATIONS FOR FATTENING POULTRY. Sci. Agr., 23: 647–650. 1943.

GUTTERIDGE, H. S., AND PRATT, J. M.: THE EFFECT OF VITAMIN D_2 AND D_3 IN FISH OIL AND OF IODOCASEIN ON SHELL QUALITY. Poultry Sci., 25: 89–91. 1946.

HANDBOOK OF OFFICIAL GRAIN STANDARDS OF THE UNITED STATES. U. S. D. A. Rev. 1949.

HART, C. P., AND STEWART, H. O.: THE EFFECT OF DIFFERENT INTAKE LEVELS OF ALFALFA MEAL IN ENHANCING HATCHABILITY. R. I. Sta. Misc. Pub. 20: 6. 1944.

HEUSER, G. F., AND NORRIS, L. C.: SOYBEAN OIL MEAL IN CHICK RATIONS. Cornell Sta. Bul. 810. 1944.

HEUSER, G. F., AND NORRIS, L. C.: OYSTER SHELLS, CALCITE GRIT, GROUND LIMESTONE, AND GRANITE GRIT IN RATIONS FOR HENS. Poultry Sci., 25: 173–179. 1946.

HEYWANG, B. W.: THE WATER CONSUMPTION OF HENS. Poultry Sci., 20: 184–187. 1941.

HOFFMANN, E., AND WHEELER, R. S.: THE VALUE OF THYROPROTEIN IN STARTING, GROWING, AND LAYING RATIONS. Poultry Sci., 27: 609–612. 1948.

HOWE, P. E., HARSHAW, H. M., AND WOODWARD, T. E.: A HANDBOOK FOR BETTER FEEDING OF LIVESTOCK. U. S. D. A. Misc. Circ. 12. 1947.

JAAP, R. G., AND THOMPSON, R. B.: FATTENING POULTRY BY FEEDING "FEMALE" HORMONES. U. S. Egg and Poultry Mag., 51: 108–110. 1945.

KEMPSTER, H. L.: THE USE OF DRIED INCUBATOR OFFAL IN CHICK RATIONS. Poultry Sci., 24: 396–398. 1945.

KENNARD, D. C., AND CHAMBERLAIN, V. D.: OATS FOR CHICKENS. Ohio Sta. Bimo. Bul., 21: 95–98. 1936.

KENNARD, D. C., BETHKE, R. M., AND CHAMBERLAIN, V. D.: BUILT-UP FLOOR LITTER A SOURCE OF DIETARY FACTORS ESSENTIAL FOR HATCHABILITY OF CHICKEN EGGS. Poultry Sci., 27: 477–481. 1948.

KENNARD, D. C., THATCHER, L. E., AND CHAMBERLAIN, V. D.: BARE YARD, CONFINEMENT, OR LEGUME RANGE FOR GROWING CHICKENS? Ohio Farm and Home Research 33: 64–66. 1948.

LEE, C. E., SCHOLES, J. C., AND HENRY, C. L.: THE EFFECT OF "FREE CHOICE" GRAIN FEEDING ON EGG PRODUCTION AND FEED CONSUMPTION. Poultry Sci., 28: 10–13. 1949.

MARCH, B. E., STUPICK, D., AND BIELY, D.: THE EVALUATION OF THE NUTRI-
TIONAL VALUE OF FISH MEALS AND MEAT MEALS. Poultry Sci., 28: 718–724. 1949.

MAW, A. J. G., AND MAW, W. A.: SOME OBSERVATIONS ON METHODS OF FAT-
TENING CHICKENS. U. S. Egg and Poultry Mag. 45, No. 6. 1939.

MCCONNELL, E. S., INSKO, W. M., AND BUCKNER, G. D.: FUSED ROCK PHOS-
PHATE FOR CHICKS. Ky. Sta. Bul. 455. 1944.

MCGINNIS, J., MACGREGOR, H. I., AND CARVER, J. S.: WOOD SUGAR MOLAS-
SES AS A FEEDSTUFF FOR CHICKS. Poultry Sci., 27: 459–461. 1948.

MORENG, R. E., AND SHAFFNER, C. S.: A THIOURACIL-THYROPROTEIN TREAT-
MENT FOR FATTENING POULTRY. Poultry Sci., 28: 504–510. 1949.

NATIONAL COTTONSEED PRODUCTS ASSOCIATION. 1950 FEEDING PRACTICES.
Bul. 27.

NELSON, N. M.: FEED INFLUENCE ON EYE COLOR IN WHITE LEGHORN CHICK-
ENS. Poultry Sci., 23: 541–543. 1944.

OHIO POULTRY FEED CONFERENCE BOARD: 1950 OHIO POULTRY RATIONS.
Ohio Ext. Poultry Pointer 103. 1950.

OTT, W. H., BOUCHER, R. V., AND KNANDEL, H. C.: FEEDING CANE MOLAS-
SES AS A CONSTITUENT OF POULTRY RATIONS. Poultry Sci., 21: 340–345.
1942.

PARKER, J. E., AND MCSPADDEN, B. J.: PASTURES FOR GROWING PULLETS.
Tenn. Sta. Bul. 188. 1944.

PAYNE, L. F., AND GISH, C. L.: GRASS AND ALFALFA AS SILAGE, FORAGE, AND
MEAL FOR POULTRY. Kan. Sta. Bul. 320. 1943.

PENSACK, J. M., BETHKE, R. M., AND KENNARD, D. C.: THE EFFECT OF FISH
MEAL AND EXTRACTS OF FISH MEAL ON HATCHABILITY OF HEN'S EGGS
AND GROWTH OF PROGENCY. Poultry Sci., 28: 398–405. 1949.

PETERSEN, C. F., WIESE, A. C., AND LAMPMAN, C. E.: THE EFFECT OF SEVERAL
PROTEIN SUPPLEMENTS ON HATCHABILITY WHEN FED TO HENS IN
OPEN PENS AND BATTERIES. Poultry Sci., 27: 471–476. 1948.

POLEY, W. E.: CAPON PRODUCTION IN SOUTH DAKOTA. S. D. Sta. Bul. 335.
1940.

POLEY, W. E., AND WILSON, W. O.: FEEDING VALUES OF HIGH- AND LOW-
TEST WEIGHT GRAINS FOR CHICKENS. S. D. Sta. Bul. 353. 1941.

POULTRY COUNCIL OF THE STATE COLLEGE OF WASHINGTON: FEEDING AND
MANAGEMENT OF LAYERS. Wash. Ext. Bul. 349. 1949.

RINGROSE, R. C., NORRIS, L. C., AND HEUSER, G. F.: THE VALUE OF CORN
GLUTEN MEAL FOR FEEDING POULTRY. Cornell Sta. Bul. 725. 1939.

ROBERTSON, E. I., CARVER, J. S., AND COOK, J. W.: METHODS OF FEEDING
LAYING HENS. Wash. Sta. Bul. 381. 1939.

SCHLAMB, K. F., AND WINTER, A. R.: AN EVALUATION OF DRIED DISTILLERS'
FEEDSTUFFS FED TO CHICKENS THROUGHOUT THEIR LIFE CYCLE. Poultry
Sci., 27: 492–505. 1948.

SKOGLUND, W. C., TOMHAVE, A. E., AND KISH, A. F.: INFLUENCE OF MAN-
AGEMENT PRACTICES ON PRODUCTION OF HATCHING EGGS. Del. Sta. Bul.
266. 1947.

SMITH, R. M.: THE USE OF RICE AND RICE BY-PRODUCTS IN THE LAYING RA-
TIONS. Ark. Sta. Bul. 478. 1948.

SOUTHERN STATES COOPERATIVE. OPEN FORMULA FEEDS. Baltimore, Md. 1949.

TEMPERTON, H., AND DUDLEY, F. J.: THE EFFECTS OF SYSTEMS OF FEEDING

ON GROWTH AND EGG PRODUCTION. Harper Adams Utility Poultry Journal, 33: 1–7. 1948.

THAYER, R. H., AND THOMPSON, R. B.: FEEDING CHICKENS. Okla. Sta. Circ. C-133. 1949.

TURNER, C. W.: FEEDING THYROPROTEIN AND SEX HORMONES TO LAYING HENS. Poultry Sci., 27: 613–620. 1948.

UPP, C. W.: CANE MOLASSES IN POULTRY RATIONS. La. Sta. Bul. 289. 1937.

VONDELL, J. H.: METHODS OF FEEDING LAYERS AND BREEDERS. Poultry Sci., 27: 531–535. 1948.

WILGUS, H. S., NORRIS, L. C., AND HEUSER, G. F.: THE RELATIVE PROTEIN EFFICIENCY AND THE RELATIVE VITAMIN G CONTENT OF COMMON PROTEIN SUPPLEMENTS USED IN POULTRY RATIONS. Jour. Agr. Res., 51: 383–399. 1935.

WILSON, W. O.: CORN, WHEAT, AND BARLEY FOR CHICKENS. S. D. Sta. Bul. 376. 1944.

WINTER, A. R., AND SCHLAMB, K. F.: INFLUENCE OF RANGE VERSUS CONFINEMENT REARING ON GROWTH, FEED CONSUMPTION, EGG PRODUCTION, AND LIVABILITY. Poultry Sci., 27: 571–578. 1948.

CHAPTER 11 |||||||||||||||||||||||||||||||||||||||||||||||||||||||

Disease and Parasite Prevention
and Control

▼

Disease may be defined as any deviation from the normal state of health, whether it be a slight ailment or one endangering life.

Poultry suffer the greatest losses from disease of all the domestic animals. It is the greatest hindrance to profitable poultry production. Losses from disease account for the relatively high prices of poultry products.

Egg-laying contests and the United States Department of Agriculture report an annual mortality of 12 to 20 per cent among layers (Table 74).

Table 74

MORTALITY IN LAYING FLOCKS

Location	Year	Breed	Mortality
			Per Cent
United States *	1939	all breeds	18.1
(all farms)	1940	all breeds	17.8
	1941	all breeds	19.1
	1942	all breeds	19.4
	1943	all breeds	16.2
	1944	all breeds	18.4
	1945	all breeds	17.7
	1946	all breeds	17.4
United States †	1948–49	White Leghorn	15.9
(all egg-laying contests)		Rhode Island Reds	13.0
		New Hampshires	10.4
		Barred Plymouth Rocks	13.2
		White Plymouth Rocks	17.5
		White Wyandottes	17.3

* U. S. D. A. Bureau of Agri. Economics, 1947.
† Council of American Official Poultry Tests, 1948–49.

Chick mortality during the growing period is also a factor of economic importance. According to the United States Department of Agriculture (Agricultural Statistics, 1944) it amounts to more than 87 million in 1943, or nearly 10 per cent of the chickens raised.

In the losses from disease, one must consider not only actual mortality but losses from poor hatchability, growth, and production; poorly finished market birds; and overhead expense of partly filled houses and idle equipment.

Disease

Terminology. A knowledge of common disease terms is needed in studying poultry diseases. A few of the most widely used terms are listed here.

Infection is the invasion of the tissues of the body by pathogenic organisms in such a way as to favor their growth and permit their toxins to injure the tissues.

Pathogenic refers to the ability of an organism to cause disease.

Immunity is the power of resistance of an animal to resist and overcome infection.

Etiology is the study of the cause of a disease.

Inflammation is the reaction of body tissues to irritation. It is characterized by swelling, heat, redness, and pain. The ending, "itis" is often used to indicate inflammation of a part; for example, enteritis means inflammation of the intestines.

A *lesion* is any hurt, wound, or local degeneration of tissue.

A *vaccine* is a suspension of living disease-producing organisms (bacteria or viruses).

A *bacterin* is a suspension of dead disease-producing organisms.

A *toxin* is a poisonous substance produced by bacterial action.

Causes. Diseases may be produced by living organisms such as parasites, protozoa, fungi, bacteria, and viruses (Fig. 137).

Parasites are here regarded as small multicellular animal organisms. Examples are lice and roundworms.

Protozoa are microscopic one-celled animals. Examples are the causative organisms of coccidiosis and blackhead.

Molds or fungi are low forms of plants. A few of the many forms which appear in nature produce diseases. Examples of poultry diseases produced by them are aspergillosis and favus.

Bacteria are microscopic one-celled plants. They are widely distributed in nature, but only a few of them produce disease. Examples of bacterial poultry diseases are pullorum and tuberculosis.

Viruses are organisms so small that they cannot be seen even with the microscope. The proof of their existence is their ability to reproduce disease by introducing substances containing them into the body of a susceptible animal. Fowl pox and laryngotracheitis are examples of poultry virus diseases.

The disease-producing organisms may gain entrance to the body by way of the mouth, nose, eye, skin, cloaca, or egg. They produce disease by irritation, inflammation, use of body nourishment, mechanical obstruction of organs, destruction of tissue, or production of toxins.

Disease may also be produced by body deformities, injury, faulty nutrition, poisons, and poor environment. This group of diseases is not transmissible from one bird to another.

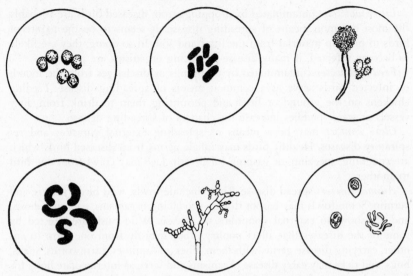

Fig. 137. Some disease-producing microorganisms, magnified several hundred times. Top: left, cocci or round bacteria, found in pus and skin lesions; center, bacilli or rod-shaped bacteria, cause pullorum disease; right, aspergillus or mold, causes aspergillosis or brooder pneumonia. Bottom: left, spirilla or curved bacteria found in some blood diseases; center, monilia or mold, causes thrush; right, protozoa, coccidia—the cause of coccidiosis.

Infections. The ability of disease-producing organisms to produce disease depends upon a number of factors.

Virulence of organisms is a determining factor in the production and severity of an infectious disease. The longer infective agents are away from the body and the more they are exposed to adverse environmental conditions, such as high and low temperatures, dryness, air, sunlight, or disinfectants, the less the chances that they will produce disease.

The *number of organisms* gaining entrance to the body influences disease production and its course. Small numbers of disease-producing organisms may be thrown off by the body, but massive doses cannot be combated by the natural body defenses.

Resistance of birds or their immunity against infection influences disease production. Immunity may be inherited or it may be acquired. It may be acquired by having had the disease or by the intake of a few organisms from time to time which stimulated the production of immune substances.

Well-fed birds have greater natural resistance against infection than improperly fed individuals.

Overcrowding, drafts, extremes of temperature, and forced production lower resistance against infection.

Spread of disease. The parasites, fungi, protozoa, bacteria, and viruses may escape from the body of diseased birds by way of the droppings, mouth, wounds, or by blood obtained by blood-sucking insects. After leaving the body of the bird, the disease-producing agents may be passed on to susceptible birds in a number of ways.

Litter and soil contaminated by droppings from diseased birds are probably the most common means of spreading disease. It seems to be the nature of birds to pick up material from the litter and soil. In so doing, they are likely to become infected, if many disease-producing organisms are present.

Feed and water contaminated by droppings or discharges from the mouth of infected birds serve as a common means of spreading disease. Feeding chickens on the ground or litter and permitting them to drink from dirty vessels or water puddles increase the chances of spreading disease.

Close contact may be a means of spreading external parasites and respiratory diseases. Healthy birds may inhale germs from diseased birds which are coughing, sneezing, or gasping for breath. Lice may crawl from one bird to another.

Animal carriers spread disease. These include fowls, wild birds, insects, and vermin. Some fowls may harbor disease-producing organisms, e.g., coccidiosis, and yet show no external symptoms of disease. Wild birds are affected by some of the diseases that affect poultry. They may fly from one farm to another, carrying disease germs with them. Flies, mosquitoes, earthworms, snails, bugs, and ticks may carry disease organisms and serve as intermediate hosts for the development of some of these organisms. Rats may also serve as a means of spreading disease. Dogs, cats, and other farm animals may carry infective material on their feet.

Movable equipment may be a means of spreading disease. This includes cleaning equipment, coops, feeders and waterers, feed sacks, and egg cases.

The *attendant* or visitors may carry disease-producing organisms on their feet and clothing.

Disease Prevention

The most efficient and economical method of controlling disease lies in the use of preventive measures. The old adage, "an ounce of prevention is worth a pound of cure," certainly applies to poultry diseases. The chicken has small unit value. Medicine and treatment often cost more than the bird is worth. Most diseases have a lasting after-effect on growth or production. Flock preventive measures should be used. These include selection for disease resistance, proper housing, clean range, proper feeding, culling out unhealthy birds, and quarantine of new stock.

Selection of stock. Select healthy fowls for breeders (p. 91). Use pullorum-tested stock (p. 116). Hatch from hens rather than from pullets; this affords more information about the livability of the parents. Use male birds in the breeding pens that come from families having good livability.

Proper housing. Provide adequate floor space (p. 181). This reduces the chances of cannibalism and the spread of disease by close contact and contaminated litter.

Provide adequate ventilation but avoid drafts. Avoid sudden changes in temperature. Drafts and extremes in temperature lower the resistance of birds and make them more susceptible to disease.

Use dropping pits or dropping boards to lessen the chances of spreading disease by droppings.

Use sanitary feeders and waterers. The more fecal material kept out of the feed and water, the less the chances of disease.

Use litter and change it often enough to keep the house reasonably clean and dry. Built-up litter may accomplish the same purpose.

Ranges and yards. The keeping of birds on the same range year after year will result in severe contamination if diseased birds are present in the flock. Some disease germs and parasite eggs will live in the soil for a year or more. Good drainage and aeration of the soil help keep down infection. Keeping the grass cut short or grazed closely provides young, tender vegetation for the birds and at the same time permits greater penetrating power of sunlight. Permanent shade is objectionable—unless there can be good rotation of range with the birds off the ground for two or more years—because it keeps out sunlight and keeps the soil damp. Shady, damp places are favorable for the protection of disease-producing organisms.

The rearing range should be changed each year so that each range has a two- or three-year period during which no birds are kept on it. The same applies to yards attached to permanent houses. Cropping unused ranges and yards assists in keeping them safe for poultry.

If only one small range is available and it becomes contaminated, keep the birds in confinement. Sun porches or cindered yards may be provided for confined birds so that they may have the benefits of fresh air and sunshine without the dangers of contaminated soil.

Sanitation. Sanitation is the establishment of environmental conditions favorable to health. Good houses, equipment, and yards need to be kept clean in order to lessen the chances of disease.

Built-up litter may be a means of controlling diseases according to Kennard and associates of the Ohio Agricultural Experiment Station (Table 75). The chicks are started on old (six months or more) used litter rather than on new litter in clean pens. When the litter becomes caked, it is stirred and a little fresh material added. The thick layer (6–12 inches) of litter keeps the floor warmer and dryer. The alkaline excretory products and/or the micro-

Table 75

INFLUENCE OF LITTER MANAGEMENT ON BROILER MORTALITY[1]

Ration	Floor Litter	Av. Wt. of Birds at 12 Wks.	Mortality 1st 12 Wks.
Complete	Old built-up	2.45 lbs.	5 *per cent*
	Fresh	2.30	7
Incomplete	Old built-up	2.34	7
	New built-up	1.88	18
	Fresh	1.64	23

[1] Kennard and Chamberlain, 1949.

organisms living in the litter may reduce the virulence or kill possible pathogens such as viruses, bacteria, and protozoa. The built-up litter also has marked B-complex vitamin and protein sparing properties (Table 72).

The use of built-up litter is an entirely opposite approach to sanitation than the following recommendations that have been in use for years.

Cleaning the drinking and feed vessels, perches, nests, floors, and the interior of a house before each new lot of birds is housed aids in disease prevention. Keeping the equipment and pens clean while birds are in them is a further precautionary measure against disease.

Removal of droppings and litter to a distant part of the farm where chickens will not range, and keeping manure storage pits screened against flies help prevent the spread of disease. Manure piles serve as breeding places for flies. These insects carry disease and serve as hosts for tapeworm larvae (p. 362).

Disinfection or the killing of any remaining disease-producing organisms will further reduce the possibilities of disease. Chemical disinfectants are not always necessary or practical for this purpose.

Most pathogenic bacteria and viruses soon lose their virulence and die when they are away from the body of the bird. Drying and exposure to air and light aid in their destruction. Thorough cleaning of the house and equipment removes many organisms mechanically and exposes the remaining ones. The action of air and light will generally destroy them, especially if the house is allowed to remain empty for a time.

Chemical disinfectants may be used to hasten the destruction of pathogenic organisms. In most cases the warmer the temperature, the longer the time of action, the stronger the solution of disinfectant, and the smaller the amount of material to be disinfected, the better the effect of the disinfectant. It must be remembered that disinfectants react with feces, litter, dust, feed, and other organic matter and may be "used up" before coming in contact with bacteria. Therefore, cleaning should be thorough before disinfectants are used.

Lye solution, consisting of 1 pound of commercial lye (94 per cent sodium hydroxide) and 2½ pounds of water-slacked lime in 5½ gallons of water, is a cheap, odorless, and efficient disinfectant for general farm use. On prolonged contact, it may be injurious to painted or varnished surfaces, some fabrics, and aluminum. It does not injure metallic and wooden fixtures generally found on the farm. The lye solution may be used for disinfecting yards by thoroughly wetting the ground and then adding ½ to 1 gallon of the disinfectant per square yard of soil surface.

Cresol and other coal tar disinfectants are stable noncorrosive products which may be used on poultry house floors and equipment. A 3 per cent solution is generally used. These products should not be used in egg, meat, or other food storage rooms because of the odor transmitted to the foods.

Feeding. Proper feeding not only protects poultry against nutritional diseases, but results in better vigor and greater resistance against infection by disease-producing organisms. Vitamin A, for instance, stimulates normal secretory power of the epithelial tissue lining the respiratory and digestive tracts and hinders secondary bacterial infections. Adequate supplies of vitamins A and B in the ration afford protection against parasite infestation. A liberal supply of protein in the growing ration increases resistance against coccidiosis and worm infestation.

Removal of unhealthy birds. Whenever unhealthy birds (Table 14) are observed in the flock, they should be removed at once. They are often carriers of disease. Unless the bird is a valuable one, it should not be returned to the flock when and if it recovers. Such birds often get out of condition again. It is better to sell them for meat purposes.

Protection against carriers of disease. Do not allow pigeons and wild birds, especially sparrows and starlings, to roost in the houses or feed with the poultry.

Avoid the use of feeds and feeding practices which attract flies or other insects in unusual numbers.

Exterminate rats and mice.

Use new feed sacks for poultry feeds, especially for the growing stock.

Use clean coops for handling birds. Clean and disinfect them before use in another house or on another farm.

Young chicks should be brooded quite a distance from old stock. If the same person must care for both the young and old stock, the shoes should be cleaned and disinfected by stepping in a pan of disinfectant, or rubbers should be put on before going into the brooder house or on the range (Fig. 138).

Quarantine of new stock. New stock to be added to the poultry flock, or birds that have been away from the farm at shows, fairs, or other exhibits, should be held in coops or pens away from the flock for about two weeks, to make sure that they do not have any disease or show symptoms of disease infection.

Disease Control

Disease may gain entrance to a flock and outbreaks occur in spite of the use of preventive measures. In case of an outbreak of disease in which the cause and control measures are unknown, a veterinarian should be consulted.

Outbreaks of disease. In case of an outbreak of disease, all sick birds should be removed from the flock and placed in another building. If the disease is general, the flock may be left intact and the entire group treated.

The litter should be changed frequently as long as an epidemic lasts. Put the birds on new range or keep them in confinement. Remember that most diseases are spread by means of contaminated litter and soil.

Fresh feed and water should be kept before the birds in clean containers. The use of a disinfectant in the drinking water is of doubtful value. There are many other ways of spreading disease than by means of water (p. 333). The use of a disinfectant in the water nearly always hinders normal water consumption.

Fig. 138. Cleaning the shoes and stepping in a pan of disinfectant, or putting on overshoes before going in the brooder house or on the chick range will lessen the chances of carrying disease from the mature birds to the young stock.

It is advisable to use milk in some form (p. 290). It adds to palatability of the ration, acts as a mild laxative, and serves as an antidote against most toxins and poisons.

In case of poisoning, diarrhea trouble, or constipation, give the flock a laxative. For flock treatment of adult birds, use a pound of Epsom salts in two gallons of water per hundred birds. Individual doses of laxatives consist of one-half teaspoonful of Epsom salts in one or two tablespoons of water, or one-half to one teaspoon of castor oil. Liquids may be given with a hollow tube provided with a bulb on one end (Fig. 139).

Other control measures to be used will depend upon diagnosis of the disease.

Table 76

PRINCIPAL DISEASES OF MATURE CHICKENS AND THE PERCENTAGE DISTRIBUTION AMONG THE AUTOPSIES [2]

DISEASE	AGE OF BIRDS		
	7–12 Months	1–2 Years	Over 2 Years
Colds and coryza	11.5	7.4	7.7
Roundworms (intestinal)	11.3	10.8	7.2
Coccidiosis	8.6	4.9	1.4
Leucosis	7.8	4.9	3.5
Fowl cholera	6.3	7.7	9.4
Enteritis	5.7	5.3	2.4
Tumors	5.6	7.2	13.4
Ruptured yolk	5.1	5.0	7.5
Paralysis	3.9	2.5	1.1
Pox	2.8	3.2	4.9
Tapeworm	2.7	1.4	1.8
Infectious laryngotracheitis	2.6	2.8	4.6
A-avitaminosis	2.2	1.4	1.2
Roundworms (gizzard)	2.0	3.2	2.0
Lice	2.0	2.2	2.9
Cannibalism	1.6	1.2	0.3
Peritonitis	1.3	1.7	1.6
Nephritis	1.1	1.9	1.4
Salpingitis	1.0	2.0	2.4
Pullorum	0.7	1.8	1.6

Diagnosis of poultry diseases. A careful observation of external symptoms and autopsy findings are valuable aids in the diagnosis of poultry diseases. Other data needed in arriving at a correct diagnosis include history of the case or outbreak, age of birds affected, per cent of flock affected, housing and yard conditions, the ration being fed, management practices used, and treatment that has been given.

The California Department of Agriculture (Calif. Dept. of Agr. Bul. 21, No. 1. 1942) report on 30,000 birds of all ages autopsied, between 1931 and 1940 inclusive, is given in Tables 76 and 77.

Mature birds showed an increase in tumors, cholera, fowl typhoid, and pullorum with increasing age.

---

[2] Hoffman and Stover, 1932.

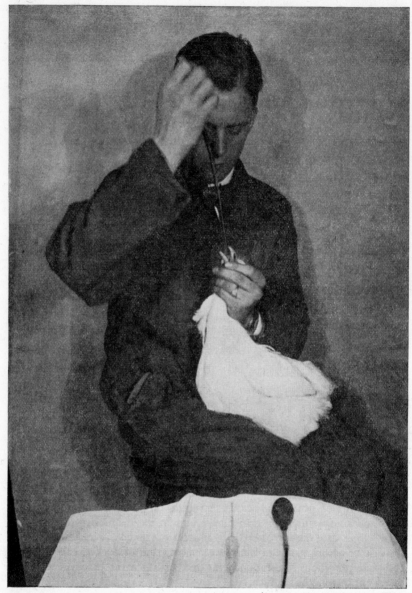

Fig. 139. Birds may be given medicine in liquid form with a hollow tube with a bulb on the end of it or with a pipette.

Growing chickens showed an increase in coccidiosis, paralysis, and worm infestation with increasing age.

External examination, while helpful, is often insufficient for accurate diagnosis. A bird may show certain symptoms that will indicate several dis-

Table 77

PRINCIPAL DISEASES OF GROWING CHICKENS AND THE PERCENTAGE
DISTRIBUTION AMONG THE AUTOPSIES [3]

DISEASE	AGE OF BIRDS		
	1–4 Weeks	5–12 Weeks	13–24 Weeks
Pullorum	27.9	0.7	0.6
Coccidiosis	20.5	49.7	24.5
Ulceration (gizzard)	10.9	4.9	0.8
Fowl typhoid	5.1	0.3	0.3
Pneumonia	3.6	0.4	0.2
Chick bronchitis	3.1	2.6	0.7
Colds and coryza	2.5	6.3	10.1
Enteritis	2.4	6.0	7.1
Nutritional dermatitis	2.3	0.2	....
Nephritis	2.1	1.0	0.8
Nutritional paralysis	1.6	0.2	....
Infectious laryngotracheitis	1.4	2.6	2.7
Rickets	1.4	1.3	....
Streptococcus infection	1.1	....	....
Paralysis	....	3.8	14.6
Roundworms (intestinal)	....	1.7	7.9
Tumors	....	0.7	3.5
Tapeworms	....	0.2	2.9
Leucosis	....	0.6	2.4

eases. As an example, lameness may indicate scaly leg, polyneuritis, vitamin A deficiency, rickets, bumblefoot, nutritional paralysis, tuberculosis, sod disease, parasites, perosis, range paralysis, or injury. External symptoms, autopsy findings, and the diseases indicated are summarized in Table 78.

Post-mortem examination generally adds additional information to that obtained from external symptoms.

The bird should be killed by breaking the neck. Cut the skin between the vent and rear of the keel around on both sides near the thighs and across the ribs. Press the legs away from the body until they are thrown out of joint. Pull the skin forward and to the sides to expose the entire breast and abdominal surface (Fig. 140).

A cut should then be made through the muscles just back of the breast-bone and forward through the ribs on each side in the direction of the attachment of the wings. Raise the rear of the keel and push it forward to expose the viscera.

The organs should be examined carefully before removal. Observe the air sacs, the pleural and peritoneal linings, the pericardium, and the mesenteries for indications of inflammation, unusual deposits, and the presence of abnormal tissue. Look for the presence of fluid, yolk material, or other abnormal substances in the body cavity.

[3] Hoffman and Stover, 1932.

Table 78

DIAGNOSIS OF DISEASES AS INDICATED BY EXTERNAL SYMPTOMS AND
AUTOPSY EXAMINATION

Structure, etc.	Abnormalities	Disease Indicated
Comb	Deep red	Cholera, botulism
	Purple	Cholera, poisoning
	Pale	Parasites, typhoid, tuberculosis, leukemia
	Blister or scabs	Fowl pox
Eyes and nostrils	Exudate in	Colds, roup, vitamin A deficiency, coccidiosis, sod disease
Mouth and throat	Ulcers in bloody mucus	Roup, fowl pox Infectious bronchitis
Feathers	Unthrifty	Worms, lice, mites, vitamin deficiency
	Falling out	Feather pulling, botulism
Wings	Drooping	Parasites, coccidiosis, vitamin deficiency, bacterial diseases
Legs	Lameness	Injury, gout, bumblefoot, vitamin deficiency, perosis
	Paralysis	Leucosis, tape worms, coccidiosis, tumors, vitamin deficiency
Neck	Limber	Botulism, poisoning, cholera
	Twisted	Worms, poisoning, tumors
Diarrhea	Green	Typhoid
	White	Pullorum, vitamin A deficiency, worms, cholera, coccidiosis
	Yellow	Cholera
	Bloody	Coccidiosis, cholera
Crop	Distended	Crop bound, sour crop
Vent	Inflamed, protruding	Prolapse
Weight	Light, emaciated	Parasitic, chronic, coccidiosis, leucosis, tuberculosis
Temperature	Elevated	Cholera, typhoid, pullorum, tuberculosis, tracheitis
	Subnormal	Botulism, vitamin deficiency
Respiration	Difficult	Bronchitis, gapes, aspergillosis, pneumonia

DIAGNOSIS OF DISEASES AS INDICATED BY EXTERNAL SYMPTOMS AND AUTOPSY EXAMINATION (cont'd.)

Structure, etc.	Abnormalities	Disease Indicated
Liver	Enlarged	Typhoid, leukemia, blackhead
	Spots	Typhoid, coccidiosis, tuberculosis, tumors, blackhead
	Yellow	Chilling, overheating
Intestinal tract	Congestion	Cholera, parasites, coccidiosis, poisons, vitamin B deficiency
	Thickened ulcers	Parasites, coccidiosis, tuberculosis, blackhead.
	Nodules	Tapeworms, tumors, tuberculosis.
Kidneys	Swollen, light colored	Vitamin A deficiency, cholera, typhoid
Ovary	Discolored or irregular ova	Pullorum, tumors
Heart	Small hemorrhages	Cholera
	Grayish spots	Typhoid
Lungs	Congested with blood	Cholera
	Pus spots	Pullorum, pneumonia
	Green or brown	Mycosis
Trachea and bronchi	Blood and pus	Infectious bronchitis
	Worms in	Gapes

The intestinal tract should be removed and split open with scissors. Look for thickened walls, hemorrhages, ulcers, worms, and other abnormalities. Observe the characteristics of the contents of the intestinal tract. Suspension of a section of the intestine in a jar of warm water helps to reveal small worms.

Open and examine the trachea for inflammation, mucus accumulation, and the presence of parasites.

By checking the abnormalities found with the diseases indicated in Table 78, it is often possible to diagnose the disease. Further proof may be secured by microscopic examination of tissues, bacterial cultures, and inoculation tests.

Nutritional Diseases

Unnatural brooding, housing, and feeding conditions; rapid growth; forced production; and the use of processed feedstuffs may often result in nutritional deficiencies.

Vitamin A deficiency. Vitamin A deficiency disease is also known as nutritional roup and avitaminosis A. It may affect poultry of all ages that are deprived of green grass range or other sources of vitamin A.

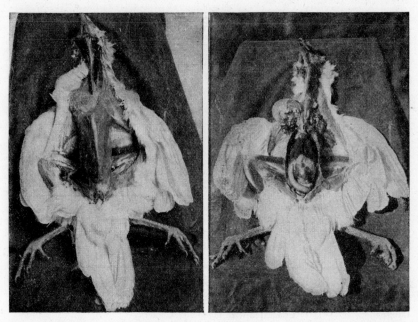

Fig. 140. Autopsy for diagnosing disease.

Symptoms among growing chicks include slow growth, ruffled feathers, paleness, drowsiness, staggering gait, inco-ordination of movements, crouching on the hocks, inflammation or dryness of the eyelids, cheesy material in the eyes, emaciation, weakness, and finally death.

Symptoms among hens include cessation of egg production, drowsiness, white cheesy material in the eyes, a nonodorous discharge from the nostrils, emaciation, weakness (Fig. 141), staggering gait, whitish droppings, and low resistance against respiratory infections.

Autopsy characteristics of vitamin A deficiency include pustule-like lesions in the mouth and gullet and swollen, grayish kidneys and ureters clogged with uric acid.

More careful study reveals a degeneration of the epithelial lining of the respiratory system and the upper digestive system, nerve degeneration, and an excess of uric acid in the blood.

Prevention of vitamin A deficiency is accomplished by providing green grass range or feeding yellow corn, dehydrated alfalfa meal, and feedstuffs containing corotene or vitamin A (Table 3, Appendix).

Fowls may be cured of vitamin A deficiency disease by feeding cod liver oil or a solution of corotene in a vegetable oil. The vitamin A requirements of poultry are given on page 278.

Vitamin B_1 deficiency disease. This disease is also known as avitaminosis B and polyneuritis. It is a nerve disease which may affect fowls of all ages deprived of green grass range and fed degerminated grains. Since most rations contain the germs of grains, vitamin B_1 deficiency is of rare occurrence.

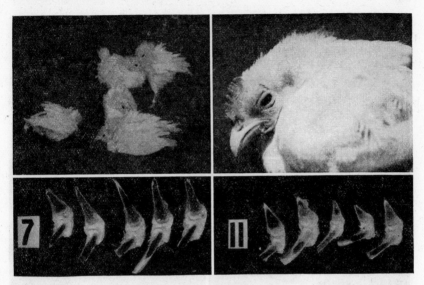

Fig. 141. Some fat-soluble vitamin deficiency diseases. Upper left, rickets. Birds walk with a wobbly gait and sit down much of the time. Upper right, vitamin A deficiency. Note the unthriftiness and pale, dry skin about the head and eyes. Lower, (7) normal bones with definite lines of calcification at the joints; (11) rachitic bones with poor calcification at the joints.

Symptoms of vitamin B_1 deficiency include loss of appetite, cessation of growth or production, spastic head contractions (Fig. 142), complete paralysis, and high mortality.

Autopsy reveals darkened and shrunken viscera and undigested food in the intestinal tract. The muscles are also darkened and shrunken. Peripheral nerves and those controlling the intestinal movements and secretory glands are partially paralyzed. Carbohydrate metabolism is affected and basal heat production is low.

Prevention of vitamin B_1 deficiency is accomplished by feeding whole or ground grains containing the germs, wheat bran, and middlings; green grass or alfalfa meal; milk; packing house by-products containing glandular tissue; or other feedstuffs containing vitamin B_1.

Fowls may be cured of polyneuritis by feeding yeast or pure vitamin B_1 (thiamin). Vitamin B_1 requirements of poultry are given on page 278.

Curled toe paralysis. This disease is most often encountered among growing birds kept in confinement or in batteries and fed rations containing a large amount of vegetable protein feedstuffs and a small amount of milk. It results from a deficiency of one of the factors of the vitamin B-G complex in poultry rations known as vitamin B_2, vitamin G, or riboflavin.

Symptoms of curled toe paralysis include slow growth, ruffled feathers, paleness, moving about on the hock joints, toes curling in, and, in advanced stages, lying on the floor with the legs sprawled out.

Vitamin B_2 or G deficiency among mature birds is indicated by poor hatch-

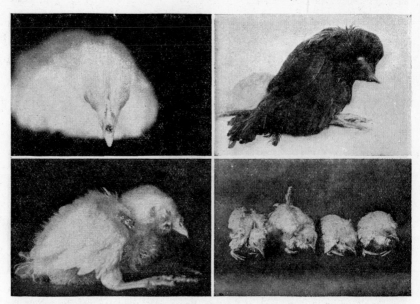

Fig. 142. Some vitamin B—G complex deficiency diseases. Upper left, "notched beak" lesion resulting from riboflavin deficiency. (University of California.) Upper right, polyneuritis resulting from vitamin B₁ deficiency. (Ohio Extension Bulletin 115.) Lower left, chick dermatitis resulting from a deficiency of pantothenic acid. (Courtesy L. C. Norris.) Lower right, curled toe paralysis and poor growth resulting from vitamin G or riboflavin deficiency.

ability with high embryo mortality the first week, and egg whites with little or no greenish opalescence.

Autopsy may reveal flabby and withered leg muscles and sciatic and brachial nerve degeneration.

Control of curled toe paralysis is accomplished by providing the birds with a green grass range or by feeding good quality alfalfa meal, milk, whey, or other feedstuffs containing vitamin G (Table 3, Appendix).

The disease may be cured by feeding yeast or riboflavin. The vitamin B_2 or G requirements of poultry are given on page 278.

Chick dermatitis. It is due to lack of the vitamin B-G complex known as the filtrate factor, or pantothenic acid. It may occur among chicks deprived of green grass and fed rations containing much vegetable protein feedstuffs and little milk, alfalfa, and wheat by-products. The disease seldom occurs, because of the wide distribution of pantothenic acid in poultry feedstuffs.

Symptoms of chick dermatitis include scabs or crustlike lesions around the eyes and corners of the mouth and on the feet, granular and constricted margins of the eyelids with a sticky exudate, peeling off of the skin on the toes, and development of wartlike protuberances on the balls of the feet.

Autopsy of chicks affected with chick dermatitis may reveal a puslike substance in the mouth and a grayish exudate in the glandular stomach, eroded lesions in the gizzard, enteritis of the duodenum, portions of the small intestine and ceca distended with gas, and pale-colored liver and kidneys.

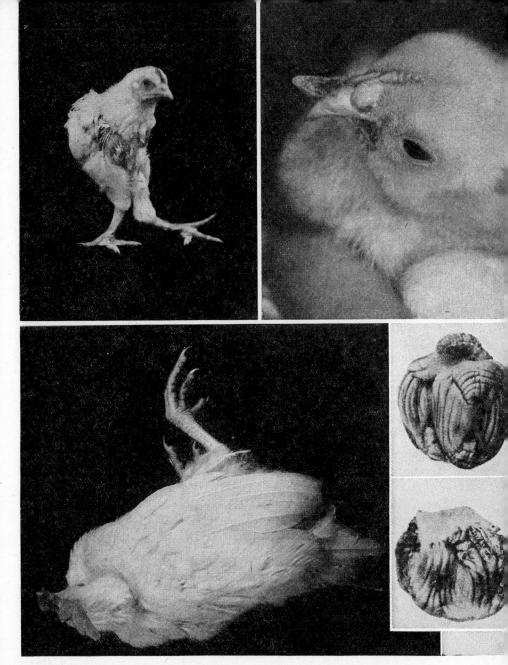

Fig. 143. Miscellaneous nutritional troubles. Upper left, perosis, also known as "slipped tendon" and hock disease. Upper right, beak necrosis. Feed sticking in the beak has caused the deformed beak. Lower left, "crazy chick" disease. Nutritional encephalomalacia shows similar symptoms. Lower right, gizzard erosion: top, normal gizzard lining; bottom, eroded lining. (Courtesy W. B. Esselen, Massachusetts State College.)

Prevention of chick dermatitis is accomplished by feeding green grass or alfalfa meal, packing house by-products rich in glandular tissue, milk, wheat bran, molasses, and other feedstuffs containing pantothenic acid.

Chick dermatitis may be cured by feeding yeast, liver, germs of grains, or pantothenic acid. The requirements of chicks and layers for pantothenic acid are given on page 278.

Nutritional encephalomalacia. This is a disease which affects chicks between two and seven weeks old (Fig. 143). It can be produced experimentally by feeding chicks rations high in animal fat content. Birds with apparently the same disease have been observed under practical farm conditions and fed many different home-mixed and commercial feeds.

Symptoms of nutritional encephalitis include ataxia, tremors, retraction of the head, spasms of the legs, inco-ordination, prostration, stupor, and finally death.

Pathology of nutritional encephalomalacia is indicated by swelling and softening of the cerebellum and sometimes other parts of the brain, edema of the brain covering, minute hemorrhages on the surface of the brain, and greenish to brownish coloration and shrinkage of the necrotic areas.

Apparently the cause of the trouble is some factor which impairs the capillary circulation of the brain.

Control for nutritional encephalomalacia involves the use of vitamin E (alpha-tocopherol). The addition of green grass, alfalfa leaf meal, and wheat bran or middlings to the ration will reduce the losses.

Experimentally produced nutritional encephalomalacia may be cured by adding certain vegetable oils to the ration, such as corn oil, cottonseed oil, hydrogenated cottonseed oil (Crisco), peanut oil, and soybean oil. These oils may prove to be of value when added to practical poultry rations.

Vitamin K deficiency disease. Vitamin K deficiency results in a blood disease characterized by hemorrhages and slow clotting time of the blood. It affects growing chicks deprived of natural feedstuffs and may also affect mature birds.

Symptoms of vitamin K deficiency include paleness or anemia, excessive hemorrhage from minor wounds, cannibalism, and feather picking.

Pathology of vitamin K deficiency is indicated by small hemorrhages beneath the skin and elsewhere in the body. The hemoglobin content of the blood is low and the clotting time of the blood is delayed.

Prevention of vitamin K deficiency is accomplished by providing birds with green grass range or by feeding alfalfa, meat scraps, or fish meal in the ration.

Rickets. This is a vitamin D deficiency disease which inhibits normal mineral assimilation. It affects birds of all ages that are kept in confinement unless vitamin D is supplied in some form.

Symptoms of rickets among growing birds include a wobbly gait, sore joints, a tendency to squat down much of the time, ruffled feathers, poor growth, crooked bones, emaciation, and death.

Rickets among mature birds is indicated by low egg production, thin eggshells, poor hatchability, crooked breastbones, and temporary paralysis.

Pathology of rickets is indicated by soft, spongy bones of low ash content; wide zone of uncalcified tissue at the ends of the tibia (Fig. 141); calluses at the junctures of the sternal and vertebral portions of the ribs, and enlarged thyroids.

Prevention or cure of rickets is accomplished by providing chickens with direct sunshine, feeding fish oils or other sources of vitamin D, and by irradiation under ultraviolet lights. The vitamin D requirements of chickens are given on page 274.

Perosis. This is also known as slipped tendon or hock disease. It is a bone disease affecting the hock joints of growing birds. It occurs most frequently among chickens which are raised on wire or in confinement and fed rations of high mineral content.

Symptoms of perosis include a slight puffiness of the tissues about the hock joint; discoloration due to subcutaneous hemorrhage; or crooked legs.

Pathology of perosis is indicated by an irregular line of ossification of the end of the tibia at the hock joint and the Achilles tendons slipped from the condyles.

Prevention of perosis is accomplished by raising chickens on range or in confinement on straw litter rather than on wire; by avoiding an excess of phosphorus in the ration; and by feeding alfalfa, oats, middlings, rice bran, or a trace of manganese in the ration.

Chickens in the early stages of perosis may return to normal if the system of feeding and management is corrected.

The mineral requirements of growing chickens are given on page 278.

Gout. Gout is a disease that may affect mature birds fed a high protein ration and deprived of exercise. It may occasionally occur among growing birds.

Symptoms of gout include swollen and painful joints; nodular or tumorlike growths at the joints which may burst, discharging a yellowish turbid material; assuming a sitting position; emaciation; weakness; and diarrhea.

Autopsy findings associated with gout include chalklike covering of the internal organs, particularly the heart and heart sac; and swollen, pale kidneys clogged with urates. The uric acid content of the blood is high.

Prevention and cure of gout is accomplished by reducing the protein in the ration and by providing range or feeding green feed.

In the articular form of the disease, the enlarged joints may be opened and the contents washed out.

Indigestion. This is the lack or failure of digestion. Mechanical obstruction to the passage of food may be a cause of indigestion.

Crop-bound trouble may result from irregular feeding, partial starvation followed by giving feed before water, change from confinement to range, and feeding coarse, dry, fibrous, or decayed feed.

Crop-bound condition may be relieved by injecting water into the crop, loosening the material by massage, and emptying the crop by gentle pressure on it with the head of the bird pointing downward. If this fails, it will be necessary to open the crop by making an incision on the upper part of the organ. Pull the skin which covers the crop wall to one side and cut through it; then push it back and cut through the crop wall. Remove the contents and sew up the crop membrane with ordinary thread which has been dipped in tincture of iodine. Sew up the skin separately. Feed soft feed for a few days.

Sour crop is indicated by distention of the crop with gases. The condition may be relieved by injection of soda water (two teaspoons of baking soda in a pint of water) into the crop and forcing the material out by massaging while holding the bird by the feet and the head down.

Constipation may be relieved by giving Epsom salts at the rate of one pound per hundred hens in two gallons of drinking water or in wet mash. Individual dosage consists of one-half teaspoon of Epsom salts in one to two tablespoons of water. It may be given with a hollow tube with a bulb on the end of it.

Poisoning. Cases of poisoning among poultry are seldom encountered. The bird's sense of taste will usually protect it if it is well fed and kept away from unusual, alluring objects. Cases of poisoning are more common among birds allowed to run at will than among those kept in confinement.

Symptoms of poisoning include sudden appearance of a large number of birds with dark red combs, elevated temperature, weakness, wobbly gait, prostration, limberneck, and high mortality.

Autopsy findings in case of poisoning may reveal a parboiled appearance of the crop, severe inflammation of the intestinal tract, and the presence of poisonous substances in the crop or gizzard.

Causes of poisoning among fowls include spray materials; rat poisons; excessive amounts of medicinal products, such as bichloride of mercury or copper sulphate in the drinking water; overdoses of parasite remedies, such as nicotine sulphate and kamala; dusting and fumigating compounds, such as cyanides; decomposed animal tissues; paint skins; and rose chafers.

Control of poisoning may be accomplished by shutting the birds off range, giving a laxative, and changing the ration.

External Parasites

Lice, mites, ticks, and fleas are the most important of the many species of external parasites that infest poultry. They cause discomfort, skin irritation, loss of plumage, stunted growth, and decreased egg production. External parasites may also serve as carriers of bacterial and virus diseases from one bird to another.

Lice. Over two thousand species of bird lice have been described, and of these, forty or fifty may be found on poultry. An individual may harbor several species. They are generally referred to as body lice, head lice, shaft lice, wing lice, etc.

Characteristics of lice. Lice are small, flattened insects seldom more than one-eighth inch in length, and yellowish or gray in color (Fig. 144). They live on birds on the skin and at the base of the feathers, and spend their entire life cycle there. Lice have biting and cutting mouth parts and feed upon scales of the skin or bits of feathers. The biting of lice, together with their sharp claws and spiny structure, causes considerable discomfort to birds on which they live. Lice seldom leave an individual except by accident or to migrate to another individual of the same species. They cannot live more than a week or so away from the body of the fowl. Lice lay eggs at the base of feathers. Body warmth hatches them, and they mature in 10–20 days after hatching.

The body louse is probably the most common parasite of poultry. It is most easily located in the region below the vent. In cases of bad infestation, the body louse may also be found on the back, breast, and under the wings. Body lice cause skin irritation and may produce scabs and blood clots. They infest chickens, turkeys, and other species of poultry.

The head louse is found on the head and neck of chickens and turkeys. It is dark gray in color and about one-tenth inch long. It may cause serious damage among young chicks and poults.

The shaft louse is found along the shaft of the feathers and seldom on the skin. It feeds on the barbs of the feathers and the scales along the shafts.

Turkeys, ducks, geese, pigeons, other fowls, and wild birds are infested with several other species of lice.

Control of lice. Poultry may be rid of lice by dusting, dipping, greasing, or fumigating. One should keep in mind that the treatment must reach the skin where the lice feed and that it must last long enough to be effective against the young ones that hatch. Otherwise, more than one application is necessary.

HCHH or hexachlorocyclohexane solution sprayed or painted on the roosts destroys both lice and their eggs by its fumigant action. It is more lethal especially for louse eggs than nicotine sulphate.

Dusting once with sodium fluoride or sodium fluosilicate kills the lice on birds and also the young lice that hatch from the eggs. The bird is held on a table while the powder is applied next to the skin under the feathers as follows: one pinch on the head, one on the neck, two on the back, one on the breast, one below the vent, one on the tail, one on each thigh, and one on the underside of each wing.

DDT used in 10 per cent strength as a dust is of about the same value as the dust form of sodium fluoride for the eradication of lice. It does not prevent reinfestation after two or three weeks, which is approximately the life cycle.

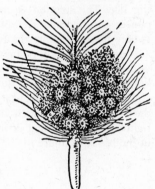

Fig. 144. Top, the male head louse, top view, greatly enlarged. (U. S. D. A.) Bottom, eggs (nits) of the common louse at the base of the feather.

Dipping once with sodium fluoride solution (one ounce per gallon of water) is done more easily and requires less material than the dusting method. The water should be about body temperature and the dipping should be done only on a warm day or when the birds can be kept in a warm place until dry. The birds should be held by the wings and plunged into a tub filled with the solution, the head being left out while the feathers are ruffled with the hand to allow the solution to penetrate to the skin. The head is then ducked once or twice; the bird held for a few seconds to drain; and then released.

Greasing with mercurial ointment (one part of metallic mercury in six to twelve parts of vaseline) is effective against lice on birds and the young lice that hatch from the eggs matted in the feathers. Take an amount of the mixture about the size of a pea and run it into the skin at a point about one inch below the vent. In severe infestations, a small amount should be applied on the back of the head for eradication of head lice. Care should be taken not to leave an excess of the ointment on the feathers where birds can pick it off, because of the danger of mercurial poisoning. The greasing method should not be used on setting hens or on breeding stock just prior to or during the breeding season.

Fumigating with nicotine sulphate has been used successfully for eradicating lice. The solution is applied to the top of the perches (about eight ounces per hundred feet of perch space) with a brush, about fifteen to twenty minutes before the birds go to roost. The heat from the bird's body aids in the liberation of fumes of nicotine which penetrate the feathers and kill the lice. The material should be used on a warm, still night. This method kills body lice and nearly all head lice, but does not harm the eggs. A second and possibly a third application at ten-day intervals will be necessary to kill the young lice that hatch from the eggs. The house should not be closed tightly during the night of the application as enough fumes may be retained in the house to injure the birds.

Mites (*Ascarina*)

Mites are closely related to spiders. There are several species which infest poultry. They have different habitats and require different methods of control.

The roost mite. The roost mite is a very small gray insect which lives in cracks and crevices about the perches, under boards, and in fecal material and litter near the perches and nests. Great numbers of mites attack a single bird at night when on the roost and suck its blood. After feeding, the mites appear red. They crawl back to their hiding places and lay eggs. A female lays about four eggs in twenty-four hours and feeds again before laying another four eggs. The cycle may be repeated eight or more times. The eggs hatch in about two days during warm weather. The young mites reach maturity in about a week (Fig. 145).

One should keep a close watch for mites in the summer time and at all times of the year in heated houses. The birds attacked by mites appear unthrifty and pale as a result of the loss of blood. Pens badly infested with

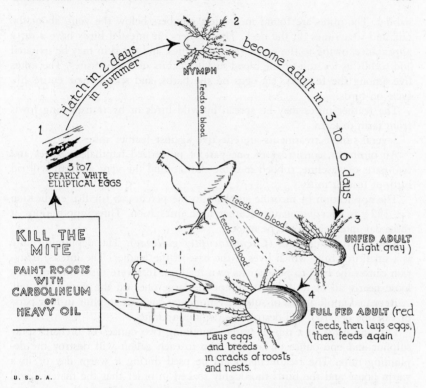

2

become adult in 3 to 6 days

Hatch in 2 days in summer

NYMPH

feeds on blood

1

3 to 7
PEARLY WHITE
ELLIPTICAL EGGS

3

UNFED ADULT
(light gray)

Feeds on blood

Feeds on blood

Feeds on blood

KILL THE
MITE

PAINT ROOSTS
WITH
CARBOLINEUM
or
HEAVY OIL

4

FULL FED ADULT (red
feeds, then lays eggs,
then feeds again)

Lays eggs
and breeds
in cracks of roosts
and nests.

U. S. D. A.

Fig. 145. The life cycle of the common roost or red mite.

mites have a characteristic odor. New houses and equipment are just as likely to become infested as old ones. Patches or colonies of the mites may be seen by lifting up the perches and looking underneath them or by loosening caked manure or litter about the perches or nests. These appear as gray or reddish masses of the small insects.

Mites are spread by English sparrows and by moving fowls from place to place, as a few mites remain on the fowls during the day. They may live without food for several months.

Clean, dry, well-ventilated and well-lighted houses are less likely to be badly infested with mites than damp, dirty, and dark houses. The dropping boards or pits should be cleaned frequently. The perches and nests should be painted once or twice a year, after thorough cleaning, with a wood preservative containing anthracene oil. This material penetrates the wood, does not evaporate readily, and retains its killing power longer than most other compounds. Painting or spraying the perches with crude petroleum or crankcase oil is also effective, but the applications have to be used more often.

The feather mite (*Liponyssus silviarum*). The feather mite, also called the northern fowl mite, has infested many flocks in recent years. It is more injurious to flocks in the northern states than elsewhere in the country. The feather mite resembles the roost mite in appearance but differs from it in habitat. The mites are found in greatest numbers below the vent, about the tail, and sometimes on the neck. The feathers on infested birds have a dirty appearance, owing to the presence of the mites, and the skin may be irritated and scabby as a result of the blood-sucking habits of the parasites. The mites live among the feathers, lay eggs on the barbs, and spend their entire life cycle on birds.

The feather mites may be spread by wild birds or by transporting fowls from farm to farm.

Several simple treatments are effective against feather mites.

An ointment, consisting of one part of pulverized napthalene flakes and two parts of vaseline, rubbed into the skin around the vent and tail will rid birds of feather mites.

The application of nicotine sulphate to the perches as for lice eradication (p. 352) is effective against feather mite infestation. Three applications at three-day intervals should be made.

The depluming mite (*Cnemidocoptes gallinae*). The depluming mite is a small itch mite which lives at the base of the feather. The intense irritation causes the bird to pull out its own feathers. In severe cases the bird may loose nearly all of its feathers except the large ones on the wings and tail.

Repeated applications of sulphur ointment (one part sulphur in four parts of vaseline or lard) will destroy the depluming mite.

Dipping birds in a tub of water containing two ounces of orchard spray sulphur and one ounce of laundry soap to each gallon will destroy the depluming mite. The treatment should be used during a warm day or in a warm house and the birds thoroughly soaked in order that the material will reach the base of the feathers and the skin.

The scaly leg mite. This is a small itch mite which burrows under the scales of the shanks. The severe irritation causes an accumulation of grayish, dry debris and a loosening of the scales. The shanks appear to be enlarged and rough (Fig. 146). In severe infestations the bird may become lame and the feet deformed. Chickens, turkeys, other species of poultry, and game birds may become infested by the scaly leg mite.

The life cycle is spent on the bird. The mites lay eggs as they burrow their channels beneath the scales. The eggs are hatched and the young grow to maturity beneath the scales of the shanks.

Birds may be cured of scaly leg mite infestation by soaking and washing off the crusts and scales with warm soapy water, drying the shanks, and then dipping them in a mixture of one part kerosene and two parts of raw linseed oil.

Chiggers. The small, almost microscopic chiggers which annoy man may also infest poultry that run on range. They collect in groups, cause extreme irritation, and small abscesses are formed where they feed. Chiggers may cause mortality among growing stock and unthriftiness among adult stock.

Chigger infestations may be prevented by hatching chicks early and by keeping them off ranges where the mites occur.

Frequent light dusting with flowers of sulphur will keep the chigger mite

Fig. 146. Legs of a chicken as they commonly appear with scaly leg. (Ohio Extension Bulletin 115.)

infestation under control. In case of severe infestation, the application of sulphur ointment as used for the depluming mite (p. 354) is effective.

Ticks and Fleas

These parasites are common infestations of poultry in the southern states.

The fowl tick (*Argas persicus*). The fowl tick generally infests chickens but may also infest other species of poultry. It is a blood-sucking insect about one-fourth inch in length. The life history of ticks is much like that of the roost mite in that they hide and lay eggs in cracks or secluded spots and attack the birds and suck blood. Ticks may live for many months without food.

A wood preservative containing anthracene oil or an oil spray applied to the perches as in the treatment for the roost mite (p. 353) is effective against tick infestation.

Fleas (*Echidnophaga gallinacea*). The chicken flea, or sticktight flea, is a common parasite of poultry in the southern states. The fleas attach themselves to the comb, face, earlobes, and wattles and remain there for several days. They lay eggs while attached to the birds. The eggs incubate in the litter or on the ground in about a week. The young fleas feed upon the droppings.

They go through a series of developmental stages and then attack birds. The entire life cycle requires thirty to sixty days.

Flea infestation is rather hard to prevent because the fleas are carried by dogs, cats, rats, and wild birds. Dust on the floor and the soil under the poultry house are ideal places for flea development.

Dogs, cats, and other carriers of fleas should be kept away from the poultry houses. In case of infestations, the houses should be cleaned and the houses and yards sprayed with creosote oil.

Fowls may be treated with the sulphur ointment recommended for depluming mites (p. 354).

Internal Parasites

Internal parasites of poultry include the round and flatworms. There are no symptoms specific enough for diagnosis. Birds should be autopsied and the worms found. Most species of worms are large enough to be seen with the naked eye.

Worms cause stunted growth, emaciation, weakness, and death among growing stock, and poor vigor and low egg production among mature birds. The extent of the injury will depend upon the age when infested and the severity of the infestation. Worms cause obstruction to the passage of food; injure body tissues, thereby making birds more susceptible to bacterial and virus infections; produce toxins; and use the bird's food for their own growth and reproduction.

Worms reproduce by eggs which are passed out with the droppings. They must undergo incubation outside the body or in an intermediate host before they are infective. Birds become infested by eating material from contaminated soil or litter and by eating intermediate hosts such as insects and worms.

Worms

Roundworms. Roundworms are usually long and cylindrical. Their location is generally more varied than that of tapeworms, different species being located in different parts of the body. There are many different species of roundworms. The principal ones are the large and small roundworms and the ceca worms.

Large roundworms (*Ascaridia lineata*). Large roundworms may be found in birds of all ages, but cause most serious damage among birds under three months of age.

Symptoms of large roundworm infestation are unthriftiness, drooping or sagging of the wings, paleness of the head, and emaciation among young stock. Lowered egg production and emaciation are symptoms among mature birds.

Autopsy of birds infested with large roundworms reveals grayish-white slender roundworms one and one-half to four inches in length in the small intestine. They may be so numerous as to completely plug the intestine (Fig.

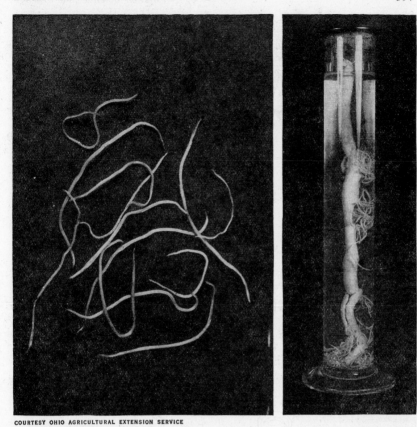

Fig. 147. Roundworms from the small intestines of a chicken and a portion of intestine filled with roundworms.

147). They may penetrate the intestinal wall during growth, thereby causing injury and loss of blood, and permitting bacterial infection.

Occasionally a roundworm may wander up the oviduct from the cloaca and become enclosed in an egg.

Life history of the large roundworm is illustrated in Figure 148. The worms lay microscopic eggs in the intestinal tract which are passed to the outside with the droppings of the bird. Under favorable conditions of warmth and moisture they incubate and become infectious in from ten to sixteen days. The embryonated worm is liberated from the shell when the egg is eaten along with other material picked up from contaminated soil or litter. The young worms may burrow into the wall of the intestine for a period after hatching and cause considerable damage to the lining. They then return to the intestine and grow to maturity in about two months from date of hatching.

Prevention of large roundworm infestation is accomplished by the use of clean range; elimination of wet, shady places in the chicken yard; isola-

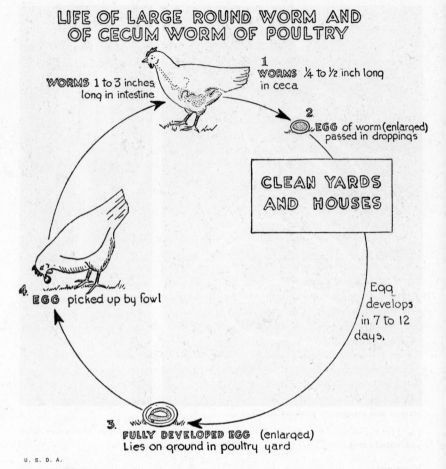

LIFE OF LARGE ROUND WORM AND OF CECUM WORM OF POULTRY

WORMS 1 to 3 inches long in intestine

1 WORMS ¼ to ½ inch long in ceca

2. EGG of worm (enlarged) passed in droppings

CLEAN YARDS AND HOUSES

Egg develops in 7 to 12 days.

4. EGG picked up by fowl

3. FULLY DEVELOPED EGG (enlarged) Lies on ground in poultry yard

U. S. D. A.

Fig. 148. Life cycle of the large roundworm and cecum worm of poultry. Note the incubation stage in soil.

tion of young birds from old ones; avoidance of wet litter in the brooder house; and the use of a starting and growing ration of good protein and vitamin content.

Treatments may be used for roundworm infestation, but they will be only temporarily effective unless the source of infestation is eliminated. Some of the treatments are as follows:

No. 1. Give each bird a No. 2 capsule containing .35 gram of a mixture of 6.6 cubic centimeters of a 40-per cent nicotine sulphate and 16 grams of Lloyd's alkaloidal reagent (a selected fuller's earth).

No. 2. Give each mature bird one cubic centimeter of tetrachlorethylene or carbon tetrachloride in a gelatin capsule or with a pipette. Reduce size of dosage for smaller birds. Care must be taken that the drug does not get into the lungs.

No. 3. A single flock treatment consists of one teaspoon of oil of chenopodium, thoroughly mixed with a moist mash for each lot of twelve birds.

No. 4. A preventive flock treatment is the addition to the mash of 2 per cent by weight of tobacco dust containing at least 1.5 per cent of nicotine, and feeding this mixture to the flock for a period of three or four weeks. Treatment may be repeated at three-week intervals as often as necessary.

Individual treatments are more effective than flock treatments. In the latter method, the birds that need the treatments the worst have a poor appetite and do not eat enough of the material for it to be effective.

For a few days following the administration of vermifuges, the birds should be confined so that the worms and eggs expelled may be removed with the litter and burned.

Gapeworms (*Syngamus trachea*). Gapeworms cause "gapes" or a gasping for breath among chicks during the brooding period.

Symptoms of gapeworm infestation are dullness, ruffled feathers, loss of appetite, stretching of the neck with a yawnlike opening of the beak, convulsive shaking of the head, sneezing cough, expulsion of frothy saliva from the beak, and high mortality.

Autopsy examination of the trachea of birds infested with gapeworms reveals inflammation of the lining, an accumulation of mucus, and the presence of small, slender, reddish roundworms one-fourth to one and one-half inches in length, clinging to the inner lining.

The *life cycle* of gapeworms is direct. The microscopic eggs are coughed up, swallowed, and expelled with the feces. They undergo incubation and may hatch outside the body. Either the embryonated eggs or the worms cause infestation when contaminated soil, litter, feed, or water is consumed. The young worms reach the lungs within a week and in another week or so will have matured and become imbedded in the trachea.

Earthworms play an important part in the spread of gapeworms. The eggs may be eaten by earthworms and these in turn by fowls. Turkeys and guinea fowls may carry gapeworms throughout their whole life and thus may serve as a source of infestation for chicks and young turkeys.

Control measures include clean range, isolation of young stock from old birds, and keeping birds shut up until the dew has dried off and the earthworms have crawled back into the soil.

Treatment consists of inhaling barium antimonyl tartrate dust for 15 to 20 minutes. Place the birds in a closed box. Pump in about one ounce of the dust to each 8 cubic feet of box space with a dust gun. Then tilt the box back and forth so that the birds will keep the dust stirred up by wing movement and will breathe more vigorously.

Cecal worms (*Heterakis gallinae*). The common cecal worm of poultry occurs in the ceca of chickens, turkeys, ducks, and geese. It is a small, white, roundworm three-tenths to one-half inch long and may occur in very large numbers, causing a serious inflammation of the ceca, especially in young chicks. This parasite may also carry the protozoan which causes blackhead in turkeys.

The *life cycle* is very similar to that of the large roundworms. The eggs voided in the droppings become embryonated in seven to twelve days. When taken into the body, they hatch in the small intestine and become encysted in the walls of the cloaca. After a short time they return to the lumen of the ceca and develop into adults. The entire life cycle requires eight or nine weeks.

The eggs have a thick shell and may remain infectious after a year or more in the soil. Earthworms ingest cecal worm eggs, and birds may become infested by eating these worms or by ingesting food contaminated with their excreta.

Prevention measures against cecal worm infestation include general sanitary measures, rotation of yards, and isolation of young chicks from old birds.

Treatment for cecal worm infestation is the use of a mash containing .5 per cent phenothiazine. The mixture is moistened with water to make a crumble mash and fed after the regular feed is withheld for two or three hours. The use of this mash for a six- to eight-hour period will remove nearly all of the cecal worms.

Small roundworms (*Capillaria amulata*). As with the large roundworms, small roundworm infestations may be found in chickens, turkeys, and game birds of all ages.

Symptoms of small roundworm infestation include droopiness, anemia, muscular weakness, loss of appetite, foul breath, emaciation, twisting of the neck, and paralysis of the legs.

Autopsy of birds infested with small roundworms reveals the presence of delicate, slender, colorless, hairlike worms one-half to one inch in length in the gullet, crop, small intestine, or ceca. The worms are hard to see with the naked eye unless the sections of the intestinal tract are suspended in clear water. Crop infestation results in milky fluid crop contents with a foul odor, inflammation and thickening of the crop wall, and the formation of a necrotic false membrane. Intestinal species may be found in the lumen of the intestine or threaded in the surface of the mucous membrane.

Life history of small roundworms varies with the species. It may be direct as in the case of the large round and ceca worms or it may require earthworms as intermediate hosts.

Prevention of small roundworm infestation should include the same sanitary measures used for large roundworm control.

Treatment for small roundworm infestation is only partially effective. Carbon tetrachloride, given in one cubic centimeter doses, as for roundworms, and repeated in seven days is partially effective.

Gizzard worms (*Cheilospirura hamulosa*). Gizzard worms infest chickens, turkeys, water fowls, and game birds.

Symptoms of gizzard worm infestation include dullness, loss of appetite, emaciation, weakness, and death.

Autopsy of birds infested with gizzard worms reveals the presence of slender, reddish, roundworms one-half to three-fourth inch in length in the musculature of the gizzard near the entrance of the proventriculus. Nodules may be present on the surface of the gizzard in this region.

The *life cycle* of the gizzard worm requires the grasshopper as an intermediate host. The eggs, passed out with the droppings, are eaten by grasshoppers. The larvae hatched from the eggs undergo development in the muscles of the grasshopper and become infective in a few weeks. If the grasshopper is eaten by a susceptible bird, the larvae are set free and grow in the gizzard of the fowl and reach maturity in two or three months.

Prevention of gizzard worm infestation includes frequent removal of the litter and droppings and confinement of birds to runs with short, thick vegetation rather free range having tall, dry vegetation.

Treatment for gizzard worm infestation is only partially effective. The carbon tetrachloride treatment used for small roundworms may also be used for gizzard worms.

Eye worms (*Oxyspirura mansoni*). Eye worms may infest chickens, turkeys, and wild birds. They are most common in the southern states.

Symptoms of eye worm infestation include constant winking of the eye, frequent rubbing of the head on the feathers of the wing, the scratching of the eye with the foot, puffy and inflamed eyes, and a discharge from the eyes and nose pasted over the feathers.

Autopsy of birds infested with eye worms reveals small, white, threadlike worms approximately one-half inch long beneath the nictitating membrane of the eye. Firm pressure applied to the tear sac at the inner corner of the eye will cause the worms to wiggle out over the eyeball, where they may be seen.

The *life history* of the eye worm requires an intermediate host. The cockroach is one of the hosts. It eats the eggs and the larvae develop in its body. When fowls eat infested cockroaches, the worms are liberated in the crop. The worms crawl up the gullet to the mouth and then through the tear ducts to the eye.

Prevention of eye worm infestation consists of eradication of hiding places for cockroaches such as boxes, boards, and other unnecessary equipment. Frequent removal of litter and droppings will also help remove the sources of the worm eggs for the roaches.

Treatment for eye worm infestation consists of dropping two or three drops of a 5 per cent solution of butyn into the eye as an anesthetic; lifting the nictitating membrane and putting a drop or two of 5 per cent creolin directly on the worms; and, immediately after applying the creolin, washing the eye thoroughly with warm water.

Glandular stomach worms (*Tropisurus americanus*). The glandular stomach worm affects chicks during the growing period.

Symptoms of glandular stomach worms include poor appetite, weakness, anemia, emaciation, diarrhea, and death.

Autopsy of birds infested with glandular stomach worms reveals a swelling of the proventriculus, inflammation, hemorrhage, and destruction of the glands.

The *life history* of glandular stomach worms requires grasshoppers and cockroaches as intermediate hosts. Eggs picked up by these insects hatch within their bodies and the larvae develop in their muscles. When fowls eat

Fig. 149. Large tape-
worms attached to the
small intestine of a
fowl.

the infested insects, the larvae are liberated and enter the glands of the proventriculus.

Prevention of glandular worm infestation consists of frequent removal of droppings and litter and keeping fowls away from cockroaches and grasshoppers.

There is no effective treatment for glandular worm infestation.

Tapeworms *(Cestoda).* Tapeworms infest chickens, turkeys, and other species of poultry and wild birds. Infestations appear to be most noticeable in the fall or early winter. Tapeworm infestation is more detrimental among young than old birds.

Symptoms of tapeworm infestation include droopiness, ruffled feathers, diarrhea, weakness, paleness of comb, twisting of the neck in unnatural positions, and lameness or paralysis in one or both legs.

Autopsy of birds infested with tapeworms reveals the presence of flat, white, segmented, ribbon-like worms fastened to the wall of the small intestine (Fig. 149). They may vary from microscopic dimensions in some species to ten inches in length in others. Numerous protuberances or nodules may be observed on the outer surface of the small intestine opposite the joints of attachment of species of small tapeworms to the inner lining. The nodules may consist of pus or greenish-yellow necrotic material. Intestinal catarrh is common.

The *life history* of tapeworms requires intermediate hosts such as flies, earthworms, beetles, grasshoppers, and ants (Fig. 150). The worms attach themselves to the intestinal wall by means of heads (scolexes) provided with hooks or suckers, or both. Segments containing eggs grow from the head or neck part of the worm. The segments break off and pass out with the droppings. The intermediate hosts eat the eggs, hatch them, and develop the young worms into a bladder worm stage. When the flies, earthworms, grasshoppers, or other carriers of tapeworm larvae are eaten by fowls, all except the heads of the bladder worms are digested. The heads attach themselves to the mucous membrane of the small intestine where they develop segments and start another generation.

Prevention of tapeworm infestation consists of using clean range or keeping birds in confinement, raising young birds separate from old birds and quite a distance from them, avoiding manure piles or keeping them screened away from flies, using well-drained and aerated range, and raising birds in screened-in brooder houses.

Treatment for tapeworm infestation is not satisfactory. Some treatments "shear" off most of the segments but leave the tapeworm heads attached. New chains of segments form and begin to pass out with the droppings in two or

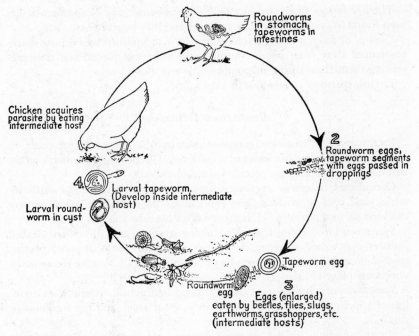

Fig. 150. Diagram of the various stages in an indirect life history of a tapeworm or round-worm, parasitic in poultry.

three weeks. Kamala and some other treatments that have been recommended in the past not only are ineffective against tapeworm removal but are harmful to the birds. No treatment can be recommended until research develops a means of reaching and killing the heads of poultry tapeworms.

Flukes (trematodes). Fluke worms are not common parasites of poultry at the present time. In recent years they have been found in the skin, proventriculus, cloaca, and oviduct of chickens in some of the North Central states. Birds having access to swamps may become infested.

Symptoms of fluke worm infestation of the cloaca and oviduct are dullness, loss of weight, paleness, and decreased egg production.

The skin fluke impairs the health of the fowl and produces cysts in the skin in the abdominal region and around the vent. The cysts are smooth and shiny, grayish-white in color, and vary from two to ten millimeters in diameter. Most of them show a small black pore through which eggs pass.

Autopsy of fowls infested with fluke worms may show peritonitis and collapsed ovules containing grayish-yellow material mixed with fibrin and pus. The proventriculus may be enlarged and inflamed.

Close examination of the affected tissues reveals the presence of small, flat, unsegmented, leaflike, reddish worms one-sixth to one-fourth inch long.

Since fluke worms infest the oviduct and cloaca, they may be found occasionally in eggs.

The *life history* of the oviduct fluke involves snails and dragonflies. It has been found in crows and English sparrows and may be spread by them.

Control of fluke worm infestation may be accomplished by keeping chickens fenced away from ponds, swamps, and other wet places, and thus preventing them from eating dragonflies.

English sparrows should also be kept away.

Protozoan Diseases

Protozoa are microscopic, single-celled animals. Many species occur in nature but only a few of them are pathogenic. The two most common protozoal diseases of poultry are coccidiosis and blackhead.

Coccidiosis (*Eimeria avium*). Coccidiosis is a disease of the small intestine and ceca of chickens and other birds. It is most injurious among chickens six to ten weeks old, but may affect older or younger birds.

Symptoms of coccidiosis among growing stock include droopiness, ruffled feathers, eyes closed, diarrhea, droppings streaked with blood, poor appetite, emaciation, paleness, and greatest losses six to ten days following the onset of symptoms (Fig. 151).

Symptoms of chronic coccidiosis among older birds include paleness, loss of appetite, ruffled feathers, droopiness, emaciation, and leg weakness or paralysis.

Autopsy findings among growing chickens infected with coccidiosis include swollen, darkened, and firm ceca; inflamed and thickened cecal walls; and contents consisting of yellowish, cheesy, blood-stained material.

Autopsy findings among older birds infected with chronic coccidosis include thickened and inflamed intestinal wall of the small intestine in the region of the duodenal loop, grayish white spots showing on the outer intestinal surface, and a sticky mucous exudate covering the inflamed and hemorrhagic areas lining this portion of the intestine.

Microscopic examination of the scrapings from inflamed areas and the intestinal contents of birds infected with coccidiosis reveals the presence of coccidia in some stage of development. The oöcysts appear as round oval bodies having a dark center, clear surrounding zone, and a double wall.

The *life cycle* of coccidiosis is direct. The oöcysts, which are the largest and most resistant stage of the organism, are passed out with the droppings from an infected fowl. Under favorable environmental conditions of warmth and moisture outside the body, the oöcysts sporulate in one to three days with the formation of sporocysts. The sporulated oöcysts are infective if picked up by a susceptible bird. Development continues after ingestion with the formation of small, spindle-shaped bodies (sporozoites). The sporozoites are released from the oöcyst shell and enter the epithelal cells of the intestine, where they develop into forms known as schizonts. The schizonts give rise to small sporelike forms called merozoites. The schizont to merozoite to schizont cycles are repeated several times in the intestinal wall with resultant hemorrhage and injury of the mucous membrane.

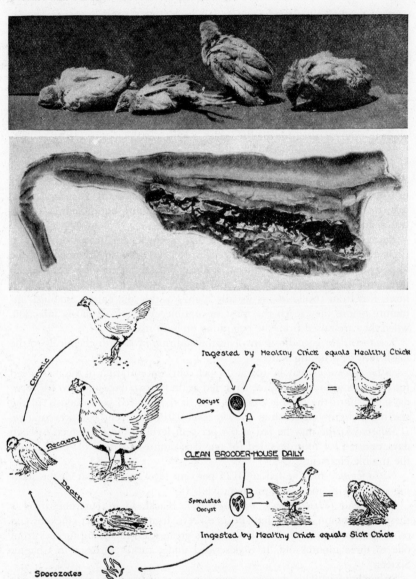

Fig. 151. Top, bad cases of coccidiosis. (Courtesy W. A. Billings, University of Minnesota.) Center, enlarged ceca from a fowl infected with coccidiosis. (Courtesy C. E. Lampman, University of Idaho.) Bottom, the life cycle of coccidiosis. (California Agricultural Experiment Station.)

The merozoites finally develop into male and female forms and, after union, oöcysts are again formed and passed out in the droppings. The complete life cycle generally requires from four to ten days.

Sporulated and nonsporulated oöcysts are quite resistant to adverse environmental conditions because of their protective shell. They may live for a year or more in the soil. Disinfectants are not very destructive to oöcysts unless they remain in contact with them for a considerable time. Coccidia oöcysts are killed by high temperature and drying and their sporulation is inhibited by low temperature.

There are at least six different species of coccidia which infect chickens. They are differentiated by their location in the intestinal tract and by differences in time required for the life cycle.

Prevention of coccidiosis is possible by the use of a clean house, equipment, and range; keeping young and old birds quite a distance apart; avoidance of damp litter or wet places on range; and the prevention of contaminated litter or soil from being carried on the brooding premises by the attendant, dogs, cats, rats, wild birds, flies and other insects, cleaning equipment, catching crates, and feed sacks.

Recent Ohio investigations indicate that, if chicks are started on built-up litter even though coccidiosis-infected birds have been on it previously, the losses will be negligible. However, if the birds are raised on wire or clean litter until six or eight weeks old and then transferred to the same built-up litter, loss from coccidiosis is usually high. Possibly the chicks establish immunity before they reach the most susceptible age for coccidiosis infection, when they are raised from the beginning on built-up litter.

Treatment for coccidiosis involves the addition of certain chemicals to the mash feed or drinking water.

Sulfaquinoxaline may be fed at 0.1 per cent concentration in the mash feed for two days; omitted for three days; fed again for two days; omitted for three days, etc., until the trouble clears up. Or, it may be fed continuously in the starting and growing mash at a lower level 0.0125 per cent as a preventative.

Sulfamethazine may be fed at 0.4 per cent level in the mash feed for two days, omitted for four days, fed for one day, omitted for four days, etc., until the trouble clears up.

Nitrophenide may be fed at .0125 per cent level continuously in the starting and growing mash as a preventative.

Blackhead (*Histomonas meleagridis*). Blackhead or enterohepatitis is the most common disease that affects turkeys. It may also infect chickens and other species of poultry. Blackhead causes greatest losses among turkeys from one to three months old. It is described under turkey diseases in Chapter Sixteen.

Spirochetosis. This disease or one similar to it has been observed among chickens in some of the southern states. It is transmitted by ticks.

Symptoms of spirochetosis include drowsiness, paleness, loss of appetite, ruffled feathers, diarrhea, weakness, prostration, paralysis, and death within three to fifteen days.

Autopsy in case of spirochetosis infection reveals an enlarged liver with small white spots, paleness of organs, and inflammation of the intestines.

The causative organism is found in the blood as a long, wavy, screwlike, microscopic protozoa.

Control of spirochetosis consists in keeping poultry away from sources of tick infestation.

Treatment with the use of arsenical drugs such as Salvarsan and atoxyl has been advocated.

Trichomoniasis. This is a protozoal disease that has been observed among growing chickens and turkeys.

Symptoms of trichomoniasis infection include paleness, droopiness, foul odor, and subnormal temperature.

Autopsy examination reveals a chronic ulceration of the crop and occasionally the gullet and proventriculus. Rough, protruding, yellowish, tumor-like projections are firmly imbedded in the mucosa and may partly close the lumen.

Control of trichomoniasis infection is accomplished by keeping growing stock on range away from dirty wet places and moldy or decomposed litter.

In case of an outbreak, change the range and give milk to drink or add copper sulphate to the drinking water (one part in two thousand).

Mold Diseases

Mold diseases are also known as mycoses. They are produced by fungi or low forms of plant life. Fungi are widely distributed in nature, but only a few of them are pathogenic for poultry. The chief mold diseases of poultry are aspergillosis, thrush, and favus.

Aspergillosis. This is a fungus disease of the lungs and air sacs. It is most common among growing chickens and turkeys, but may affect any species of poultry of any age.

Symptoms of aspergillosis infection include poor appetite, darkened comb, droopiness, high temperature, diarrhea, sneezing, gasping for breath with a croupy sound, suffocation, and death.

If the infection has reached the small air sacs and hollow spaces of the bones, there may be lameness and swollen, inflamed joints among the infected birds.

Aspergillosis may affect a single bird or a large percentage of the flock. Young chicks die within a few days after the onset of symptoms. Older birds may live for three or four weeks.

Autopsy of birds infected with aspergillosis shows whitish or yellowish nodules in the trachea, lungs, and air sacs in the early stages of the disease. They may be easily confused with lesions caused by pullorum infection or brooder pneumonia. Later the walls of the respiratory passages are covered by elevated, dirty-yellow or greenish layers of mold growth, and the air sacs may become filled with yellow pus.

Microscopic examination of material taken from the lesions reveals the presence of the filaments and spores of the fungus, *Aspergillus fumigatus.*

Control of aspergillosis infection is accomplished by preventing birds from inhaling or eating the mold spores of the fungus. Birds showing symptoms of the disease should be removed as soon as noticed.

Aspergillosis mold may be found in moldy litter, feed, droppings, and dust

material. Healthy fowls may inhale the spores without injury, but when resistance is lowered through faulty nutrition or close confinement in damp
quarters, inhaling the organisms may cause mortality.

There is no satisfactory treatment for aspergillosis infection.

Thrush. Thrush is a yeastlike fungus disease of the mouth and upper digestive tract. It has been observed most frequently among young birds, but
may affect poultry of any age.

Symptoms of thrush infection include poor appetite, weakness, emaciation,
and a slimy mucous material in the mouth.

Autopsy examination of birds affected with thrush reveals the presence of
grayish-white or yellowish patches on the mucous membrane of the mouth,
whitish ulcers in the crop, brownish or mucoid deposits in the glandular
stomach, and ulcers in the gizzard. The lesions may be so small in young
chicks that they may be overlooked.

Microscopic examination of the lesions reveals the presence of the yeastlike fungus, *Monilia albicans* or *Oidium.*

Control of thrush infection consists of the prevention of healthy birds from
eating contaminated feed or litter and drinking from contaminated vessels.

The fungus may be spread by way of the feeders, drinking vessels, litter,
and possibly by eggshells. The period of incubation is about a month.

In case of an outbreak, use one part copper sulphate in 2000 parts water as
the drink for a few days, dispose of sick birds, and clean and disinfect the
premises.

Favus. Favus is a rather uncommon fungus disease of the unfeathered part
of the head, particularly the comb.

Symptoms of favus infection include yellowish-white scaly lesions on the
surface of the skin of the head, and, in bad cases, loss of feathers or broken
ones on the neck and body.

Control of favus infection is most easily attained by disposal of all infected
birds. Since the disease may be transmitted to man, one should use care in
handling affected birds in order to avoid the introduction of the organism into
cuts or scratches.

Favus infection may be cured by one or more applications of an ointment
of formaldehyde and vaseline (one part formalin in twenty parts of vaseline).

Bacterial Diseases

Bacteria are widely distributed in nature. Most of them are beneficial to
man and animals. A few are pathogenic. The principal bacterial diseases of
poultry are pullorum, fowl typhoid, cholera, and tuberculosis.

Pullorum (bacillary white diarrhea). Pullorum is a common and widespread disease which may affect poultry of all ages. It is the most frequent
cause of mortality in the first three weeks after hatching. Pullorum may also
cause economic losses by reduced egg production and hatchability, and mortality of mature birds (Fig. 152).

Symptoms. One of the chief symptoms of pullorum infection among

Fig. 152. Pullorum disease. Left—upper, chicks infected with pullorum disease in the incubator may show necrotic spots in the lungs. (Courtesy L. P. Doyle, Purdue University.) Left—lower, appearance of chicks infected with pullorum disease. (Courtesy L. P. Doyle, Purdue University.) Right—upper, graphic illustration of pullorum control. (U. S. D. A. Farmers' Bulletin 1652.) Right—lower, normal ovary above and an ovary from a bird with pullorum disease below. (After Rettger.)

chicks is high mortality in the first three weeks after hatching, with the peak about the tenth day. Chicks may die suddenly without apparent symptoms. In most cases, however, they huddle under the hover with closed eyes and drooping wings. Their droppings may be whitish, foamy, and sticky, or sometimes brownish in color. The material may stick to the down in the region of the vent, resulting in the condition known as "pasting up behind." Chilling or overheating of chicks causes a diarrhea very similar to that produced by pullorum.

Mature birds generally show no outward symptoms, since the disease is usually localized in the ovaries. Some of the diseased hens lay at a low rate or quit laying entirely, while others become thin and weak and show signs of diarrhea.

Autopsy examination. Pullorum-infected chicks that die during the first four or five days often fail to show any lesions. Those dying after this time may show firm, whitish spots in the lungs. This is often the case when chicks become infected in the incubator by inhaling down or dust which carries the germs. The lung lesions may be confused with those caused by brooder pneumonia or mold infection. Abscesses may be found in the wall of the gizzard, in the liver, and in the heart muscles. A white stringy material may cover the heart. While all of these changes are typical of pullorum in the chick, the only sure diagnosis is to find the organism (*Salmonella pullorum*). It is found most often by making bacterial cultures from the heart blood, liver, lung lesions, and unabsorbed yolk.

Hens usually show lesions in the ovaries. Some of the yolks are angular, shrunken, hard, and brownish or greenish in color. Pullorum infection in the ovary may be confused with ovarian tumors. Definite diagnosis depends on isolation of the pullorum organism from the ovary by bacterial culture. The bacteria may localize in other parts of the body. Pullorum infection may cause discolored testes in males and inflammation of the heart muscles of males and females.

Control. Pullorum disease may be controlled by removing birds which have the disease from the breeding flock and selling them for meat. Carriers of pullorum disease may be detected by a blood test. There are two practical tests in use.

The *whole blood test* involves a drop of blood from the bird and a drop of stained pullorum antigen. A drop of antigen is placed on a test plate; a drop of blood obtained with a wire loop from a pricked wing vein is added and the mixture stirred with the loop. If the bird has the disease, flakes appear in the mixture within a minute (Fig. 153). If the bird does not have the disease, no flakes appear in the mixture.

The *standard tube test* involves the use of definite amounts of blood serum and a pullorum antigen. A few cubic centimeters of blood are collected in a vial by puncturing the brachial vein. After the blood has clotted, a definite amount of serum (usually .04 or .08 cc.) is removed and added to an agglutination tube. Two cubic centimeters of pullorum antigen (a suspension of dead pullorum bacteria) are added to the agglutination tube, the mixture shaken, and incubated over night. If the bird has the disease, the bacteria are agglutinated and settle to the bottom, leaving a clear liquid in the tube. If the bird does not have the disease, the suspension in the tube remains turbid.

The whole blood test is gaining in popularity because it involves less labor and necessitates only one handling of the birds.

Sanitation in the incubator is a further means of controlling the spread of pullorum disease. Increasing the humidity in the incubator to 90 to 95° F. wet bulb reading during the hatch will help to keep dust and down from flying in the machine.

Thorough cleaning of the incubator between hatches will also lessen the changes of spreading pullorum by means of dust and down.

Fig. 153. The whole blood pullorum test. Upper left, a general view of a set-up for testing. (U. S. D. A.) Upper right, a table for holding birds. Lower left, a testing cabinet containing a can of hot water and holder for the antigen bottle; test plate or paper; stock bottle of antigen; loop and needle holder; and antigen dropper. Lower right, a section of a test paper showing positive (+) and negative reactions. (Courtesy Columbus Vaccine Company.)

Fumigation of the incubator with formalin between hatches is a good means of killing pullorum bacteria and other microörganisms that may be present in the machine or on the eggshells (p. 167).

The use of sanitary feeders and waterers help reduce the spread of the disease.

Treatment of an infected group of chicks by adding .5 per cent sulfamerazine in the mash feed for about a week will reduce the mortality.

Fowl typhoid. This is an infectious septicemic disease of chickens and other domestic birds. It is most common among mature birds but may also affect young stock.

Symptoms of birds infected with fowl typhoid are drowsiness, ruffled feathers (Fig. 154), paleness, and yellowish or greenish diarrhea. The course of the infection in acute cases is from two to ten days. In chronic cases the birds may live for several weeks and show few visible symptoms of the disease.

Autopsy examination of birds infected with fowl typhoid reveals enlarged livers, dark in color, and often with a greenish sheen. The liver is usually dotted with tiny grayish spots and has a tendency to break easily. The spleen and kidneys are usually enlarged. The heart may be pale and have grayish, firm nodules of varying size in the heart wall. The blood is thin, pale red, and does not clot easily. The lining of the intestine is pale or may show a slight inflammation. The intestinal contents are usually slimy and yellowish.

Definite diagnosis depends on isolation of the causative organism of fowl typhoid (*Salmonella gallinarum*) by bacteriological culture methods, from the tissues of the body.

Spread of fowl typhoid is by way of the droppings from infected to healthy chicks. It may be spread from one bird to another by contaminated soil, litter, feed, or water. It may be introduced into the flock by infected fowls, wild birds, or on the feet of animals or people.

Control of fowl typhoid consists in the removal of all infected or suspicious birds as soon as symptoms of ill health are noticed; use of clean, sanitary feeders and waterers; frequent change of litter and the use of a liberal amount of it; and keeping birds away from contaminated yards and range. In other words, use every means possible to keep healthy chickens from coming in contact with the droppings from infected birds.

In case of a fowl typhoid epidemic in a community, it is advisable to vaccinate the flock as a preventive measure. One to two cubic centimeters (depending on size of bird) of a fowl-typhoid bacterin, made from *Salmonella gallinarum,* are injected beneath the skin. The inoculation is usually made beneath the skin covering the breast muscles on the bare spot beneath the wing.

The pullorum test used for detecting carriers of pullorum also detects carriers of fowl typhoid. This is true because the organisms causing the two diseases are much alike and produce cross agglutination.

Carriers of other *Salmonella* infections, such as aertrycke and paratyphi, may also be detected by the pullorum test.

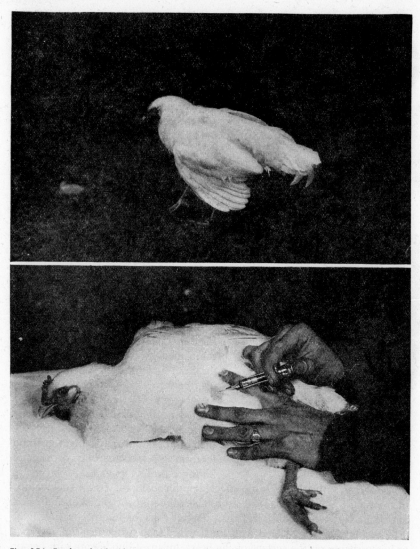

Fig. 154. Fowl typhoid. Above, symptoms include drowsiness, pale or darkened comb, and drooping wings. Below, technique for preventive vaccination.

Birds vaccinated against fowl typhoid infection should not be tested for pullorum infection for at least three weeks after the vaccination.

Fowl cholera. Fowl cholera is a highly infectious septicemic disease of all domestic birds. It may affect birds of all ages and appear in acute or chronic form.

Symptoms of fowl cholera vary with the severity of infection. In acute outbreaks, the finding of dead birds on the roosts or in the nests may be the first

Fig. 155. Hemorrhages and red spots may be found on the hearts of chickens that die of cholera. (Illinois Station Circular 441.)

indication of infection. These birds may have appeared perfectly healthy only a short time before. In the less acute forms, the first symptom is yellowish coloration of the droppings. This is followed by yellowish, brownish, or greenish diarrhea. The comb turns a bluish-red, the body temperature increases, and there is loss of appetite and increased thirst. The bird becomes drowsy and sleeps a great deal of the time with the head drawn down to the body or tucked backward and resting on the feathers about the wing. Respiration is difficult and at times an accumulation of mucus in the mouth and air passages may cause a rattling noise as the bird breathes.

The chronic form of fowl cholera infection is indicated by paleness, emaciation, and a lack of activity. Lameness may be present in prolonged cases as a result of joint infection by the germs. In some cases the birds have "colds" accompanied by gasping and swelling of the head and wattles. When first swollen, the wattles are soft and warm; later they become hard and cold.

Cholera may destroy a large number of birds in the flock in a few days and then disappear, or may remain in chronic form for months, only occasionally killing a bird.

Autopsy examination of birds infected with cholera may show sticky mucus in the mouth and air passages, reddish discoloration of the skin and breast muscles, a congested and darker than normal color of internal organs, light- or dark-colored liver covered with small white foci, swollen spleen, red spots or hemorrhages on the surface of the heart, inflamed duodenum with hemorrhages of the inner lining, congested blood vessels supplying the visceral organs, congestion and small hemorrhages in the lungs, and yellow cheesy deposits in various parts of the body (Fig. 155).

In chronic cholera cases there may be pus in the lungs and air sacs; soft, flabby, and irregular ova; and rupture of ova in the body cavity.

Positive diagnosis depends on finding the *Pasteurella avicida* bacteria in the heart blood or organs of the body.

Spread of fowl cholera is by way of the droppings from infected to healthy birds. It may be carried by wild birds and insects and on the feet of animals

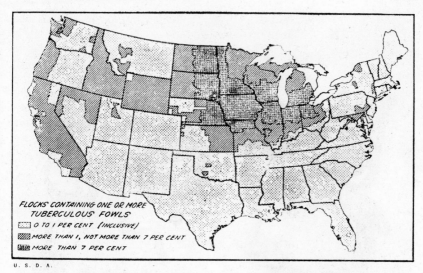

FLOCKS CONTAINING ONE OR MORE
TUBERCULOUS FOWLS
▢ O TO I PER CENT (INCLUSIVE)
▨ MORE THAN I, NOT MORE THAN 7 PER CENT
▩ MORE THAN 7 PER CENT

U. S. D. A.

Fig. 156. Extent of avian tuberculosis in the United States.

and on equipment. Birds that have recovered from the disease may be carriers.

Control of fowl cholera is accomplished by killing and burning any birds that have the acute feverish symptoms. Remove the litter frequently. Use clean, sanitary feeders and waterers. Avoid the use of contaminated yards or range. Keep flies and wild birds away from the premises in so far as possible. Infected flocks recover with less mortality if kept in warm, sanitary, and uncrowded houses.

Infected wattles may be removed by surgical amputation.

A whole blood test with the use of *Pasteurella avicida* stained antigen may be used to detect chronic carriers of fowl cholera.

Treatment consists of the use of a sulfa drug in the mash or drinking water.

Sulfaquinoxaline may be added to the mash at 0.05 per cent level; fed for two or three days; discontinued for two or three days; and, repeated if the trouble has not been checked.

Sulfamethazine may be added to the mash at 0.5 per cent level and fed for two days. The medicated mash is discontinued for four days and then fed again for a day.

Sodium sulfamethazine may be added to the drinking water at 0.1 per cent level and used. The medicated water is used two days; discontinued four days; and used again for a day.

Fowl tuberculosis. Avian tuberculosis is a chronic infectious disease of poultry and wild birds. It is most commonly observed in birds more than a year old. The chief areas of avian tuberculosis infection are shown in Figure 156.

Symptoms of fowl tuberculosis include paleness, weakness, emaciation, loss of muscle meat from the breastbone, lameness, diarrhea, complete exhaustion,

COURTESY OHIO AGRICULTURAL EXTENSION SERVICE

Fig. 157. Lesions of the viscera indicating tuberculosis. Left, viscera of a normal bird; right, the liver, spleen, and mesentery of the small intestine show grayish, granular, tubercular lesions.

and death. In a few instances the disease may be well established in birds that appear to be in good condition.

Autopsy examination reveals characteristic grayish-white or yellowish tumors of varying sizes in the liver, spleen, and intestines (Fig. 157). These tubercles when cut open show a solid, grayish, or glistening interior. Those in advanced stages of development show yellowish, cheesy, or crumbly masses in their interior.

Positive diagnosis depends on finding *Mycobacterium tuberculosus avium* in the lesions.

Spread of avian tuberculosis infection is by way of contaminated water, feed, litter, or soil. It may be carried from flock to flock by infected fowls, wild birds, rabbits, rats, mice, and equipment. Swine are susceptible to avian tuberculosis and cattle may become infected from swine.

Control of avian tuberculosis is accomplished most satisfactorily by disposal of the entire flock. The birds in good condition may be sold for meat purposes and the thin ones should be killed and burned.

The old birds may be disposed of in the spring and the building, equipment, and yard thoroughly cleaned and allowed to remain empty during the summer. Young chicks may be raised on clean range and later housed in the buildings that have been idle. It is a good plan to dispose of all old birds at least a month before chicks are brought on the farm.

Fig. 158. Chronic cold and ocular roup. Note the swollen face, exudate from the nostril, and mouth open for forced breathing. (Ohio Extension Bulletin 115.)

Colds (coryza) and roup. Colds are common respiratory infections that affect poultry and wild birds of all ages. A chronic cold is also known as ocular roup. Colds cause lowered egg production.

Symptoms of coryza are watery eyes; thin serous discharge and then a thick, sticky, foul-smelling discharge from the nostrils; sinuses filled with mucus which dries to a cheesy form, causing a swelling of the face about the eye (Fig. 158); and yellowish patches in the mouth.

Autopsy examination reveals no additional characteristics.

Hemophilus gallinarum bacteria may be isolated from cultures taken from the respiratory tract.

Control of colds and roup may be accomplished by removing all sick birds as soon as symptoms are observed, feeding a good ration containing an abundance of vitamin A, eradication of external and internal parasites, prevention of drafts and sudden changes in temperature in the house, keeping the house clean and dry, and preventing overcrowding. The use of cold and roup bacterins are of doubtful value.

In case of an outbreak, feed .5 per cent sulfathiazole in the ration for a period of four or five days and use clean drinking vessels. Set up a brooder

Fig. 159. Limberneck or botulism. (Ohio Extension Bulletin 115.)

stove in the house to keep the birds warm, the house dry, and to secure ventilation without drafts. The birds may be sprayed at night with one of the sprays recommended for colds or bronchitis. These sprays will not cure the trouble, but may relieve discomfort by drying up the discharge of mucus. *Individual treatment* may be used if the bird is valuable enough to warrant it. Wash the nostrils and eyes with a warm solution of baking soda (one teaspoon in a cup of water) or salt water (one teaspoon in a quart). Irrigate the nasal passages with one of the above solutions by means of a special nasal irrigator. In case of severe swelling beneath the eye, open the spot with a sharp knife; press out the cheesy material; and wash the wound with one of the above solutions.

Botulism (limberneck). Botulism is an acute disease of poultry and wild birds characterized by weakness and prostration. The first symptoms are dullness and leg weakness. These are soon followed by paralysis of the neck, wing, and leg muscles (Fig. 159). The bird appears lifeless. The feathers are loose and may be plucked easily. Death may be sudden or the bird may linger for several hours.

Botulism is caused by a toxin produced by the *Clostridium botulinum* bacteria. It is a soil organism that grows out of contact with air. It may grow and produce toxin in dead animals, closely packed hay, and in canned foods not thoroughly cooked.

In case of an outbreak, shut the birds off the range until the source of the trouble has been located and removed. Give the birds a laxative as in case of poisoning. Do not feed spoiled canned food to chickens unless it has been thoroughly cooked to destroy the toxin.

Navel infection (omphalitis). Navel infection is also known as "mushy chick disease" among hatcherymen. It is a rather uncommon disease that occurs among chicks the first day or so after hatching.

Symptoms of navel infection among chicks are drowsiness, mushy and puffed appearance of the abdomen, death within a few hours after the first symptoms, and high mortality the first seventy-two hours after hatching.

Autopsy examination of birds having navel infection shows a parboiled red color of the abdominal skin and muscles, accumulation of water and gas in the abdominal cavity, pale and swollen liver and kidneys, and fluid, putrid contents of the yolk sac.

Several kinds of bacteria have been isolated from cases of navel infection. The causative organism has not been definitely established.

Control of navel infection may be accomplished by the use of strict sanitation in incubators. Incubators should be thoroughly cleaned and fumigated between hatches (p. 167).

In case of an outbreak, fumigate the incubators between hatches with three times the strength of formalin used at hatching time. It may also be necessary to clean, disinfect, and fumigate the egg, incubator, and battery rooms to destroy the disease germs in the chick hatchery.

Apoplectiform septicemia. This is a rapidly fatal bacterial disease which may affect chickens, turkeys, pigeons, and other fowls.

Symptoms include sudden death or depression, listlessness, staggering gait, prostration, and finally death.

Autopsy examination of infected birds shows discoloration of the skin of the breast and neck caused by subcutaneous hemorrhages; serous or bloody exudates in the heart sac and body cavity; swollen liver, spleen, and kidneys; and congested intestines and lungs.

Bacterial cultures from the blood reveal the presence of *Streptococcus capsulatus gallinarum.*

Control of apoplectiform septicemia infection involves the use of the same sanitary measures as used for the control of cholera and fowl typhoid.

Healthy fowls may be vaccinated against apoplectiform septicemia by the intravenous injection of a killed culture of the causative organism.

Virus Diseases

Viruses are believed to be living organisms, so small that they cannot be seen with the microscope. The proof of their existence is the ability to produce disease by introducing body tissue, or fluid which contains them. All infectious diseases, where a causative organism has not been isolated, are generally classed as virus diseases. The principal poultry virus diseases are fowl pox, infectious bronchitis, range paralysis, and fowl plague.

Fowl pox. Fowl pox has also been called chicken pox, contagious epithelioma, canker, avian diphtheria, and sore head. It is a highly infectious disease affecting the head and mouth of chickens, turkeys, other poultry, and wild birds.

Fowl pox usually occurs in the fall and winter, but may occur at any time. It generally affects birds during the first year of production, but may affect younger or older birds. Fowl pox slows up and may stop production. The losses may vary all the way from few or no deaths to rather high mortality.

Symptoms of fowl pox are watery eyes and a discharge from the nostrils, as in the case of colds; and small, grayish, raised blister-like spots that appear on the comb, face, and wattles and are followed by a drying and darkening of the lesions to form warty-like scabs (Fig. 160).

The severity of the disease depends on the extent of diptheric deposits in the mouth. These are first thin, whitish, or yellowish in color, and then become thicker, firmer, and harder to remove.

The period between exposure to fowl pox and the appearance of the first symptoms of the disease varies from three to fifteen days. The duration of the disease varies from two or three days to as many weeks in acute cases and may last in a flock in chronic form for several months.

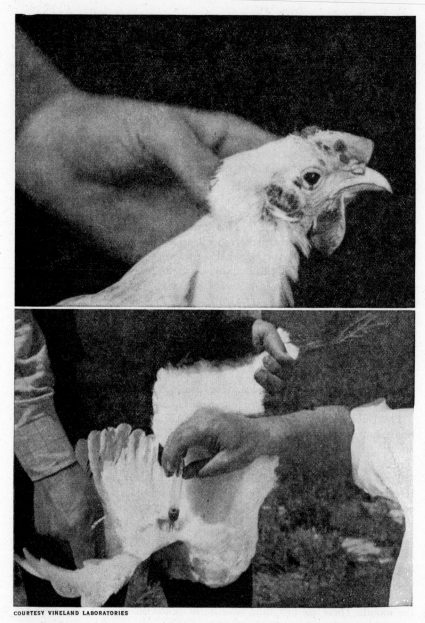

Fig. 160. Fowl pox and its control. Above, the dark nodules or scabs are fowl pox lesions. Below, wing vaccination by the stab method for prevention of fowl pox.

The fowl pox virus gains entrance to the body through a break in the skin. *Spread* of fowl pox is by contaminated material and by close contact. The disease may be carried from farm to farm by fowls that have had the disease or have been vaccinated recently, by mosquitoes and other biting insects, by wild birds, and by equipment.

Control of fowl pox is accomplished by using preventive measures. There is no satisfactory treatment. If the disease is present in the flock in chronic form or if it has caused trouble during the past two or three years, it is advisable to vaccinate all birds that have not had the disease.

In case of an outbreak of pox among birds that are already in production, the flock should be vaccinated with the pigeon strain of fowl pox vaccine. Its action is milder than that of the fowl strain and does not cause so great a loss in egg production.

In preventive vaccination in pullet flocks, the birds should be vaccinated with a fowl strain of pox vaccine when the birds are six to fifteen weeks old. Later, vaccination gives the birds a "set back" in development. While the fowl strain of pox vaccine is more severe in its action than the pigeon strain, it is believed to provide more lasting immunity.

Vaccination for prevention of fowl pox is carried out by making a break in the skin and introducing a little of the vaccine mixture. In the feather follicle method, three or four leg feathers are plucked and the vaccine added to the spot with a brush. In the more recent stab method, two sewing machine needles are pushed through a cork with the points about one-fourth inch apart. The wing is stretched out and the web is pierced from the underside, thus making four vaccination points through the double layer of skin simultaneously. The eyes of the needles take up sufficient vaccine to make the single stab effective.

The reaction denoting a "take" may be observed in five to seven days. The site of vaccination will show inflammation and later the formation of a scab which will drop off in three or four weeks.

Infectious bronchitis (laryngotracheitis). Infectious bronchitis is also known as infectious tracheitis, influenza, or flu. It is a highly infectious respiratory disease of chickens, but may also affect turkeys, ducks, pheasants, and wild birds. The disease is widely distributed in the United States. Losses may run from less than 5 per cent to as high as 80 per cent of the flock. Infectious bronchitis is more prevalent, lasts longer, and causes greater mortality among birds six months to one year old than among older or younger birds. It occurs most frequently during the fall and winter months. Infectious bronchitis, common among birds three to twelve months old, appears to be a different disease from chick bronchitis (p. 383).

Symptoms of laryngotracheitis are watery eyes, lack of activity, coughing, sneezing, shaking the head, gasping for breath (Fig. 161), coughing up of bloody mucus, strangulation, and possibly sudden death.

The disease may go through the flock in one to two weeks or it may continue for a month or more.

Autopsy examination of birds infected with laryngotracheitis reveals an

Fig. 161. Infectious bronchitis (laryngotracheitis). Above, typical symptoms. Below, cloacal vaccination for prevention.

inflamed glottis and trachea, presence of yellow cheesy material, and the nostrils and mouth filled with a sticky mucoid exudate.

Spread of infectious bronchitis is by way of contaminated feed, water, and litter, and by close contact. The virus is present in the exudate in the mouth. It may be carried by apparently healthy birds, that have recovered from the disease, and by wild birds and equipment.

Control of laryngotracheitis is accomplished by strict sanitary measures and by preventive vaccination. Birds showing symptoms of bronchitis should be removed from the flock as soon as noticed. Prevent drafts, sudden changes in temperature, and overcrowding in the house.

In case of an outbreak, use the same measures as for colds (p. 377). Inhalents will check the discharge of mucus in the respiratory passages. If the mucous discharge can be checked, fewer birds will die as a result of strangulation.

Vaccination with laryngotracheitis vaccine may be used for prevention of the disease. It should be used only on farms where the trouble has caused losses during the past two or three years. Vaccines should be used only when there is a definite need for them, because they are a means of introducing the living virus diseases on the farm.

Cloacal vaccination is used for the prevention of infectious bronchitis in a flock and for preventing the spread from infected birds to healthy ones in case of an outbreak. The bird is held by an assistant and the upper part of the vent is rolled open with the thumb and forefinger. A stiff brush moistened with vaccine is rubbed back and forth across the mucous membrane until a slight redness is produced.

Five days after vaccination a "take" is indicated by a reddened and swollen membrane at the point of vaccination, which is also covered with mucus.

Birds may be vaccinated for both fowl pox and infectious bronchitis at the same time (between six and fifteen weeks of age).

Chick bronchitis. An infectious bronchitis is sometimes found in hatcheries, battery brooder rooms, and in brooder houses. It is caused by a different virus from that which causes laryngotracheitis in older birds.

The causative organism is probably carried into the hatchery on eggshells or egg cases. Fumigation of incubators and eggs between hatches (p. 167) will prevent the spread of disease in machines. In case of an outbreak in a hatchery, it may be necessary to fumigate the incubator room as well as the incubators.

In case of an outbreak of chick bronchitis in a battery room or brooder house, use an inhalent until the chicks are removed. Then the room and equipment should be thoroughly cleaned and fumigated. Use forty cubic centimeters of formalin and twenty grams of potassium permanganate crystals per hundred cubic feet of room space. Have the room closed tightly, the temperature 70° F. or higher, and the floor wet with hot water. Pour the formalin over the potassium permanganate crystals in earthernware vessels, spaced at various points about the room. Leave the room closed for three or four hours after fumigation. Do not return infected chicks or those that have had the disease to the room after fumigation. They are carriers of the disease and will return it to the premises.

Fowl paralysis (leucosis). Fowl paralysis is also known as range paralysis, lymphomatosis, neurolymphomatosis, and leucosis. The disease here described is a distinct virus disease and should not be confused with various types of paralysis, lameness, or leg weakness resulting from vitamin deficiencies, parasite infestations, or bacterial infections. It affects chickens between the ages of six weeks and eighteen months, but the highest incidence of the disease occurs between the ages of four and twelve months. The mortality may reach as high as 75 per cent.

Symptoms. The symptoms of leucosis vary with the strain of the infective agent and the course of the disease.

The *paralysis form* is first indicated by a drooping of the wing or a partial paralysis of one or both legs (Fig. 162). In a short time the bird is unable to stand and is not able to reach feed or water. The muscles of an affected leg often shrink or wither. Affected birds generally have a healthy appearance, except for the paralysis, and a good appetite. They may show digestive disturbances as indicated by diarrhea.

The *blindness form* is indicated by a fading of the color of the eye. It changes from the usual reddish-bay to a gray. In severe cases the pupils fail to respond to light. The eye sometimes bulges out and the bird becomes totally blind. The birds may continue to find the feed and water and lay well for a time after they lose their eyesight.

The *leucosis or leukemic form* is indicated by paleness, loss of weight, and weakness. The affected birds resemble those affected with chronic coccidiosis. The birds may live for several weeks.

The *tumor form* seldom shows any external symptoms. Lumps may be found in a few instances on almost any part of the body.

The above forms of the disease may be due to the same or different viruses. Investigators are not in agreement on this point at the present time.

Birds infected with leucosis seldom, if ever, recover.

Autopsy examination. In case of leucosis accompanied by paralysis, the plexuses and large nerves leading to the affected legs or wings may be enlarged and yellowish-gray instead of the normal whitish-gray color. The cross striations characteristic of normal nerves are lost, and nodules may be present anywhere along the affected nerve.

In case of the leukemic form of the disease, the liver, spleen, and kidneys are usually enlarged, grayish-red in color, and soft and flabby. The liver may be spotted with brownish or gray areas and easily ruptured.

In case of the tumor form of leucosis, the masses of abnormal tissue may be found about the ovary, liver, spleen, kidneys, and other tissues of the body. The tumors vary greatly in size. They are generally grayish or yellowish in color. The centers of the tumors are generally necrotic and yellowish in color.

Microscopic examination of the blood generally reveals the presence of an unusually large number of white blood cells. Examination of the nerves

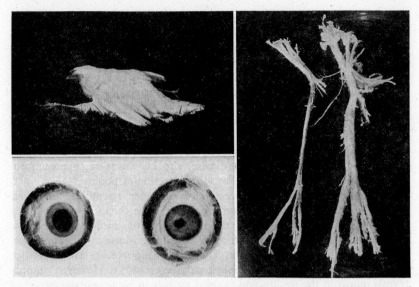

Fig. 162. Fowl paralysis or leucosis. (See also Figure 33.) Left—upper, typical symptoms of the paralysis form. Left—lower, "white eye" lesion, a symptom of leukemia. Normal eye at left and diseased eye at right. Right, leg nerves of normal fowl at left and of leucemic fowl at right. (Courtesy W. R. Graham, University of Illinois.)

and other tissues of the body shows infiltration of massive numbers of white blood cells.

Control. There is no known treatment for leucosis. It is generally believed that chickens become infected when quite young. The development of symptoms of the disease requires a month or more after infection. Old birds are believed to be carriers of the disease. Young chicks probably become infected by contaminated feed, litter, water, or range. The disease may be carried by flies and other insects, wild birds, animals, and equipment. Young stock should be raised separate from old stock and as far away from them as possible.

Birds showing any of the symptoms of leucosis should be removed from the flock as soon as noticed. Those showing only the eye symptoms of the disease may be sold for meat.

In case of an outbreak which may cause heavy losses, dispose of the entire flock. Clean and disinfect the buildings and allow them to remain idle for a month or more. Restock the farm with birds from a flock where the disease has not occurred or from one that is no longer bothered with losses from leucosis.

Another procedure is to hatch from hens and cocks rather than from pullets and cockerels. Birds that live through an outbreak of paralysis have some immunity against the disease. Data being obtained in various parts of the country indicate that it may be possible to breed strains of chickens that will have resistance against leucosis infection.

Fowl plague. Fowl plague, also known as fowl pest, is a common virus disease in Europe. A few outbreaks have occurred in the United States.

Symptoms of fowl plague include ruffled plumage, loss of appetite, droopiness, darkening and swelling of the comb and wattles, and, in advanced cases, a clogging of the eyes and nostrils with a sticky exudate. Death usually occurs in from two to five days. A high percentage of the flock may die within a few days.

Control of fowl plague requires rigid sanitation. Remove, kill, and burn diseased birds. Remove the remainder of the flock to clean quarters. Thoroughly clean and disinfect buildings and equipment.

Newcastle disease. Newcastle disease, also known as avian pneumoencephalitis, is a respiratory and nerve virus infection of poultry.

Symptoms in chicks is first a respiratory infection resembling infectious bronchitis (p. 000). As the disease progresses, some chicks develop nervous symptoms such as distortions of the neck, shivering, inco-ordination, convulsive seizures, circling, and sometimes paralysis. Mortality may be slight or it may reach 30 or 40 per cent. The nerve symptoms are somewhat like those in case of nutritional encephalomalacia (p. 348). However, autopsy reveals mucus in the trachea and clouded air sacs in Newcastle disease.

Symptoms in adult birds resemble those of a cold or infectious bronchitis. The infection spreads rapidly. There is a drop in feed consumption and a sudden drop in egg production to nearly zero in one or two days. The eggs laid during the period are generally rough-shelled or soft-shelled and the white is often of poor quality. The respiratory symptoms last from four to eight days and egg production is affected for three to eight weeks. Mortality is usually low, two per cent or less.

Control should be based on preventative vaccination rather than on treatment. Growing chickens may be vaccinated when eight to twelve weeks old in the same manner and at the same time they are vaccinated for fowl pox. If a live attenuated vaccine is used, immunity will carry through the following laying season. Chicks hatched from immunized birds will have some immunity. However, it disappears and the chicks are susceptible to Newcastle infection by the time they are two to four weeks old. In some broiler areas where Newcastle losses have been heavy, the chicks are vaccinated when received or during the first two weeks with a killed Newcastle vaccine. A live virus vaccine produces too severe a reaction on young chicks.

If an outbreak occurs, try to stimulate feed consumption by feeding pellets in a wet mash moistened with milk. A mild spray may also be used to give relief from the mucus in the respiratory passages.

Psittacosis. This is a virus disease of parrots and some other species of birds. It may be spread to laboratory animals and man.

In parrots the disease is characterized by weakness, prostration, diarrhea, and death. Persons contracting the disease from birds or laboratory animals develop pneumonia.

Strict sanitary measures are necessary for the control of psittacosis.

Epidemic tremors. This is a disease of chicks up to six weeks of age. It is probably caused by a virus.

Affected chicks show a constant trembling. Handling increases it. The trouble stops during sleep. Mortality may reach 50 per cent. No method of control is known.

Diseases Associated with Egg Production

Diseases of the reproductive organs, associated with egg production, account for most of the losses of noninfectious nature among laying hens. The principal diseases associated with egg production are "pick outs," rupture of the oviduct, egg bound, and ruptured yolks.

Pick outs. This trouble is usually encountered among pullets during the first weeks of egg production. If the bird, after laying an egg, does not remain on the nest or away from the other birds until the everted cloacal membrane is withdrawn, the other birds are attracted by the red membrane and begin picking it. The cloacal membrane becomes bruised and swollen and hemorrhage may result. In bad cases, the entire cloacal area is picked away and the bird dies from hemorrhage.

Injured birds should be removed as soon as noticed. Pullets should be trained to lay in nests by placing birds in them that have a habit of laying on the floor. Bright light should be excluded from the house in case "pick out" trouble is encountered.

Feeding oats, using built-up litter, and keeping legume hay or green feed available may help to prevent "pick outs." If the trouble starts and persists in spite of all of the precautionary measures, it may be necessary to trim the upper part of the beak, especially of the offenders, back to the tender undercoating.

Prolapse of oviduct. The oviduct may come loose and protrude from the vent when a bird lays an egg. The blood which accompanies the prolapse and the oviduct itself attract other birds and the injured one is picked to death unless it is promptly isolated. The trouble is most common during the late winter or early spring and affects high-producing birds.

There is no satisfactory treatment. Affected birds, observed and removed soon after the prolapse, may be used for meat.

Feeding vitamin D and oyster shell and encouraging exercise by the use of range reduce the troubles from prolapse.

Rupture of oviduct. Internal rupture of the oviduct may result from severe inflammation, an attempt to pass large eggs, or from injury. The breaking of the oviduct permits yolks or fully formed eggs to pass into the body cavity. The yolks may rupture and the contents dry out, forming a yellow coating over the viscera. The material interferes with the normal functioning of the abdominal organs.

Yolks or even whole eggs may get loose in the body cavity and cause a protruding abdomen (Fig. 163).

There is no treatment for rupture of the oviduct. The use of low perches and nests, careful handling of birds, and feeding well-balanced rations will reduce the number of cases.

Data being collected at Ohio State University indicate that rupture of the

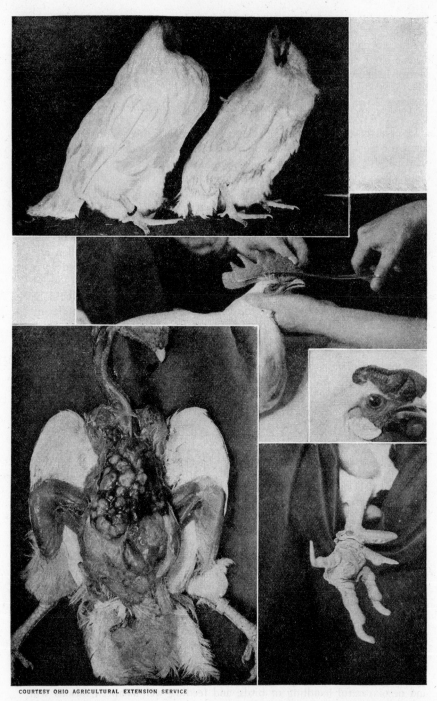

Fig. 163. Miscellaneous poultry troubles. Top, posture of birds with ruptured oviduct and eggs loose in the body cavity. Center: procedure for amputation of frozen combs or for dubbing. Bottom—left, tumors of the viscera. Note the light-colored masses throughout the liver and small intestine. Bottom—right, bumble foot. Note the swollen foot and the lesion on the bottom and between the toes.

oviduct and other reproductive troubles is largely a family characteristic and may be controlled through breeding.

Egg bound. Egg-bound trouble occurs most frequently among pullets. It results from attempts to pass large or double-yolked eggs through an oviduct that is too small for their passage. Birds appear listless and make frequent attempts to lay.

As a means of treatment, the bird may be placed on its back, a finger greased and inserted into the oviduct, and the egg worked toward the cloaca by the finger and pressure on the abdomen.

Several eggs may collect in the oviduct, resulting in its rupture, and may cause a bird to assume the posture of a penguin.

Ruptured yolks. A yolk may rupture and flow into the body cavity or into the oviduct. When it flows into the body cavity, it covers the internal organs and gives them a yellowish cast. The accumulation of yolk material in the peritoneal cavity may result in peritonitis and death.

If the yolk ruptures in the oviduct, it adheres to the walls, causes a thickening of the membranes, and leads to a catarrhal peritonitis.

Rupture of yolks may be caused by cholera (p. 373), rough handling, fright, flying on and off of high perches and nests, and by faulty nutrition.

Miscellaneous Diseases

A number of diseases of poultry are caused by injury or undesirable environment, while still others are caused by microörganisms or conditions that are not well understood. These diseases have been classed as miscellaneous. They include blue comb, cannibalism, heat prostration, frozen combs and wattles, edema of the wattles, necrosis of the beak, pendulous crop, sod disease, bumblefoot, vent gleet, and tumors.

Blue comb. This disease of unknown cause is also known as pullet disease, X disease, cholera-like disease, contagious indigestion, and avian monocytosis. It usually occurs in pullets just coming into production either on range or after being housed. However, males may also be affected, as well as chicks as young as four weeks and hens up to two years. Vigorous, well-nourished pullets are most frequently attacked. The disease occurs more often in hot weather.

Symptoms include a loss in appetite, diarrhea, and a severe drop in egg production. There may be shrivelling of the skin, darkening of the comb (blue comb), and fever in the later stages of an acute attack. Mortality varies from 0 to 50 per cent with an average of 5 per cent. The disease lasts for about 2 weeks but egg production may be below normal for several weeks.

The liver often shows yellowish pin-point spots. Most organs are reddish. The bird is usually in good flesh. The intestines contain a mucous material. The kidneys are usually swollen, pale, and contain chalklike deposits. The ovary may contain flabby ova and some may be broken.

Control of blue comb disease is difficult. No specific treatment is known. Wet-mash feeding, containing 40 per cent blackstrap cane molasses and 60 per cent mash, twice daily with other feed withheld for two hours before feeding has been advocated. Feed about as much of the mash mixture as the birds will clean up in 10 to 20 minutes. Continue the treatment until the trouble clears up.

Potassium chloride or a good grade of muriate of potash fertilizer (containing at least 60 per cent potassium oxide) may be used at the rate of 0.5 per cent in the drinking water for 7 days, and, if necessary, at the rate of 1.5 per cent in the feed for an additional 7 days.

Cannibalism. Cannibalism may be encountered among birds of all ages. Among chicks, the trouble is confined to toe and tail picking. Among mature birds, the vent, tail, and comb are the regions most frequently picked.

The trouble generally breaks out among overcrowded birds that are kept in close confinement. Birds picking at a wound of an injured chick or picking at the tails of birds in front of them at the feeders, may get the habit of cannibalism started. Housing pullets of different ages or stages of maturity together, birds laying eggs on the floor, and prolapse of oviduct or hemorrhage from egg laying are other things that may lead to cannibalism.

Cannibalism may be controlled by darkening the windows in the house, providing range, use of oats in the ration, and the removal of all injured birds as soon as observed. Sometimes a few birds are the cause of all the trouble. It is desirable to watch for them and remove them from the flock. At times the use of one of the above suggestions is sufficient for control of the trouble, while in other cases more than one of them need to be used.

The wounds of injured birds should be painted with pine tar or an "anti-pick" compound. One such compound consists of a mixture of four ounces of vaseline, one-fourth ounce of carmine, and one-half ounce of aloes.

Heat prostration. Mature fowls are better able to withstand extremely cold than extremely hot weather. During extremely warm days, apparently healthy hens may die of heat prostration.

Helpful preventive measures against heat prostration are shade, ventilated nests, and an ample supply of water.

Frozen combs and wattles. Birds having large combs and wattles may have them frozen during extremely cold temperatures in the house. The frosted parts become swollen and painful, bluish-red in color, and the severely frozen portions slough off.

If discovered early, the affected parts may be thawed out with cold water and thoroughly greased with vaseline.

Amputation of badly frozen combs and wattles will hasten recovery (Fig. 163). The comb or wattle is cut off with tinners' shears or some other dull shears which crush as they cut. The crushing of the tissues and blood vessels helps to prevent hemorrhage. Searing the cut surface with a hot knife, addition of a few drops of an alcoholic solution of ferric chloride, dusting with powdered alum, or the application of a little ground mash feed to the wound will aid in stopping the bleeding which may result from the operation.

Dubbing is the term commonly used to designate the removal of the combs and wattles of growing stock to prevent freezing during the ensuing winter. The combs and wattles may be trimmed from young Leghorns by means of small sharp scissors when the birds are about four weeks old. There is little or no bleeding when the operation is performed at this age.

Edema of the wattles. This disease is characterized by a hot, swollen wattle filled with a fluid which later changes to a hard cheesy nodule. Edema of the wattle is more common among males than females.

The cause of edema of the wattle is not known. The causative organism for fowl cholera (p. 373) and other bacteria have been isolated from the lesions. The trouble may start from an infection in a wound of the wattle.

The affected wattle may be removed like frozen wattles.

Necrosis of the beak. This trouble is caused by the packing of finely ground mash feed in the mouth. It may accumulate under the tongue or along the edges of the upper and lower mandibles. The accumulation of feed interferes with the closing of the mouth and results in abnormal respiration. The mouth becomes dry, inflammation sets in at the site of feed deposit, and secondary bacterial infections may result.

The trouble may be prevented by avoiding the use of finely ground mash or by using more fiber in the mash. The use of a large amount of ground wheat in the ration may cause the feed to stick in the mouth.

Affected chicks may be cured by removing the adhering food material and washing out the mouth with salt water.

Pendulous crop. Enlarged pendulous crops may be found among birds of the heavy breeds of chickens and among growing poults two to three months of age.

The trouble may be caused by irregular feeding. Consumption of a large quantity of feed or water or both at a given time may cause a weakening of the crop wall which will not return to normal.

Keeping feed and water before birds of all ages at all times, preventing overheating in houses, and providing shade on range will help prevent the trouble.

Sod disease. This is a rather uncommon disease that affects the feet of young chickens and even mature birds that have access to grass range.

Symptoms of sod disease are blisters between the toes, swollen and tender feet, thick scabs, and possibly the loss of a part of the foot.

The disease is known as vesicular dermatitis, but the causative organism is unknown.

In case of an outbreak, confine the birds to plowed ground or to the house.

Bumblefoot. Bumblefoot is a term applied to a swollen foot of a fowl. The condition, described here, is found most often among laying hens.

The ball of the foot is hot and swollen. The bird may limp and hold the affected foot up. In some cases, both feet are affected. The swollen condition is followed by an accumulation of cheesy material in the ball of the foot and between the toes.

Bacteriological examination reveals the presence of different kinds of bacteria. They probably gain entrance through a break in the skin on the foot.

In treating birds for bumblefoot, the lesions should be lanced, the cheesy material pressed or picked out, the cavity washed with salt water or 5 per cent carbolic acid solution, and the foot bandaged. The wound should be dressed daily until the bird recovers.

Vent gleet. Vent gleet is a disease of mature birds. It is characterized by a severe irritation, a watery discharge that becomes foul smelling, and a reddened area around the vent. The fowl will pick at the irritated surface, and other birds may pick at the swollen and reddened area, causing ulceration.

Affected birds should be removed from the flock, the feathers clipped around the vent, the scabs removed by washing with warm soapy water, and zinc oxide or mercurial ointment applied to the inflamed area.

Tumors. Tumors are masses of unorganized tissue which grow independently of surrounding structures and have no physiologic use. Old birds are quite likely to have tumors. They are found most frequently in the oviduct and ovary, but may occur anywhere in the body or on the surface. They vary all the way from baglike structures filled with fluid to hard meaty or even bony tissue. Tumors may press on nerves, causing paralysis; rupture blood vessels, causing hemorrhage; close the respiratory passages, causing suffocation; and cause injury or death in many other ways.

There is no treatment for internal tumors. Some external tumors may be removed satisfactorily by surgical means.

REVIEW QUESTIONS

1. Which may be used with more safety on a farm, a bacterin or a virus? Why?
2. What are some of the factors influencing the severity of an infection?
3. What are the chief means of spreading poultry diseases?
4. What are the principal diseases that affect growing stock? Mature birds?
5. Why is prevention of poultry diseases more practical than treatment?
6. Is it easier to free the poultry yards from internal parasites or from pathogenic bacteria? Why?
7. Name a practical disinfectant and describe its use in the poultry house in case of an outbreak of disease.
8. What nutritional disease is most likely to be encountered in poultry production? Why?
9. Differentiate between nutritional and ocular roup.
10. Differentiate between rickets and perosis.
11. Differentiate between chick dermatitis and fowl pox.
12. What is the control for curled-toe paralysis?
13. Nutritional encephalomalacia may be confused with what other chick diseases?
14. What are some of the indications of rickets among laying hens?
15. What should be done in case of poisoning in the flock?
16. Differentiate between the life cycles of lice and red mites.
17. What is the most efficient method of treating birds for lice?
18. In what ways do internal parasites cause injury to fowls?
19. Which is harder to control, roundworm or tapeworm infestation? Why?
20. What other troubles may be confused with tapeworm infestation?

21. Why are cecal worms a menace to turkey production?
22. Symptoms of tapeworm infestation may be confused with those of what other disease?
23. Lesions caused by tapeworm infestation may be confused with lesions caused by what other diseases?
24. Do confined or range birds suffer more from internal parasite infestation? Why?
25. Do winter- or spring-hatched poultry suffer more from infectious diseases? Why?
26. Chronic coccidiosis infection may be confused with what other diseases?
27. What is the method of controlling coccidiosis infection?
28. What is the life cycle of blackhead?
29. How are mold diseases spread?
30. What are the principal bacterial diseases of poultry?
31. What are the steps in the National Poultry Breeding Plan for the control of pullorum disease?
32. How may one differentiate between egg and incubator pullorum-infected chicks?
33. What are some of the benefits to be gained by incubator fumigation?
34. Which is the most practical of the three official pullorum tests? Why?
35. In testing birds for pullorum infection, what is the tester looking for in the blood?
36. What other disease is so closely related to pullorum that the pullorum test also detects birds having the disease?
37. What are the chief diagnostic characteristics of cholera?
38. What is the recommended plan for the control of avian tuberculosis?
39. Differentiate between a cold and ocular roup.
40. What is the cause of botulism?
41. Give directions for vaccination of birds for prevention of fowl pox.
42. What is the most reliable diagnostic characteristic of laryngotracheitis infection?
43. What is the procedure for controlling an outbreak of chick bronchitis in a hatchery?
44. What are the principal forms of leucosis as indicated by symptoms?
45. What are the recommendations for the control of leucosis?
46. How may "pick outs" be controlled?
47. Why "dub" cockerels?

REFERENCES

General References

BARGER, E. H., AND CARD, L. E.: Diseases and Parasites of Poultry, 3rd ed. Lea and Febiger, Philadelphia, Pa. 1943.

BEACH, J. R. AND STEWART, M. A.: DISEASES OF CHICKENS. Calif. Sta. Bul. 674. 1942.

BIESTER, H. E., AND SCHWARTZ, L. H.: Diseases of Poultry, 2nd ed. Iowa State College Press, Ames, Iowa. 1948.

BLOUNT, W. P.: Poultry Diseases. The Williams and Wilkins Co., Baltimore, Md. 1947.

BRANDLY, C. A., AND WALTERS, Y. F.: INHERITANCE AS A FACTOR IN POULTRY DISEASE RESEARCH. Amer. Jour. Vet. Res., 3: 105–110. 1942.

BRYANT, R. L.: BREEDING LEGHORN CHICKENS TO INCREASE THE LIFE SPAN. Va. Sta. Tech. Bul. 99. 1946.

BUSHNELL, L. D., AND TWIEHAUS, M. J.: POULTRY DISEASES—THEIR PREVENTION AND CONTROL. Kan. Sta. Bul. 326. 1945.

DELAPLANE, J. P.: THE DIFFERENTIATION OF THE RESPIRATORY DISEASES OF CHICKENS. Rhode Island Sta. Bul. 288. 1943.

HALL, W. J., AND WEHR, E. E.: DISEASES AND PARASITES OF POULTRY. U. S. D. A. Farmers' Bul. 1652. Revised, 1949.

HAYS, F. A.: MORTALITY RATE IN RELATION TO EGG PRODUCTION. Poultry Sci., 28: 707–712. 1949.

HINSHAW, W. R.: DISEASES OF TURKEYS. Calif. Sta. Bul. 613. Revised, 1943.

HOFFMAN, H. A., AND STOVER, D. E.: AN ANALYSIS OF THIRTY THOUSAND AUTOPSIES ON CHICKENS. Calif. State Dept. Agr. Bul. 31: No. 1, 7–30. 1942.

HULL, T. G.: Diseases Transmitted from Animals to Man. Charles C. Thomas, Springfield, Illinois. 1941.

KAUPP, B. F., AND SURFACE, R. C.: Poultry Sanitation and Disease Control. Kaupp and Surface, Minneapolis, Minnesota. 1943.

KENNARD, D. C., AND CHAMBERLAIN, V. D.: BUILT-UP FLOOR LITTER, SANITATION, AND NUTRITION. Ohio Farm and Home Res. Vol. 34, No. 261: 162–166. 1949.

LUBBEHUSEN, R. E., AND BEACH, J. R.: ADULT POULTRY MORTALITY OF NONINFECTIOUS ORIGIN. Jour. Amer. Vet. Med. Assoc., 94: 209–222. 1939.

SCHILLINGER, J. E., AND MORLEY, L. C.: DISEASES OF UPLAND GAME BIRDS. U. S. D. A. Farmers' Bul. 1781. 1937.

SEEGER, K. C., AND TOMHAVE, A. E.: CAUSES OF MORTALITY IN FOUR SUCCESSIVE FLOCKS OF BROILERS AT THE SUBSTATION. Del. Sta. Bul. 249. 1944.

STURKIE, PAUL D.: FIVE YEARS OF SELECTION FOR VIABILITY IN WHITE LEGHORN CHICKENS. Poultry Sci., 22: 155–160. 1943.

TILLEY, F. W.: THE USE OF DISINFECTANTS ON THE FARM. U. S. D. A. Farmers' Bul. 1991. 1947.

U. S. D. A. YEAR BOOK of AGR., pp. 931–1108. 1942. *Or,* YEAR BOOK SEPARATE NO. 1891, Part 7: COMMON DISEASES AND PARASITES OF POULTRY.

UNITED STATES DEPARTMENT OF AGRICULTURE REGIONAL POULTRY RESEARCH LABORATORY STAFF. POULTRY DISEASE INVESTIGATIONS AT THE U. S. REGIONAL POULTRY RESEARCH LABORATORY. Misc. Pub. 609. 1946.

VAN ES, L., AND OLNEY, J. F.: AN INQUIRY INTO THE INFLUENCE OF ENVIRONMENT ON THE INCIDENCE OF POULTRY DISEASES. Neb. Sta. Res. Bul. 118. 1940.

VAN ES, L., AND OLNEY, J. F.: POULTRY DISEASES AND PARASITES. Neb. Sta. Bul. 332. 1941.

WINTER, A. R.: PREVENTION AND CONTROL OF POULTRY DISEASES. Ohio Ext. Bul. 115. Revised, 1943.

Nutritional Diseases

BUCKNER, G. D., AND INSKO, W. M.: DEFORMED BONES OF CHICKENS. Ky. Sta. Bul. 492. 1946.

CLARK, P. F., McCLUNG, L. S., PINKERTON, H., PRICE, W. H., SCHNEIDER, H. A., AND TRAGER, W.: INFLUENCE OF NUTRITION IN EXPERIMENTAL INFECTION. Bact. Rev., 13: 99–134. 1949.

DURRELL, W. B.: AVITAMINOSIS A IN POULTRY. Canad. Jour. Compar. Med. and Vet. Sci., 9: 163–165. 1945.

MANN, T. B.: CHICK REARING. I. THE EFFECT OF THE DIET ON MORTALITY WITH REFERENCE TO SIX-DAY DISEASES. Jour. Agr. Sci. (Eng.) 35: 95–97. 1945.

MAXON, A. L., AND RHIAN, M.: SELENIUM POISONING. Physiol. Rev., 23: 305–337. 1943.

PAPPENHEIMER, A. M., GOETTSCH, M., AND JUNGHERR, E.: NUTRITIONAL ENCEPHALOMALACIA IN CHICKS AND CERTAIN RELATED DISORDERS OF DOMESTIC BIRDS. Storrs Sta. Bul. 229. 1939.

STOKSTAD, E. L. R., AND MANNING, P. V. D.: THE EFFECT OF RIBOFLAVIN ON THE INCIDENCE OF CURLED TOE PARALYSIS IN CHICKS. Jour. Nutrition 16: 279–283. 1938.

TEPPER, A. E., AND BIRD, H. R.: GIZZARD LESIONS IN DAY-OLD CHICKS. Poultry Sci., 21: 108–110. 1942.

External and Internal Parasites

BISHOP, F. C., AND HENDERSON, L. S.: HOUSE FLY CONTROL. U. S. Dept. Agr. Leaflet, 182. Revised, 1946.

EDGAR, S. A., WALSH, W. L., AND JOHNSON, L. W.: COMPARATIVE EFFICACY OF SEVERAL INSECTICIDES AND METHODS OF APPLICATION IN THE CONTROL OF LICE ON CHICKENS. Poultry Sci., 28: 320–338. 1949.

GRAHAM, R., TORRY, J. P., MIZELLA, J. D., AND MICHAEL, V. M.: INTERNAL PARASITES OF POULTRY. Ill. Sta. Circ. 469. 1937.

JAQUETTE, D. S., AND WEHR, E. E.: NICOTINE-BENTONITE AND PHENOTHIAZINE MIXTURE AS TREATMENT FOR ROUNDWORMS OF CHICKENS. Poultry Sci., 28: 821–825. 1949.

MCDOUGLE, H. C., AND DURANT, A. J.: COMMON INTERNAL AND EXTERNAL PARASITES OF POULTRY. Mo. Sta. Bul. 473. 1943.

POULTRY COUNCIL OF THE STATE COLLEGE OF WASHINGTON. COMMON EXTERNAL PARASITES OF CHICKENS AND TURKEYS. Wash. Ext. Bul. 370. 1947.

RITCHER, P. O., AND INSKO, W. M.: EXTERNAL PARASITES OF CHICKENS AND THEIR CONTROL. Ky. Sta. Bul. 517. 1948.

ROBERTS, I. H., AND PETERSON, H. O.: HEXACHLOROCYCLOHEXANE—A FUMIGANT FOR THE CONTROL OF CHICKEN LICE. Poultry Sci., 26: 588–593. 1947.

SMITH, R. M.: VERMIFUGE TREATMENTS AND EGG PRODUCTION. Ark. Sta. Bul. 431. 1943.

STAFSETH, H. J.: ON THE CONTROL OF TAPEWORM INFESTATION IN CHICKENS WITH NOTES ON THE PATHOLOGY OF THE HOSTS. Mich. Sta. Tech. Bul. 148. 1935.

TODD, A. C.: WORM PARASITES OF TENNESSEE CHICKENS. Tenn. Sta. Bul. 205. 1948.

WALLER, E. F.: BLUE COMB DISEASE. N. H. Sta. Tech. Bul. 85. 1945.

WARREN, D. C.: THE VALUE OF DDT FOR THE CONTROL OF THE COMMON CHICKEN LOUSE. Poultry Sci., 24: 473–476. 1945.

WEHR, E. E.: CONTROLLING GAPEWORMS IN POULTRY. U. S. D. A. Leaflet 207: 1–6. 1941.

Protozoan Diseases

BECKER, E. R.: COCCIDIA AND COCCIDIOSIS OF DOMESTICATED, GAME AND LABORATORY ANIMALS AND OF MAN. Collegiate Press, Inc., Ames, Iowa. 1934.

DEVOLT, H. M., AND HOLST, A. P.: COMPARATIVE VALUE OF CHLOROHY-
DROXYGUINOLINE AND VIOFORM AS PREVENTIVES OF BLACKHEAD (IN-
FECTIOUS ENTEROHEPATITIS) OF TURKEYS. Poultry Sci., 28: 641–643. 1949.

DICKINSON, E. M.: THE EFFECT OF SULFAQUINOXALINE ON EIMERIA ACER-
VULINA INFECTION IN PULLETS IN EGG PRODUCTION. Poultry Sci., 28:
670–674. 1949.

DURANT, A. J., AND MCDOUGLE, H. C.: COCCIDIOSIS IN CHICKENS AND OTHER
BIRDS. Mo. Sta. Bul. 512. 1948.

HART, C. P., WILEY, W. H., DELAPLANE, J. P., GRUMBLES, L. C., AND HIGGINS,
T. C.: MEDICATION VERSUS SANITATION IN THE CONTROL OF COCCIDIOSIS.
Poultry Sci., 28: 686–690. 1949.

HARWOOD, P. D., AND STUNZ, D. I.: NITROFURAZONE IN THE MEDICATION
OF AVIAN COCCIDIOSIS. Jour. Parasitol. 35: 175–182. 1949.

HAWKINS, P. A., AND DUNLAP, J. S.: BISPHENOLS FOR THE CONTROL OF
COCCIDIOSIS. Poultry Sci., 28: 818–820. 1949.

HEWITT, R. I.: RECENT RESEARCH IN AVIAN AND SIMIAN MALARIA. Jour.
Natl. Malaria Soc., 3: 95–109. 1944.

KNIGHT, D. R., MCDOUGLE, H. C., AND DURANT, A. J.: TRICHOMONIASIS OF
TURKEYS. Mo. Sta. Bul. 456. 1942.

KOUTZ, F. R.: IMMUNITY STUDIES IN AVIAN COCCIDIOSIS. Poultry Sci., 27:
793–797. 1948.

MARSHALL, E. K.: CHEMOTHERAPY IN AVIAN MALARIA. Physiol. Rev. 22:
190–204. 1942.

TYZZER, E. E.: STUDIES ON HISTOMONIASIS OR BLACKHEAD INFECTION IN
THE CHICKEN AND TURKEY. Proc. Amer. Acad. Arts and Sci., 69: 189–264.
1943.

Diseases Due to Molds and Yeasts

ASTHANA, R. P.: ASPERGILLOSIS IN FOWLS. Indiana Acad. Sci. Proc., 20: 43–
47. 1944.

DURANT, A. J.: MOLD DISEASES OF CHICKENS AND TURKEYS. Mo. Sta. Bul.
481. 1949.

HENRICI, A. T.: Molds, Yeast, and Actinomycetes, 2nd ed. John Wiley & Sons,
Inc., New York. 1948.

JUNGHERR, E. L.: STUDIES ON YEASTLIKE FUNGI FROM GALLINACEOUS BIRDS.
Storrs Sta. Bul. 188. 1933.

JUNGHERR, E. L.: OBSERVATIONS ON A SEVERE OUTBREAK OF MYCOSIS IN
CHICKS. Jour. Agr. Res., 46: 169–178. 1933.

PETTY, M. A., AND QUIGLEY, G. D.: THE MICROFLORA OF WHEAT FEEDS AS
RELATED TO THE INCIDENCE OF BLUE COMB IN CHICKENS. Poultry Sci., 26:
7–13. 1947.

RONK, S. E., AND CARRICK, C. W.: FEEDING MOLDY CORN TO YOUNG CHICK-
ENS. Poultry Sci., 10: 236–244. 1931.

THOMPSON, W. W., AND FABIAN, F. W.: MOLDS IN RESPIRATORY TRACT OF
CHICKENS. Jour. Amer. Vet. Med. Assoc., 80: 921–922. 1932.

Bacterial Diseases

CARPENTER, J. A., ANDERSON, G. W., JOHNSTON, R. A. AND GARRARD, E. H.:
PULLORUM DISEASE IN TURKEYS. Poultry Sci., 28: 270–275. 1949.

DEBLIECK, L.: THE PRESENT STANDPOINT ON CORYZA INFECTION. Proc. 8th
World's Poultry Cong., pp. 586–592. 1948.

DURRELL, W. B.: STUDIES ON PULLORUM DISEASE USING VARIOUS RAPID ANTIGENS. Canad. Jour. Compar. Med. and Vet. Sci., 10: 143–148. 1946.

EDWARDS, P. R., BRUNER, D. W., AND MORAN, ALICE: THE GENUS SALMONELLA: ITS OCCURRENCE AND DISTRIBUTION IN THE UNITED STATES. Ky. Sta. Bul. 525. 1948.

EMMEL, M. W., AND MEHRHOF, N. R.: PULLORUM DISEASE IN CHICKENS. Fla. Ext. Circ. 84. 1948.

FELDMAN, W. H.: Avian Tuberculosis Infection. The Williams & Wilkins Co., Baltimore. 1938.

GARLAND, F. W., WINTER, A. R., AND AMIET, E. R.: A COMPARISON OF METHODS OF TESTING TURKEYS FOR SALMONELLA PULLORUM INFECTION. Poultry Sci., 28: 63–68. 1949.

GARRARD, E. H., BURTON, W. H., AND CARPENTER, J. A.: NON-PULLORUM AGGLUTINATION REACTIONS. Proc. 8th World's Poultry Cong., pp. 626–631. 1948.

GODFREY, G. S., BUSS, R., AND WINTER, A. R.: FORMALIN FUMIGATION OF INCUBATORS BY THE CHEESECLOTH METHOD. Poultry Sci., 24: 417–422. 1945.

GRAHAM, R.: FOWL CHOLERA. Ill. Sta. Circ. 441. 1935.

HALL, W. J.: FOWL TYPHOID. U. S. D. A. Circ. 755. 1946.

HALL, W. J., MACDONALD, A. D., AND HENLEY, R. R.: USE OF THE RAPID WHOLE BLOOD TEST FOR PULLORUM DISEASE. U. S. D. A. Misc. Pub. 349. Revised, 1946.

HALL, W. J., MACDONALD, A. D., AND LEGENHAUSEN, D. H.: STUDIES ON FOWL TYPHOID. II. CONTROL OF THE DISEASE. Poultry Sci., 28: 789–801. 1949.

HAMILTON, C. M.: TREATMENT OF INFECTIOUS CORYZA IN CHICKENS WITH SULFATHIAZOLE. Jour. Amer. Vet. Med. Assoc., 103: 144–146. 1943.

HILBERT, K. F., AND KISER, J. S.: CHEMOTHERAPY OF DUCK DISEASES WITH SULFONAMIDES. Cornell Vet. 38: 148–155. 1948.

HOLTMAN, D. F., AND FISHER, GLADYS: THE APPLICATION OF SULFONAMIDES TO THE CONTROL OF TYPHOID IN POULTRY. Poultry Sci., 26: 478–488. 1947.

KISER, J. S., PRIER, J., BOTTORFF, C. A., AND GREENE, L. M.: TREATMENT OF EXPERIMENTAL AND NATURALLY OCCURRING FOWL CHOLERA WITH SULFAMETHAZINE. Poultry Sci., 27: 257–262. 1948.

MCNEIL, ETHEL, AND HINSHAW, W. R.: THE EFFECT OF STREPTOMYCIN ON PASTEURELLA MULTOCIDA IN VITRO, AND ON FOWL CHOLERA IN TURKEYS. Cornell Vet. 28: 239–246. 1948.

POMEROY, B. S., AND FENSTERMACHER, R.: SALMONELLA INFECTIONS IN TURKEYS. Amer. Jour. Vet. Res., 5282–288. 1944.

POULTRY COUNCIL OF THE STATE COLLEGE OF WASHINGTON. CORYZA OF CHICKENS AND SINUSITIS OF TURKEYS. Wash. Ext. Bul. 358. 1947.

ROBERTS, E., CARD, L. E., AND ALBERTS, J. O.: THE USE OF SULFONAMIDES IN THE CONTROL OF PULLORUM DISEASE. Poultry Sci., 27: 194–200. 1948.

WINTER, A. R., AND NADAL, REYNALDO: THE INFLUENCE OF SALMONELLA SPECIES ON THE WHOLE BLOOD PULLORUM TEST. Poultry Sci., 19: 143–146. 1940.

Virus Diseases

BEACH, J. R., QUORTRUP, E. R., ROSENWALD, A., ARMSTRONG, W. H., DELAY, P. D., JONES, E. E. ET AL.: RESULTS OF CONTROLLED FIELD TRIALS OF LIVE

VIRUS AVIAN PNEUMOENCEPHALITIS (NEW CASTLE) VACCINE IN CALIFORNIA. Special Rpt. Dept. Vet. Sci., Univ. Calif. and State Dept. of Agr. of Calif. 1949.

BRANDLY, C. A., GRAHAM, R., AND MICHAEL, V. M.: LEUKEMIA OF FOWLS. Ill. Sta. Circ. 467. 1937.

BRANDLY, C. A.: PROPAGATION OF FOWL- AND PIGEON-POX VIRUSES IN AVIAN EGGS AND USE OF EGG-CULTIVATED VIRUSES FOR IMMUNIZATION. Ill. Sta. Bul. 478. 1941.

CLANCY, C. F., COX, H. R., AND BOTTORFF, C. A.: LABORATORY EXPERIMENTS WITH LIVING NEWCASTLE DISEASE VACCINE. Poultry Sci., 28: 58–62. 1949.

COLE, R. K.: THE EGG AND AVIAN LEUCOSIS. Poultry Sci., 28: 31–44. 1949.

DELAPLANE, J. P.: THE DIFFERENTIATION OF THE RESPIRATORY DISEASES OF CHICKENS. R. I. Sta. Bul. 288. 1943.

DICKINSON, E. M.: FOWL POX IN DOMESTIC POULTRY. Ore. Sta. Bul. 411. 1942.

EMMEL, W. M.: THE ETIOLOGY OF FOWL PARALYSIS, LEUKEMIA, AND ALLIED CONDITIONS IN ANIMALS. Fla. Sta. Bul. 425. 1946.

HALL, W. J.: FOWL PARALYSIS. U. S. D. A. Circ. 628. 1942.

HOFSTAD, M. S.: A STUDY OF INFECTIOUS BRONCHITIS IN CHICKENS, I–III. Cornell Vet., 35: 22–31. 1945.

HUTT, F. B., AND COLE, R. K.: GENETIC CONTROL OF LYMPHOMATOSIS. Science 106: 379–384. 1947.

JOHNSON, E. P.: FOWL LEUCOSIS. Va. Sta. Tech. Bul. 76. 1941.

MOLGARD, P. C., AND CAVETT, J. W.: THE FEATHER FOLLICLE METHOD OF VACCINATING WITH FOWL LARYNGOTRACHEITIS VACCINE. Poultry Sci., 26: 563–572. 1946.

POULTRY COUNCIL OF THE STATE COLLEGE OF WASHINGTON. INFECTIOUS LARYNGOTRACHEITIS AND BRONCHITIS OF CHICKENS. Wash. Ext. Bul. 372. 1948.

WATERS, N. F.: BREEDING FOR RESISTANCE AND SUSCEPTIBILITY TO AVIAN LYMPHOMATOSIS. Poultry Sci., 24: 259–269. 1945.

WATERS, N. F., AND BYWATERS, J. H.: INFLUENCE OF AGE OF CHICKENS AT CONTACT EXPOSURE ON INCIDENCE OF LYMPHOMATOSIS. Poultry Sci., 28: 254–261. 1949.

Miscellaneous Diseases

CLAUDE, A., AND MURPHY, J. B.: TRANSMISSIBLE TUMORS OF THE FOWL. Physiol. Rev., 13: 245–275. 1933.

JUNGHERR, E., AND LEVINE, J. M.: THE PATHOLOGY OF SO-CALLED PULLET DISEASE. Amer. Jour. Vet. Res., 2: 261. 1941.

KNOWLTON, F. L.: CONGENITAL LOCO IN CHICKS. Ore. Sta. Bul. 253. 1939.

LUKE, D.: ROUND HEART DISEASE IN POULTRY. Proc. 8th World's Poultry Cong., pp. 692–696. 1948.

ROBERTSON, E. I., ANGSTROM, C. I., CLARK, H. C., AND SHIMM, M.: FIELD RESEARCH ON STUNTED CHICK DISEASE. Poultry Sci., 28: 14–18. 1949.

SCHALM, O. W.: SPECIAL TECHNIQUES FOR DUBBING AND CROPPING CHICKENS. Jour. Amer. Vet. Med. Assoc., 89: 713–716. 1936.

SCOTT, H. M., JUNGHERR, E., AND MATTERSON, L. D: POSSIBLE ROLE OF POTASSIUM IN PULLET DISEASE. Soc. Exp. Biol. and Med. Proc., 57: 7–10. 1944.

WALLER, E. F.: BLUE COMB DISEASE. N. H. Sta. Tech. Bul. 85. 1945.

CHAPTER 12 ||||||||||||||||||||||||||||||||||||||||||||||||||||||

Marketing Eggs

▼

Marketing Problems

Problems in marketing poultry products arise from (1) the location of these products with respect to consumption centers, (2) their seasonal distribution relative to the time of consumption, and (3) the maintenance of quality through the marketing channels while they are being held or transported. The difference between production and consumption centers gives rise to problems in transportation. Seasonal production without corresponding seasonal consumption necessitates cold storage with its problems. The physical and chemical nature of poultry and eggs with their consequent changes resulting in deterioration inaugurates a multiplicity of problems pertaining to the maintenance of quality in poultry and eggs.

Production and consumption centers. In a primitive or more self-sufficing agriculture, food products are consumed by those who produce them or by nearby consumers. In colonial times in America each family produced the eggs and poultry used in its fare, but as our national life became more complex diversified poultry raising became more specialized. Poultry followed the grain regions, particularly the Corn Belt, and thus the production centers for poultry and eggs shifted far west of the industrial cities where the great bulk of the surplus poultry and eggs is consumed. To visualize the relationship of poultry and human populations in the respective states, egg production per capita has been calculated and shown in Figure 164. Since the United States as a nation may be considered self-sufficient as to poultry and eggs, it may be assumed that the per capita production also represents the per capita consumption of eggs for the United States. From 1931 to 1936 about 370 chickens were required to produce the poultry and eggs consumed by 100 people living in the United States. If we may assume that consumption of poultry and eggs is about the same in all states, we may determine very readily those states which produce the surpluses and those states which require additional supplies. However, surplus-producing states probably have a somewhat higher per capita consumption of eggs and poultry than do deficit-producing states. Figure 164 shows that the surplus egg-producing areas center in the Middle West. The centers of consumption for eggs and poultry are located east of the production centers because the more populous areas

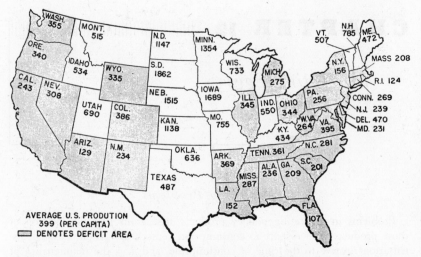

Fig. 164. Egg production per capita (1946).

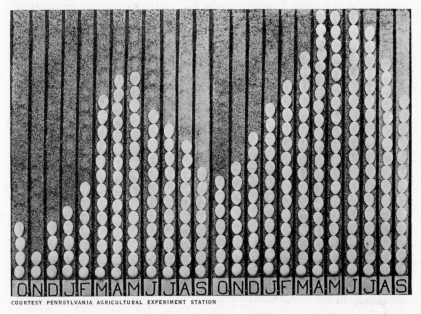

Fig. 165. Seasonal production of low- and high-producing hens.

are in the eastern part of the United States. There is considerable movement of eggs to and from states which produce sufficient quantities of eggs for their population. This movement is due to a lack of coördination in the marketing of eggs and also because the supply and demand for the different grades do not coincide.

MILLION CASES

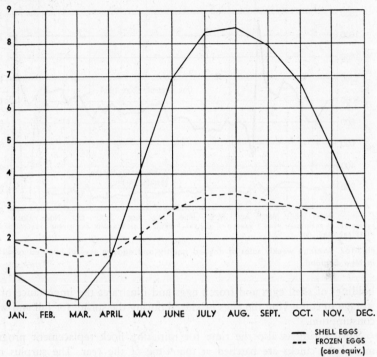

SHELL EGGS
FROZEN EGGS
(case equiv.)

Fig. 166. Seasonal variation in cold-storage holdings, 1929–1938. (Data from Agricultural Statistics, U. S. D. A.)

Seasonal distribution of production. The production of poultry and eggs in the United States is highly seasonal. Spring, the natural reproductive season for birds, is the time of the year when great surpluses of eggs are produced. While the wild fowl from which the domesticated chickens descended continue to produce only enough eggs during the spring to reproduce their species, the egg production of their domesticated relatives has been greatly modified by man. Figure 165 shows the seasonal production of eggs by hens of different productive abilities. As production has been increased, it has been extended over longer periods of the year. With genetically improved birds which receive the proper management and nutrition we may expect more eggs per bird and less seasonal variation in production. Commercial poultry raisers are smoothing out the production curve of their flocks by hatching chicks at different seasons of the year and by other management practices. Just how far and rapid this smoothing out process will go is problematical, but for the present and during the near future the great bulk of the eggs will continue to be produced during the spring months. Thus the problem of conserving eggs from periods of overproduction to periods of underproduction remains a major one. Figure 166 shows the cold-storage

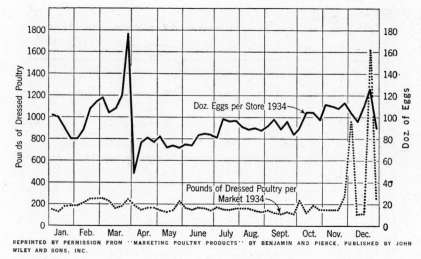

REPRINTED BY PERMISSION FROM ''MARKETING POULTRY PRODUCTS'' BY BENJAMIN AND PIERCE, PUBLISHED BY JOHN WILEY AND SONS, INC.

Fig. 167. Average weekly sales of dressed poultry and eggs in several hundred retail stores in New England.

holdings of shell eggs and frozen eggs and illustrates the importance of cold storage in conserving the eggs produced during the spring for fall and winter consumption.

Since spring is also the time for initiating flock replacement programs, most baby chicks are hatched at that time of the year. The surplus males and pullets which are raised reach the markets during the late summer and fall months. The culling of flocks, which is most generally done during the fall, adds its quota of poultry to the surplus accumulations of poultry meat at that season. The seasonal marketing of poultry is indicated by Figure 195, which shows the cold-storage holdings of poultry in the United States.

Consumption of poultry and eggs. If the consumption of poultry and eggs coincided in time with their seasonal production, the marketing services required for storing these products could be eliminated or reduced to a minimum. Consumption of these products, however, as illustrated by Figure 167, varies considerably throughout the year and these variations do not coincide with the seasonal variation in production. Certain products, such as turkeys and live poultry, have special holiday demands which cause the bulk of these products to be marketed for these occasions. The relation of the production and consumption of eggs throughout the year is shown by Figure 168.

The problem of quality. An ideal marketing system would give the most remote consumer eggs and poultry of the finest quality during all seasons of the year. Such an ideal may never be attained, but it should be the goal of marketing agencies. Eggs and market poultry are nonliving biological products subject to the natural laws of decomposition which cause deterioration in quality. That these products are never better than soon after their origin is generally admitted. The maintenance of quality of eggs and poultry is a

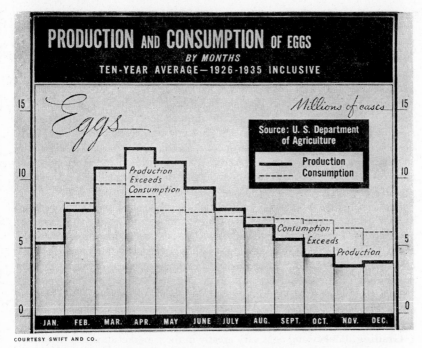

Fig. 168. The relation of production and consumption of eggs by months.

major problem in the industry. Since the production and consumption centers are widely separated, considerable time is required to transport these products to the retail markets. During such time quality of the products is being decreased to an extent depending upon the conditions under which they are being moved to market.

Surpluses, arising above consumption requirements at different seasons of the year, necessitate the storage of great quantities of poultry and eggs. The maintenance of quality over an extended period is an important storage problem. Since temperature and humidity are highly variable climatic conditions and are of the utmost importance in the maintenance of quality in poultry and eggs, these two factors must be controlled if suitable results are to be obtained. That the problem of quality in eggs and poultry is also one of breeding is recognized by the industry. Therefore, quality and its maintenance in poultry products is one of the important problems with which the industry will always be concerned. A satisfactory solution of this problem requires the co-operation of producers, marketing agencies, and consumers. Due to its complexity, neither an early nor perfect solution is anticipated.

Marketing Services

Before considering the marketing of poultry products, the economic basis of marketing should be understood. Marketing is the rendering of essential services such as assembling, processing, grading, packing, transporting, storing, financing, and distributing. The agencies providing these services may be private or co-operative and their methods may be direct, integrated, or regular, but the services are essential and cannot be eliminated.

Assembling. From more than 5 million farms come eggs and poultry, mostly in small quantities. These products, comprised of small units and marketed in small lots, make the problem of assembling an important one. The producer of a few dozen eggs each week cannot afford to send the eggs to the distant cities, but they must be shipped long distances to market if suitable prices are to be received. Someone must assemble these small quantities of eggs and poultry in car lots and ship them to market. By so doing, sufficient volume is obtained to reduce transportation and other operating costs. Assembling provides volume of the different qualities and makes grading possible.

Processing. By processing, the form of the unfinished product is changed to that of the finished product. This is an important service in marketing poultry. The farmer prefers to sell live chickens, while most consumers demand poultry prepared for cooking. Marketing agencies purchase the birds from the producers and prepare them to meet the consumers' demands. Fattening, killing, and dressing are the processing services required for poultry. Whole shell eggs, which represent the bulk of eggs marketed, do not require processing services. There is, however, an increasing demand for frozen egg products which require breaking and freezing.

Grading. Poultry and eggs vary greatly in their market qualities. Grouping these products according to their respective qualities constitutes grading. While grading is not used as extensively in the poultry industry as it should be, there is a growing demand for graded poultry and eggs. Grading is an economical procedure because it facilitates the sale of products on a quality basis and thereby stimulates the production of better quality products and encourages the maintenance of quality while the products are passing through the marketing channels. Graded products are more easily financed, traded in, and advertised than are ungraded products. The costs of marketing are reduced and demand is stimulated by the sale of graded products. The elimination of cull poultry and inedible and inferior eggs by careful grading at the point of origin would prevent products from being marketed which frequently do not pay transportation costs.

Packing. The poultry and egg packing industry renders distinct marketing services, including packaging these products in suitable containers under proper conditions so that they will retain their quality. Standard containers are thirty dozen cases for eggs, and boxes holding twelve dressed birds. By proper packaging, handling is facilitated, transportation and storing costs are reduced, shrinkage and spoilage are minimized, and the price of the product is increased.

Transporting. Transportation is a major problem in marketing poultry products because production areas are so far removed from the consumption centers. Improved transportation facilities reduce marketing costs and narrow the price margins between the producer and the consumer. The magnitude of the transportation problem is indicated by the fact that one state (Iowa) alone ships annually approximately two thousand carloads of eggs to New York City. In recent years the use of trucks, even on long hauls, has been increasing.

Storing. The highly seasonal nature of poultry and egg production makes storage a necessity. By storing these products from periods of overproduction so that they may be used when production is low, marketing operations and prices are stabilized and the supply of these commodities is better adjusted to consumer needs.

Financing. To provide the necessary marketing services, adequate financing is needed. Several million dollars each year must be invested in the eggs and poultry which are marketed and stored. Vast sums are invested also in the facilities required for marketing these products.

Distributing. The problem of moving several million cases of eggs and several hundred million pounds of poultry from more than 5 million farms to 150 million consumers is no small task. Some of the finest quality breakfast eggs have been delivered to consumers in New York City from poultry farms in California. The housewife in Boston may purchase a turkey for Thanksgiving which was raised by a Minnesota farmer. Agencies highly specialized in the marketing of such products maintain a constant flow of these commodities from producer to consumer.

Assuming risk. Egg and poultry prices often fluctuate greatly between the time these products are produced and the time they are consumed. Someone must assume the risks involved in price fluctuations as well as losses incurred from spoilage and the hazards of nature.

The Egg as an Article of Commerce

The egg, though designed by nature solely for reproductive purposes, has become one of the leading agricultural commodities in the world's markets. In the United States alone more than 100,000,000 cases of eggs are produced annually, and more than 20,000,000,000 eggs enter the channels of trade each year. New York City alone receives annually about 7,000,000 cases of eggs which, if shipped by rail, would require 17,500 freight cars for their transportation. Thousands of people are employed in transporting and handling eggs.

More than 7,000,000 cases of shell eggs and 100,000,000 pounds of frozen eggs are usually held in cold storage warehouses on August 1 each year. Millions of cubic feet of storage space are required for these products. Eggs are sold to millions of customers by thousands of retail stores throughout the nation. They provide an income to American farmers of nearly two billion dollars annually. This income represents purchasing power for innumerable quantities of other goods. The egg is therefore a very important article of commerce in the United States. This importance can be attributed to the fact that in preparing a self-contained reproductive unit, nature had to endow the egg with all the nutrients needed for developing a living organism. Man, not unlike other living organisms, has need for these same essential nutrients, and therefore eggs are important in the human diet. The importance of the egg in human nutrition may be more fully appreciated if the structure and composition of the egg are better understood.

Structure of the egg. The detailed structure of the egg and its formation are discussed in Chapter Three; therefore, at this point only the gross structure as related to the egg as a food product will be reviewed. The egg in the commercial channels of trade divides quite naturally into the following proportional major parts: shell (10), white (60), and yolk (30). In marketing, the shell becomes a waste product, the disposal of which represents a loss to the industry. However, it is an inexpensive container for egg meat. The white is made up of thick white, the outer thin white, and the inner thin white. The yolk is surrounded by and floats in the white of the egg. The structure of the egg is such that the shell can be removed with the loss of only a small amount of albumen, and the yolk can be readily separated from the white. The ease by which the parts of the egg can be separated makes possible the freezing and drying of yolk and albumen. The yolk of the egg is made up of many layers and contains the germ spot from which the chick embryo develops.

Composition of the egg. In the marketing of eggs the composition of the egg in its relation to human nutrition is important. The fact that the hen's egg contains many essential nutrients should interest those engaged in marketing eggs. They should stress in their sales work the importance of the egg in human nutrition. Eggs are rich in proteins, fats, and mineral elements (Table 1, Appendix). The vitamins required by humans which are found in eggs are vitamins A, B_1, D, riboflavin and B_{12}. Since the egg contains all of the nutrients except oxygen necessary to develop a perfect animal (the chick), its importance in the human diet would be indicated without reference to experimental data. There is, however, ample scientific evidence to show the importance of the egg in the human diet.

Judging Quality in Eggs

For many years eggs have been described as having good quality or poor quality, but only within recent years have investigators attempted to refine the methods used for determining egg quality. Candling has been the commercial method used and until recent years the only method available for judging the quality of shell eggs. Other tests of quality are chemical, biological, and bacteriological analysis, measurements of interior egg quality, and cooking tests.

Candling. Candling consists of the examination of shell eggs before a light strong enough to reveal the appearance of the contents of the egg. Experienced candlers, working with eggs which pass through the regular egg-marketing channels, can detect most of the inedible eggs, note the size of the air cell and thereby estimate the age of the egg, detect tremulous and movable air cells, observe any germ development on the yolk, estimate the condition of the white, and observe any imperfections in the shell. They can detect most meat spots, blood clots, and eggs having bloody albumen. From these observations they can group the eggs into commercial grades with a reasonable degree of accuracy.

The relation of average interior egg quality to the commercial grade arrived at by candling is shown in Table 79.

Table 79

THE RELATION OF THE COMMERCIAL GRADE OF FERTILE EGGS TO THEIR INTERIOR QUALITY. FEB.–MAY, 1942 [1]

	Grade A	Grade B	Grade C
Number of eggs measured...................	100	100	53
Albumen score........	2.33	2.76	4.02
Diameter of germinal disc...................	5.05	4.48	8.29
Percentage of apparent thick white.............	73.63	70.44	52.89
Yolk index................................	.38	.37	.22
Pressure per square centimeter required to rupture the vitelline membrane.	11.6	9.8	6.7

Measurements for interior egg quality. During recent years several investigators have developed methods for measuring the quality of eggs after they are broken out. These so-called measures of interior quality are used to determine the effects of different factors on the interior condition of the eggs as revealed after the egg is broken out. By using such methods the investigator can better determine the effect of different rations on the shell, yolk, or white. He can determine more accurately the results from exposing eggs to different environmental conditions, temperature effects, etc. A better understanding of the interior quality of eggs has led to the study of the factors which influence quality. The determinations of interior quality which are more commonly made are (1) the percentage of thick and thin white in the egg, (2) the yolk color, (3) the yolk index, (4) albumen index, and (5) the albumen score. Figure 169 shows the albumen scores which were developed at Cornell University for eggs of different quality.

Cooking tests. The real test for egg quality is the kind of product produced when the egg is prepared for human consumption. Other measures of quality are useless unless they are correlated with the edible qualities of the egg. Some institutions are using cooking tests for the determination of quality in eggs and poultry used in experiments or produced by feeding experiments. An egg with an albumen score of 1.0 is excellent as a breakfast egg, but a lower-quality egg may be equally as good for other uses. Certain feeds impart undesirable flavors to eggs and poultry meat. Cooking tests

---

[1] Mo. Sta. Res. Bul. 382.

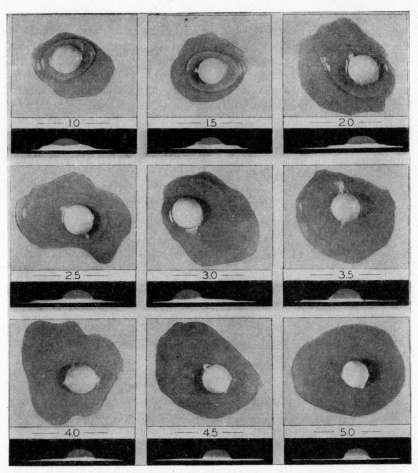

Fig. 169. Albumen scores prepared by Van Wagenen of Cornell University.

can be used for detecting such effects. The entire problem of quality in eggs is one which should be attacked from the viewpoint of the ultimate consumer, who should be guided by nutritive as well as aesthetic values.

Chemical, biological, and bacteriological tests. Chemical analyses for determining egg quality have not as yet been perfected so that they have practical application in the industry. Tests for free ammonia may be made to detect decomposed eggs; and pH values are used by investigators to determine such changes in eggs stored.

Biological assays for the determination of the vitamin content of eggs are being used. In such work, the products studied are fed to such laboratory animals as rats or chicks. Work in this field will likely be expanded as research in poultry products is developed.

The use of bacteriological analyses for studying quality in eggs and poultry is limited, as yet, primarily to research work. Producers of frozen and dried eggs are interested in the bacterial count of these eggs.

Factors Affecting Quality in Fresh-Laid Eggs

Since investigators have developed methods for measuring egg quality, research workers have devoted more attention to the factors which influence egg quality. They have found wide variations in quality and many factors which influence the quality of an egg.

Inheritance

An examination of fresh-laid eggs shows that they differ considerably in quality and if the eggs are traced to the individual hens that laid them, it will be found that they differ as to the quality of the eggs they produce. Table 80 shows some of the differences in quality of eggs laid by different hens. Hen 126 produced eggs with fine albumen and yolk quality and no meat or blood spots were found in an examination of her eggs. The eggs laid by hen 368 contained practically no thick white and every egg examined had from one to four meat spots. Hen 473 though she produced eggs having good albumen quality was undesirable because of the meat spots found in her eggs.

Table 80

THE QUALITY OF EGGS LAID BY DIFFERENT HENS
(Eggs cooled and examined within 24 hours after laying) [2]

Hen No.	Date	Weight (grams)	Albumen Quality				Yolk			Meat and Blood Spots
			Score	Height	Width	Index	Height	Width	Index	
126...	5–16–49	59.6	1.0	9.5	63.3	.150	20.6	44.5	.463	None
126...	5–19–49	59.2	1.0	9.8	70.5	.139	19.6	45.3	.432	None
126...	5–20–49	57.5	1.0	9.7	73.4	.132	20.3	44.2	.459	None
126...	5–21–49	61.4	1.0	8.5	76.0	.112	19.5	44.0	.443	None
126...	5–22–49	64.6	1.0	9.5	78.9	.120	19.6	45.7	.429	None
368...	5–15–49	62.5	4.5	3.8	120+	.032	16.4	43.8	.374	4 Large meat spots
368...	5–17–49	68.1	4.5	2.8	120+	.023	19.3	42.1	.458	1 Medium-size meat spot
368...	5–19–49	70.9	5.0	2.2	120+	.018	17.4	45.1	.386	1 Medium-size meat spot
368...	5–23–49	71.8	5.0	2.2	120+	.018	17.1	44.2	.387	3 Medium-size meat spots
368...	5–24–49	72.4	5.0	2.0	120+	.017	18.6	40.7	.457	2 Small meat spots
473...	5–23–49	58.4	1.5	7.3	75.8	.096	20.1	44.3	.454	2 Medium-size meat spots
473...	5–24–49	58.5	1.5	7.6	74.7	.101	20.4	44.8	.455	4 Small meat spots
473...	5–25–49	56.2	1.5	7.3	76.8	.095	20.8	43.5	.478	4 Small meat spots
473...	5–26–49	55.6	1.5	7.4	71.8	.103	20.2	44.8	.451	4 Small meat spots
473...	5–27–49	54.1	1.5	7.9	72.3	.109	19.9	42.9	.464	3 Small meat spots

It has been shown by the United States Department of Agriculture that the ability to produce eggs containing a high or low percentage of thick albumen as well as meat and blood spots is inherited and that the problem must be attacked by breeding.

[2] Unpublished data from the University of Missouri.

It has been established by the Beltsville Agricultural Research Center that shell quality and the ability of thick white to withstand high temperature are also inherited and therefore are breeding problems.

The Massachusetts Agricultural Experiment Station has reported that some hens tend to produce eggs with a "fishy" flavor. These birds may be detected by the odor (old silage) of their breath. Their results also indicate that this characteristic is inherited.

Therefore any fundamental progress in improving the original quality of fresh-laid eggs must be made by the poultry breeder.

Nutrition

The composition and quality of an egg are affected by the feed the hen consumes.

Yolk color. The color of the yolk of an egg is determined by the feed the hen eats. Layers receiving a ration containing a high percentage of green feed and yellow corn produce eggs containing yolks with more yellow color than do hens eating less of these feedstuffs.

Hens sometimes lay eggs containing olive-colored yolks. This condition is nutritional. Acorn meat or hulls will produce this condition. Some of the eggs laid by hens eating acorns contain yolks which are brown. The Kansas Station has reported that the feeding of molasses-oat-grass silage caused olive-colored yolks.

Cottonseed meal when fed at high levels to laying hens will cause an olive-colored yolk to develop after the shell egg has been stored for four weeks or longer. This condition does not develop in the frozen egg products. The agent in cottonseed meal which causes the olive-colored yolk is gossypol.

Cottonseed meal will also cause a reddish color to develop in the yolks of stored shell eggs.

Yolks can be made dark reddish-brown by feeding pimento peppers.

Albumen color. The color of the albumen may be affected by feeding. Hens receiving an abundance of riboflavin produce eggs containing albumen which shows a very light greenish cast.

Shell eggs stored for one month or longer sometimes contain pink whites. The California Agricultural Experiment Station has established that these pink whites may arise when the layers consume rations containing cottonseed meal, or the seeds of cheeseweed or hollyhock.

The eating of onions, rape, turnips, and cabbage has been reported to cause off-flavors and odors in eggs.

Shell quality. The quality of the shell is affected by the ration. Hens consuming rations deficient in calcium or vitamin D will lay eggs with thin shells.

Mineral content. Research workers have shown that the percentage of calcium, iodine, copper, iron, and manganese in eggs can be influenced by feeding.

Vitamin content. The vitamin content of eggs can be influenced by nutrition. The feeding of green feed, yellow corn, or cod liver oil will increase the vitamin A content of eggs. The feeding of the fish oils will also increase the vitamin D in eggs. The other vitamins required by poultry are deposited in the egg and the relative amount can be influenced by feeding.

Season

Eggs laid in the summer when the temperatures are high are smaller in size, have weaker shells, and generally contain less thick white than those laid during the preceding spring.

Disease

Outbreaks of Newcastle disease in laying flocks are followed by the production of misshapen eggs containing mostly watery whites and abnormal air cells (bubbly).

Maintaining Quality in Eggs

The maintenance of quality in shell eggs is one of the major marketing problems. Fresh-laid eggs are generally of good quality with the exception of meat and blood spots. Most of the loss in quality results from the effect of the environment in which the eggs are held.

Temperature. One of the biggest marketing problems is to maintain a suitable temperature where the eggs are held after they are laid and before they are consumed. High temperature probably causes more spoilage in eggs than any other factor. Fertile eggs when held at temperatures above 80° F. soon develop embryonically to a point where they are inedible. The rate of growth is shown in Chapter Six. Millions of dozens of eggs become total loss in the United States each summer because fertile eggs develop into inedible eggs.

High temperature causes a very rapid break down of the thick white into thin white. It also results in a flattening of the yolk (Figs. 169 and 170). The yolk index (height ÷ width) decreases very rapidly when eggs are held at 90° F. or 100° F. Such high temperatures also result in very weak yolk membranes.

From work done at the Missouri Agricultural Experiment Station the following conclusions may be drawn:

Temperature was found to be a very important factor affecting egg quality.

Thick albumen was converted to thin albumen very slowly at temperatures of 30° F. and 50° F. but quite rapidly at temperatures of 80° F. to 100° F. Liquefaction of the thick white proceeded at a more rapid rate in fertile than in infertile eggs if the temperature was high enough for rapid embryonic development.

Shell eggs held at 30° F. and 50° F. maintained relatively low albumen scores throughout the 70 days of the experiment but these scores went up very rapidly

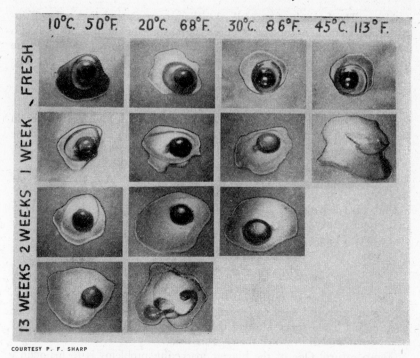

COURTESY P. F. SHARP

Fig. 170. Effect of temperature on changes in egg quality.

for eggs held at 70° F. to 100° F. and more rapidly in fertile than in infertile eggs.

The yolk of shell eggs held at 80° F. to 100° F. flattened very rapidly as compared to those held at 30° F. and 50° F. These data did not show any significant difference between fertile and infertile eggs. The vitelline membrane of the yolk retained its strength remarkably well at 30° F. and 50° F., but deteriorated quite rapidly at the higher temperatures, especially in fertile eggs.

The data obtained showed that macroscopically germ development in fertile eggs cannot be detected in shell eggs held at temperatures below 80° F. Discernible germ development occurred only after the temperature was raised to above 80° F. At 85° F. embryonic development proceeded very rapidly.

A very practical problem is to remove the animal heat from the egg as soon as possible after the egg is laid. The manner in which the egg is exposed while being cooled is an important factor affecting the rate of cooling. Figure 171 shows the rate at which eggs cool when exposed as individual eggs or in different containers. Eggs held in wire baskets cooled to 70° F. within 5 hours while 13 hours was required to cool eggs an equal amount if the eggs were cased before being cooled.

Humidity. Natural eggs held in a dry atmosphere lose moisture quite rapidly and soon develop large air cells. The size of the air cell is an important consideration in grading shell eggs because it indicates age and hold-

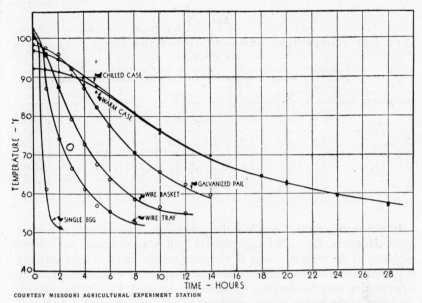

Fig. 171. Effect of container on the rate of cooling in eggs. (Egg room at 50° F.)

ing conditions. Eggs should therefore be held where the humidity is relatively high so that the air cell will remain small. A basement or cellar where the floor can be kept damp is a satisfactory place to hold eggs on the farm. Humidity has but little if any effect on the quality of the yolk or albumen. The effect on evaporation of both temperature and humidity is shown by Table 81.

Age of egg. The aging of an egg brings deterioration. Under ideal holding conditions changes in quality are very slow and eggs may possess excellent quality after several weeks or months but under adverse conditions they may become inedible within a few days.

Producers should hold their eggs under the most favorable conditions available and market them at least once each week. Marketing agencies should speed up delivery so that a minimum of time elapses between production and consumption.

Handling. Rough handling is detrimental to egg quality, resulting in tremulous and movable air cells as well as checked and cracked eggs. Eggs shipped long distances develop tremulous air cells. Eggs cased small end down develop fewer tremulous air cells than eggs placed in the cases with the large (air cell) end down.

The problem of soiled eggs. Million of dozens of soiled eggs enter the channels of trade each year. They constitute a major marketing problem. They should not be offered to consumers because they have a depressing effect on consumer demand for shell eggs. Fortunately most of them come into the markets during the spring when the egg-breaking plants can use them.

Table 81

EFFECT OF TEMPERATURE AND HUMIDITY ON THE DEPTH (MM) OF THE
AIR CELL [3]

Time Held in Days	Storage Temperatures and Percentage of Relative Humidity								
	60° F.			70° F.			80° F.		
	Per Cent 40–45	Per Cent 60–70	Per Cent 85–90	Per Cent 37–42	Per Cent 60–70	Per Cent 88–93	Per Cent 32–35	Per Cent 60–70	Per Cent 85–92
0	1.2	1.2	1.2	1.4	1.4	1.4	.9	.9	.9
1							2.2	2.1	1.5
3	3.3	2.5	2.3		2.6	2.0	3.2	2.5	2.0
7	3.3	2.9	2.2	4.1	3.3	2.8	4.7	3.8	2.9
14	4.8	4.1	1.0	5.7	4.7	2.7	7.0	5.3	3.3

Proper management can reduce the percentage of soiled eggs to a minimum. However, the soiled egg problem will always remain one of the problems of the industry. Some of the management practices most effective in preventing soiled eggs are: frequent gathering (3 or 4 times daily); using clean nesting material; keeping the house dry by using deep litter; confining the layers to the houses at least until most of the eggs have been laid; providing dropping pits so the birds cannot walk over the droppings; and providing sufficient nests and keeping them darkened.

Despite all the educational work done with producers the number of dirty eggs coming into the markets during the spring months is very discouraging. What can be done with them? Can they be cleaned so they will keep if they are marketed as current receipts or if they should go into storage? Work done at the Missouri Agricultural Experiment Station showed that dirty eggs passing through the regular channels of trade cleaned by washing or by dry cleaning did not keep well in storage unless they were thermostabilized (heated for 15 minutes in water held at 130° F.). Reports from producers indicate that soiled eggs cleaned, soon after gathering, by washing in warm water can be handled as current receipt eggs to the consumers without trouble.

The Missouri Station (1948) reported the results of ten years of investigations on the cleaning of soiled eggs for storage with the following conclusions:

1. Clean eggs keep unusually well in storage as far as spoilage is concerned.
2. Soiled eggs keep better than soiled eggs which have been washed in cold water or water below 100° F.
3. The results with disinfectants were erratic and show that surface cleaning with disinfecting agents does not effectively prevent spoilage in storage.
4. Shell eggs dry cleaned do not keep well in storage.
5. Flash pasteurizing does not protect eggs, that have been washed, against spoilage in storage.

---

[3] Mo. Agr. Exp. Sta. Res. Bul. 382.

6. The only method found to be effective in all cases in preventing spoilage in storage was thermostabilization, applied either during the process of washing or soon thereafter. This means complete immersion in water or oil for several minutes and does not refer to merely sprinkling or spraying warm water over eggs. The heat must penetrate the eggs in order to be effective.

Maintaining Egg Quality

The maintenance of egg quality is a major problem of the industry, particularly for those production areas most remote from their principal markets.

Quality egg programs. The Agricultural Extension Service and other agencies have carried on rather extensive educational campaigns designed to improve the quality of eggs produced. While these programs have accomplished much where the marketing agencies have provided suitable price differentials for the different grades of eggs, they have failed where eggs were not bought by grade. The Producers Produce Company, Springfield, Missouri, co-operating with the Missouri Agricultural Extension Service, has done much to improve the quality of eggs marketed in that territory. In their program they emphasized the following points:

1. Produce clean eggs.
2. Feed a complete ration all the time.
3. Produce infertile eggs after the hatching season.
4. Maintain the original quality of eggs.
   a. Gather eggs three times daily.
   b. Confine broody hens to coops.
   c. Keep eggs in a cellar, basement, or egg cooler.
   d. Maintain high humidity where eggs are held.
   e. Cool eggs before placing them in cases.
5. Pack and market eggs with care.
   a. Case eggs with small end down.
   b. Place top on case when full.
   c. Deliver eggs at least twice each week.
   d. Protect eggs against sun and rain.
   e. Handle carefully.
6. Breed for large egg size.

Cold storage. One of the greatest advances made by man has been in the storage of a food supply from the time of an abundant harvest to a period of scarcity. The development of cold storage has made possible the storage of such perishable foods as eggs and dressed poultry.

The use which is made of cold storage for the preservation of egg quality is shown in Figures 166, 172, 173, and 174.

Since half of the eggs produced in the United States annually are produced during the four months of March, April, May, and June, some form of storage is essential to consumers as well as producers. Storage makes possible a satisfactory market for eggs during the spring, when a great surplus of eggs occurs, and it also provides eggs for the consumers at reasonable prices during the fall and winter when fresh eggs are scarce. For best results, eggs should

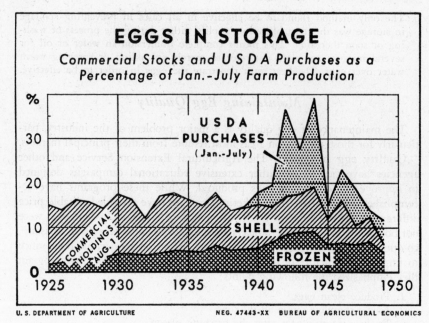

EGGS IN STORAGE

Commercial Stocks and U S D A Purchases as a
Percentage of Jan.-July Farm Production

U. S. DEPARTMENT OF AGRICULTURE   NEG. 47443-XX   BUREAU OF AGRICULTURAL ECONOMICS

Fig. 172. Storage holdings of eggs, 1925–1949.

be stored in cold-storage warehouses where the temperature is held at 29° F.
to 30° F. and the relative humidity is kept at 90 to 94 per cent. Eggs should
be stored alone as they absorb odors if stored in rooms with substances which
emit odors.

The estimated cost of storing shell eggs for six months in a cold storage
warehouse in Chicago in 1948 for eggs valued at 35 cents per dozen was:
storage and handling 60 cents per case, interest (5%) 26¼ cents, and insurance 1¼ cents, making a total of 87½ cents per 30-dozen case. There is
also the depreciation in quality which occurs during storage. This is a variable
cost which depends upon the quality of the eggs placed in storage and the
storage conditions maintained while the eggs are in storage.

Shell treatment of eggs. To prevent evaporation while eggs are held and
to reduce the gaseous exchange which naturally occurs when eggs are surrounded by air, the practice of treating the shells with an oil coating has
arisen (Fig. 175). Special oil-dipping machines have been designed to speed
up the process and therefore make it applicable to packing-plant conditions.
The oils used are lightweight petroleum oils which are tasteless, odorless, colorless, and suitable for human consumption. The eggs treated with these oils
retain their quality exceedingly well because very little evaporation occurs and
most of the carbon dioxide is retained in the egg and therefore the change in
pH is retarded.

Freezing eggs. The frozen-egg industry of the United States has developed
rapidly during the past twenty-five years. The relative growth of the industry

Fig. 173. Cold storage warehouse owned by the United States Cold Storage Company, Kansas City, Missouri.

in relation to shell eggs is shown in Figure 166. Yolks, whites, and mixed whole eggs are preserved by freezing and holding at low temperatures. Bakers, confectioners, and other commercial users of eggs prefer eggs which have already been broken and the yolks and whites separated. The demand for frozen eggs has continued to increase. Approximately a third of the eggs stored annually in the United States are now stored as frozen eggs.

The egg-breaking plants where eggs are frozen are located in the production areas where shell eggs are relatively cheap. They are usually operated as a part of the commercial egg-packing plants, though many specialized breaking and freezing plants are found in these areas.

A modern egg-breaking plant is operated under strictly sanitary conditions, and only high-quality eggs are placed in the cans. Figure 176 shows a modern egg-breaking plant in operation.

Drying eggs. Dried eggs have many uses: dried albumen is used by confectioners, dried yolk in prepared flours, dried whole egg in bakery products, and during the war millions of pounds of whole dried egg were used as food for the men and women in the military services and for feeding the peoples of Europe. The dried-egg industry was not technically prepared for the tremendous expansion which skyrocketed the annual production of dried eggs to over 320,000,000 pounds in 1944.

There are three methods used in drying eggs: the belt, spray, and pan drying. The egg spray driers are similar to milk driers. This method is used for producing dried yolk and dried whole egg. Pan drying is generally used for albumen, but the spray method is now also used for producing dried albumen.

The amount of dried-egg products produced by a case of average market eggs is nine to ten pounds of dried whole egg, or seven to seven and one-half pounds dried yolk and two to two and one-half pounds of dried albumen.

The dried-egg industry of the United States remained rather unimportant

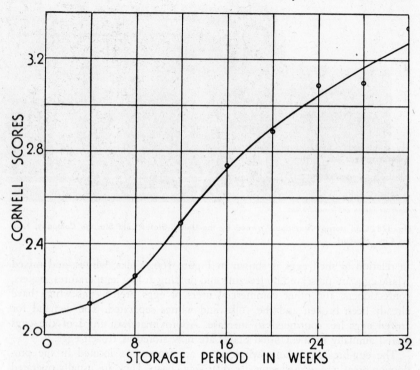

Fig. 174. Change in albumen score of eggs held in cold storage. See Figure 160 for albumen scores.

until the Japanese invasion of China in 1937. The Chinese source of dried eggs to this country was cut off, and the egg driers of the United States expanded their output to take care of the needs of this country, which was approximately 10,000,000 pounds annually. With the war there came a demand for tremendous quantities of dried whole egg and annual production expanded (Table 82). After the war there came the inevitable let down which most people expected, and while more dried eggs will, no doubt, be used than before the war, the amount will be only a fraction of what was produced in 1944.

Thermostabilization of quality in shell eggs. One of the problems confronting the poultry industry is the maintenance of the fresh-laid quality of shell eggs from the time of production until such eggs are consumed. The

Table 82

THOUSAND POUNDS OF DRIED EGGS PRODUCED IN THE UNITED STATES, 1940–48

1940............ 7,487	1943............261,972	1946............125,466
1941............ 45,280	1944............320,742	1947............ 85,561
1942............235,649	1945............105,863	1948 (10 mo.)...... 42,083

Fig. 175. *Right,* eggs may be dipped in a can of oil on the farm and allowed to drain.

Below, oil-dipping machines in use in an egg-packing plant.

COURTESY THE CAR-PRO CO.

Missouri Agricultural Experiment Station in 1943 announced a new process for maintaining egg quality, which was termed thermostabilization (stabilized by heat) by the conference which received the announcement. This process accomplishes the following important objectives in egg marketing: (1)

Fig. 176. Modern egg-breaking plant in operation.

Stabilizes the thick albumen so that the egg retains its fresh appearance much longer when broken out. (2) Devitalizes the fertile egg so that it reacts as an infertile egg. (3) Has a pasteurizing effect on shell eggs so that spoilage in storage is minimized.

The process is extremely simple and consists of immersing shell eggs for about 15 minutes in water held at 130° F. The beneficial results and the simplicity of the process would appear to make this process readily applicable in the industry.

Grading Eggs

Proposed government standards for eggs. The Production and Marketing Administration has proposed standards and grades for eggs. (Table 83). For a number of years a uniform grading system using government standards and grades for eggs has been advocated by the United States Department of Agriculture and other disinterested agencies. The industry has been slow to adopt these grades because the larger handlers of eggs have their own private trade names and grades which might be overshadowed by the government grades and therefore lose their advertising value.

Egg grades used in the industry. There is much confusion in the grading of eggs because there is little uniformity in the system of grading. All large packing organizations as well as retail organizations have their own grades, usually clothed in terms which without clarification give the consumer

Table 83

SUMMARY OF UNITED STATES STANDARDS FOR QUALITY OF INDIVIDUAL SHELL EGGS (1949–50)

Quality Factor	Specifications for Each Quality Factor			
	AA Quality	A Quality	B Quality	C Quality
Shell	Clean; unbroken; practically normal	Clean; unbroken; practically normal	Clean; unbroken; may be slightly abnormal	Clean; unbroken; may be abnormal
Air Cell	One-eighth inch or less in depth; practically regular	Two-eighths inch or less in depth; practically regular	Three-eighths inch or less in depth; may show movement not over three-eighths inch; if not over two-eighths inch may be free	May be over three-eighths inch in depth; may be free or bubbly
White	Clear; firm	Clear; may be reasonably firm	Clear; may be slightly weak	Clear; may be weak and watery; small blood clots or spots may be present
Yolk	Well centered; outline slightly defined; free from defects	May be fairly well centered; outline may be fairly well defined; practically free from defects	May be off-center; outline may be well defined; may be slightly enlarged and flattened; definite but not serious defects	May be off-center; outline may be plainly visible; may be enlarged and flattened; may show clearly visible germ development but no blood; may show other serious defects

but little if any idea of the quality of the eggs designated by the different grades.

A glance at the price quotation on eggs in the central markets shows that each market has a different set of grades. The adoption of a uniform system for grading eggs would be of great benefit to the industry. Slight modifications to fit local conditions may be necessary in a country as large and diverse in climatic conditions as the United States.

Market definitions. Benjamin and Pierce give the following definitions for market terms applied to eggs:

Fresh. Fresh eggs are those which have not been held or delayed in their movement to market so as to make it necessary to distinguish them as "refrigerator" in accordance with the definitions given below.

Hennery. Hennery eggs are so-called because they originate on farms where special attention is given to poultry. From such farms the eggs move to market with reasonable promptness.

Storage packed. Eggs are said to be "storage packed" when they have been packed especially for storage. The ordinary method for this packing is to sort out small, checked, and washed eggs, and to place the good ones in new cases and fillers of the kind prescribed by trade specifications.

Held. As generally understood by the trade, eggs are said to be "held" when they have been delayed in their movement to market sufficiently so that they are of distinctly lower quality than fresh (lower than U. S. Grade A), and have not been held under refrigeration long enough to be labeled "cold storage" or "refrigerator."

Current receipt. Unsorted lots including small, checked, and dirty eggs and rots, just as they are purchased from the farmer, are called "current receipts."

Rehandled current receipt. If the current receipts have been sorted, and those of poorest qualities removed, they are said to be rehandled current receipts. "Loose grading" or "slight grading" mean the same thing.

Rehandled and repacked current receipt. This term indicates that the eggs have been repacked in new or standard cases and fillers, in addition to the rehandling.

Graded. Eggs which have been sorted closely are referred to as graded eggs. The degree of sorting must be further explained in order to make the meaning sufficiently clear to a prospective buyer.

Undergrades. All qualities below the best are termed "undergrades." These may be checks, dirties, seconds, and the like.

Packing Eggs

The egg packer is one who operates an establishment in the surplus producing areas where eggs are received from farmers and affiliated dealers, candled, graded, cased according to grades, and sold to wholesale or other dealers in the central markets.

Containers used for eggs. The standard container for eggs is the thirty-

Fig. 177. Containers for marketing eggs. Upper left, frozen eggs (in foreground) being loaded in refrigerator car. (Courtesy Henderson Produce Company.) Upper right, egg cases made of wood and fiberboard for shipping eggs. Lower, egg cartons for retailing eggs.

dozen wooden case. Both fifteen-dozen and thirty-dozen fiberboard cases are being used but they have not as yet been adopted generally (Fig. 177). During recent years egg case liners have been introduced into the trade. These liners are made of two layers of heavy kraft paper between which there is a thin layer of asphalt. Such liners reduce evaporation and minimize the loss of carbon dioxide from the eggs and thereby help maintain the original quality of the eggs.

Fillers and flats for egg cases have been improved; less breakage occurs in transit now than formerly because better packing materials are available for packaging eggs. The cup flat or the embossed flat and the honeycomb filler make a firm pack. The filler-flat makes an even more rigid pack and reduces breakage and jarring. The plain flat and excelsior pads which were once universally used are gradually disappearing from the trade.

Eggs are retailed either in cartons or as loose eggs in paper bags. Egg cartons for twelve eggs or six eggs are becoming the standard container in the retail trade. Their convenience more than offsets their cost.

Many labor-saving devices for cartoning eggs are used. Special lifters (Fig. 175) may be used in transferring eggs from cases to cartons. Automatic machines for closing cartons and wrapping them in cellophane are sometimes used.

Transportation of Eggs

The great volume of eggs is shipped by rail in car lots. However, trucks now handle large quantities of eggs especially from production areas located within a few hundred miles of the central markets. A carload of eggs is about 400 standard thirty-dozen cases. It is estimated that in 1935, 11,000,000 cases of eggs were handled by railroads. Large quantities of frozen eggs are also shipped by rail. In warm weather eggs shipped long distances are kept under refrigeration. During cold weather the cars must be heated to prevent freezing of the eggs. Refrigerated trucks are being used for transporting eggs short distances where quality eggs are marketed.

Egg Prices

The price of eggs is determined by the supply of eggs of different qualities and the demand for such eggs. The price of eggs tends to move with the general price level. The price of eggs is also related to the price of feed, since feed cost represents the greater part of the cost of producing eggs. The purchasing power of eggs in terms of feed tends to move in normal times in a cycle of about three years' duration.

The price of eggs varies seasonally, with the peak prices being reached in October or November and the lowest prices being paid during the spring and summer months (Fig. 178).

Merchandising Eggs

The methods used in selling eggs are of vital concern to both the producer and the consumer. If inefficient methods add to the cost of selling eggs, the producer will receive less and the consumer probably pay more than they

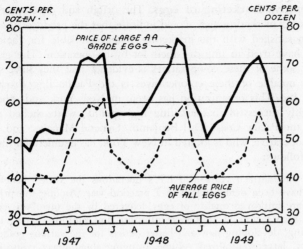

Fig. 178. Egg prices in Ohio: average all eggs and large AA grade at farm, 1947–49.

should for eggs. Eggs are marketed directly by the producer, by established private marketing agencies, and by co-operatives.

Direct marketing. While the total volume of eggs sold by the producer directly to the consumer is relatively small and very likely decreasing, to individuals who have a suitable location this method has proved to be a profitable way of selling eggs. As society has become more specialized in America and the consumers of the cities have lost contact with producers, specialized marketing agencies have arisen which can perform the services of marketing more efficiently and more economically than can the producer.

Regular egg-marketing system. The great volume of eggs marketed in the United States is handled by private marketing agencies. These eggs are usually delivered by the producers to local buyers or small stores where eggs are purchased. The eggs bought by the stores are sold to local buyers who are affiliated with a concentration or packing plant. The eggs are generally picked up at the buying stations by trucks which are operated by the packing plants. In the packing plants the eggs are candled, graded, cased, cooled, and shipped by truck or rail to the wholesalers located in the large consuming centers. The packing plant may be owned by or affiliated with the wholesale organization which handles the sales to jobbers and retailers. Briefly this is the route taken by most eggs marketed in the United States. Car-lot packers of eggs and poultry are located primarily in the Middle West, where large surpluses of eggs are produced. In 1939, Iowa had 118 of these plants, Missouri 77, and Illinois 50. Production areas near the consuming centers and deficit egg-producing areas do not have these car-lot shippers of eggs and poultry.

Private marketing agencies have been responsive to the needs of the industry and have been, on the whole, progressive—because the industry is competitive.

Co-operative marketing of eggs. The origin and development of co-operatives for marketing eggs would indicate that the producers have not always been satisfied with the marketing system available for their use and that they have tried to improve their lot by co-operation. The growth and success of some of these co-operatives is evidence that they have succeeded. The most notable of these co-operatives is the Pacific Egg Producers Co-operative, Inc. This organization has been, in New York and other eastern cities, highly successful in marketing high-quality, white-shelled eggs produced on the Pacific Coast. Earl Benjamin, General Manager and Treasurer of this co-operative, who is located in New York, has enumerated their attainments as follows:

During the fourteen years of P.E.P.'s operations the varied benefits of co-operation have been demonstrated in a practical way. Among the principal attainments are improved quality of eggs delivered by the members, particularly as regards such factors as freshness, infertility and uniform flavor; more uniform grading; developing new and better outlets for the various grades of eggs and poultry; larger centralized volume, bringing about lower costs; economies in shipping due to heavier loading; improved packages; new methods of handling eggs and poultry such as "protecting," sand-cleaning, and packing in lined cases or boxes; careful studying of conditions to determine the proper price level for the product (use is made of an auction at certain seasons, to aid in determining the correct price level); and continuance of technical and economic research in order to bring about a constant improvement of methods.

From this list of achievements it is evident that the co-operative has been progressive and has pioneered in improving egg marketing. Unless the co-operatives can render such economic services, their existence cannot be justified.

The Missouri Farmers Association, a more general type of co-operative which originated in a general farming region, has developed into one of the largest handlers of eggs and poultry in the United States. At Springfield, Missouri, they maintain one of the largest and most modern poultry- and egg-packing plants in the world. This co-operative organization handles feed, fertilizers, groceries, and other commodities through their local exchanges.

More than twenty co-operative egg auctions have been established in the East. These auctions have provided an outlet for high-quality eggs from relatively large producers and a source of good eggs for dealers and retailers located in the nearby cities. The auctions provide a trading place for producers and dealers at a minimum cost. Those auctions which have been most successful have been located in commercialized producing areas and near large consuming centers.

The farmers of some districts in Indiana have developed the co-operative shipping of eggs. Each producer maintains the identity of his eggs and sells to his preferred outlet in New York City. By shipping jointly, these producers have been able to make appreciable savings on transportation costs.

Consumer preferences and demands for eggs. Since egg prices are determined by the demand for and the supply of eggs of the different grades, it behooves the producers to know the consumers' demands for eggs and their buying habits. The producer must also know the demands of the dealers through whom they reach the consumer.

Several interesting studies of consumer preferences for eggs have been made. It should be noted that a preference expresses merely a desire, but it is not a demand since demand is a preference plus a purchase at a price. The poultry industry needs scientific demand studies which will measure the demand for various grades of eggs and poultry under different environmental and competitive conditions. The buying habits of consumers also need to be more fully understood by producers and marketing agencies.

The consumer preference studies which have been made indicate that in some cities consumers prefer eggs with white shells and in others they prefer brown-shelled eggs. These preferences are based upon the belief that shell color and interior quality are related. Consumers in the principal markets are about equally divided as to their preference for yolk color. It is doubtful if the consumers would pay any appreciable amount more for eggs with either white or brown shells merely because of shell color, or for eggs with yolks of different shades of yellow as long as the egg yolks appear edible and uniform in color. Since the dealers reflect the demand of the consumers to the producers it is necessary for the producers to cater to the dealer demand. This demand reflects not only the total demand for eggs of different qualities but it reflects a protective demand against any eggs which may cause complaints. The idea has developed in some markets that eggs which have light yellow-colored yolks are preferred to those which have dark-colored yolks. If the dealers can avoid complaints by supplying eggs with yolks which do not arouse suspicion, though the suspicion be based on erroneous assumptions, they will quite naturally do so. A dissatisfied customer can arouse more dealer demand than one hundred satisfied customers.

Creating new demands for eggs. If the per capita production of poultry and eggs in the United States continues to increase, one of the future problems of the poultry industry will be the stimulation of a greater demand for eggs and poultry. Before much can be accomplished along this line, research work will be needed for determining the demand by the various income groups for the different grades of these products. The amount of money spent for poultry and eggs varies with the family income, as shown by Figure 179.

That there are untapped markets for eggs in the United States among the lower income groups is indicated by the response of consumers in these groups to the Food Stamp Plan of the Federal Surplus Commodities Corporation. Table 84 gives the uses to which these consumers applied their increased income in the purchase of surplus commodities. These preliminary studies indicated that of the surplus commodities available in Rochester, Dayton, Seattle, and Shawnee, from May 16 to August 26, 1939, eggs and butter were the two commodities in greatest demand, approximately 50 per cent of the food stamps being used to purchase these products.

A well-established grading system probably would stimulate the demand for eggs. The adoption of a uniform grading system throughout the United

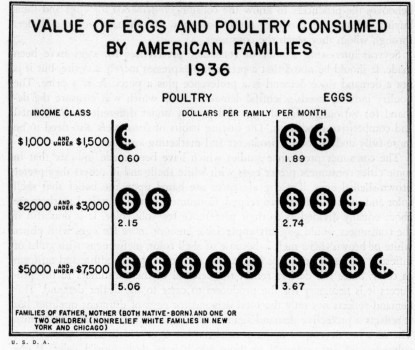

VALUE OF EGGS AND POULTRY CONSUMED BY AMERICAN FAMILIES 1936

POULTRY   EGGS

INCOME CLASS   DOLLARS PER FAMILY PER MONTH

$1,000 AND UNDER $1,500   0.60   1.89

$2,000 AND UNDER $3,000   2.15   2.74

$5,000 AND UNDER $7,500   5.06   3.67

FAMILIES OF FATHER, MOTHER (BOTH NATIVE-BORN) AND ONE OR TWO CHILDREN (NONRELIEF WHITE FAMILIES IN NEW YORK AND CHICAGO)

U. S. D. A.

Fig. 179. The relation of income to the value of poultry and eggs purchased by American consumers (1936).

States would educate the consumers to the qualities of the different grades and give them confidence in their purchases. The removal of uncertainty in egg quality should stimulate the demand for eggs. Making available to the consumers eggs of various grades with proper price differentials would provide eggs for the various income groups at prices which they could afford to pay. (Fig. 180.) To offer consumers eggs at only the highest prevailing prices will eliminate many purchasers and therefore reduce the consumption of eggs. The adoption of a uniform grading system with suitable price differentials would no doubt be helpful in increasing the total demand for eggs.

International Egg Trade

The exchange of eggs and egg products between the various nations is quite general, as is indicated by the fact that importing nations such as Germany and Great Britain in normal years each import eggs from more than thirty different nations. The exports from the United States have been primarily shell eggs shipped to Mexico and the other Latin American countries. They have never reached 1.5 per cent of our total production in normal times. The egg imports received in the United States have been principally dried- and frozen-egg products from China. They have never reached 2 per cent of our

Fig. 180. Eggs attractively displayed in a refrigerated case.

total production. The disruption of trade in China since 1937 by the war has greatly reduced the production and exportation of such products. The American dried- and frozen-egg industries have benefited by the decrease in imports of these products and the dried-egg industry has been reëstablished in the United States.

Table 84

COMMODITIES PURCHASED WITH BLUE STAMPS ISSUED
BY THE FEDERAL SURPLUS COMMODITIES CORPORATION,
MAY 16 TO AUGUST 26, 1939

Commodity	Percentage of Total Purchases
Eggs	24.7
Butter	23.4
Flour	10.1
Corn meal	2.2
Rice	2.4
Dry beans	3.8
Dried prunes	2.2
Fresh fruits	12.0
Fresh vegetables	19.2
	100.0

There has been considerable agitation by producers and distributors in the United States for more adequate protection against the importation of shell eggs and egg products, particularly when egg prices in this country are high enough so that the importers can pay the import tax.

The United States tariff rates on eggs made effective in 1948: shell eggs, five cents per dozen; frozen eggs, seven cents per pound; and dried eggs, 17 cents per pound.

The total imports of eggs into the United States are usually less than two per cent of the total production of this country. This volume, added to surpluses which sometimes exist, no doubt exerts a depressing effect on prices of the domestic products, although no greater than an expansion of the domestic production by an equivalent amount.

Industrial Uses for Eggs

In recent years the term "chemurgy" has appeared in the discussion of the farm problem, particularly as related to surpluses of farm products. This term applies to the science of developing industrial uses for agricultural products and thereby reducing surpluses by diverting some of these products from human food uses to industrial uses. There are certain industrial uses for eggs and egg products which are receiving increasing attention. (See Chapter One.)

Recently, considerable progress has been made in the use of fertile eggs for preparing vaccines. The virus which causes sleeping sickness in horses is now grown almost exclusively on live chick embryos and vaccines developed in this manner are very effectively preventing this disease.

It has been demonstrated that the virus for fowl pox and also for laryngotracheitis can be grown on chick embryos and effective vaccines for these diseases can be developed by this method. It is highly probable that the egg, because of economic and sanitary advantages, will become important in the development of immunizing agents for the diseases of humans as well as farm animals. Already millions of eggs are being used in this new field.

There is also experimental evidence that the egg may become an important agent for the study of disease, serving as a medium in which disease organisms may be grown and studied.

REVIEW QUESTIONS

1. Where are the surplus egg-producing areas of the United States located?
2. Show graphically the seasonal marketing of eggs and poultry.
3. Name the essential marketing services in marketing eggs and poultry.
4. Name the methods used in determining egg quality.
5. Can the color of egg yolks be controlled?
6. Explain how the vitamin content of eggs may be influenced.
7. What is the origin of "meat spots" in eggs?
8. List in the order of importance the environmental factors which affect egg quality during the summer months; the fall months.

9. List the essentials of a county or state quality egg program.
10. How should soiled shell eggs be marketed?
11. What effect does shell treatment have on the pH of the shell egg?
12. Why are eggs broken and frozen?
13. Is the dried-egg industry of the United States now increasing or decreasing? Why?
14. Name the U. S. D. A. egg grades. Describe each.
15. Show graphically the seasonal variation in egg prices.
16. Where have egg auctions developed? Why?
17. How does an increase in consumer income affect the consumption of eggs?
18. What effect would a uniform grading system for eggs have on egg consumption?
19. Discuss the international egg trade of the United States.
20. What are some of the more important industrial uses for eggs?

REFERENCES

BENJAMIN, E. W., PIERCE, H. C., AND TERMOHLEN, W. D.: Marketing Poultry Products, 4th ed. John Wiley & Sons, Inc., New York. 1949.

BIRD, H. R.: NUTRITIVE VALUE OF EGGS AND POULTRY MEAT. U. S. Egg and Poultry Mag., 49: 402, 419, 427, 458, 477. 1943.

BOTSFORD, H. E.: HANDLING EGGS FOR MARKET. Cornell Sta. Bul. 416. Revised, 1943.

BUMZAKNOV, A. D.: THE DEHYDRATION OF EGG PRODUCTS. U. S. Egg and Poultry Mag., 50. Spec. Reprint. 1944.

BUSTER, M. W., AND HAMMANN, H. G. F.: UNIFORM LABELS FOR CONSUMER GRADES OF EGGS. U. S. D. A. Misc. Pub. 560. 1945.

CARD, L. E., AND NALBANDOV, A. V.: A STUDY OF INTERIOR EGG QUALITY IN TWENTY MIDWESTERN FLOCKS. Poultry Sci., 26: 219–220. 1947.

CHARKEY, L. W., DYAR, ELIZABETH, AND WILGUS, H. S.: THE NUTRIENT CONTENT OF HIGH- AND LOW-QUALITY FRESH EGGS. Poultry Sci., 26: 626–631. 1947.

CONRAD, R. M., VAIL, GLADYS, OLSEN, A. L., TINKLIN, GWENDOLIN, GREENE, J. W., AND WAGONER, C.: IMPROVED DRIED WHOLE EGG PRODUCTS. Kan. Sta. Tech. Bul. 64. 1948.

DAVIDSON, J. A.: SHELL TREATING AND MAINTENANCE OF EGG QUALITY IN STORAGE. Mich. Sta. Quart. Bul. 29: 208. 1948.

EVANS, R. J., BUTTS, HELEN, DAVIDSON, J. A., AND BANDEMER, SELMA: THE AMINO ACID CONTENT OF FRESH AND STORED SHELL EGGS. Poultry Sci., 28: 691–696. 1949.

FUNK, E. M.: STABILIZING QUALITY IN SHELL EGGS. Mo. Sta. Res. Bul. 362. 1943.

FUNK, E. M.: PASTEURIZATION OF SHELL EGGS. Mo. Sta. Res. Bul. 364. 1943.

FUNK, E. M.: EFFECTS OF TEMPERATURE AND HUMIDITY ON THE KEEPING QUALITY OF EGGS. Mo. Res. Bul. 382. 1944.

FUNK, E. M.: EXPERIMENTS IN CLEANING SOILED EGGS FOR STORAGE. Mo. Sta. Res. Bul. 426. 1948.

GIBBONS, N. E., MICHAEL, RUTH, AND IRISH, URSULA: PRESERVATION OF EGGS. VI. EFFECT OF VARIOUS OILS AND OILING TEMPERATURES ON THE KEEPING QUALITY OF SHELL EGGS STORED AT 70° F. AND 30° F. Canad. Jour. Res. 25F. 141–148. 1947.

GROSS, C. R., HALL, G. O., AND SMOCK, R. M.: ODOR SOURCE IN EGG STORAGE AND METHOD OF REMOVAL. Food Ind. 19: 919–921. 1947.

HAINES, R. B.: MICROBIOLOGY IN THE PRESERVATION OF THE HEN'S EGG. Dept. Sci. Ind. Res. Food Inves. Spec. Rpt. 47. Cambridge. London, Eng. 1939.

HUDSON, R. A.: WHAT COMMERCIAL USERS EXPECT OF DRIED EGGS. U. S. Egg and Poultry Mag., 55. No. 3, 14–15, 26. 1949.

JACKSON, M. E., AND SEATON, M. A.: PRODUCING AND MARKETING QUALITY EGGS IN KANSAS. Kan. Ext. Circ. 196. 1949.

JOHNDREW, O. F.: REDUCING DAMAGE TO EGGS AND EGG CASES. U. S. D. A. Misc. Pub. 564. 1945.

JOHNS, C. K., AND BERARD, H. L.: EFFECT OF CERTAIN METHODS OF HANDLING UPON THE BACTERIAL CONTENT OF DIRTY EGGS. Sci. Agr. 26: 11–15. 1946.

JOHNSON, A. S., AND CAVERS, J. R.: A SURVEY OF FARM EGG QUALITY. Sci. Agr. 28: 533–544. 1948.

JOHNSON, E. O.: EGG HANDLING COST ANALYSIS BY LARGE MIDWESTERN PLANT. Am. Egg. and Poultry Rev. 10, No. 2: 83–84. 1949.

KALOYEREAS, S.: FREEZING EGGS IN THE SHELL. Am. Egg and Poultry Rev. 10, No. 3: 26, 28. 1949.

KINGHORNE, J. W.: MARKETING EGGS. U. S. D. A. Farmers' Bul. 1378. Revised, 1947.

LEPPER, H. A., BARTRAN, M. T., AND HELLIG, F.: DETECTION OF DECOMPOSITION IN LIQUID, FROZEN, AND DRIED EGGS. Jour. Assoc. Offic. Agr. Chem. 27: 204–223. 1944.

LINEWEAVER, H., MORRIS, H. J., KLINE, LEO AND BEAN, R. S.: ENZYMES OF FRESH HEN EGGS. Arch. Biochem. 16: 443–472. 1948.

LORENZ, F. W.: THE APPLICATION OF MECHANICAL REFRIGERATION TO RANCH EGG COOLING. Agr. Eng. 27, No. 2: 69–73. 1946.

LORENZ, F. W.: ON THE EFFICIENCY OF EGG PROCESSING OILS. Poultry Sci., 28: 119–127. 1949.

MAYFIELD, H. L., AND HALBROOK, E. R.: MEASUREMENT OF YOLK COLOR BY MEANS OF THE COLORIMETER. Poultry Sci., 28: 462–463. 1949.

MCFARLANE, V. H., WATSON, ALICE, AND GORESLINE, H. E.: MICROBIOLOGICAL CONTROL IN THE PRODUCTION OF SPRAY-DRIED WHOLE EGG POWDER. U. S. Egg and Poultry Mag., 51: 250–257, 270–286. 1945.

MILLER, CORA, AND WINTER, A. R.: FUNCTIONAL PROPERITIES AND BACTERIAL CONTENT OF FROZEN AND PASTEURIZED WHOLE EGG AND YOLK. Poultry Sci., 29: 88–97. 1950.

MURPHY, W., AND SUTTON, W. S.: THE PASTEURIZATION OF SHELL EGGS TO PREVENT STORAGE ROT AND MAINTAIN QUALITY. Agri. Gazette of N. S. Wales, Misc. Pub. 3317. 1947.

NALBANDOV, A. V., AND CARD, L. E.: THE PROBLEM OF BLOOD AND MEAT SPOTS IN EGGS. Poultry Sci., 26: 400–409. 1947.

NORTON, L. J., HATHORN, S., AND BROADBENT, E.: GRADING WILL IMPROVE THE MARKET FOR ILLINOIS EGGS. Ill. Sta. Circ. 631. 1948.

PEARCE, J. A., REID, M., METCALFE, B., AND TESSIER, H.: DRIED WHOLE EGG POWDER XX. THE EFFECT OF GRADE OF EGGS, LOCALITY AND MONTH OF PRODUCTION, AND CLIMATIC CONDITIONS ON THE SOLIDS CONTENT OF LIQUID EGG AND ON THE QUALITY OF THE POWDER PRODUCED. Canad. Jour. Res. 24F: 215–223. 1946.

PEARCE, J. A., AND LAVERS, C. G.: LIQUID AND FROZEN EGGS. V. VISCOSITY, BAKING QUALITY, AND OTHER MEASUREMENTS IN FROZEN-EGG PRODUCTS. Canad. Jour. Res. 27F: 231–240. 1949.

PENNISTON, VIRGINIA A., AND HEDRICK, L. R.: THE REDUCTION OF BACTE-RIAL COUNT IN EGG PULP BY THE USE OF GERMICIDES IN WASHING DIRTY EGGS. Food Tech. 1: 240–244. 1947.

POULTRY COUNCIL OF THE STATE COLLEGE OF WASHINGTON: EGGS AND THEIR CARE. Wash. Ext. Bul. 358. 1949.

ROBERTS, J. B.: MARKETING AND PRICING EGGS IN KENTUCKY. Ky. Sta. Bul. 441. 1943.

ROMANOFF, A. L., AND ROMANOFF, A. J.: The Avian Egg. John Wiley & Sons, Inc., New York, 1949.

SCHNEITER, R., BARTRAM, M. R., AND LEPPER, H. A.: BACTERIOLOGICAL AND CHEMICAL CHANGES OCCURRING IN FROZEN EGGS. Jour. Assoc. Offic. Agr. Chem., 26: 172–182. 1943.

SHARP, P. F., STEWART, G. F., AND HUTTAR, J. C.: EFFECT OF PACKING MA-TERIALS ON THE FLAVOR OF STORAGE EGGS. Cornell Univ. Memoir 189. 1936.

SLOSBERG, H. M., HANSON, HELEN, STEWART, G. F., AND LOWE, BELLE: FACTORS INFLUENCING THE EFFECTS OF HEAT TREATMENT ON THE LEAV-ENING POWER OF EGG WHITE. Poultry Sci., 27: 294–301. 1948.

SNYDER, E. S.: EGGS, THE PRODUCTION, IDENTIFICATION, AND RETENTION OF QUALITY IN EGGS. Ontario Col. of Agr. and Ontario Dept. of Agr. Bul. 446. 1945.

STEWART, G. F., AND BOSE, S.: FACTORS INFLUENCING THE EFFICIENCY OF SOLVENT OIL MIXTURES IN THE PRESERVATION OF SHELL EGGS. Poultry Sci., 27: 270–276. 1948.

STEWART, G. F.: HEAT TREATING LIQUID EGG. U. S. Egg and Poultry Mag., 55, No. 6: 10–13, 30. 1949.

UNITED STATES DEPARTMENT OF AGRICULTURE POULTRY AND EGG SPECIAL-ISTS. EGGS AND EGG PRODUCTS. U. S. D. A. Circ. 583. 1941.

UPP, C. W., HATHAWAY, H. E., BARR, H. T., AND KRAMER, H.: EGG COOLERS FOR THE FARM. La. Sta. Circ. 32. 1943.

VAN WAGENEN, A.: CHANGES IN SEASONAL VARIATION OF THE WHOLESALE PRICE OF EGGS IN NEW YORK CITY. Cornell Sta. Bul. 808. 1944.

VONDELL, J. J., AND PUTNAM, J. N.: THE EFFECT OF CERTAIN FEEDSTUFFS ON THE FLAVOR, ALBUMEN CONDITION, AND YOLK COLOR OF EGGS. Poultry Sci., 24: 284–287. 1945.

WILKIN, MARIAN, AND WINTER, A. R.: PASTEURIZATION OF EGG YOLK AND WHITE. Poultry Sci., 26: 136–142. 1947.

WILLIAMS, I. L., AND MUSSEHL, F. E.: THE NEBRASKA EGG COOLER. Neb. Sta. Circ. 82. 1946.

WINNER, E. B., AND CLIZER, N. R.: PRODUCING AND MARKETING QUALITY EGGS. Mo. Ext. Circ. 544. 1947.

WINTER, A. R.: BLACK ROT IN FRESH SHELL EGGS. U. S. Egg and Poultry Mag., 48: 506–509, 520. 1942.

WINTER, A. R., AND COTTERILL, O. J.: THE PRESERVATION OF SHELL EGG QUALITY BY OIL DIPPING RIGHT ON THE FARM. Am. Egg and Poultry Rev. 10, No. 3: 14–16. 1949.

WINTER, A. R., AND WRINKLE, CAROLYN: THE CONTROL OF BACTERIA IN

FROZEN-EGG PRODUCTS. U. S. Egg and Poultry Mag., 55: No. 1, 7–9, 18–19; No. 2, 20–24, 30; No. 3, 28–31, 44. 1949.

YUSHOK, W. D., AND ROMANOFF, A. L.: STUDIES ON PRESERVATION OF SHELL EGGS BY COATING WITH PLASTICS. Food Res. 14: 113–122. 1949.

ZAGAEVSKY, J. S., AND LUTIHOVA, R. O.: SANITARY MEASURES IN THE EGG-BREAKING PLANT. U. S. Egg and Poultry Mag., 50: 17–20, 43–46, 75–77, 88–90, 121–123. 1944.

CHAPTER 13 |||||||||||||||||||||||||||||||||||||||||||||||||||

Marketing Poultry

▼

The marketing of poultry in suitable forms for satisfying all market requirements is a major problem and one which is of vital concern to the producer as well as to the consumer. Great strides have been made in developing a suitable system for marketing poultry in the United States. No other nation has made such rapid progress in this field. The development of special railroad cars and motor trucks has revolutionized the shipping of live poultry. The establishment of large packing plants in the Middle West, where millions of pounds of dressed poultry are prepared, is peculiar to the poultry industry of the United States. The use of machinery in the killing and dressing of poultry has reduced not only the labor involved but has improved the quality of the poultry packed. Modern refrigeration is essential to the marketing of high-quality poultry, and millions of dollars have been invested in refrigeration equipment and cold-storage warehouses for preserving the quality of dressed poultry.

Inefficient marketing methods may penalize the producer with lower prices and the consumer with an inferior product. The development of better methods of marketing will benefit both producer and consumer. Reluctance on the part of marketing agencies to adopt improved methods may initiate producer or consumer coöperatives. The marketing agencies of the future will be those that render the marketing services in the most efficient manner and at the least cost for the services given.

Live Poultry

Producers prefer to sell live poultry because they are neither trained nor equipped to do the dressing. Therefore the killing and dressing are done usually after poultry leaves the farm. Since there are special demands for live poultry in the cities, large quantities of such poultry are transported from the eastern and middle western states to these markets (Fig. 181).

Seasonal production. Most of the poultry meat produced is the by-product of egg production, coming from the cockerels which were the hatch mates of pullets intended for layers and also from the discarded layers. Since most chicks are started in the spring and mature in the fall and most culling of laying flocks is done in the fall, receipts of poultry are greatest during the fall

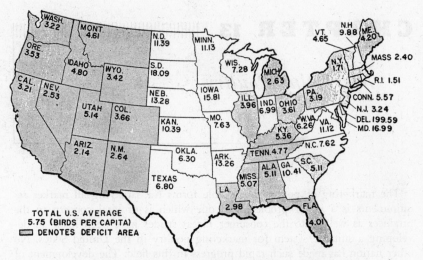

Fig. 181. Per capita production of chickens, 1946.

months. Turkeys also increase the receipts during the fall. The purchase of more early and sexed chicks and year round broiler production are tending to result in more uniform meat production throughout the year.

Care. Live poultry should be handled carefully while being moved to market. Heavy mortality and losses in quality frequently result from rough handling and failure to protect the birds against unfavorable weather conditions. The birds should be protected against rain or snow in cold weather and against heat during the summer. Birds exposed to drafts while in transit often develop colds when placed in the feeding stations and therefore lose weight.

Coops. The coops used for marketing live poultry are usually made of wood. They are purchased from poultry equipment houses. Producers should be very careful about bringing contaminated coops on their premises and thereby introducing disease in their flocks. There is a temptation to use coops many times and often until they become contaminated with disease. The spread of poultry diseases could be reduced if coops were never moved from farm to farm or from the poultry markets back to the farm. Steel coops which can be disinfected easily are gaining favor. The general use of a one-way coop which could be destroyed instead of returning it to the farm would help prevent the spread of poultry diseases.

Transportation

Live poultry moves from the farm to the local market mainly by truck or automobile. That which is shipped long distances by the producer is often sent by truck or railway express. Poultry dealers ship in large quantities by truck or special live-poultry cars. (Fig. 182.)

Large quantities of live poultry going to New York and other eastern cities come from the Middle West and are shipped by freight in live-poultry cars

Fig. 182. Transportation of live poultry. From top to bottom: pick-up truck used by receiving station (U. S. D. A.); early live poultry car (U. S. D. A.); live poultry truck (R. M. Smith, University of Arkansas); modern live poultry cars (U. S. D. A.).

or by live-poultry trucks. Many of these shipments originate in plants where dressing facilities are not available, and therefore the birds must be sold as live poultry. In plants where dressing is done, only vigorous birds, which are in condition to make the trip, should be selected for shipment.

Market classes of poultry. Market terms are often confusing to the producers because words which have certain general meanings have in some cases been given specific, and what may appear to be illogical, meaning by market men. The breed name Leghorn is used to designate all small birds, while "colored" is used to indicate medium and heavy breeds even though they are white. Plymouth Rock refers to Barred Rocks, and the term "black" is used to designate chickens which have black or greenish-black shanks.

The Production and Marketing Administration (U. S. D. A.) in 1949 proposed the following market classes for poultry: *Kinds and classes for live, dressed, and ready-to-cook poultry.*

a. Chickens
1. **Broilers and fryers:** Young chickens of either sex (usually under sixteen weeks of age), tender-meated, with soft, pliable, smooth-textured skin, and flexible breastbone cartilage.
2. **Roasters:** Young chickens of either sex (usually under eight months of age), tender-meated, with soft, pliable, smooth-textured skin. Breastbone cartilage somewhat less flexible than in broilers and fryers.
3. **Capons:** Unsexed male chickens (usually under ten months of age), tender-meated, with soft, pliable, smooth-textured skin.
4. **Stags:** Male chickens (usually under ten months of age) with somewhat toughened and darkened flesh, coarse skin, and considerable hardening of the breastbone cartilage. Stags show a condition of fleshing and maturity intermediate between that of roasters and cocks.
5. **Hens, stewing chickens, fowl:** Mature female chickens (usually more than ten months old) with meat less tender than young chickens, and with a nonflexible breastbone.
6. **Cocks (old roosters).** Mature male chickens with toughened and darkened meat and hardened breastbone.
b. Turkeys
1. **Fryers:** Young turkeys of either sex (usually under fourteen weeks of age), tender-meated, with soft, pliable, smooth-textured skin, and flexible breastbone cartilage.
2. **Young hen turkeys:** Young female turkeys (usually under eight months of age), tender-meated, with soft, pliable, smooth-textured skin, and flexible breastbone cartilage.
3. **Young tom turkeys:** Young male turkeys (usually under eight months of age), tender-meated, with soft, pliable, smooth-textured skin, and flexible breastbone cartilage.
4. **Mature (old) hen turkeys:** Mature female turkeys (usually over ten months of age), with toughened flesh and hardened breastbone. May have coarse or dry skin and patchy areas of surface fat.
5. **Mature (old) tom turkeys:** Mature male turkeys (usually over ten months of age), with toughened flesh, coarse skin, and hardened breastbone.
c. Ducks
1. **Broiler and fryer ducklings:** Young ducklings of either sex (usually under eight weeks of age), tender-meated and with soft bills and windpipes.
2. **Young roasting ducklings:** Young ducks of either sex (usually under twelve weeks of age), tender-meated, and with bills not completely hardened and easily dented windpipes.

3. **Mature (old) ducks:** Mature ducks of either sex (usually over twelve weeks of age), with toughened flesh, hardened bills, and hardened windpipes.

d. Geese
1. **Young geese:** Young geese of either sex, tender-meated and with easily dented windpipes.
2. **Mature (old) geese:** Mature geese of either sex, with toughened flesh and hardened windpipes.

e. Guineas
1. **Young guineas:** Young guineas of either sex, and tender-meated.
2. **Mature (old) guineas:** Mature geese of either sex, with toughened flesh.

f. Pigeons
1. **Squabs:** Young, immature pigeons of either sex, extra tender-meated, that have not flown.
2. **Pigeons:** Mature pigeons of either sex, with toughened flesh and coarse skin.

Marketing direct. The sale of live poultry to the consumer by the producer has been decreasing. However, the development of roadside markets by poultrymen suitably located has proved profitable in many cases. Direct sales usually net the producer better prices and effect a saving for the consumer. Direct marketing of live poultry may be expected to decline except for those poultrymen who can establish successful roadside markets.

Commission merchants. Live poultry commission merchants act as selling agents for the shippers, charging from 4 to 5 per cent of the sale price for their services. They may specialize in car-lot shipments, in products from certain sections, or in certain classes of live or dressed poultry (fowl, roasters, turkeys, etc.).

Truckers or hucksters. In some sections hucksters collect considerable quantities of live poultry and truck the birds to the city markets. Hucksters may sell to the city dealers or direct to retailers and consumers.

Jobbers. The receivers known as jobbers purchase live poultry from the shippers and sell it on their own account.

Slaughterhouse operators. Live poultry marketed in the large cities is killed and it also may be dressed in the slaughterhouses. They keep a supply of live poultry on hand from which purchasers may select the birds they desire.

Retail markets. The live poultry which is marketed in the larger cities may be retailed through slaughterhouses, chicken stores, chicken stands in public markets, or butcher shops.

Demand for live poultry. The demand for live poultry is decreasing even in such cities as New York, where there is a large Jewish population. Consumers are being educated to use dressed poultry and American-born Jews apparently are discarding some of the more orthodox views of their ancestors relative to food.

Kosher poultry. The Hebrew religion requires that only poultry meeting specified requirements, and killed in accordance with the Hebrew laws under the supervision of the rabbi, shall be used for Jewish consumption. The representative of the rabbi who does kosher killing is called a "schochet." Recently in New York City a metal leg band called a "plumba" has been required on poultry to show that it has met the Hebrew dietary laws. A Jewish organization maintains a representative where poultry is being kosher killed to band the kosher poultry with "plumbas," charging one cent per bird. Extra marketing costs imposed by these regulations serve to still further handicap a diminishing live-poultry trade.

Hebrew holidays. The demand for live poultry is greatest during the Jewish holidays, principal of which are the Passover in the spring and the Day of Atonement in the fall.

Standards and grades for live poultry. Live poultry is more difficult to grade than dressed poultry because the feathers interfere with the observations of the grader. The following United States Department of Agriculture standards and grades for live poultry became effective January 1, 1950:

U. S. STANDARDS FOR QUALITY FOR INDIVIDUAL LIVE BIRDS

A or No. 1 Quality: Each bird shall: (1) be alert and have bright eyes with other conditions indicating health and vigor; (2) be well-feathered (with feathers showing luster or sheen quite thoroughly covering all parts of the body), and may have a slight scattering of pinfeathers; (3) be of normal physical conformation but may have a slightly crooked back, also a slight curve or abnormality in the shape of the breastbone if it does not interfere with the normal distribution of the flesh (a dent in the breastbone shall not exceed ¼ inch in depth for turkey classes and ⅛ inch in depth for other classes of poultry); (4) have a well-developed, moderately broad and long breast, well-fleshed throughout its entire length, and thighs and back well covered with flesh according to age and sex with no appreciable toughening of flesh (if tender meat is a class requirement); (5) have breast, back, hips, and pinbones, in the classes of young chickens and turkey toms, showing fat, and in other classes of poultry have these parts well covered with fat (a chicken hen shall not have excessive abdominal fat); (6) be free of tears, broken bones, and external evidence of disease, but may have slightly scaly legs, slight scratches, bruises, or calluses (slightly thickened, hardened, and darkened areas of skin over the breastbone), which must not materially affect its appearance, especially the breast, when feathers are removed.

B or No. 2 Quality: Each bird shall: (1) be of good health and vigor; (2) be fairly well-feathered (feathers may be lacking on some parts of the body), and may have a moderate number of pinfeathers; (3) be of normal physical conformation but may have a moderately crooked back, slightly misshapen legs or wings, also a slightly crooked breastbone if it does not seriously interfere with the normal distribution of the flesh; (4) be fairly well-fleshed in relation to length and depth of body and over all parts according to age and sex with no appreciable toughening of flesh (if tender meat is a class requirement); (5) have sufficient coverage of fat to prevent a dark appearance (a chicken hen may have excessive abdominal fat); (6) be free of tears, broken bones, and external evidence of disease, but may have seriously scaly legs, slight breast blisters, and heavy calluses (thickened, hardened, and darkened areas of skin over the breastbone).

C or No. 3 Quality: Each bird may: (1) be lacking in vigor; (2) have a large number of pinfeathers over all parts and a complete lack of feathers on the back;

(3) have crooked breastbone, hunchback, and other definite deformities; (4) have poorly developed, narrow breast, and thin covering of flesh over all parts of the bird; (5) have only small amount of fat in feather tracts and be completely lacking in fat on back and thighs; (6) have large skin bruises, small flesh bruises, and severe breast blisters. It may be slightly crippled but must be free of external evidence of disease or any other condition which would render it unfit for food.

Reject: Any bird below C or No. 3 shall be classified as a reject (a reject is a bird that shows evidence of disease, large flesh bruises, severe discolorations, severe injury, emaciation, or other similar conditions which render it unfit for human food).

U. S. SPECIFICATIONS FOR GRADES OF LIVE POULTRY

U. S. Grade A or No. 1: Each lot shall consist of A or No. 1 quality birds, except that a tolerance of 10 per cent B or No. 2 quality birds shall be allowed, provided no individual container in the lot shall have more birds of B or No. 2 quality than specified below in Table of Maximum Tolerances, and shall contain no rejects.

U. S. Grade B or No. 2: Each lot shall consist of B or No. 2 quality or better, except that a tolerance of 10 per cent of C quality or No. 3 shall be allowed, provided no individual container in the lot shall have more birds of C or No. 3 quality than specified below in Table of Maximum Tolerances, and shall contain no rejects.

U. S. Grade C or No. 3: All edible birds below B or No. 2 quality. No rejects allowed.

No Grade: Lots of poultry containing rejects shall be classed as "No grade."

Tolerances: All poultry having excessive feed in the crops shall be considered as "overcropped" and may be subject to dockings. "Excessive" feed shall be interpreted to mean more than an average of (1) 1 ounce of feed in crops of birds weighing not more than 2½ pounds; (2) 2 ounces of feed in crops of birds weighing more than 2½ pounds (except turkeys); (3) 3 ounces of feed in crops of turkeys.

TABLE OF MAXIMUM TOLERANCES PER INDIVIDUAL CONTAINERS

No. of birds in container	Maximum no. of birds of next lower quality allowed
Less than 10	1
10 to 15	2
16 to 20	3
21 to 25	4
26 to 30	5

Market inspection and regulation. The United States Department of Agriculture provides inspectors in the principal live-poultry markets. The inspectors examine the poultry for the amount of feed in the crops. If the birds in a car have an average of two ounces or more of feed in their crops they cannot be unloaded on the day of inspection. These inspectors examine the birds for disease and supervise the disposal of dead and diseased birds.

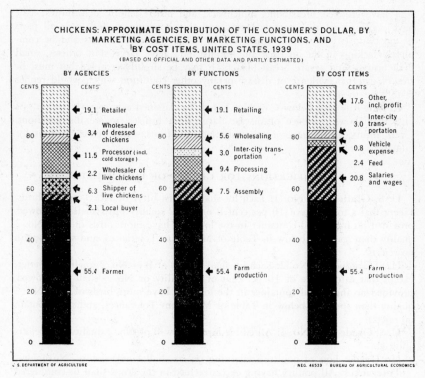

CHICKENS: APPROXIMATE DISTRIBUTION OF THE CONSUMER'S DOLLAR, BY
MARKETING AGENCIES, BY MARKETING FUNCTIONS, AND
BY COST ITEMS, UNITED STATES, 1939
(BASED ON OFFICIAL AND OTHER DATA AND PARTLY ESTIMATED)

BY AGENCIES

CENTS		CENTS	
		19.1	Retailer
80		3.4	Wholesaler of dressed chickens
		11.5	Processor (incl. cold storage)
		2.2	Wholesaler of live chickens
60		6.3	Shipper of live chickens
		2.1	Local buyer
40			
		55.4	Farmer
20			
0			

BY FUNCTIONS

CENTS		CENTS	
		19.1	Retailing
80		5.6	Wholesaling
		3.0	Inter-city transportation
		9.4	Processing
60		7.5	Assembly
40			
		55.4	Farm production
20			
0			

BY COST ITEMS

CENTS		CENTS	
		17.6	Other, incl. profit
		3.0	Inter-city transportation
80		0.8	Vehicle expense
		2.4	Feed
		20.8	Salaries and wages
60			
40			
		55.4	Farm production
20			
0			

U. S. DEPARTMENT OF AGRICULTURE   NEG. 46533   BUREAU OF AGRICULTURAL ECONOMICS

Fig. 183. Distribution of the consumer's dollar spent for chicken.

The live-poultry industry in some of the larger markets, notably New York City, has been subject to rackets, combines in restraint of trade, and other abuses. Under the Packers and Stockyard Act, the federal government has been given authority to regulate these markets. The Secretary of Agriculture has placed several markets under federal supervision, and it is hoped that proper regulation will correct the abuses which have arisen.

Improving the quality of market poultry. Any observer of live poultry received at the markets will find a wide variation in the quality of such poultry, with much of it definitely inferior. It is not likely that much progress can be made in improving the market quality of poultry as long as those who produce poultry are paid the same price per pound for grade A poultry as for grade C poultry. The factors which determine quality are complex, and improvement in quality will be slow; but the first requisite is an economic motive which graded buying with suitable price differentials would provide. The quality of market poultry can be improved by the selection of more suitable strains of poultry, by breeding for desirable market characters, by using well-balanced rations, by controlling diseases and parasites, and by following other good management practices.

Costs of marketing poultry. The goal of the marketing agencies that handle poultry and eggs should be to render efficient marketing services at minimum costs consistent with sound business finances.

Figure 183 shows that the retail cost of handling poultry is the most expensive part of the marketing process; in 1939 it cost 19.1 cents of the consumer's dollar spent for chickens. Table 85 shows that farmers in 1945 received 68 cents out of the consumer's dollar spent for poultry, but by 1947 the farmer's share had declined to 57 cents. This was due principally to the decline in prices. When prices are high, farmers receive a higher percentage of the consumer's dollar than when prices are low.

The cost per pound of marketing live poultry shipped from the Middle West to New York City was estimated in 1938 by the Consumers Service Division, Department of Markets, New York City to be as follows:

Price paid the farmer	17.000 cents
County agent or buyer	1.000
Transportation	1.750
Shrinkage	1.080
Stand men (unloading, etc.)	.240
Weighmaster	.050
Inspection (U. S. D. A.)	.044
Coops	.361
Loaders	.142
Receivers	1.000
Wholesalers truck	.500
Slaughterhouse labor	.750
Schochet	.500
Slaughterhouse administration	.750
Plumba, etc.	.250
Slaughterhouse operators margin	.250
Retailer	7.000
Pluckers charge to consumer	1.250
Total	33.917 cents

Feeding Station Management

The purpose of fattening. There are two main objectives in fattening poultry: (1) improve the quality of the flesh, and (2) increase the weight of the birds.

Location of feeding stations. Feeding stations in the United States are located primarily in the poultry-packing plants in the producing areas of the Middle West. While feeding batteries are used in poultry plants located in the cities, their principal use there is for holding poultry, but they are also used for fattening poultry (Fig. 184).

Selection of stock. Only healthy, vigorous birds should be placed or kept in fattening batteries. Birds which develop "gapes" or go "off feed" from any other cause should be removed from the batteries. The caretaker should inspect the birds on feed at least once each day and remove birds which are out of condition or "off feed."

Table 85

CHICKENS: RETAIL PRICE PER POUND, FARM VALUE OF 1.136 POUNDS
LIVE CHICKEN, MARKETING MARGIN, AND FARMER'S SHARE OF RETAIL
PRICE, UNITED STATES, 1929–47

Year	Retail Price Per Pound	Farm Value of 1.136 Pounds	Marketing Margin	Farmer's Share of Retail Price
	Cents	*Cents*	*Cents*	*Per Cent*
1929	43.7	25.4	18.3	58
1930	39.0	21.0	18.0	54
1931	34.9	17.6	17.3	50
1932	26.7	13.2	13.5	49
1933	23.5	10.8	12.7	46
1934	29.0	12.8	16.2	44
1935	29.9	16.8	13.1	56
1936	31.1	17.6	13.5	57
1937	31.3	17.7	13.6	57
1938	30.1	17.1	13.0	57
1939	27.6	15.3	12.3	55
1940	28.1	14.8	13.3	53
1941	30.2	17.7	12.5	59
1942	36.1	21.4	14.7	59
1943	41.5	27.6	13.9	67
1944	41.7	27.2	14.5	65
1945	43.1	29.3	13.8	68
1946	48.7	30.4	18.3	62
1947	53.6	30.3	23.3	57

Sanitation. An outbreak of disease may cause serious losses in a feeding station. Therefore sanitation, though difficult, is very important. Batteries, after each lot of birds has gone through them, should be thoroughly cleaned and disinfected. At least once each year the entire feeding station should be carefully cleaned and disinfected. If the plant is having trouble with colds among the birds, or as a safeguard against such an outbreak, the birds should be sprayed with a fine formaldehyde spray. This spray mixture for use in cold weather consists of glycerine 3, 50% formalin solution 15, warm water 82 (parts by weight). For use in warm weather 3 parts of denatured alcohol are added and the other materials as listed above are changed to 2, 7, and 88 parts respectively.

Fattening poultry. Satisfactory gains are necessary for the economical operation of feeding stations. During recent years feeding stations have been used primarily for holding birds for a few days until they could be killed, instead of holding them for a long feeding period. The problem of economical gains from fattening in feeding stations has become more difficult in recent years.

Rations. The rations used for fattening poultry should be palatable, highly digestible, free from ingredients which impart undesirable flavors to the meat, not too expensive or complex, and they should contain the materials necessary to insure gains and produce the type of carcass preferred by consumers (p. 324).

Gains in weight from feeding. The gains made depend upon the condition of the birds, their age, their size, and the rations which they receive. The Missouri Agricultural Experiment Station reported in 1932 the results given in Tables 86 and 87, which show that young chickens such as broilers usually make larger gains than hens. It was also found that the small or medium-sized broilers, roasters, or hens made greater gains than did large birds of the same classes.

Table 86

GAINS MADE BY ROCK BROILERS FED TEN DAYS [1]

Lot	Number of Birds	Ration	Initial Weight	Final Weight	Gain	Dressed Weight	Dressing Loss	Percentage of Initial Weight Packed
			Pounds	*Pounds*	*Per Cent*	*Pounds*	*Per Cent*	
46	94	Basal + Condensed Buttermilk	195.6	236.3	20.1	204.7	13.4	104.7
1	98	Basal + Liquid Buttermilk	211.9	262.3	23.8	234.8	10.5	110.8
7	100	Basal + 5% Dried Skim Milk	208.0	248.1	19.3	222.0	10.5	106.7
13	98	Basal + 10% Dried Skim Milk	185.3	242.7	31.0	213.3	12.1	115.1
19	96	Basal + 15% Dried Skim Milk	201.6	271.3	34.6	238.5	12.1	118.3
25	98	Basal + 20% Dried Skim Milk	215.7	270.3	25.3	240.9	10.9	111.7
Total........................			1218.1	1531.0	25.7	1354.2	11.5	111.2

Gains made today as compared to twenty-five years ago. Why do chickens make smaller gains when fed in the feeding stations of the packing plants now than they did twenty-five years ago? This is a much discussed problem among poultry packers. Some feeders believe that the birds received at the feeding stations today do not possess the vitality that similar receipts did a quarter of a century ago. The more plausible explanation is that today most poultry as raised receives better growing and fattening rations than poultry did before 1920. Whereas during the earlier period the growing stock foraged for much of their living and those fed received rather inferior rations so that growth was slow and very little fat was stored, today young growing chickens have high protein mashes before them continually and in many cases grain is also kept in hoppers before them.

The poultry of 1900 to 1920 grew slowly and developed a framework on which the packer could quickly add fat and therefore get rapid gains. Today young chickens come to feeding stations from full feeders. They are relatively fat and they are not hungry. Too often it is true they come infested with worms or infected with disease, conditions which, of course, cause losses in-

---

[1] Mo. Agr. Expt. Sta. Bul. 309, 1932.

Table 87

GAINS MADE BY ROCK HENS FED SEVEN DAYS [2]

Lot	Number of Birds	Ration	Initial Weight	Final Weight	Gain	Dressed Weight	Dressing Loss	Percentage of Initial Weight Packed
			Pounds	*Pounds*	*Per Cent*	*Pounds*	*Per Cent*	
49	90	Basal + Condensed Buttermilk	347.4	408.1	17.5	363.1	11.0	104.5
4	89	Basal + Liquid Buttermilk	352.5	401.6	13.9	364.1	9.3	103.3
10	95	Basal + 5% Dried Skim Milk	416.6	456.5	9.6	419.1	8.2	100.6
16	95	Basal + 10% Dried Skim Milk	360.6	421.7	16.9	377.1	10.6	104.6
22	91	Basal + 15% Dried Skim Milk	361.8	395.5	9.3	357.0	9.7	98.7
28	96	Basal + 20% Dried Skim Milk	414.3	454.4	9.7	408.9	10.0	98.7
Total............			2253.2	2537.8	12.6	2289.3	9.8	101.6

stead of gains in weight. The occurrence of the "gapes" in recent years has also interfered with long feeding periods.

Feeding period. The length of time poultry can be fed profitably in the feeding stations depends on their fatness when received, size, age, and season of the year. Under Missouri conditions, which are probably representative of the section of the United States where most of the large feeding stations are located, it is no longer profitable to feed poultry after October 1. Satisfactory gains can be obtained from April 1 to October 1. After October 1 "gapes" and other diseases are common. From April 1 to October 1 springs may be fed for four to seven days and fowl from four to six days. The following statement by a poultry packer located in the Middle West describes the change in fattening which has occurred:

During the past twenty-five years, we have certainly had a radical change in our feeding station methods, the big change coming about 1925 when the "gapes" hit this part of the country, and our feeding period being reduced accordingly. Prior to 1924, disease was practically unknown to us, except occasional cases of roup, and we could feed broilers and fryers up to fourteen days profitably, and of course could make some very fine poultry which is not possible to do now. Prior to 1925, it was not necessary to use the same strict sanitary methods in the feeding stations that we have to now, nor was it necessary to watch the ventilation so closely. But now with the very best systems of ventilation, the closest watch, better feeds, and the strictest methods of sanitation, it is almost impossible to feed the chickens long enough to get any profitable gains on poultry except during the summer months, and even then it does not compare with what we had prior to the time when the "gapes" struck this part of the country.

[2] Mo. Agr. Expt. Sta. Bul. 309, 1932.

Feed consumption. The amount of feed required to produce each pound of gain determines quite largely the profits from fattening poultry. If small gains are made, feed cost per pound of gain becomes excessive and feeding unprofitable. Feed consumption per bird and economy of gains is given in Table 88 for broilers, roasters, and hens. These results show that under favorable conditions gains may be very economical.

Table 88

FEED CONSUMPTION AND GAINS WHEN BIRDS WERE FED LIQUID BUTTER-
MILK. HENS AND ROASTERS FED SEVEN DAYS
AND BROILERS FED TEN DAYS [3]

Lot	Number	Stock	Feed Consumed *		Pounds of Gain	Pounds of Feed per Pound Gain
			Total Pounds of Feed	Pounds of Feed per Bird per Day		
1	98	Rock Broilers...........	157.9	.1611	50.4	3.1
2	95	Red Broilers............	159.9	.1683	52.6	3.0
3	100	Leghorn Broilers........	166.9	.1669	57.8	2.9
4	89	Rock Hens..............	137.4	.2205	49.1	2.8
5	93	Red Hens..............	142.7	.2192	53.5	2.7
6	97	Leghorn Hens..........	159.3	.2346	42.0	3.8
31	95	Rock Roasters..........	126.6	.1904	33.1	3.8
33	88	Red Roasters...........	123.9	.2011	34.0	3.6
32	86	Rock Roasters.........	120.7	.2005	35.8	3.4
Average.............................			143.9	.1914	45.4	3.2

* Feed consumption was calculated by considering liquid buttermilk as containing 10 per cent solids.

Source of fat and its distribution. Results secured at MacDonald College showed that the distribution of fat in the carcass of the fattened bird was influenced by the kind of grain used in the fattening ration. Corn, as shown in Table 89, gave a very satisfactory distribution of fat, while birds fed oats and wheat had much less fat stored in the flesh.

Cramming. Forced feeding of poultry is not practiced in America because

Table 89

PER CENT DISTRIBUTION OF FAT IN THE BODY [4]

Cereal	Total Fat to Dressed Weight	In Flesh	In Skin	Abdominal Fat
Corn.................	13.4	30.0	55.0	15.0
Barley...............	12.1	26.0	59.0	15.0
Oats.................	12.1	22.0	57.0	21.0
Wheat...............	12.9	20.0	60.0	20.0

[3] Mo. Agr. Expt. Sta. Bul. 309, 1932.
[4] Maw, 1935.

Fig. 184. One of the many rows of fattening batteries in a modern fattening station.

of the labor cost of the gains secured. In Europe this method is used to secure extra gains. The birds are fed by the use of cramming machines which are used to force soft feed through a tube into the crop of the bird. Evidently the appetite of a bird is not a true indication of what it can digest since birds crammed make satisfactory gains.

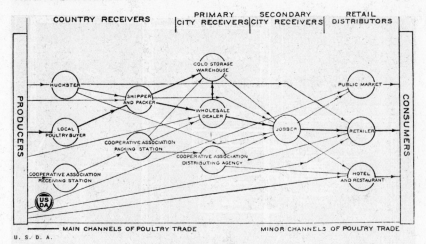

Fig. 185. Market channels for poultry.

Recently some feeders in packing plants have been cramming turkeys. Such a procedure will, no doubt, increase weight by filling an empty digestive tract but it is doubtful if any improvement in the quality or quantity of turkey meat can be made by cramming.

Equipment. While being fattened, the birds are usually held in sixteen-compartment portable steel batteries, as shown in Figure 184. These batteries are durable and they can be easily cleaned and disinfected. The capacity of these batteries is ninety-six mature birds. Feeding vats in which the wet mashes are mixed and moved are standard equipment in feeding stations. Buckets with spouts for pouring feed are used for distributing the feed to the feeding troughs. Scales are needed for weighing batteries containing birds and for weighing small lots of birds as they are received. Other equipment needed are the tools necessary for keeping the plant clean.

Dressed Poultry

Since most consumers do not wish to be bothered with killing and dressing poultry, they now purchase dressed poultry. Improvements in killing and dressing and in preserving dressed poultry have gained for it the confidence of the consumers. As the industry continues to improve the quality of dressed poultry, consumer demand for such poultry will be increased.

Marketing channels. The channels by which poultry moves to market are shown in Figure 185. Most of the dressed poultry is killed and dressed in the poultry-packing plants located in the producing areas. It is subsequently transported to the consuming markets or placed in cold-storage warehouses.

Dressing plants. Facilities for dressing and processing poultry vary all the way from one or two rooms (Fig. 186) which handle a few birds per hour to large line operated plants (Fig. 187) which handle 3000 or more per hour.

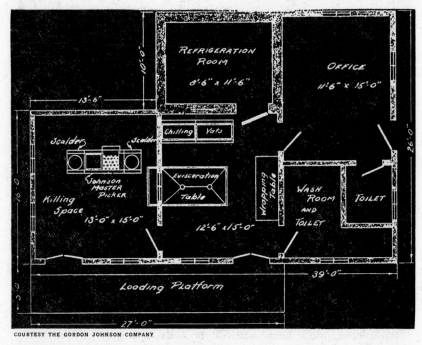

COURTESY THE GORDON JOHNSON COMPANY

Fig. 186. Suggested plan for a small poultry eviscerating plant. Note that the eviscerating and wrapping room is separate from the killing room.

Equipment should include holding batteries for live birds, track and shackles for holding birds, scalder, wing stripper, ducking machine, pinning track, singer, chilling vats, eviscerating table, wash sink, meat saw, drying and wrapping bench, and freezer.

Tools (Fig. 188) should include sticking and eviscerating knives, pinning knife, kidney and lung remover, and bone shears.

Sanitation standards must be met before poultry may be inspected for wholesomeness and/or graded for quality under United States Department of Agriculture supervision. General plant sanitation requirements include: (1) proper drainage and facilities for disposal of sewage and plant wastes; (2) freedom from filth and objectionable odors; (3) construction to keep out rodents and flies; (4) floors and side walls that may be hosed easily; (5) adequate light, ventilation, washroom, and toilet facilities; (6) arrangements to protect products and equipment from contamination by handling operations, insects, rodents, pets, etc.; (7) adequate supply of clean and potable water; (8) separation of the feeding and holding room from the eviscerating, grading, inspection, and packaging room.

Plant operation and sanitary requirements include: (1) adequate supply of hot water (180° F. or above); (2) clean rooms and equipment kept in proper repair; (3) removal of feed from the crop, fecal material from the cloaca, and blood from the head followed by washing the carcass before chilling or packing; (4) chilling vats maintained not higher than 40° F. (birds not to remain in vat after internal temperature has reached 36° F. or longer than 6 hours without a change of water); (5) air chilling of birds to an internal temperature of 36 to 40° F. within 24 hours; (6) holding of poultry not longer than 72 hours at temperatures not above 36° F.; (7) freezing poultry solid within 60 hours and storing at 0° F. or below.

Killing and Bleeding Poultry

Where dry picking is used, poultry should be killed by bleeding and by piercing the hind brain with a sharp pointed knife inserted through the cleft in the roof of the mouth or through the opening in the skull by which the optic nerve enters the eye. Proper sticking destroys the nerve tissue and relaxes the muscles which hold the feathers, thereby loosening them so that they may be more easily plucked. Piercing the brain is not necessary when poultry is scalded or semi-scalded.

Bleeding. Bleeding may be accomplished by severing the neck, by dislocating the neck, or by severing the large blood vessels of the neck either by cutting the throat of the bird or by making the cut inside the bird's mouth. Dislocating the neck, as shown in Figure 189, is a simple and sanitary method of killing poultry for home use. Birds killed for the kosher trade must have their throats cut with a sharp knife so that the windpipe, gullet, and jugular vein are completely severed. In commercial packing plants where dressed poultry is prepared, bleeding (where dry picking is practiced) is accomplished by inserting the knife into the mouth and severing the blood vessels as indicated in Figure 190. Where semi-scalding is used, bleeding is sometimes accomplished by cutting the bird's throat. Making the incision on the outside of the neck is believed by some operators to give better bleeding than severing the veins through the mouth.

Improper bleeding results in inferior dressed poultry, particularly after it has been held for some time. Poor bleeding may be detected by blood showing in the feather follicles of the thighs, hips, neck, and wings of the birds which have been improperly bled. High-quality dressed poultry must be well bled.

Electrocution. Recently there has been developed a machine for killing poultry by electrocution and for bleeding the poultry electrocuted. It is too early to evaluate this method, but its development indicates the alertness of American inventors in developing new machines for improving marketing methods.

Dressing

The value of dressed poultry may be greatly reduced because of faulty dressing. Skilled workmen, employing correct methods, can dress poultry so that maximum prices may be obtained.

Hard scalding. One of the earliest methods developed for removing the feathers from freshly killed poultry was that of immersing the birds in hot

Fig. 187. Steps in semi-scald and wax picking of poultry. Upper left, sticking, debraining, and removal of main tail and wing feathers before the birds are passed through the semi-scalding tank. Upper right, a bird ready to be dipped into the wax bath and one that has been withdrawn. Lower, removal of main body feathers before the birds are passed through the wax tank.

Upper, removal of wax after birds have passed through the dipping tanks. Lower left, dressed birds on racks in the chill room. Lower right, grading dressed poultry before packing or evisceration. The birds are graded according to weight and quality of carcass. Compartments are provided for several weights and different grades of each.

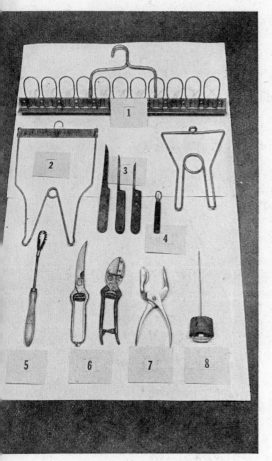

Fig 188. Poultry dressing and eviscerating equipment:
1 and 2. Shackles for holding birds.
3. Sticking and eviscerating knives.
4. Pinning knife.
5. Kidney and lung remover.
6. Shears used in evisceration.
7. Bleeding and debraining instrument.
8. Dial thermometer for use in scalding tank.

water (180° F. to 190° F.). While hard scalding expedites the removal of feathers, it destroys some of the food value of the poultry and produces an unattractive carcass after the surface of the body has thoroughly dried. While hard scalding is still used for home dressing and for dressing birds which are to be delivered to the kitchens of hotels and restaurants, this method is not used for preparing dressed poultry for the regular market channels.

Dry picking. Hard scalding was replaced by dry picking and for many years prior to 1925 the poultry which was dressed in the packing plants was dry picked. Birds which were properly killed by piercing the brain could be picked without being scalded. The pickers were divided into two groups: the "roughers," who removed the large wing, tail, and body feathers, and the "pinners," who removed all of the remaining feathers, including the pinfeathers. Plants using this method paid the workers for the number of birds roughed and pinned. A dry-picking machine has been used in Europe for removing the feathers of market poultry.

Semi-scalding. The development of the semi-scald method for removing feathers from poultry was very rapid and from 1925 to 1935 practically all the larger packing plants adopted this newer method for picking poultry. Special machinery for handling the birds was installed in most plants using this method. Some of the instructions supplied by the manufacturers of the machines are as follows: (1) Good bleeding is essential; this means severing both the vein and artery. By this method, bloody crops are impossible. Some operators simply cut the throat, from inside or outside the mouth. (2) Birds, according to age, may be placed on the shackles and bled from twenty seconds to two minutes before reaching the scalding tank. (3) Time of immersion: the machine may be changed at will by the operator; broilers may be immersed twenty to thirty seconds, older birds from twenty up to forty seconds. (4) The temperature of the water is controlled by an automatic thermostat on the steam intake line. When set at 128° F. for ordinary scald, or with special 185° thermostat for hard scald, the temperature will automatically be maintained. (5) Birds should be picked in a reasonable time after leaving the tank. Pickers should pick, never scrape or rub. (6) Heads should be dry before wrapping. (7) Birds should be put in coolers within one hour after being picked.

Those engaged in packing poultry prefer the semi-scald method for removing feathers because it (1) reduces labor costs, (2) improves the appearance of the dressed bird, and (3) increases the number of birds which go into the higher grades.

Semi-scald and wax picking. Soon after the semi-scald method of picking came into general use, C. V. Rosenberger, Independence, Iowa, patented (in 1929) the wax method of removing the feathers (Fig. 187). This special wax may be purchased from the manufacturers. This method has been combined with the semi-scald method, but results released by the National Research Council of Canada in 1935 indicate that wax picking may be devel-

Fig. 189. Killing a chicken by dislocating the neck. This method is satisfactory for killing birds for home use.

oped so that semi-scalding can be eliminated and dry-picked birds dipped in the wax.

Birds from which the large feathers have been removed are dipped in melted wax and then sprayed with cold water to harden the wax. Some waxes in use harden without being sprayed with cold water. When the hardened wax is peeled away the feathers, pinfeathers, "hair," and scales are removed, and an attractive dressed bird is produced at a greatly reduced labor cost. The hardened wax in which the feathers are embedded is reclaimed by boiling away the water and removing the feathers so that the wax may continue to be used.

Picking machines. A more recent development is the feather-picking machine. (Fig. 191.) This machine is used in conjunction with semi-scalding. Such a machine removes the feathers very efficiently and with a minimum of labor. The machines may be located along "the line" so that the birds are

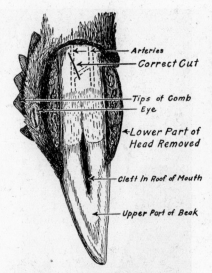

Arteries
Correct Cut
Tips of Comb
Eye
Lower Part of Head Removed
Cleft In Roof of Mouth
Upper Part of Beak

Fig. 190. Bleeding of poultry is accomplished by inserting a special knife through the mouth and severing the blood vessels as indicated. (Drawing by Noel Hall.)

carried by conveyors through these machines.

Dressing problems. Dressing is a processing service whereby live poultry is converted into a consumable form. In dressing, every effort should be made to avoid bruises, tears, and broken bones. To insure more attractive birds for the consumer the head should be wrapped as shown in Figure 192, the feet should be cleaned by washing, and the lower intestines emptied by applying pressure on the abdomen and forcing their contents out through the vent.

Grading Dressed Poultry

Grading is essential to economical and intelligent trading in dressed poultry because traders located several hundred miles apart trade in the poultry meat of several species which varies from that which is worthless to that which is excellent. The packing plant is fortunate which employs a well-trained grader who knows how to separate the birds into their respective grades to realize the greatest returns.

Quality standards for individual dressed and ready-to-cook poultry. The United States Department of Agriculture, in co-operation with the poultry industry, formulated the following standards of quality for individual birds which became effective January 1, 1950.

A Quality. (Fig. 192.) 1. *Shape.* Is of normal physical conformation except that it may have a lightly curved breastbone or other slight abnormality in the shape of the breastbone which does not interfere with the normal distribution of the flesh. The carcass may also have a very slightly curved back. There may be a dent in the breastbone which does not exceed ⅛ inch in depth except that for turkeys the depth does not exceed ¼ inch.

2. *Fleshing.* Has a well-developed, moderately broad and long breast, well-fleshed throughout its entire length, with the flesh carrying sufficiently well up to the crest of the breastbone so that the breastbone is not prominent; and, with respect to young tom turkeys, there may be a slight thickening and slight pouchiness of the skin on the forepart of the breast. The legs are well covered with flesh.

3. *Fat.* Has the breast, back hips, and pinbones well covered with fat except that chicken broilers or fryers, turkey fryers, and young tom turkeys may have only a moderate amount of fat covering these parts, but a hen, stewing chicken, or fowl may not have excessive abdominal fat.

4. *Pinfeathers.* Is practically free from pinfeathers, especially on the breast,

Fig. 191. Poultry pickers for small dressing plants.

and from vestigial feathers (i.e., hair or down, as the case may be) if the carcass is dressed poultry. If the carcass is ready-to-cook poultry, it is free from protruding pinfeathers, practically free from nonprotruding pinfeathers, especially on the breast, and free from vestigial feathers.

5. *Skin tears.* Is free from skin tears and cuts on the breast and legs; however, elsewhere on the carcass there may be tears and cuts (exclusive of the cuts usually made to remove the neck and viscera in the production of eviscerated poultry) the aggregate length of which does not exceed 1½ inches except that, with respect to any turkey carcass or goose carcass, such aggregate length does not exceed 3 inches. There are no sewn tears or cuts. The carcass has no disjointed bones or broken bones except that it may have one disjointed bone in either a leg or wing but only if there is no evidence of a related bruise or blood clot; and, if the carcass is of a chicken broiler or fryer, it may have one nonprotruding broken bone in a wing in addition to such disjointed bone but only if there is no evidence of a related bruise or blood clot. The wing tips may have been removed.

6. *Bruises.* Is free from bruises and discolorations of the flesh on the breast and legs; however, elsewhere on the carcass there may be bruises and discolorations of the flesh showing not more than a slightly reddened color the aggregate area of which does not exceed the area of a circle ½ inch in diameter, except that, with respect to any turkey or goose carcass, such aggregate area does not exceed the area of a circle 1 inch in diameter. The carcass is free from skin bruises, on the breast and legs, the aggregate area of which exceeds the area of a circle ½ inch in diameter, and from skin bruises, elsewhere on the carcass, the aggregate area of which exceeds the area of a circle ¾ inch in diameter. With respect to any turkey or goose carcass, such aggregate area on the breast and legs does not exceed the area of a circle ¾ inch in diameter; and elsewhere on the carcass such aggregate area does not exceed the area of a circle 1½ inches in diameter. Notwithstanding the foregoing, the total aggregate area, on the breast and legs, of all

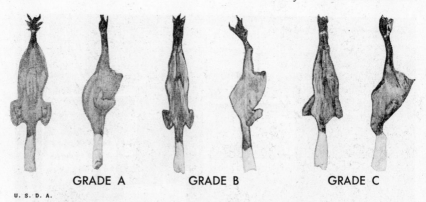

GRADE A   GRADE B   GRADE C

Fig. 192. U. S. standards for dressed fowl (effective January 1, 1950).

such flesh bruises, skin bruises, and all other discolorations and blemishes of the skin, is not in excess of the area of a circle 1 inch in diameter; and elsewhere on the carcass such total aggregate area is not in excess of the area of a circle 1½ inches in diameter. Furthermore, with respect to any turkey or goose carcass, such total aggregate area on the breast and legs is not in excess of the area of a circle 2 inches in diameter; and elsewhere on the carcass such total aggregate area is not in excess of the area of a circle 3 inches in diameter. The skin may show only slight reddening in the feather follicles on the neck, near the head, and on the wings because of improper bleeding.

7. *Freezer burn.* Shows only slight "freezer burn," (i.e., a few pockmarks, or evidence thereof, none of which exceeds the area of a circle ⅛ inch in diameter).

B Quality. 1. *Shape.* Is of at least practically normal physical conformation except that it may have a dented, curved, and slightly crooked breastbone which does not seriously interfere with the normal distribution of the flesh. The carcass may also have a moderately crooked back or misshapen legs or misshapen wings.

2. *Fleshing.* Is sufficiently well-fleshed on the breast and legs so as to prevent a thin appearance and a prominent breastbone; however, a young tom turkey may have a pouchy, thick, and somewhat flabby skin on the forepart of the breast.

3. *Fat.* Has a sufficient coverage of fat on the breast and legs to prevent a distinct appearance of the flesh through the skin.

4. *Pinfeathers.* Has not more than a slight scattering of pinfeathers over the entire carcass with only relatively few on the breast and is free from vestigial feathers (i.e., hair or down, as the case may be) if the carcass is dressed poultry. If the carcass is ready-to-cook poultry, it is free from protruding pinfeathers and vestigial feathers but may have not more than a few scattered, nonprotruding pinfeathers.

5. *Skin tears.* Is free from tears and cuts, on the breast and legs, the aggregate length of which exceeds 1½ inches; however, elsewhere on the carcass there may be tears and cuts (exclusive of the cuts usually made to remove the neck and viscera in the production of eviscerated poultry), the aggregate length of which does not exceed 3 inches except that, with respect to any turkey or goose carcass, such aggregate lengths do not exceed 3 inches on the breast and legs and 6 inches elsewhere on the carcass. There are no sewn tears or cuts. The carcass may have not more than a total of two disjointed bones in either the legs or wings, or both,

but only if there is no evidence of a related bruise or blood clot, and, in addition, one broken bone in a leg or wing, but only if it is nonprotruding and does not show an excessive related bruise or blood clot. The wing tips may have been removed.

6. *Bruises.* Is free from bruises and discolorations, on the flesh of the breast and legs, showing not more than a slightly darkened color and which in the aggregate is in excess of the area of a circle ½ inch in diameter; however, elsewhere on the carcass there may be bruises and discolorations of the flesh the aggregate area of which does not exceed the area of a circle 1½ inches in diameter, except that, with respect to any turkey or goose carcass, such aggregate area on the breast and legs does not exceed the area of a circle 1 inch in diameter, and, elsewhere on the carcass, it does not exceed the area of a circle 3 inches in diameter. The carcass is free from skin bruises, on the breast and legs, the aggregate area of which exceeds the area of a circle ¾ inch in diameter, and from skin bruises, elsewhere on the carcass, the aggregate area of which exceeds the area of a circle 1½ inches in diameter. With respect to any turkey or goose carcass, such aggregate area on the breast and legs does not exceed the area of a circle 1½ inches in diameter, and, elsewhere on the carcass, such aggregate area does not exceed the area of a circle 3 inches in diameter. Notwithstanding the foregoing, the total aggregate area on the breast and legs of all such flesh bruises, skin bruises, and all other discolorations and blemishes of the skin is not in excess of the area of a circle 1½ inches in diameter; and elsewhere on the carcass such total aggregate area is not in excess of the area of a circle 3 inches in diameter. Furthermore, with respect to any turkey or goose carcass, such total aggregate area on the breast and legs is not in excess of the area of a circle 3 inches in diameter; and elsewhere on the carcass such total aggregate area is not in excess of the area of a circle 6 inches in diameter. The skin may show not more than moderate reddening in the feather follicles on the neck, near the head, and on the wings because of improper bleeding.

7. *Freezer burn.* Shows no more than moderate "freezer burn," or evidence thereof, on any part of the carcass and no dried area in excess of the area of a circle ½ inch in diameter.

C. Quality. 1. *Shape.* Is of abnormal physical conformation (i.e., possesses serious abnormal physical conditions, including, but not being limited to, a crooked back and brooked breastbone) if it is fairly well-fleshed.

2. *Fleshing.* Be poorly fleshed and a young tom turkey may have a thick coarse skin and extended breast that is pouchy or flabby.

3. *Fat.* Be lacking in fat covering over all parts of the carcass.

4. *Pinfeathers.* Has numerous pinfeathers and vestigial feathers (i.e., hair or down, as the case may be) scattered over the entire carcass if the carcass is dressed poultry; if ready-to-cook poultry, the carcass is free from protruding pinfeathers and vestigial feathers, but may have nonprotruding pinfeathers that do not seriously detract from the appearance of the carcass.

5. *Skin tears.* Has torn skin, disjointed bones, and broken bones but only if there is no evidence of a related severe bruise or blood clot. Wing tips may have been removed.

6. *Bruises.* Has numerous and large discolored areas or blemishes of the skin which may be accompanied by some reddening and darkening of the flesh beneath, if such discolored areas and blemishes do not render any part of the carcass unfit for food.

7. *Freezer burn.* Shows more than moderate "freezer burn" or evidence thereof (including, but not being limited to, numerous pockmarks or large dried areas) on any part of the carcass.

Grade standards for dressed and ready-to-cook poultry. The United States Department of Agriculture formulated the following grade standards which became effective January 1, 1950.

U. S. Grade A. Any lot of dressed poultry or ready-to-cook poultry composed of one or more containers of carcasses of the same kind and class may be designated as U. S. Grade A if not less than 90 per cent, by count, of the carcasses in such lot are of A quality, the remainder is of B quality, and no individual container in such lot contains more carcasses of B quality than in the proportion of 2 to each 12 carcasses in the container.

U. S. Grade B. Any lot of dressed poultry or ready-to-cook poultry composed of one or more containers of carcasses of the same kind and class may be designated as U. S. Grade B if not less than 90 per cent, by count, of the carcasses in such lot are of at least B quality, the remainder is of C quality, and no individual container in such lot contains more carcasses of C quality than in the proportion of 2 to each 12 carcasses in the container.

U. S. Grade C. Any lot of dressed poultry or ready-to-cook poultry may be designated as U. S. Grade C if it consists of carcasses of not less than C quality.

Weight ranges. The suggested weight specifications for ready-to-cook chickens are given in Table 90.

Grades used by the packers. The packers have not all adopted the grades proposed by the Bureau of Agricultural Economics. Most of them have special grade names which they have advertised over a period of years and they are reluctant to discontinue such established grade names as Priebe Quality Brand, Swift's Premium, etc.

Packing Poultry

The process of packaging poultry together with allied processes is known in the poultry trade as packing poultry.

Containers. The containers in which poultry is packed may be wooden barrels or boxes made out of wood or fiberboard. Barrels are used primarily for shipping nearby poultry to the eastern markets and for shipping turkeys. Barrels are also used for packing cocks and lower-grade poultry in the large packing plants. However, boxes are replacing barrels for the packing of turkeys. Types of containers most generally used for dressed poultry are shown in Figure 193. Boxes of many different dimensions are required for packing the different sizes of birds.

Style of pack. While other types of packs are used in arranging the dressed birds in their respective containers, the great bulk of the poultry killed and dressed in the United States is packed breast up in boxes with twelve birds to each box. The style of pack generally used is the breast pack shown in Figure 193. With the development of quick freezing and full drawing, there has come the use of individual bird wrappers made out of cello-

Table 90

READY-TO-COOK POULTRY

Kinds and Classes	Weight Range Per Carcass	
	Minimum	Maximum
Broilers or fryers	None	1 pound 8 ounces
	Over 1 pound 8 ounces	2 pounds
	Over 2 pounds	2 pounds 8 ounces
	Over 2 pounds 8 ounces	3 pounds
	Over 3 pounds	3 pounds 8 ounces
Roasters	Over 2 pounds 8 ounces	3 pounds
	Over 3 pounds	3 pounds 8 ounces
	Over 3 pounds 8 ounces	4 pounds
	Over 4 pounds	4 pounds 8 ounces
	Over 4 pounds 8 ounces	5 pounds
	Over 5 pounds	None
Hens or stewing chickens or fowl	None	2 pounds
	Over 2 pounds	2 pounds 8 ounces
	Over 2 pounds 8 ounces	3 pounds
	Over 3 pounds	3 pounds 8 ounces
	Over 3 pounds 8 ounces	4 pounds
	Over 4 pounds	4 pounds 8 ounces
	Over 4 pounds 8 ounces	5 pounds
	Over 5 pounds	5 pounds 8 ounces
	Over 5 pounds 8 ounces	None
Cocks or old roosters	None	2 pounds 8 ounces
	Over 2 pounds 8 ounces	3 pounds 8 ounces
	Over 3 pounds 8 ounces	4 pounds 8 ounces
	Over 4 pounds 8 ounces	5 pounds 8 ounces
	Over 5 pounds 8 ounces	None
Turkeys and geese (all classes)	None	4 pounds
	Over 4 pounds	6 pounds
	Over 6 pounds	8 pounds
	Over 8 pounds	10 pounds
	Over 10 pounds	12 pounds
	Over 12 pounds	14 pounds
	Over 14 pounds	16 pounds
	Over 16 pounds	18 pounds
	Over 18 pounds	20 pounds
	Over 20 pounds	None
Ducks (all classes)	None	3 pounds
	Over 3 pounds	3 pounds 8 ounces
	Over 3 pounds 8 ounces	4 pounds
	Over 4 pounds	None
Guineas (all classes)	None	12 ounces
	Over 12 ounces	1 pound
	Over 1 pound	1 pound 4 ounces
	Over 1 pound 4 ounces	1 pound 8 ounces
	Over 1 pound 8 ounces	None
Pigeons (all classes)	None	6 ounces
	Over 6 ounces	10 ounces
	Over 10 ounces	14 ounces
	Over 14 ounces	None

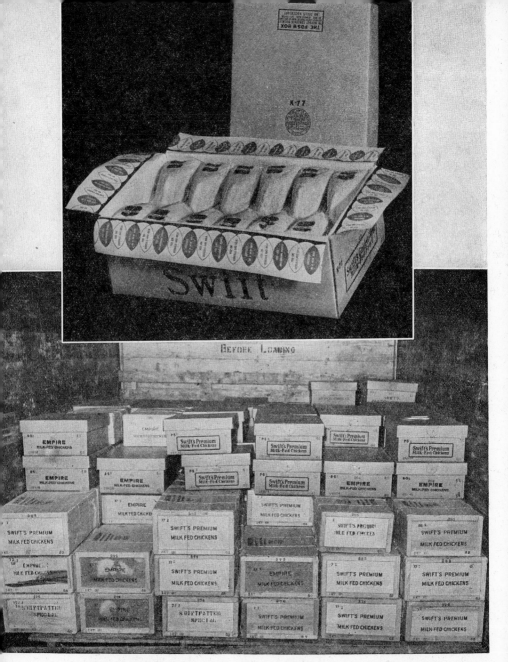

Fig. 193. Packing dressed poultry. Above, the breast pack generally used for all classes of dressed chickens. Below, two types of containers used for dressed poultry, the wire-bound wooden box and the fiberboard box. (Courtesy National Container Association.)

phane, cloth, and parchment paper. Attractive packages containing individual birds are also being used. Poultry is being packed and displayed with a greater consumer appeal each year. Eviscerated poultry is being packed in some plants in cardboard containers, six birds per box.

Maintaining the Quality of Dressed Poultry

The maintenance of the quality of the freshly killed bird until it is consumed constitutes an important marketing problem. Research agencies both governmental and industrial have contributed to its solution.

Cooling. Freshly killed poultry should be cooled as soon as possible. Cooling in cold water is sometimes used when the birds are killed for local consumption or nearby markets. Because several hours are required for cooling and the keeping qualities of the birds are reduced, water cooling has limited usage in poultry-packing plants; however, it is used in some plants as a supplement to dry chilling. In commercial poultry-packing plants most of the dressed poultry is cooled in the coolers where the temperature ranges from 30° F. to 34° F. The dressed birds are hung on portable steel racks which hold from 150 to 180 mature chickens and then rolled from the dressing room to the cooler. When the internal temperature of the carcasses has been reduced to 35° F. or lower, the birds may be packed. The rate of cooling may be increased by circulating the air in the cooling room.

Ready-to-cook poultry. For many years it was maintained that undrawn poultry would keep better than poultry which was drawn. Under the conditions which prevailed in the industry when the research work on this problem was done by Dr. Mary Pennington and her associates in the Bureau of Chemistry of the United States Department of Agriculture, this was no doubt true. With improved refrigeration and the advent of the quick-freezing process, the drawing or evisceration of poultry which was to be marketed or stored became possible. While much consumer education will be required before a great demand for oven-dressed and frozen poultry can be created, this new industry is developing. The operation of an eviscerating room is shown in Figure 194. It is believed by those who have studied the problem that the quality of poultry can be maintained better in full-drawn and quick-frozen birds which are properly refrigerated than in the undrawn poultry.

The future of ready-to-cook poultry prepared in the production areas appears bright because this is sound marketing procedure.

Quick freezing. There are three processes of quick-freezing poultry used in the United States. The "Z" process uses a brine mist at 0° F. or lower, which is sprayed over the birds, thereby freezing them. The Birdseye process freezes poultry under pressure and at low temperatures ($-25°$ to $-50°$ F.) by bringing the product in contact with hollow metal plates which are cooled by the direct expansion of ammonia. Another process used for freezing poultry is the use of strong cold ($-40°$ F.) air blast blown against the birds.

Quick freezing does not injure the quality of the meat as does slow freezing, because rapid freezing prevents the formation of large ice crystals which rupture the cells.

Refrigeration. Artificial refrigeration is essential to the proper marketing of poultry in the United States. The seasonal nature of production makes it necessary to have in storage on January 1 of each year usually more than 100,-

Fig. 194. Preparation of ready-to-cook poultry. Top, eviscerated and cellophane-wrapped turkeys being placed in a fast-freezing chamber. (Courtesy Frosted Food Sales Corp.) Center, packing eviscerated and cellophane-wrapped broilers. (Courtesy Swift and Company.) Bottom, preparing ready-to-cook poultry before fast-freezing. (Courtesy Fairmont Creamery Company.)

000,000 pounds of poultry. Cold-storage warehouses render this service to the industry. The seasonal holdings of dressed poultry in cold storage for 1945–1950 is shown in Figure 195.

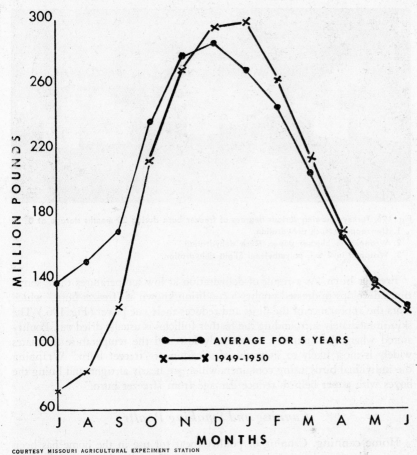

AVERAGE FOR 5 YEARS
1949-1950

COURTESY MISSOURI AGRICULTURAL EXPERIMENT STATION

Fig. 195. Seasonal variation in cold storage holdings of dressed poultry in the United States, 1945–50.

Freezing. Dressed poultry may be rapidly frozen when delivered to the cold-storage warehouse by placing it in a room where the temperature is −20° F. Since low temperatures are more expensive than high temperatures in a cold-storage warehouse and it has been believed that too low temperatures are injurious to the quality of dressed poultry, poultry has been frozen at 0° F. and stored at temperatures above zero. More recently it has been learned that the quality of dressed poultry is improved when it is quickly frozen at very low temperatures (−20° F.) and held at temperatures well below 0° F. Poultry stored for three years at −20° F. has been found to retain its quality in splendid condition. At present the tendency is for the more progressive warehouses to use temperatures below 0° F. for freezing and storing poultry. The average temperature of most cold-storage warehouse poultry rooms is about 0° F.

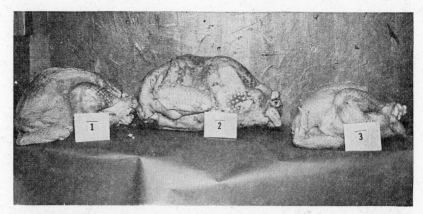

Fig. 196. Turkeys showing various degrees of freezer burn during 20 months storage at 0° F.:
1. Unwrapped. Much dehydration.
2. Wrapped in butcher paper. Much dehydration.
3. Wrapped in 2 mil. polyethylene. Slight dehydration.

Freezer burn. As a result of dehydration at low temperatures there some-times develops in dressed poultry a condition known as "freezer burn," which mars the appearance of the birds and reduces their sale price. (Fig. 196.) The skin immediately surrounding the feather follicles is usually dried out. Poultry stored where the humidity is relatively low and the temperature fluctuates widely is most likely to show this dessication or "freezer burn." Wrapping the individual birds, using containers which are nearly airtight, and lining the boxes with paper help to reduce damage from "freezer burn."

Canning and Smoking Poultry

Home canning. Canning of poultry meat for use in the home has been practiced by farm housewives for many years. The following instructions for home canning are taken from Directions for Canning Chicken at Home, supplied by the Institute of American Poultry Industries.

Preparing the meat. Prepare the chickens as for cooking. Pick, singe, re-move pinfeathers, wash, and cut into the usual pieces for serving. Clean thoroughly, taking care not to break the gall bladder, which would make the meat unfit for use. The lungs, kidneys, eggs, and liver should not be used for canning, but the gizzard and heart may be, if desired. Trim off any large pieces of fat, so that it may not interfere with the penetration of heat. Cut the white meat in large pieces from the breastbone and shoulders, but leave the meat on the bones in other pieces. Cut the neck off close to the body. Use the very bony pieces, such as back, neck, and perhaps the feet, after they have been skinned, for making broth to fill up the containers. Make the broth by covering the bony pieces with lightly salted cold water, bring to the sim-mering point, and simmer until the meat becomes tender.

Preheating and packing. Preheating may be done in several ways, the aim in all of which, however, is to heat the meat thoroughly until no red color shows. It is not necessary nor desirable to preheat until the meat is cooked to doneness, since a subsequent canning process will then overcook the meat. Either tin cans or pint glass jars may be used as containers. Wash glass jars, lids, and tin cans before using. Keep lids for tin cans dry.

Pack the chicken without cramming, and use some pieces with bone in each container. Leave space for liquid to circulate around the meat.

Preheating may be done by the following method: Place the chicken in a small quantity of boiling water, lower the heat, and simmer. After thoroughly heating, pack in tin cans, or glass jars, bring the broth to boiling, and pour over the meat to within one-half inch from the top of the container. Add salt, one-half to one teaspoon per pint, and if it is desired, a small quantity of gelatin, one tablespoon per pint softened in cold liquid, may be added to the broth. Fully seal tin cans or partially seal glass jars, and place each as prepared in the hot cooker so that the meat will not be cooled.

Commercial canning. This is a relatively new field, but several million pounds of poultry are canned annually by the commercial canners. The Hormel Packing Company, Austin, Minnesota, was one of the pioneers in the field of canning whole chicken. Canned poultry meat, chicken and noodles, and chicken soup are sold quite generally by retail food stores and the demand for such products is increasing.

Smoking poultry meat. This method of preserving meat has been used quite generally in the past for preserving pork on the farm. Benjamin and Pierce report that smoked chickens are sold in the Chinese sections of the United States. They also report that "smoked turkeys, prepared by pickling in brine and smoking like hams, are also obtainable from hotel supply houses." Directions for smoking poultry meat as suggested by the United States Department of Agriculture may be summarized as follows: Kill, pick, and draw the birds in the usual manner. The curing mixture consists of 6 lbs. salt, 3 lbs. sugar, and 3 oz. saltpeter dissolved in 4½ gallons of water. About four times this indicated quantity of pickle is required to cover 100 lbs. of turkeys, when carefully packed in a 50-gallon barrel.

The turkeys should be packed carefully and close together in a suitable container, such as a crock or a clean odorless hardwood barrel, and weighted down so that they will not float when the curing solution is added. Then pour the solution over the turkeys until they are covered with a slight excess of liquid. It is important to hold the temperature as near to 38° F. as possible. Remove the turkeys once each week, and repack to remix the solution and to make sure that it comes in contact with all parts of the birds.

Depending on the weight of the turkeys, the meat should be sufficiently cured in two to four weeks to be removed from the pickle and prepared for smoking. It is suggested that the individual turkey remain in the pickle from one and one-third to one and one-half days per pound of dressed weight.

The cured turkey should be washed, hung up to dry, then smoked, using hardwood, at a suggested smokehouse temperature of 100° to 110° F. Several hours in hardwood smoke may give sufficient flavor, although some may prefer to smoke the meat longer, even to the extent of having a fire under it eight to ten hours each day for several days.

Distribution of Live and Dressed Poultry

The efficiency of the system of distribution used in moving poultry from the producer to the consumer affects very materially the prices received by the producer and the quality of the products received by the consumer. While the methods employed in distributing poultry have improved, progress will no doubt continue to be made and a more efficient system of distributing poultry will be evolved.

Live Poultry

The system of distributing live poultry in the central markets has not kept pace with marketing in other fields. Excessive and unnecessary charges are often applied in marketing live poultry. Unscrupulous buyers and racketeering labor organizations have too often preyed upon this industry.

The government is attempting to curb unfair practices in the marketing of live poultry. By suitable regulation a diminishing live poultry trade may be restored to its rightful place in poultry marketing. The cost of marketing live poultry is given on page 443. The charges made by the different agencies for services rendered appear reasonable with the exception of the retailers' charge of seven cents per pound. To the producer such a charge implies either an exhorbitant profit or an inefficient marketing system. This charge is justified in some cases because the volume is relatively small.

Dressed Poultry

The great bulk of the dressed poultry is received in the central markets as New York dressed, i.e., bled and picked, but otherwise unprepared for consumption. Most of the poultry received in the cities is prepared for cooking in the butcher shops. There the birds are thawed if frozen, drawn, and otherwise prepared for the oven.

Drawing and preparing poultry for cooking. Two general methods of preparing poultry for cooking are used, depending upon the age of the bird and the purpose for which the carcass is intended. Roasting chickens, turkeys, ducks, and geese are prepared roaster style, the process being as follows: Remove the shanks and feet by cutting the legs off at the hock joint or slightly below this joint. If the tendons are pulled, this must be done before the shanks are removed. The neck skin should be slit down the back side and the neck bone cut off at the shoulder. Cutting the head off will leave the skin for covering the opening where the neck was removed. The internal organs are removed through a short cut made in the abdomen and around the vent. Roasting chickens should be trussed by tying or sewing them together to make a compact carcass (Fig. 197).

Fryers and broilers are prepared for cooking by splitting the broilers into two parts and fryers first into two parts and then each of the halves into several parts, depending upon the size of bird and the size of servings desired (Fig. 198).

Consumer education. Since the economic welfare of the poultry producer is dependent upon the demands of the consumer for poultry products, the producer should be vitally interested in seeing that consumers are properly educated on poultry consumption

REPRINTED BY PERMISSION FROM "MARKETING POULTRY PRODUCTS" BY BENJAMIN AND PIERCE, PUBLISHED BY JOHN WILEY AND SONS, INC.

Fig. 197. Roasting chicken ready for the oven.

problems. The consumers should be familiar with the grades employed. It would facilitate education on grades if a simplified and uniform system of grading were used. The consumer should be taught to evaluate quality in poultry meats. Suitable recipes for the preparation of poultry meats should be made available to consumers. Simple and easy methods for cooking poultry will create a greater demand for poultry meat. Consumer education should receive greater emphasis in the future than it has in the past. Such education is essential for the stimulation of greater consumption of poultry (Fig. 199).

The Poultry and Egg National Board. In 1941 the Poultry and Egg National Board, Chicago, Illinois, was established by the industry for the primary purpose of promoting the consumption of poultry and eggs. This was the first national co-operative effort of the poultry industry to promote its products. The results have been excellent and the support received particularly from the hatcheries has been very liberal and indicates that the industry realizes the value of consumer education and promotion and is willing to support such a program.

The P.E.N.B. is serving the poultry industry as the Meat Board serves the livestock industry.

Improved Methods of Handling Poultry

Improved facilities and better methods of marketing are continually being developed. The future will bring changes probably equally as important as those made in the past.

Refrigeration. The development of small mechanical refrigerators suitable

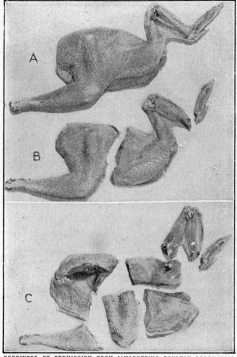

REPRINTED BY PERMISSION FROM "MARKETING POULTRY PRODUCTS"
BY BENJAMIN AND PIERCE, PUBLISHED BY JOHN WILEY AND SONS, INC.

Fig. 198. Broiler and fryers prepared for cooking.

for retail stores and the home has greatly improved the quality of poultry ultimately consumed. Every retail store which handles any appreciable amount of dressed poultry has refrigeration for holding meats at low temperatures. The number of homes where refrigeration is available is increasing each year. The housewife and the storekeeper hold poultry meat under refrigeration because they know that high temperatures lower the quality of poultry meat (Fig. 200).

Ready-to-cook poultry. The introduction of ready-to-cook poultry has simplified the sale of poultry in the retail markets because this poultry comes from the packing plants ready to be used by the housewife. Such poultry is proving popular with retailers as well as with housewives (Fig. 194). Some large Midwest poultry-packing plants are preparing 100 per cent of their poultry ready-to-cook.

Sale of poultry cuts. The sale of different cuts of meat from the larger domestic animals has long been an accepted practice, but all poultry from one and one-half pound broilers to forty-pound turkey toms has been sold as a whole carcass. In recent years some retailers have stimulated the demand for poultry meat by offering for sale the different parts of the bird (Fig. 200).

Rolls made of turkey meat have been developed and sold in some markets. Since 1945, half-turkeys have sold well.

Poultry meat imports and exports. The United States exports less than 0.3 per cent of the poultry meat produced. For instance, in 1948, 1,240,000 pounds of live poultry, 6,799,000 pounds of dressed poultry, and 400,000 pounds of canned poultry were exported.

The imports of poultry meat amount to about the same as the exports.

REVIEW QUESTIONS

1. How is live poultry transported to market? Have any changes in methods of transportation occurred in recent years?

Fig. 199. Poultry cooking demonstrations stimulate interest in the use of poultry products.

Fig. 200. A market where parts of the chicken are sold instead of the whole chicken.

2. What is the capacity of a live-poultry railroad car?
3. Name the more important channels by which live poultry moves from producer to consumer.
4. Why is New York an important live-poultry market?
5. Name and describe the live market grades of poultry as given by the United States Department of Agriculture.
6. Distinguish between market inspection and the operation of the Packers and Stockyard Act.
7. What motive do you think is most important to stimulate, to improve the quality of poultry? Why?
8. Name several of the more important costs of marketing live poultry from the producer located in the Middle West to the consumer in the East.
9. What are some of the factors which influence the gains obtained by fattening poultry?
10. Some operators state that the gains they get today are below those obtained in the early days of commercial fattening. What explanation could you offer for this change?
11. Does the kind of feed used in fattening rations influence the distribution and the consistency of the fat deposited?
12. Illustrate graphically the seasonal production of poultry meat.
13. Name and discuss the methods used in removing the feathers of poultry.

REFERENCES

ALEXANDER, L. M.: POULTRY COOKING. U. S. D. A. Farmers' Bul. 1888. 1941.

APPEL, V. O.: FREEZING AND REFRIGERATED STORAGE OF POULTRY AND POULTRY PRODUCTS IN THE UNITED STATES. Proc. 8th World's Poultry Cong., pp. 531–536. 1948.

BAILEY, R. L., STEWART, GEO. F., AND LOWE, BELLE: ICE SLUSH COOLING OF DRESSED POULTRY. Refrig. Engin. 55: 369–371–A. 1948.

BEERY, ISABEL, PRUDENT, INEZ, AND WILSON, EVA DONELSON: FOUR METHODS OF DEFROSTING POULTRY STUDIED. Jour. of Home Ec. 41: 203–204. 1949.

BENJAMIN, E. W., PIERCE, H. C., AND TERMOHLEN, W. D.: Marketing Poultry Products, 4th ed. John Wiley & Sons, Inc., New York. 1949.

BIRD, H. R.: THE NUTRITIVE VALUE OF EGGS AND POULTRY MEAT. U. S. Egg and Poultry Mag., 49: 402, 419, 427, 458, 477. 1943.

BROWN, H. D., KUNKLE, L. E., AND WINTER, A. R.: Frozen Foods. Processing and Handling. S. F. Hinkle and Sons, Asheville, Ohio. 1946.

CANNED POULTRY. Amer. Egg and Poultry Rev. 10, No. 3: 42–44. 1949.

CARLIN, FRANCES, LOWE, BELLE, AND STEWART, G. F.: THE EFFECT OF AGING VERSUS AGING, FREEZING, AND THAWING ON THE PALATABILITY OF EVISCERATED POULTRY. Food Tech. 3: 156–159. 1949.

CHESSHER, L. H.: WHY I SELL MY PRODUCTS CLOSE HOME. U. S. Egg and Poultry Mag., 55: No. 4, pp. 9–11, 26. 1949.

DAVIDSON, J. A., SCHAIBLE, P. J., AND PILLAR, R.: BONING POULTRY. Mich. Sta. Quart. Bul. 24: 11–19. 1941.

DIEHL, H. C., AND WARNER, K. F.: FREEZING TO PRESERVE HOME GROWN FOODS. U. S. D. A. Circ. 709. 1945.

DUNN, M. S., CAMIEN, M. N., MALIN, RUTH B., MURPHY, E. A., AND REINER, P. J.: PERCENTAGES OF TWELVE AMINO ACIDS IN BLOOD, CARCASS, HEART,

KIDNEY, LIVER, MUSCLE, AND SKIN OF EIGHT ANIMALS. Univ. Cal. Pub. Physiol. 8: 293–326. 1949.

ECHTERLING, C. J.: EFFECT OF SURFACE TREATMENT IN THE PRESERVATION OF FROZEN POULTRY. Poultry Sci., 28: 929–930. 1949.

ESSELEN, W. B., LAWLER, KATHERINE M., AND FELLERS, C. R.: HOME FREEZING IN MASSACHUSETTS. Mass. Sta. Bul. 437. Revised, 1948.

FENTON, FAITH, AND DARFLER, JUNE: FOODS FROM THE FREEZER. Cornell Sta. Bul. 692. 1946.

FREEZING MEAT AND POULTRY FOR HOME USE. U. S. D. A. Bur. An. Ind. A W I–75. 1944.

GRACE, N. H.: A COMPARATIVE STUDY OF SEMI-SCALDING AND DRY ROUGHING IN RELATION TO THE EASE OF REMOVING PINFEATHERS BY WAX DRESSING. Sci. Agr., 17: 50–53. 1936.

GUNDERSON, M. F., SCHWARTZ, PAULINE M., AND ROSE, K. D.: HOW MUCH DRESSED POULTRY IS AS CLEAN AS IT LOOKS. U. S. Egg and Poultry Mag., 52: 389–391, 418, 420, 422, 424–425. 1946.

GUTTERIDGE, H. S., AND O'NEIL, J. B.: METHODS AND RATIONS FOR FATTEN-ING POULTRY, III. THE EFFECTS OF VARIOUS FATS, NUMBER OF FEEDINGS, AND LENGTH OF FATTENING PERIOD. Sci. Agr., 21: 6. 1941.

GWIN, JAMES M., NEWELL, GEO. W., AND JULL, MORLEY A.: SOME OBSERVA-TIONS CONCERNING THE PERIOD OF FASTING POULTRY BEFORE SLAUGHTER. Poultry Sci., 28: 229–231. 1949.

HARSHAW, H. M.: WEIGHTS OF PARTS AND PER CENT EDIBLE MEAT OBTAINED FROM CUT-UP CHICKENS. U. S. Egg and Poultry Mag., 49: 405. 1943.

HENDERSON, E. W.: FREEZER BURN PREVENTED BY WATER. Mich. Sta. Quart. Bul. 24: 304–307. 1942.

HENDERSON, E. W.: PERCENTAGE OF EDIBLE MEAT IN RELATION TO MEAT TYPE SCORE OF CHICKENS. Mich. Sta. Quart. Bul. 28: 176. 1946.

HITE, J. P., KLAXIN, S. E., KUMMEROW, F. A., VAIL, G. E., AND AVERY, T. B.: FAT RANCIDITY IN EVISCERATED POULTRY, III AND IV. Poultry Sci., 28: 244–253. 1949.

HOPPINGARNER, A. L.: WHAT IT COSTS TO PROCESS POULTRY TODAY. U. S. Egg and Poultry Mag., 55: No. 3, pp. 15–16, 42. 1949.

HURST, W. M.: LAYOUT AND OPERATIONS OF COOPERATIVE POULTRY DRESS-ING PLANTS. Farm Credit Admin. U. S. D. A. Misc. Rpt. 101. 1948.

JEWELL, J. D.: WHICH SHALL IT BE—FRESH OR FROZEN? U. S. Egg and Poultry Mag., 55: No. 5, pp. 8–9, 27. 1949.

JOHNSON, R. D.: IS STATION FEEDING PRACTICAL? U. S. Egg and Poultry Mag., 55: No. 3, pp. 17–19, 38. 1949.

KILPATRICK, MARY E., MOUNTJOY, BEATRICE M., AND DAVIS, EMILY C.: CHICKEN IN THE FREEZER. A I S–74. Bur. Human Nutr. and Home Ec., U. S. D. A. 1948.

KOONZ, C. H., AND RAMSBOTTOM, J. M.: INFLUENCE OF FREEZING ON COLOR OF BONES AND ADJACENT TISSUES. Food Res., 12: 393–399. 1947.

KOONZ, C. H., TRELEASE, R. D., AND ROBINSON, H. E.: LOW TEMPERATURES KEEP DRESSED POULTRY GOOD LONGER. U. S. Egg and Poultry Mag., 53: No. 12, pp. 12–13, 38. 1947.

LARZELERE, H. E., AND LEAVER, J. B.: CONSUMER RESPONSE TO CHICKENS IN 1948. Mich. Sta. Quart. Bul. 31: 409–415. 1949.

MATLACK, M. B.: INSTRUCTIONS ON PROCESSING FOR COMMUNITY FROZEN-FOOD LOCKER PLANTS. U. S. D. A. Misc. Pub. 588. 1946.

MAW, W. A., PUDDINGTON, I. E., AND MAW, A. J. G.: SUPPLEMENTARY FATS IN THE FATTENING RATION. Sci. Agr., 18: 2. 1937.

MAW, W. A.: SANITARY POULTRY DRAWING. HOW TO MINIMIZE CONTAMINATION FROM BACTERIA. U. S. Egg and Poultry Mag., 45: 595–598. 1939.

MAW, W. A., AND MAW, A. J. G.: EFFECT OF INITIAL WEIGHT, RANGE-FEEDING, AND FATTENING ON GRAIN AND EDIBLE PORTION IN BARRED PLYMOUTH ROCK COCKERELS. Sci. Agr., 19: 11. 1939.

MAW, A. J. G., AND MAW, W. A.: SOME OBSERVATIONS ON METHODS OF FATTENING CHICKENS. U. S. Egg and Poultry Mag., 45: 332, 333, 334, 378. 1939.

MAW, W. A., AND NIKOLAICZUK, N.: A BILE DEPLETION METHOD TO ELIMINATE LIVER STAIN IN STORED DRESSED POULTRY. U. S. Egg and Poultry Mag., 48: 275–278. 1942.

MCALLISTER, W. T., AND BAUSMAN, R. O.: THE RETAIL MARKETING OF FRYING CHICKENS IN PHILADELPHIA. Del. Sta. Bul. 275. 1948.

MCNALLY, E. H., AND SPICKNALL, N. H.: MEAT YIELD FROM FINE, DRESSED, AND EVISCERATED RHODE ISLAND RED MALES OF BROILER, FRYER, AND LIGHT ROASTER WEIGHTS. Poultry Sci., 28: 562–565. 1949.

MEHRHOF, N. R., WARD, W. F., AND MOORE, O. K.: COMPARISON OF PUREBRED AND CROSSBRED COCKERELS WITH RESPECT TO FATTENING AND DRESSING QUALITIES. Fla. Sta. Bul. 410. 1945.

MILLARES, R., AND FELLERS, C. R.: VITAMIN AND AMINO ACID CONTENT OF PROCESSED CHICKEN MEAT PRODUCTS. Food Res., 14: 131–143. 1949.

NEWELL, G. W., GWIN, J. M., AND JULL, M. A.: THE EFFECT OF CERTAIN HOLDING CONDITIONS ON THE QUALITY OF DRESSED POULTRY. Poultry Sci., 27: 251–256. 1948.

OCOMA FOOD COMPANY'S JERSEY CITY EVISCERATING PLANT. Amer. Egg and Poultry Rev. 10, No. 2: 56–58. 1949.

PEARCE, J. A., AND LAVERS, C. G.: FROZEN STORAGE OF POULTRY, V. EFFECT OF SOME PROCESSING FACTORS ON QUALITY. Canad. Jour. Res. 27F: 253–265. 1949.

PRIEBE, E. W.: POULTRY HANDLING AND PROCESSING COSTS. U. S. Egg and Poultry Mag., 53: No. 3, pp. 3–8, 43–44. 1947.

PRIEBE, E.: COST OF FEEDING PLUS COST OF SHRINKAGE IS MAJOR ITEM IN PROCESSING COST. U. S. Egg and Poultry Mag., 54: No. 2, pp. 7–9. 1948.

REGULATIONS GOVERNING THE GRADING AND INSPECTION OF POULTRY AND DOMESTIC RABBITS AND EDIBLE PRODUCTS THEREOF AND UNITED STATES SPECIFICATIONS FOR CLASSES, STANDARDS, AND GRADES WITH RESPECT THERETO, EFFECTIVE JANUARY 1, 1950. Reprinted from the Federal Register November 15, 1949. U. S. D. A. Prod. and Marketing Adm., Poultry Branch.

REYNOLDS, H. J.: POULTRY PROCESSING IMPROVEMENTS AND CHANGES. Amer. Egg and Poultry Rev. 10, No. 2: 100, 102–104. 1949.

REYNOLDS, H. J.: EFFICIENCY IN PROCESSING. U. S. Egg and Poultry Mag., 55: No. 6, pp. 18–19. 1949.

ROBERTS, J. B.: MARKETING AND PRICING CHICKENS IN KENTUCKY. Ky. Sta. Bul. 433. 1942.

ROBERTS, J., AND ROBERTSON, E. I.: A COMPARISON OF WET AND DRY COOLING OF DRESSED POULTRY. Wash. Sta. Bul. 403. 1941.

SEARLS, E. N.: MARKETING OF DRESSED CHICKENS A PROFITABLE ENTERPRISE. Cornell Farm Res., 15: 7. Jan., 1949.

SLOCUM, R. R.: MARKETING POULTRY. U. S. D. A. Farmers' Bul. 1377. 1943.
SMITH, E. Y., SCHOLES, J. C., AND HALL, G. O.: SMOKE-FLAVORING TURKEY AND POULTRY MEATS. Cornell Ext. Bul. 446. 1940.
STEWART, GEO. F., AND MUSSEHL, FRANK E.: THE RECOVERY OF BY-PRODUCTS FROM POULTRY EVISCERATION WASTES. Poultry Sci., 20: 450–453. 1941.
STEWART, G. F., HANSON, H. L., AND LOWE, BELLE: EFFECTS OF AGING, FREEZING RATE, AND STORAGE PERIOD ON PALATABILITY OF BROILERS. Food Res., 10: 16–27. 1945.
SWEET, M. H., AND STEWART, G. F.: REFRIGERATED BRINE SPRAYS FOR COOLING DRESSED POULTRY. U. S. Egg and Poultry Mag., 48: 261–265, 308–313. 1942.
TERMOHLEN, W. D.: INTERNATIONAL STANDARDIZATION AND GRADING OF EGGS AND POULTRY AND UNIFORMITY OF PACKAGES. Proc. 8th World's Poultry Cong., pp. 59–70. 1948.
TRELEASE, R. D., KOONZ, C. H., AND ROBINSON, H. E.: PROMPT EVISCERATION IS BEST GUARD AGAINST THE DEVELOPMENT OF VISCERAL TAINTS. U. S. Egg and Poultry Mag., 54: No. 10, pp. 12, 22–23. 1948.
TRESSLER, D. K., AND EVERS, E. F.: The Freezing Preservation of Foods. The Avi Publishing Co., New York. 1943.
TRUCK FLEET BUILDS BUSINESS IN FRESH POULTRY. Food Ind., 21: 1078–1079. 1949.
WAGONER, C. E., VAIL, GLADYS E., AND CONRAD, R. M.: THE EFFECT OF DEGREE OF SURFACE EXPOSURE ON DETERIORATION OF FROZEN POULTRY. Poultry Sci., 26: 173–175. 1947.
WAGONER, C. E., VAIL, GLADYS E., AND CONRAD, R. M.: THE EFFECT OF PREMORTAL FAST ON DETERIORATION OF FROZEN POULTRY. Poultry Sci., 26: 167–169. 1947.
WARREN, SARA, MARGOLF, P. H., AND ZIEGLER, P. T.: FREEZE MEAT AND POULTRY. Penn. Ext. Circ. 304. 1947.
WATSON, ANDREW E.: POULTRY PRODUCTS USED BY THE SUMMER TRADE IN MAINE. Maine Sta. Bul. 452. 1947.
WILLIAMS, I. L.: KILLING, DRESSING AND DRAWING POULTRY. Neb. Sta. Circ. 85. 1947.
WILLIAMS, I. L., AND FUNK, E. M.: FACTORS AFFECTING TEMPERATURE CHANGES IN DRESSED POULTRY DURING REFRIGERATION. Mo. Sta. Res. Bul. 334. 1941.
WILLS, RENA, LOWE, BELLE, SLOSBERG, HARRY, AND STEWART, GEO. F.: FROZEN STORAGE OF POULTRY. Refrig. Engin. 56: 49–51. 1948.
WILSON, W. T., AND SMITH, R. M.: BROILER PRODUCTION AND MARKETING IN NORTHWESTERN ARKANSAS. Ark. Sta. Bul. 412. 1941.
WINTER, E. P.: MARKETING MARGINS AND COSTS FOR POULTRY AND EGGS. U. S. D. A. Tech. Bul. 969. 1948.
WOODROOF, J. G.: PRESERVING FOODS BY FREEZING. Ga. Sta. Bul. 233. 1944.
WOODROOF, J. C., AND SHELOR, ETHYL: PREVENTION OF BONE DARKENING IN FROZEN PACKED CHICKEN. Food Ind., 20: 116, 120, 222, 224. 1948.

CHAPTER 14 ||||||||||||||||||||||||||||||||||||||||||||||||||||||

Poultry Farm Management

▼

The successful management of a poultry enterprise requires the application of the principles and practices discussed throughout this book, which apply to the various phases of poultry production. In this chapter the effect of management on profits in poultry farming will be considered. People engage in poultry raising primarily because of the profit motive—the desire to make a living out of the poultry business. Therefore, this chapter will discuss the effect of various factors on profits in the major poultry farming enterprises.

The Poultry and Egg Outlook

Poultry production has a definite place in American agriculture and its relative importance as one of the livestock enterprises may be expected to increase. As with other economic phenomena, there are cycles in production. These cycles are generally short because the life cycle of poultry is short and poultry raisers can get in and out of the business in a relatively short time. One measure of the relative profitableness of poultry raising is the feed-egg ratio. Figure 201 shows these ratios. These ratios show the number of dozens of eggs required to purchase one hundred pounds of poultry ration at prevailing prices. Since feed cost is the largest item of expense for the poultry producer, the feed-egg ratio shows the relative profitableness of egg production. However, when feed prices are extremely low, as they were in 1932, even though the feed-egg ratio is very low, poultry raising is not profitable because the total income of poultrymen is small and their purchasing power of other necessary commodities is low.

The response of poultry producers to these ratios is shown by the average number of layers kept in farm flocks (Fig. 202). It will be observed that in 1937 a very unfavorable price situation, as measured by feed-egg ratios, prevailed and the following year (1938) the number of layers per flock was the lowest since 1925. Poultry farmers respond to unfavorable price situations by reducing their production, but unfortunately they may get in and out at the wrong time. The poultrymen should use these ratios to govern their production by increasing production when most farmers are reducing their flocks, and decreasing production when farmers generally are expanding their operations. When the feed-egg ratio is low the industry may expect an expansion as

476

soon as such an ex-
pansion can be initi-
ated, and likewise
when prices become
unfavorable a general
reduction may be ex-
pected.

Relation of indus-
trial activity to prof-
its in poultry rais-
ing. Poultrymen who
have been in the busi-

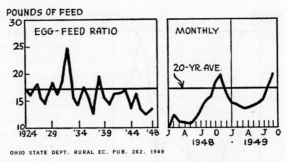

OHIO STATE DEPT. RURAL EC. PUB. 262. 1949

Fig. 201. Egg-feed ratio, 1924–1949.

ness of poultry raising for a period of years know that when business activity
is high their income from poultry and eggs is also relatively high. When the
income of industrial workers is low the demand for poultry products is cur-
tailed, and the poultry industry suffers accordingly. The very close relationship which exists between national income, farm prices for eggs, and egg
consumption is shown in Fig. 203. Using 1924–29 as a base (100) and comparing the more prosperous era of 1925–30 with the depression period of
1931–38, it will be found that from 1925 to 1930 the average index of income for industrial workers was 99.5 and the index for income to farmers
for chickens and eggs was 101.3 whereas from 1931 to 1938 these respective
indexes were 67.4 and 63.6. It is apparent from these data that the economic
welfare of the poultry raiser is closely associated with the income of industrial
workers. During the war period, this relationship was particularly apparent.

Labor Income from Poultry Raising

Missouri farm flock records (Fig. 204) show that since 1919 poultry raising
has returned a labor income every year and that the income per dollar invested
in feed for poultry was equal to or exceeded that invested in feed for other
livestock. During the depression years labor income for all agriculture was
low. Records from California show that from 1938 to 1947 commercial egg
flocks averaged 1928 hens and returned a farm income of $2.02 per hen or a
total of $3914.76 per flock.

The Poultry Plant Layout

The layout of the poultry enterprise on each farm must be adjusted to the
farm and to the convenience of the manager. There are, however, certain principles of management which apply to the plan for any poultry enterprise. The
farm should be laid out so that labor can be utilized most efficiently and so
that the best management practices can be followed with a minimum of effort.

General farm. Though poultry on general farms is usually given but little
attention, the layout should be such as will encourage a sanitation program
and make the best possible use of the labor available. Figure 205 shows four

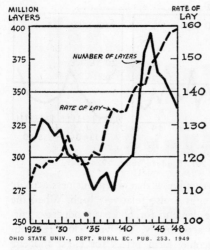

Fig. 202. Average number of laying hens and rate of lay per hen, U. S., 1925–1948.

different yarding systems for laying flocks. Such a plan contemplates the yarding of the old stock and the growing of young stock on free range which is used only once every three years, the chicks therefore being reared on fresh ground each year.

Commercial poultry farms. The commercial poultry farm is quite generally a one-man unit and the entire farm is devoted to poultry raising with a small acreage for growing vegetables and fruits. Figure 206 shows the layout for a poultry farm with a capacity of 1,500 layers and facilities for brooding 3,000 chicks each season on fresh ground. Ten colony brooder houses are used for brooding and rearing to maturity 1,200 pullets which are housed as layers each fall. For those who wish to use a long brooder house, range shelters may be used instead of colony brooder houses. The colony brooder houses or the long brooder house could be used for growing broilers during the winter months. Some poultrymen prefer to reduce the laying flock and use part of the laying house for brooding, placing the pullets in range shelters after they no longer require heat.

Other poultry farms. The specialized broiler producer will probably use a long brooder house or the colony system of brooding. The birds may be given range or confined, depending upon the freedom of the range from disease and parasites. The specialized poultry breeder may use the layout for the commercial poultryman, modifying it to provide additional range for rearing male birds.

Selecting a Breed and Variety

The beginner is confronted with the problem of selecting a breed and variety to raise. His success may be determined by the choice made. It is best to choose from a limited number of established breeds. Actual records kept on several hundred farm flocks in Missouri show that the breeds most commonly raised are the most profitable. Table 91 shows that the farmers who raised White Leghorns, Barred Rocks, Rhode Island Reds, White Rocks, and New Hampshires had a much higher labor income per hen than did those who raised the less common varieties. New and odd varieties should be given proper consideration, but the beginner will do well to choose one of the established varieties which has proved its ability to make money under the conditions under which he plans to raise them.

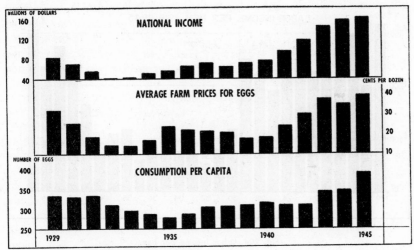

COURTESY MERRIL, LYNCH, PIERCE, FENNER, AND BEANE

Fig. 203. Relation of income to egg prices and consumption.

Probably more important than the choice of the breed and variety is the choice of a strain within the variety chosen. It is well to know the flock and the breeding of the flock from which the stock comes. Most beginners give too little attention to selection of the strain they raise. The livability of the adult stock as well as of the young stock is important. Egg production, egg size, and market quality of the stock should also be considered.

Table 91

COMPARISON OF BREEDS BY EGG PRODUCTION, CAPITAL INVESTMENT, FEED COST, SELLING PRICE PER DOZEN, ITEMIZED TOTAL RECEIPTS, TOTAL EXPENSE, AND LABOR INCOME PER HEN (1934–1945) [1]

Breeds	Num-ber of Flocks	Hens Per Flock	Egg Pro. Per Hen	Capi-tal In-vest. Per Hen	Feed Cost Per Hen	Feed Cost Per Dozen	Egg	Fowl	+ or − Inven.	Total Rec't	Total Exp. Per Hen	Labor In-come Per Hen
Whi. Wyan....	63	137	125	$2.79	$1.62	15.6¢	$2.24	$ .77	−.003¢	$3.01	$2.02	$ .99
R. I. Reds.....	166	142	143	3.09	2.34	19.6¢	2.86	1.20	+.07¢	4.13	2.80	1.33
New Hamp. *..	42	190	160	3.71	2.64	19.8¢	4.10	1.22	+.41¢	5.73	3.17	2.56
Bar'd Rocks...	101	133	133	3.55	1.85	16.7¢	2.57	.93	+.08¢	3.58	2.31	1.27
White Rocks...	146	128	140	3.75	2.36	20.0¢	2.86	1.31	+.04¢	4.21	2.93	1.28
All Heavy B....	518	139	140	3.39	2.20	18.8¢	2.87	1.13	+.11¢	4.11	2.69	1.42
Misc..........	265	160	130	2.93	1.77	16.3¢	2.25	.83	+.004¢	3.08	2.20	.88
White Leg.....	801	275	159	2.81	1.82	13.7¢	2.89	.46	+.02¢	3.37	2.22	1.15
Grand Total All Breeds...	1,584	211	151	$2.95	$1.90	15.0¢	$2.80	$ .65	+.04¢	$3.49	$2.33	$1.16

* A majority of the New Hampshire records were made during the war period.

[1] Mo. Sta. Circ. 554.

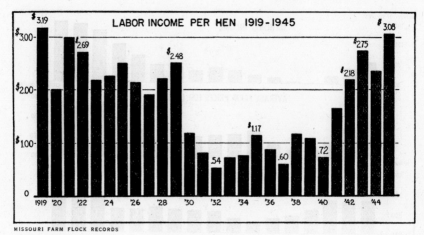

Fig. 204. Labor income per hen.

Record Keeping

Some system of keeping records is essential to the management of any business enterprise. Every poultryman who keeps a flock for profit should at least keep a simple set of records which will show the annual net profit or loss from the flock. A number of states through the Agricultural Extension Service have prepared record forms for flock owners who desire to know more about their poultry business.

The commercial poultrymen should keep more detailed records which give more specific information as to costs and income. The poultry breeder will need to keep the various records indicated in the chapter on breeding. Those who operate diversified poultry enterprises should keep records which show the relative profitableness of the different phases of the business. The hatcherymen should have a complete set of books which should be analyzed each year.

Factors Influencing Profits in Poultry Raising

Profits in poultry raising are dependent upon sound management practices. Several states have collected and analyzed flock records to show the relation of management practices to profits and income in poultry raising. The major factors are reviewed here.

Size of flock. It is evident that if poultry is to return any sizeable income to the producer the flock must be of sufficient size to do that. Records from New Hampshire as given in Table 92 show that though the return per hen was about the same in small and large flocks more than 600 hens were required to provide a labor income of more than $1000 per year. Fifteen flocks averaging 1750 layers returned an annual labor income of $2831.36.

Yearly egg production. High egg production is essential to a profitable

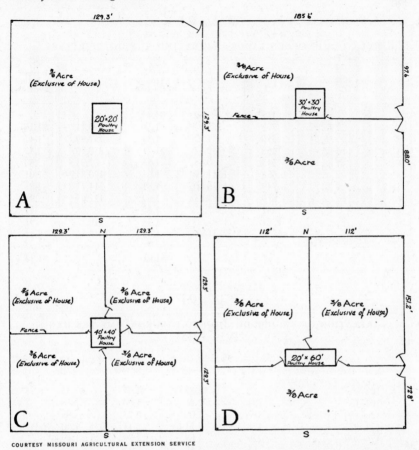

Fig. 205. These diagrams show four different types of yarding arrangement: A, single yards are often used with small flocks; B, by rotating the runs, more sanitary conditions are assured and more green feed provided; C, the four-yard system may be used either for the large square house or the long rectangular type of building; D, the triple yarding system is especially suitable for the long rectangular house.

flock. Fig. 207 shows that annual egg production is closely related to the cost of producing eggs. Records collected from Missouri flocks show (Table 93) that from 1934 to 1945 flocks averaging 101 to 125 eggs returned 56 cents labor income per hen while flocks averaging 176 to 200 eggs per hen returned $1.89 per hen.

In Washington in 1945 the relationship between average annual egg production and labor income per bird was:

154 eggs or less $2.24
155–174 .... 2.70
175–194 .... 3.08
195 and over 3.41

Table 92

RELATION BETWEEN LABOR INCOME AND NUMBER OF LAYERS [2]

Number of Farms	Number of Layers	Labor Income Per Farm	Labor Income Per Hen	Increase in Income for Each Increase in Layers	Increase in Return Per Hen
17...................	145	$ 264.82	$1.83	....	...
30...................	239	373.93	1.56	$ 109.11	$1.16
22...................	350	531.82	1.52	157.89	1.42
21...................	458	782.52	1.71	250.70	2.32
29...................	543	850.45	1.57	67.93	.80
24...................	638	1041.29	1.63	190.84	2.01
31...................	749	1356.00	1.81	314.71	2.83
26...................	879	1483.65	1.69	127.65	.98
18...................	1081	1567.33	1.45	83.68	.41
10...................	1321	1785.50	1.35	218.17	.91
15...................	1750	2831.86	1.62	1046.36	2.44
243..................			$1.61		$1.53

Table 93

RELATION OF EGG PRODUCTION TO LABOR INCOME PER HEN
(1934–1945)

Average Yearly Egg Production	Number Flocks	Total Income	Total Expenses	Labor Income Per Hen
100 or less..........	81	$1.87	$1.54	$ .33
101–125............	274	2.46	1.90	.56
126–150...'........	487	3.08	2.23	.85
151–175............	428	3.71	2.41	1.30
176–200............	229	4.68	2.79	1.89
201 or over.........	85	4.45	2.61	1.84
All Flocks..........	1584	$3.49	$2.33	$1.16

Fall egg production. Farms where fall egg production is high are more profitable than those where the fall production is low. Washington records for 1945 show that flocks with a fall lay of less than 34 per cent returned a labor income of $2.33 per hen as compared to $3.50 for flocks having a fall lay of over 54 per cent.

Percentage of pullets in the flock. Within recent years the idea of all-pullet flocks has been gaining. The advantages are: (1) Pullets lay more eggs than older birds. (2) They lay more fall eggs when eggs are higher in price. (3) The control of tuberculosis is improved. (4) Carry-over of disease infection is reduced. (5) Housing is simplified. The disadvantages are: (1)

[2] N. H. Sta. Circ. 75. 1947.

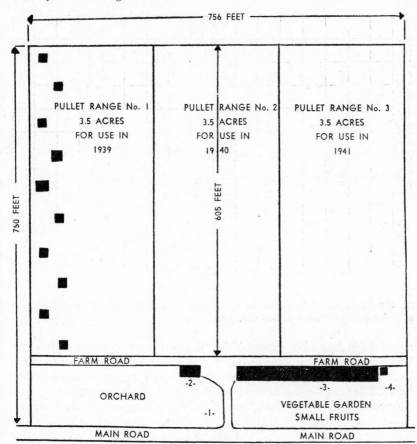

Fig. 206. Commercial poultry farm layout.

More chicks must be started each year which means more labor and expense for flock replacements. (2) More brooding and rearing equipment is needed. (3) Many productive and profitable hens must be marketed. Records kept in Iowa (Table 94) indicate that the general farmer would have a more profitable flock if all-pullet flocks were kept. Records from Indiana and Washington show that a high percentage of pullets in the flock was associated with higher labor income.

Mortality. To be profitable a flock must have a low death loss. The relation of mortality to labor income per hen as reported for flocks located in New Hampshire as presented in Table 95 shows that in depression as well as in more prosperous times the profits returned were closely related to the percentage of mortality experiencd by the flock.

Use of labor. The most efficiently organized and managed poultry farms

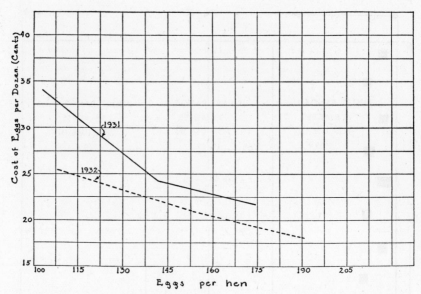

Fig. 207. The relation of production per hen and cost of producing eggs. (From Virginia Agricultural Experiment Station Bulletin 300, 1936.)

return the highest labor income. Table 96 presents the results of a Michigan Study which show that some producers realized three times as much for their labor in producing eggs as others. New York reports the time required to care for 1000 hens as ranging from 41 minutes to 125 minutes per day.

Attention has recently been focused on labor saving devices which are ur-

Table 94

COMPARISON OF ALL-PULLET AND MIXED FLOCKS [3]

Item	All-Pullet Flock	Mixed Hen and Pullet Flock
Number of birds in flock	256	293
Average eggs per hen	194	167
Per cent mortality of laying flock	20.7	27.4
Investment per hen	4.22	4.28
Expense per hen	3.85	3.70
Pounds of feed per hen	106.2	97.3
Average price rec'd. for eggs	.42	.42
Average cost per dozen eggs	.237	.265
Net income except labor	498.67	283.02
Net income per hen except labor	1.95	.96
Net income per hour for labor	1.80	.80
Days labor (10 hour day)	27.7	35.3

[3] Iowa Agri. Ext. Service, 760.

Table 95

RELATION OF ADULT MORTALITY TO LABOR INCOME PER HEN [4]

Per Cent Mortality			Labor Income Per Hen		
1932–35	1936–41	1942–45	1932–35	1936–41	1942–45
21.9........	17.9	17.9	$ .84	$ .78	$2.29
13.2........	12.8	9.9	1.20	1.42	2.73
8.8........	8.8	6.8	1.45	1.59	3.08
4.9........	3.3	4.4	1.55	1.74	3.99

Table 96

INFLUENCE OF LABOR EFFICIENCY ON LAYING
FLOCK COSTS AND RETURNS, 1932–35 [5]

ITEM	HOURS SPENT PER DOZEN EGGS		
	0.10 or Less	0.11 to 0.15	0.16 Up
Number of flocks.................	78	87	111
Number of hens at start..........	393	319	266
Average number of hens..........	299	232	188
Hours labor per dozen eggs........	.08	.13	.20
Labor charge per dozen eggs.......	1.5¢	2.4¢	3.5¢
Eggs laid per hen.................	162	158	148
Hours labor per hen..............	1.1	1.7	2.4
Labor charge per hen.............	$0.20	$0.31	$0.43
Total charge per hen.............	2.15	2.34	2.51
Net return per hen...............	.48	.40	.06
Return per hour labor............	.64	.42	.20

gently needed on most poultry farms. The drudgery of caring for poultry needs to be eliminated.

Marketing. It is evident that other factors being the same those receiving the highest prices will have the highest returns. Indiana reported the results given in Table 97 which show that those producers who received in 1945–46 41 to 51 cents per dozen for their eggs had a labor return per hen of more than 6 times that of producers receiving 32 to 38 cents per dozen; $1.24 to 19 cents.

Efficiency in poultry farm management. The efficient producer will always find poultry raising profitable because there are always so many inefficient producers who are marginal and therefore have to discontinue poultry raising when prices become unfavorable for them. Possibly no other class of livestock is so sensitive to changes in management as poultry.

[4] N. H. Sta. Circ. 75. 1947.
[5] Mich. Agr. Expt. Sta. Spec. Bul. 294.

Table 97

PRICE RECEIVED PER DOZEN EGGS RELATED TO VARIOUS FACTORS ON 100
FARM FLOCKS IN CENTRAL INDIANA, 1945–46 [6]

Item	Cents Per Dozen		
	32.0–37.9	38.0–40.9	41.0–50.9
Number of farms......................	35	35	30
Price received per dozen eggs (cents)...........	34	39	44
Egg production per hen.....................	152	162	155
Feed fed per hen (pounds)...................	103	98	108
Average number of hens....................	127	178	174
Mortality (per cent)......................	13	11	11
First-year hens (per cent)..................	92	91	93
Labor per hen (hours).....................	3.1	3.1	2.3
Labor returns per 100 hens (dollars)...........	19	104	124
Labor returns per hour (dollars)...............	.05	.45	.69

Misner and Lee in 1937 outlined an efficiency program for New York poultry farms as follows:

Favorable size of business:
1. An average number of 1,500 birds or more. This necessitates the housing of more than 1,800 layers in the fall.
2. Annual egg production of more than 18,000 dozens.
3. Combination of chicks and pullets to sell, with market-egg production.
4. As little capital as necessary to provide a favorable size of business. Usually $10,000 or more is required.

Good rate of production:
5. Egg production of more than 150 eggs per hen, based on the average number of birds for the year.
6. More than 25 per cent production during October-December.
7. Hatchability of more than 60 per cent of total eggs incubated.
8. Successful rearing of more than 80 per cent of the original number of chicks.
9. Mortality of less than 20 per cent of the original number or less than 25 per cent of the average number of layers.
10. Value of eggs more than double the laying-flock feed costs.

Diversity or balance of the poultry enterprise:
11. More than 20 per cent of the income from the poultry enterprise derived from the sale of pullets and chicks.

Efficiency in use of labor:
12. More than 1,000 layers per man.
13. A gross income of more than $5,000 per man.
14. A labor charge, including the value of operator's time, of less than 25 per cent of the receipts.

Efficiency in use of capital:
15. A rapid capital turnover, requiring less than two years for receipts to equal capital.

[6] Purdue S. B. 531.

The Cost of Producing Eggs

The cost of producing eggs is highly variable and depends upon a number of factors. Costs determined at any time and place have only relative value when considered at other times and for other regions. The relative cost of producing eggs in different parts of New York State for 1926 and 1929–33 has been calculated by Misner and Lee (Table 98). These data show that more than 80 per cent of the cost of producing eggs is accounted for by feed, labor, and depreciation on flocks. Feed costs were slightly less than one-half of the total costs, while labor costs and depreciation of flocks each accounted for about one-fifth of the total cost of producing eggs. For those years the actual cost of producing eggs was 38, 35, 32, and 31 cents per dozen, respectively, for the four regions.

Table 98

THE RELATIVE COSTS IN PRODUCING EGGS, 1926 AND 1929–33 [7]

	Long Island	East and Southeast	Central Dairy Region	Central Grain Region
Number of records.....	83	159	261	199
Birds per farm.........	1,679	1,277	1,422	1,154
Dozen eggs produced...	19,345	14,879	16,663	13,136
Costs	*Per Cent*	*Per Cent*	*Per Cent*	*Per Cent*
Feed...............	39.0	44.8	46.0	43.9
Litter..............	1.2	1.4	1.2	1.1
Human labor........	22.0	20.8	20.3	20.4
Horse labor.........	.1	.4	.4	.6
Use of automobile....	1.5	2.0	1.7	1.6
Use of land.........	.7	.2	.2	.3
Use of buildings......	7.5	7.4	6.7	7.0
Use of equipment....	.8	.7	.6	.6
Depreciation on flock.	21.8	17.0	17.5	18.9
Interest on flock.....	1.8	1.7	1.7	1.9
Miscellaneous........	3.6	3.6	3.7	3.7
Total.............	100	100	100	100

California egg production costs during 1938–1947 are summarized in Table 99.

Flock Replacement

Chickens are short-lived animals and their profitable life is limited. There is a greater turnover in the poultry flock than in any other livestock enterprise.

[7] Cornell Agr. Expt. Sta. Bul. 684.

Table 99

POULTRY MANAGEMENT STUDY RECORD AVERAGES, 1938–1947 [8]

Record Year	Average Number Hens Per Flock	Per Cent of Hens — Died and Lost	Per Cent of Hens — Culled and Sold	Eggs — Number Laid Per Hen	Eggs — Price Per Dozen, Cents	Feed — Pounds Per Hen	Feed — Cost Per Cwt., Dollars	Hours of Labor Per Hen	Net Stock Income Per Hen	Total Income	Total Cost	Management Income	Farm Income
										Dollars Per Hen			
Commercial Egg Flocks													
1938	1,339	20.9	60.7	164	23.9	109	1.73	2.1	.17	3.81	3.11	.70	1.36
1939	1,451	20.1	68.3	174	20.5	110	1.65	2.0	.18	3.42	2.97	.45	1.03
1940	1,767	20.8	60.9	178	20.5	110	1.65	1.8	.11	3.41	2.91	.50	1.03
1941	1,795	18.7	63.1	174	28.2	115	1.89	1.9	.27	4.68	3.45	1.23	1.80
1942	2,000	18.7	65.2	175	35.2	115	2.23	1.8	.26	5.69	4.11	1.58	2.33
1943	2,328	17.5	76.2	176	41.5	115	2.52	1.9	.39	6.86	4.62	2.24	3.00
1944	2,427	18.8	83.3	183	38.6	119	2.88	1.8	.43	6.75	5.33	1.42	2.25
1945	2,401	16.1	81.1	179	42.6	120	2.94	1.7	.60	7.48	5.55	1.93	2.78
1946	2,406	14.6	89.1	166	44.8	118	3.64	1.6	.43	7.11	6.45	.66	1.52
1947	2,185	15.5	76.7	187	53.1	123	4.22	1.7	.44	9.26	7.49	1.77	2.81
10-year average	1,928	18.2	71.7	176	34.8	115	2.55	1.8	.32	5.84	4.56	1.28	2.02
Combined Egg and Meat Flocks													
1938	583	16.7	87.3	172	24.9	172	1.86	4.0	2.05	6.69	5.45	1.24	2.66
1939	724	24.0	93.9	170	20.6	181	1.80	4.1	2.02	5.78	5.53	.25	1.60
1940	1,114	22.8	69.3	157	21.0	166	1.74	3.7	1.53	4.80	4.78	.02	1.08
1941	1,178	26.2	80.6	181	28.4	162	2.03	3.7	1.65	6.42	5.35	1.07	2.03
1942	1,062	28.1	73.9	168	34.3	148	2.32	3.5	1.72	7.26	5.68	1.58	2.79
1943	535	22.3	93.2	165	43.3	184	2.74	3.9	4.00	10.25	8.49	1.76	3.79
1944	783	29.2	100.9	175	37.4	182	3.23	2.9	2.90	9.02	9.10	-.08	1.93
1945	554	20.4	185.5	187	48.3	240	3.26	3.8	6.50	14.77	12.86	1.91	4.55
1946	1,056	24.4	102.6	192	45.9	189	3.61	2.1	2.30	10.27	9.58	.69	2.26
1947	1,110	16.0	84.9	197	56.9	187	4.27	1.9	3.43	13.53	10.97	2.56	4.49
10-year average	879	23.8	94.3	177	37.5	179	2.80	3.2	2.63	8.77	7.73	1.04	2.59

Source: Poultry Management Studies are based on detailed records provided by poultrymen and compiled by local offices of the Agricultural Extension Service in several counties. Above figures represent averages of 89 egg flock records, and eight combined egg and meat flock records, for the ten years.

[8] Cal. Agr. Ext. Cir. 147.

PULLET COST ITEMS

ITEM	COST PER: PULLET	COST PER: POUND	PER CENT OF TOTAL COST
FEED	28.4c	8.1c	47
BABY CHICKS	13.0	3.7	21
LABOR	8.4	2.4	14
BLDGS. AND EQUIP. USE	3.8	1.1	6
FUEL	2.4	.7	3
OTHER ITEMS	4.2	1.2	9
TOTAL	60.2c	17.2c	

Fig. 208. Average cost per pullet and per pound poultry on 316 Michigan farms, 1931–35. (Michigan Agricultural Experiment Station Special Bulletin 294.)

In most flocks more than one-half the birds are replaced each year and in many flocks 100 per cent of the layers are replaced annually. The cost of growing pullets to renew the flock is a relatively important item for all poultry producers. According to a study on the cost of renewing the poultry flock made by the Michigan Agricultural Experiment Station, cost of feed represents practically one half and cost of baby chicks 21 per cent of the total cost of producing pullets. The distribution of various cost items on the 316 Michigan farms is shown in Figure 208. The actual cost per pullet raised was 60 cents, but these costs may be lower than usual because low feed prices prevailed from 1931 to 1935.

Wright, who reported the Michigan results, lists six major factors as affecting the cost of producing pullets: (1) feeding efficiency, (2) death losses, (3) cost of baby chicks, (4) breed, (5) hatching date, and (6) number of chicks raised.

Feeding efficiency. Table 100 shows that it cost some farmers 50 per cent more for feed to grow pullets than other farmers. These figures suggest that

Table 100

RELATION OF FEEDING EFFICIENCY TO PULLET COSTS, 1931–35 [9]

ITEM	POUNDS FEED PER POUND OF POULTRY		
	4.5 or Less	4.6–5.5	5.6 Up
Number of farms...................	130	112	74
Mash per pound poultry produced (lbs.)............................	2.5	3.1	4.4
Mash and scratch per pound poultry (lbs.)...........................	3.8	5.0	6.4
Feed cost per pound poultry..........	6.6¢	8.4¢	10.5¢
Total cost per pound poultry.........	14.4	17.6	21.7
Average hatching date..............	Apr. 19	Apr. 14	Apr. 12
Average death loss (per cent)........	14	14	18
Net cost per pullet.................	46¢	59¢	74¢

[9] Mich. Agr. Expt. Sta. Spec. Bul. 294.

some farmers are more efficient feeders than other farmers. The most efficient were able to grow pullets at a feed cost of 46 cents per bird as compared to a feed cost of 74 cents per bird for the least efficient. Possibly a better system of pastures and less waste of feed account for most of the difference in the feed cost of raising pullets.

Influence of mortality on cost of producing pullets. Disease and parasites not only lower the quality of the pullets produced but they also increase the cost of producing pullets. The relation of mortality among the growing stock to pullet cost is given in Table 101. Mortality in the young stock on these Michigan farms varied from practically none to 40 per cent, with an average of 15 per cent. Farmers who controlled mortality losses not only reduced pullet costs significantly but the quality of the pullets raised was superior to that of pullets raised in flocks where mortality was high. The Michigan study showed that flocks which had high mortality in the young stock also had heavy losses from mortality in the adult stock.

Table 101

INFLUENCE OF MORTALITY ON PULLET COST, 1931–35 [10]

ITEM	PER CENT DEATH LOSS		
	10.0 or Less	10.1–20.0	20.1 Up
Number of farms......................	111	136	69
Per cent having clean ground............	58	64	51
Number of chicks started per farm.......	626	702	651
Chickens died (per cent)...............	7.0	14.0	27.7
Average hatching date.................	Apr. 20	Apr. 15	Apr. 9
Baby chick cost per 100................	$7.94	$8.45	$8.04
Brooder floor space per 100 chicks (sq. ft.)...	39	35	37
Cost per pound poultry produced.........	16.3¢	17.2¢	19.1¢
Net cost per pullet....................	55	57	65

Relation of breed to cost of producing pullets. Table 102 shows the cost of producing pullets of the light breeds and heavy breeds. The difference in the cost of production was due to the fact that the income from the heavy-breed broilers averaged 16 cents more per chick started than the income from light-breed broilers. The actual cost of producing the pullets to twenty-four weeks of age was about the same for the light and heavy breeds; but when the income from broilers was credited to the pullets, the cost of producing heavy-breed pullets was about 16 cents less per chick started than for the smaller breeds.

Relation of hatching date to cost of producing pullets. A general discussion of time of hatching is presented in Chapter Seven. It was mentioned there that pullets could be produced at a lower cost during the summer than during the winter. The Michigan Agricultural Experiment Station has obtained records on the cost of raising pullets which were hatched on the general

[10] Mich. Agr. Expt. Sta. Special Bul. 294.

Table 102

COMPARISON OF COSTS AND RETURNS BY BREEDS, 1931–35 [11]

Item	Light Breeds	Heavy Breeds
Number of farms.........................	249	49
Number chicks started per farm................	700	504
Chickens died (per cent)....................	14	19
Broiler age when sold (weeks).................	12	15
Broiler weight when sold (lbs.)................	1.7	3.1
Broiler sale price per pound....................	14¢	19¢
Broiler income per 100 chicks..................	$11.17	$26.96
Pullet weight at 24 weeks (lbs.)................	3.3	4.4
Cost per pound poultry produced...............	17.6¢	16.0¢
Net cost per pullet............................	60	45

farms in March, April, and May. Table 103 gives a summary of those results. It cost slightly more to raise March- and April-hatched pullets than May-hatched pullets. The Michigan results showed that from 1931 to 1935 the average income per dozen for the eggs laid by the pullets hatched in March, April, and May was 20.4 cents, 21.3 cents, and 18.4 cents, respectively. Therefore, the extra returns from April-hatched pullets more than paid for the extra cost of raising those pullets.

Table 103

INFLUENCE OF HATCHING DATE ON PULLET COST, 1931–35 [12]

ITEM	HATCHING DATE OF BABY CHICKS			
	March	April 1–15	April 16–30	May
Number of farms..................	61	94	79	80
Average hatching date..............	Mar. 17	Apr. 7	Apr. 23	May 10
Number of chicks per farm..........	711	819	546	566
Chickens died (per cent)...........	16	15	14	13
Baby chick cost per 100...........	$9.39	$8.47	$8.00	$6.68
Broiler income per 100 chicks........	15.06	14.25	12.57	10.36
Labor hours per 100 chicks..........	31	30	29	25
Cost per pound poultry.............	18.8¢	17.6¢	17.2¢	15.0¢
Net cost per pullet.................	63	60	58	49
Estimated value of pullet..........	84	83	79	74

The relation of cost of chicks to pullet cost. The Michigan data for 1931 to 1935 showed that the chick cost was 21 per cent of the total cost of producing pullets. The average price paid for chicks was $8.67 per 100. It was more profitable for Michigan farmers to purchase chicks than to produce them,

[11] Mich. Agr. Expt. Sta. Spec. Bul. 294.
[12] Mich. Agr. Expt. Sta. Spec. Bul. 294.

since those who purchased chicks had flock averages of 164 eggs per bird as compared to 147 eggs per bird for those flocks where the chicks were hatched on the farms. Medium-priced chicks were more profitable than either low-priced or high-priced chicks.

Relation of number of chicks raised to the cost of producing pullets. As long as the farmer has at least one brooding unit of chicks the cost of producing pullets is apparently at a minimum. Table 104 shows that there was no significant difference in the cost of raising pullets when starting from 400 to 800 chicks or more than 800 (an average of 1,376). Those farmers who started less than 400 chicks had higher labor costs but only slightly higher costs of production than those who started larger numbers of chicks. Evidently with the colony brooding system the small producer who has one brooding unit can produce pullets as cheaply as the larger producers.

Table 104

INFLUENCE OF NUMBER OF CHICKS ON PULLET COST, 1931–35 [13]

ITEM	NUMBER OF CHICKS STARTED		
	400 or Less	401 to 800	801 and Over
Number of farms...........................	65	183	68
Average number of chicks per farm...........	282	535	1,376
Chickens died (per cent)....................	16	14	15
Pullets per 100 chicks......................	43	40	37
Feed fed per pound poultry (lbs.)............	4.7	4.8	5.0
Labor charge per 100 chicks.................	$7.77	$6.14	$4.30
Buildings and equipment charge per 100 chicks..	2.82	2.22	2.46
Net cost per pullet.........................	.64	.56	.58

Management Practices Related to Profits in the Broiler Industry

Specialized broiler production has developed within recent years into an important business in several states. Profits realized by the growers are highly variable from season to season, year to year, and between individual producers (Fig. 209). An analysis of records kept in several states shows the relation of a number of practices to the profits realized by the growers.

Costs in producing broilers. The cost of producing broilers in variable but an examination of some average costs (Table 105) from 120 lots of Delaware broilers shows that feed represents more than 70 per cent of the cost of producing broilers, chicks another 11.7 per cent, and labor 7.4 per cent. These three items of cost were 92 per cent of the cost of producing broilers.

The factors found to be related to profits in the broiler business will be discussed below.

Size of enterprise. The Delaware Station reported (1947) that the minimum size flock from which the producer may expect a reasonable return was

[13] Mich. Agr. Expt. Sta. Spec. Bul. 294.

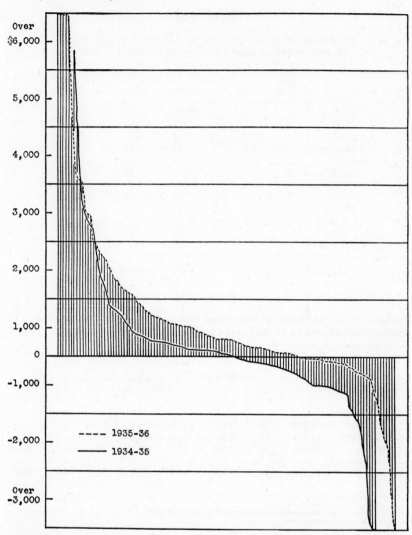

Fig. 209. Profit and loss in the broiler business. (Maryland Agricultural Experiment Station Bulletin 410.)

from 20,000 to 25,000 broilers. (Table 106.) This was considered a two-man flock. More recent developments with labor saving devices would indicate that one man could handle that number of birds.

Efficient use of feed. Since feed represents almost three-fourths of the cost of producing broilers, it is most important that feed costs be held to a minimum cost per pound of broiler produced. The Delaware results (Table 107) show 31 per cent variation in the feed required to produce a pound of gain between two groups of growers. There were greater differences between

Table 105

ITEMIZED COSTS OF PRODUCING 120 LOTS OF BROILERS
IN DELAWARE, FEBRUARY 1–SEPTEMBER 15, 1946[14]

ITEM	PER LOT	PER 1,000 BROILERS	
	Dollars	Dollars	Per Cent
Feed......................	7,079	650	72.9
Chicks.....................	1,128	104	11.7
Labor *	714	66	7.4
Medicine †	241	22	2.5
Fuel.......................	158	14	1.6
Building costs ‡.............	122	11	1.2
Equipment costs ‡...........	113	10	1.1
Litter......................	61	6	0.7
Misc.......................	92	8	0.9
Total....................	9,708	891	100.0

* Value of operator's time, family labor, and hired labor.
† Drugs, vaccines, and labor administering vaccines.
‡ Repairs, depreciation, insurance, and interest on capital.

Table 106

INFLUENCE OF NUMBER OF BROILERS PER LOT ON COSTS AND RETURNS IN
PRODUCING BROILERS IN DELAWARE, FEBRUARY 1–SEPTEMBER 15, 1946[15]

BROILERS PER LOT *		LOTS	GAIN PER WEEK	MOR- TALITY	COSTS †		NET RETURNS ‡	
					Per Pound	Per 1,000 Broilers	Per Lb.	Per 1,000 Broilers
Range	Av.	No.	Lbs.	%	c	$	c	$
0–9,349....	6,768	28	0.196	15.5	31.6	954	2.8	86
9,350–15,349...	12,134	27	0.205	11.8	30.2	890	3.2	99
15,350–over....	20,570	28	0.201	11.9	29.2	903	5.2	169
Tot. or av......	13,170	83	0.199	13.1	30.3	916	3.7	118

* Number started
† Including value of operator's time.
‡ Total returns less total expenses including value of operator's time.
Selbyville and Dagsboro areas.

individual growers. Much of this difference was no doubt due to the strains raised, but much of it can be attributed to management practices on the farms.

Price of chicks. That cheap chicks are less profitable than more expensive chicks for producing broilers was also shown by the Delaware study (Table 108). The price paid for chicks indicated their quality. The cheap chicks grew more slowly, required more time to reach market size, experienced higher mortality, and required more feed per pound of gain than the chicks that cost more as baby chicks.

---

[14] Del. Agr. Expt. Sta. Bul. 270. 1947.
[15] Del. Agr. Expt. Sta. Bul. 270. 1947.

Table 107

RELATION BETWEEN FEED PER POUND OF BROILER AND COSTS
AND RETURNS IN PRODUCING BROILERS IN DELAWARE,
FEBRUARY 1–SEPTEMBER 15, 1946 [16]

Feed Per Lb. of Broiler Produced		Lots	Broilers Per Lot *	Gain Per Week	Age "Loaded Out"	Mortality		Costs †		Net Returns ‡	
						For Period	Per Week	Per Pound	Per 1,000 Br'lers	Per Pound	Per 1,000 Br'lers
Range	Av.	No.	No.	Lbs.	Wks.	%	%	c	$	c	$
0–4.4.....	4.2	28	14,627	0.204	14.7	9.6	0.65	27.5	838	5.6	177
4.5–4.9.....	4.7	30	11,033	0.200	15.0	12.5	0.83	30.0	903	4.3	130
5.0–over...	5.5	25	14,102	0.190	15.8	17.6	1.11	33.8	1,019	0.9	38
Tot. or av...	4.8	83	13,170	0.199	15.1	13.1	0.87	30.3	916	3.7	118

* Number started.
† Including value of operator's time.
‡ Total returns less total expenses including value of operator's time.
Selbyville and Dagsboro areas.

Table 108

INFLUENCE OF PRICE PAID PER CHICK ON FEED CONSUMPTION, RATE OF
GAIN, AND MORTALITY IN PRODUCING BROILERS IN DELAWARE,
FEBRUARY 1–SEPTEMBER 15, 1946 [17]

Price Paid Per Chick		Lots	Broilers Per Lot [1]	Gain Per Week	Age "Loaded Out"	Feed Per Lb. of Wt.	Mortality	
							For Period	Per Week
Range	Av.	No.	No.	Lbs.	Wks.	Lbs.	%	%
Lots with 10,999 broilers per lot and less *								
0–8.9........	6.8	12	7,642	0.199	15.1	4.90	18.8	1.24
0–9.9........	9.3	16	7,548	0.201	14.4	4.83	13.2	0.92
10–over.......	10.2	32	7,216	0.205	14.6	4.76	13.6	0.93
Tot. or av.....	9.3	60	7,390	0.203	14.6	4.81	14.5	0.99
Lots with 11,000 broilers per lot and more *								
Tot. 0–8.9........	7.7	17	18,358	0.197	15.7	4.92	13.9	0.88
9–9.9........	9.3	19	18,211	0.203	14.8	4.51	12.3	0.83
10–over.......	10.3	24	16,428	0.203	14.8	4.50	9.8	0.66
Tot. or av.....	9.2	60	17,539	0.202	15.1	4.62	11.8	0.78
Tot. or av. all groups...	9.2	120	12,464	0.203	14.8	4.68	13.1	0.88

* Number started.

[16] Del. Agr. Expt. Sta. Bul. 270. 1947.
[17] Del. Agr. Expt. Sta. Bul. 270. 1947.

Use of labor. Since labor is one of the major costs in producing broilers it is important that it be used most efficiently. The Delaware results (Table 109) show that net returns per 1000 broilers were closely related to the num-

Table 109

INFLUENCE OF NUMBER OF BROILERS PER MAN ON COSTS AND RETURNS
IN PRODUCING BROILERS IN DELAWARE,
FEBRUARY 1–SEPTEMBER 15, 1946[18]

BROILERS PER MAN *		LOTS	BROILERS PER LOT *	GAIN PER WEEK	MOR-TALITY	COST PER POUND †	NET RETURNS ‡	
							Per Lb.	Per 1,000 Broilers
Range	Av.	No.	No.	Lbs.	%	c	c	$
0–7,999...	6,787	29	8,796	0.208	12.0	30.2	3.9	118
8,000–9,999...	9,018	28	10,022	0.205	13.7	29.6	4.2	129
10,000–11,999.	10,906	39	14,314	0.207	13.1	29.0	4.8	148
12,000–over....	13,195	24	16,741	0.201	14.1	28.6	6.0	199
Tot. or av......	9,977	120	12,464	0.203	13.1	29.6	4.7	147

* Number started.
† Including value of operator's time.
‡ Total returns less total expenses including value of operator's time.

Table 110

INFLUENCE OF MORTALITY ON COSTS AND RETURNS IN PRODUCING
BROILERS IN DELAWARE, FEBRUARY 1–SEPTEMBER 15, 1946[19]

MORTALITY		LOTS	BROILERS PER LOT *	GAIN PER WEEK	AGE "LOADED OUT"	FEED PER LB. OF WEIGHT	COSTS PER LB. †	NET RETURNS ‡	
								Per Pound	Pr 1,000 Br'lers
Range	Av.	No.	No.	Lbs.	Wks.	Lbs.	c	c	$
Lots with 10,999 broilers per lot and less *									
0–8.9......	5.9	15	6,709	0.218	14.2	4.55	28.4	5.4	170
9.0–14.9.....	12.0	19	7,815	0.208	14.4	4.76	29.8	5.0	145
15.0–over.....	21.4	26	7,472	0.193	15.0	5.02	31.7	2.5	78
Tot. or av.....	14.5	60	7,390	0.203	14.6	4.81	30.3	4.0	122
Lots with 11,000 broilers per lot and more *									
0–8.9......	6.5	29	16,830	0.208	14.4	4.46	27.3	7.5	228
9.0–14.9.....	11.4	18	18,518	0.207	15.9	4.65	29.8	5.1	176
15.0–over.....	24.0	13	17,766	0.182	15.4	5.02	31.6	0.8	38
Tot. or av.....	11.8	60	17,539	0.203	15.1	4.62	29.0	5.3	171
Tot. or av. all gr'ps.......	13.1	120	12,464	0.203	14.8	4.68	29.6	4.7	147

* Number started.
† Including value of operator's time.
‡ Total returns less total expenses including value of operator's time.

[18] Del. Agr. Expt. Sta. Bul. 270. 1947.
[19] Del. Agr. Expt. Sta. Bul. 270. 1947.

Table 111

INFLUENCE OF AGE "LOADED OUT" ON COSTS AND RETURNS IN PRODUCING BROILERS IN DELAWARE, FEBRUARY 1–SEPTEMBER 15, 1946[20]

AGE "LOADED OUT"		LOTS	BROILERS PER LOT*	GAIN PER WEEK	FEED PER LB. OF WGT.	WGT. "LOADED OUT"	MORTALITY		PRICE REC'D FOR BROILERS PER LB.	COSTS†		NET RETURNS‡	
Range	Av.	No.	No.	Lbs.	Lbs.	Lbs.	For Period %	Per Week %	c	Per Lb. c	Per 1,000 Br'lers $	Per Lb. c	Per 1,000 Br'lers $
0–13.9	13.0	32	11,229	0.215	4.55	2.8	11.7	0.90	33.4	28.5	789	4.9	149
14–14.9	14.2	29	12,592	0.211	4.46	3.0	10.9	0.77	34.0	28.6	842	5.4	161
15–15.9	15.2	26	13,190	0.204	4.63	3.1	12.8	0.84	34.1	29.5	905	4.6	148
16–over	17.0	33	12,979	0.194	4.98	3.3	16.8	0.99	35.5	31.7	1,041	3.8	131
Tot. or av.	14.8	120	12,464	0.203	4.68	3.0	13.1	0.88	34.2	29.6	896	4.7	147

* Number started.
† Including value of operator's time.
‡ Total returns less total expenses including value of operator's time.

[20] Del. Agr. Expt. Sta. Bul. 270. 1947.

ber of broilers cared for per man; $199 per 1000 broilers when one man cared for 12,000 or more broilers but only $118 per 1000 when one man handled less than 8,000 broilers.

Mortality. It is apparent that heavy mortality among broilers will result in loss instead of profit. Actual records kept in several states bear this out and show that mortality must be kept under 15 per cent if the broiler enterprise is to be profitable. Table 110 shows that Delaware growers who raised over 11,000 broilers per lot and had less than 9 per cent mortality made more than 6 times as much profit per 1000 broilers as those growers who experienced more than 15 per cent mortality.

Age and size when ready for market. It is evident that birds which reach market size at an early age will be more profitable than those that grow less rapidly. Table 111 shows the relation of the age "loaded out" to costs and returns. Broilers weighing 3.0 lbs. at 14–15 weeks were the most profitable.

Data from Maryland (Table 112) also show that broilers should not be sold until they weigh three pounds or more.

Table 112

RELATION OF WEIGHT OF BROILERS AT SELLING TIME TO PROFIT
(Two-year Average, 1934–1936) [21]

ITEM	AVERAGE WEIGHT PER BIRD, POUNDS					
	2.24 and Under	2.25 to 2.49	2.5 to 2.74	2.75 to 2.99	3 and Over	Average of All Farms
Number of birds per farm...............	9,778	5,845	7,600	8,548	12,095	8,494
Number of farms......	17	32	93	52	37	115
Average per farm:						
Income...............	$4,967.53	$2,535.37	$4,034.93	$5,366.71	$9,035.54	$4,630.21
Cost...............	5,159.47	2,832.06	3,714.89	4,715.38	7,402.24	4,148.37
Profit...............	−191.94	−296.69	320.04	651.33	1,633.30	481.84
Average per bird, cents:						
Income...............	50.8	43.4	53.1	62.8	74.7	54.5
Cost...............	52.8	48.5	48.9	55.2	61.2	48.8
Profit...............	−2.0	−5.1	4.2	7.6	13.5	5.7

Space. Crowding is conducive to slower growth and increased costs. However, maximum use should be made of floor space and most records indicate from .7 to 1.0 square foot per broiler should be allowed.

Breed. The strain is more important than the breed in determining profits; the best chicken for broiler production is one that has been bred to produce meat efficiently. Records, however, are available on the basis of breeds (Table 113). The crosses have been giving very good results, but the broiler strains of New Hampshire are also quite efficient.

---

[21] Md. Agr. Expt. Sta. Bul. 410.

Table 113

RELATIONSHIP BETWEEN BREEDS AND PRODUCTION FACTORS, COSTS, AND RETURNS [22]

Item	Broiler Cross (Barred Rock X R. I. R. or N. H.)	Plymouth Rock	Sex-Linked Cross	Rhode Island Red	New Hampshire
Number of lots...............	115	22	53	65	35
Number of chicks started per lot........................	3,115	721	1,219	1,111	1,319
Per cent mortality............	10.3	13.9	11.2	14.2	13.0
Age at sale, weeks............	14.2	14.2	15.4	15.1	15.0
Weight at sale, pounds.........	3.9	3.9	3.9	3.8	4.0
Feed per pound, meat.........	4.4	4.3	4.9	4.5	4.8
Daily grain per 100 birds, lbs....	3.9	3.9	3.6	3.6	3.8
Labor daily per 1,000 birds, hrs..	1.97	2.89	2.25	2.54	2.96
Price per baby chick...........	12.7¢	13.3¢	12.2¢	9.9¢	11.6¢
Cost per pound meat..........	23.3	25.6	25.4	25.9	27.5
Returns per pound meat.......	28.9	30.2	29.0	29.1	30.3
Profit per pound meat.........	5.6	4.6	3.6	3.2	2.8
Labor return per hr...........	$1.69	$1.19	$1.13	$1.03	$1.01

The Hatchery Business

The hatchery business of the United States has in recent years become an important branch of the poultry industry. The Maryland Agricultural Experiment Station in 1939 and the United States Department of Agriculture in 1935 reported economic studies of this industry. Table 114 summarizes the costs and profits of 110 Maryland hatcheries for 1936 to 1938.

Poffenberger and DeVault, authors of the Maryland report, list the following factors as influencing profits in the hatchery business: (1) gross income and cost, (2) efficiency in the use of fuel, (3) efficiency in the use of labor, (4) investment, (5) egg cost, (6) hatchability of eggs, (7) source from which eggs were obtained for hatching, (8) premium paid for eggs, (9) number of chicks hatched, (10) hatchery capacity and capacity utilized, (11) selling costs, (12) cost of allowances, (13) length of the hatchery operation, and (14) marketing practices.

Volume of business. As in all industries there is a minimum volume of business necessary before profits can be realized in the hatchery business. Under Maryland conditions (1936–38) the most profitable hatcheries ($3600 per year) had an average output of 120,000 chicks per year and the least profitable (loss of $307 per year) produced about 30,000 chicks annually. The relation of number of chicks hatched to profits realized by hatcheries is shown in Table 115. Hatcheries which produced a large number of chicks

[22] Me. Agri. Expt. Sta. Bul. 441. 1945.

Table 114

SUMMARY OF COSTS AND PROFITS IN THE HATCHERY BUSINESS
(Two-year Average, 1936–38) [23]

Item	Average of All Hatcheries	Average per 100 Chicks Hatched	Average of Most Profitable Hatcheries	Average of Least Profitable Hatcheries
Number of hatcheries................	110	...	27	27
Number of chicks hatched............	109,392	...	112,845	29,894
Number of chicks custom hatched.....	7,536	...	7,188	4,035
Per cent of hatchability.............	71.6	...	72.6	67.2
Total hatchery investment...........	$5,119.56	...	$ 4,826.88	$3,654.64
Hatchery investment as per cent of total investment......................	38.4	...	28.4	40.8
Income:				
Value of pullorum-tested chicks sold..	$7,790.82	$7.62	$ 8,412.36	$1,959.95
Value of non-pullorum-tested chicks sold.........................	527.52	.55	1,550.10	125.52
Value of chicks kept...............	394.16	.40	628.76	277.64
Income from custom hatching.......	248.18	.24	219.44	117.39
Total.......................	$8,960.68	$8.81	$10,810.66	$2,480.50
Costs:				
General expenses:				
Fuel.........................	$ 177.82	$0.18	$ 147.30	$ 98.85
Light, water, disinfectants and misc.........................	48.04	.04	67.16	29.89
Total.......................	$ 225.86	$0.22	$ 214.46	$ 128.74
Hatchery overhead:				
Taxes.........................	$ 60.83	$0.06	$ 60.83	$ 39.41
Insurance.....................	27.98	.03	20.41	14.13
Depreciation...................	393.80	.38	350.22	247.09
Interest on investment............	241.22	.24	217.43	158.19
Office supplies, misc..............	7.68	.01	9.15	4.22
Total.......................	$ 731.51	$0.72	$ 658.04	$ 463.04
Labor:				
Hired.........................	$ 254.34	$0.25	$ 190.65	$ 143.30
Family.........................	432.98	.43	356.40	251.13
Total.......................	$ 687.32	$0.68	$ 547.05	$ 394.43
Selling Cost:				
Advertising.....................	$ 116.12	$0.11	$ 75.89	$ 38.98
Telephone and telegraph..........	30.82	.03	16.41	24.54
Transportation (truck).............	87.94	.09	38.63	69.87
Express and parcel post...........	43.18	.04	38.39	4.96
Stamps, stationery and misc.........	29.26	.03	13.64	10.09
Total.......................	$ 307.32	$0.30	$ 182.96	$ 148.44
Allowances:				
Value of extras...................	$ 195.88	$0.19	$ 236.56	$ 55.54
Replacements...................	41.62	.04	20.46	41.64
Bad debts.....................	52.06	.05	46.00	30.28
Total.......................	$ 289.56	$0.29	$ 303.02	$ 127.46
Cost of eggs....................	$4,508.07	$4.44	$ 4,993.82	$1,300.58
Cost of containers................	$ 132.52	$0.13	$ 117.35	$ 49.30
Cost of breed improvement........	$ 58.21	$0.06	$ 67.72	$ 21.88
Cost of custom hatching...........	$ 132.42	$0.13	$ 90.39	$ 153.65
Total hatchery cost................	$7,072.79	$6.97	$ 7,174.81	$2,787.52
Total net profit or loss..............	$1,887.89	$1.84	$ 3,635.85	—$307.02
Per cent return on investment........	36.9	35.5	75.3	—8.4

[23] Md. Agr. Expt. Sta. Bul. 410.

Table 115

RELATION OF NUMBER OF CHICKS HATCHED TO PROFIT
(Two-year Average, 1936–38) [24]

ITEM	NUMBER OF CHICKS HATCHED					AVERAGE OF ALL HATCHERIES
	9,999 and Under	10,000 to 19,999	20,000 to 39,999	40,000 to 79,999	80,000 and Over	
Average number of chicks hatched per hatchery...........	4,974	13,951	30,598	57,482	372,228	116,928
Number of hatcheries..	25	19	20	20	26	110
Average per hatchery:						
Income.............	$504	$1,100	$2,658	$4,222	$30,704	$8,960
Cost..............	550	1,036	2,185	3,425	23,896	7,072
Profit.............	−46	64	473	797	6,808	1,888
Average per 100 chicks hatched:						
Income.............	$10.16	$7.88	$8.68	$7.34	$8.24	$8.38
Cost..............	11.04	7.42	7.15	5.95	6.42	6.62
Profit.............	−.88	.46	1.53	1.39	1.82	1.76

not only had more total profit but they also had a higher profit per chick than did the hatcheries with a smaller output. Maryland hatcheries with an egg capacity of 80,000 or more realized very good profits per hatchery, but those having less than 40,000 egg capacity realized an average annual income of from $78 to $1025. Capacity must be utilized to return a profit. The total egg capacity of a hatchery should be utilized at least two times and preferably more often during the hatching season. The average rate of capacity utilization in the United States during the 1934 season was 2.7, while in 1943 an average of 467 eggs was set per 100-egg capacity.

Those hatcheries in position to extend the hatching season and thereby increase the utilization of their capacity and reduce the overhead charges per chick can realize more net profit than those less favorably located or operated. The Maryland results show that profits were directly related to length of season. Hatcheries which operated less than ninety days realized very little net profit.

Egg cost. Egg cost of producing chicks for the United States in 1934 was 50 per cent of the total cost of production. Figure 210 shows the distribution of costs of producing and selling chicks in Maryland for 1936 to 1938. There the egg cost represented 63.7 per cent of the total cost. The Maryland study showed that those hatcheries which paid the highest premiums for hatching eggs also realized the most profit per hundred chicks because by selling quality chicks they were able to command a price which more than compensated for the extra cost of producing the chicks.

[24] Md. Agr. Expt. Sta. Bul. 426.

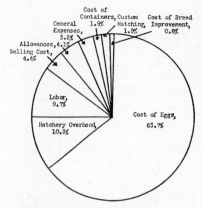

Fig. 210. Percentage distribution of the cost of producing and selling baby chicks, 1936–38. (Maryland Agricultural Experiment Station Bulletin 426.)

Hatchability is an important factor determining the egg cost of chicks. With eggs costing 30 cents per dozen the cost of producing chicks can be reduced 51 cents per hundred by increasing hatchability from 65 per cent to 75 per cent of all eggs set. Proper flock supervision will more than pay for its cost by improving hatching results.

Labor cost. The efficient utilization of labor is a problem for hatcheries because of the seasonal nature of the work. Hatcheries with relatively large capacities which operate through a long season can use labor most effectively. The most profitable hatcheries reported in the Maryland study had an average labor cost of 46 cents per hundred chicks hatched as compared to $1.53 for the least profitable hatcheries. The average labor cost for Maryland hatcheries was 68 cents per hundred chicks as compared to $1.29 for the United States in 1934.

Fuel cost. The cost of fuel is an important item in the cost of producing chicks and, according to the Maryland study, is highly variable, ranging from less than 15 cents per hundred to more than 60 cents per hundred. The average fuel cost for 110 Maryland hatcheries was 18 cents per hundred chicks. The cost per kilowatt-hour for electricity is important in determining the cost of producing chicks with electricity. Though electric incubators are relatively expensive to operate, they have advantages which have caused most hatcherymen to turn to them.

Capital investment. Figure 210 shows that about 10 per cent of the cost of producing chicks is overhead charges. About 85 per cent of these charges is interest on investment and depreciation. The average investment per hundred chicks produced by the hatcheries reported in the Maryland study was $5.02. Sixty-nine per cent of this was invested in incubators and 22 per cent in buildings. Some hatcherymen could, no doubt, increase their profits by investing in modern equipment. Equipment which gives satisfactory results should not be replaced by some that is more expensive merely because it is fashionable to have new equipment.

Marketing. Methods used in marketing chicks vary with the location of the hatchery and the type of hatchery. Local hatcheries sell most of their chicks at the hatchery or deliver them directly to the customer. Large hatcheries sell by mail most of the chicks they produce, shipping them by parcel post or express. The average cost of selling chicks by the Maryland hatcheries was 30 cents per hundred and distributed as shown in Table 116. Large commer-

Table 116

SELECTING COST

(Two-year Average, 1936–38) [25]

Item	Average Cost Per Hatchery	Average Cost Per 100 Chicks Hatched	Per Cent of Total
Advertising....................	$116.12	$0.11	37.7
Telephone and telegraph..........	30.82	.03	10.1
Transportation (truck)..........	87.94	.09	28.6
Express.......................	13.92	.01	4.5
Parcel post....................	29.26	.03	9.5
Stamps.......................	14.69	.02	4.8
Stationery....................	3.43	...	1.1
Miscellaneous.................	11.14	.01	3.7
Total......................	$307.32	$0.30	100.0

cial hatcheries expend more in selling their chicks, particularly for advertising.

Replacements. Every hatcheryman should try to satisfy his customers, but this should not lead to a sacrifice of profits through too lenient a policy in including extra chicks and making replacements. The value of these two items in some seasons is the difference between profit and loss in the hatchery business. In Maryland from 1936 to 1938 these two items cost the hatcherymen 23 cents per hundred chicks hatched. The purchaser of one hundred chicks does not pay for more chicks. Some allowance should be made for normal shipping losses, of course. Hatcherymen can very easily train their customers to expect a large number of extra chicks with each order. Losses which can be attributed to the chicks should be made good by the hatcherymen, but losses which are due to the mistakes of the poultryman should be borne by him and they should not be assumed by the hatchery.

The sale of sex-separated chicks. Since the art of sex determination of baby chicks was made known to the hatchery industry of the United States there has been an expansion in the sale of sex-separated chicks. Large hatcheries can afford to keep a "sexer" (one trained to make sex determinations), but hatcheries with a small volume of business cannot profitably use the services of a "sexer." Few hatcheries located in New England and the southern states sell sex-separated chicks, but 63.5 per cent of the hatcheries located on the Pacific Coast where the Leghorn breed predominates sell these chicks. The sale of sexed chicks is increasing in all parts of the United States.

The disposal of cockerel chicks becomes a major problem where there is a surplus of Leghorn male chicks. In the Pacific states many of these cockerel chicks are destroyed. Fifty per cent of the hatcherymen located in Oregon reporting for the season of 1937–38 stated that they destroyed some chicks.

The sale of started chicks. In the early days of the hatchery business orders for chicks were placed far enough ahead of the delivery date so that

[25] Md. Agr. Expt. Sta. Bul. 426.

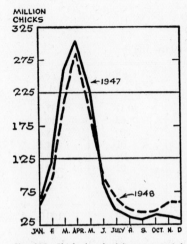

MILLION
CHICKS

Fig. 211. Chicks hatched by commercial hatcheries, U. S., by months, 1947–1948.

the eggs could be set after the order was received. In recent years the purchasers of chicks have found that hatcherymen anticipate their orders and make settings accordingly. Therefore, chicks could be obtained on short notice or by merely calling at the hatchery for them. In some communities they have found that they can purchase started chicks at the same price as day-old chicks. During a poor season started chicks may be purchased for less than the regular price of day-old chicks. Thus, the started chick business has grown into what most hatcherymen consider a nuisance. The sale of started chicks is growing because poultry raisers do not like to brood chicks and suffer the losses they have to take from pullorum disease.

Seasonal operation. Some hatcheries supplying chicks for broiler production operate throughout the entire year but most hatcheries have a highly seasonal business. This is because approximately 60 per cent of the chicks hatched annually in the United States are produced in March, April, and May. (Fig. 211.)

REVIEW QUESTIONS

1. Why do people raise chickens?
2. What does the feed-egg ratio mean?
3. How does poultry production respond to changes in these ratios?
4. What is the relation of farmers' income from poultry and eggs to the income of industrial workers?
5. Make a sketch of a poultry plant layout for 1500 layers.
6. What factors should be considered when selecting poultry stock?
7. List the factors which affect profits from poultry raising on the general farm.
8. Why do flocks of certain size tend to be located in different regions of the United States?
9. Is commercial poultry farming profitable?
10. List the factors which profits most.
11. What are the major factors influencing the cost of producing pullets?
12. Can the general farmer produce pullets as cheaply as the commercial poultryman?
13. When do specialized broiler producers start their chicks?
14. What size bird is most economical for broiler raisers to sell? Is this bird a broiler?
15. What percentage of the cost of producing chicks is egg cost?
16. Should hatcheries make good all chick losses which their customers suffer during the first two weeks after the chicks are purchased?

17. What is a "chick sexer"?
18. Why are cockerel chicks destroyed in some regions?
19. Why do most hatcherymen sell started chicks?

REFERENCES

ABELL, MAX F.: ECONOMIC ANALYSIS OF FOURTEEN YEARS OF POULTRY RECORDS. N. H. Sta. Circ. 75. 1947.

BAUSMAN, R. O.: INFLUENCE OF MANAGEMENT PRACTICES ON COST OF PRODUCING BROILERS IN DELAWARE. Del. Sta. Bul. 270. 1947.

BIERLY, I. R., AND HURD, L. M.: MORE EGGS PRODUCED PER MAN HOUR. Farm Res., (N. Y.) 12: No. 3, 16. 1946.

BROADBENT, DEE A., PRESTON, THOMAS W., AND BLANCK. GEO. T.: AN ECONOMIC ANALYSIS OF TURKEY PRODUCTION IN UTAH. Utah Sta. Bul. 318. 1945.

CREEK, C. R.: RETURNS FROM POULTRY FARMING IN MASSACHUSETTS IN 1943. Mass. Sta. F. M. 17. 1944.

DARRACK, L. B.: FACTORS THAT AFFECT INCOMES ON COMMERCIAL POULTRY FARMS, 1940–1941. Cornell Sta. Bul. 803. 1943.

DAVIES, T. J., POFFENBERGER, P. R., AND DeVAULT, S. H.: THE BROILER INDUSTRY IN MARYLAND. Md. Sta. Bul. A16. 1942.

EMBLETON, H.: EGG PROFIT CALCULATOR. Ariz. Sta. Bul. 180. 1942.

EMBLETON, H.: THE COST OF PRODUCTION OF EGGS AND PULLETS IN SOUTHERN ARIZONA. Ariz. Sta. Bul. 208. Revised, 1947.

EVANS, MORRIS: SO YOU'RE GOING TO RAISE CHICKENS. N. M. Sta. Bull. 339. 1947.

FALCONER, J. I.: OHIO FARM LEASES. Ohio Res. Bul. 683. 1948.

THE FARMER'S SHARE OF THE CONSUMER'S FOOD DOLLAR. U. S. D. A. Leaflet 123. Revised, 1946.

GOODING, P. H.: A GUIDE TO POULTRY FARMING IN SOUTH CAROLINA. TWENTY YEARS OF POULTRY RECORDS. S. C. Ext. Circ. 318. 1948.

GOODSELL, W. D.: TYPICAL FAMILY-OPERATED FARMS, 1930–45. ADJUSTMENTS, COSTS, AND RETURNS. U. S. D. A. Bur. Agr. Econ. F. M. 55. 1946.

HANNAH, H. W.: Law on the Farm. The Macmillan Co., New York. 1948.

HARRIS, M., THARP, M. M., AND TURNER, H. A.: BETTER FARM LEASES. U. S. D. A. Farmers' Bul. 1969. 1945.

HARTMAN, R. C., AND VICKERS, G. S.: Hatchery Management. Orange Judd Co., New York. Revised, 1950.

HAWTHORNE, J. G., AND MILLER, L. F.: AN ECONOMIC ANALYSIS OF 32 POULTRY COST ACCOUNTS, PENNSYLVANIA, 1946–47. Pa. Sta. Bul. 511. 1949.

HEADINGTON, R. C., AND MOORE, H. R.: FATHER-SON FARMING. Ohio Sta. Res. Bul. 686. 1949.

HOECKER, R. W.: THE ECONOMICS OF THE POULTRY ENTERPRISE ON KANSAS FARMS. Kan. Sta. Bul. 308. 1942.

HOGLUND, C. R., AND ANDERSON, A. W.: FATHER-SON FARMING PLANS. S. D. Sta. Bul. 390. 1948.

HURD, L. M., AND BIERLY, IVAN R.: SAVING STEPS AND TIME IN CARING FOR HENS. Poultry Sci., 26: 25–29. 1947.

JOHNSON, H. A.: THE BROILER INDUSTRY IN DELAWARE. Del. Sta. Bul. 250. 1944.

JOHNSON, HUGH A., ROBERTSON, LYNN S., AND SICER, J. W.: SMALL POUL-
TRY FLOCKS IN CENTRAL INDIANA. Ind. Sta. Bul. 532. 1948.
JOHNSON, HUGH A., ROBERTSON, LYNN S., AND SICER, J. W.: PROFITAB' E
POULTRY MANAGEMENT ON CENTRAL INDIANA FARMS. Ind. Sta. Bul. 531.
KIMBALL, E. S., MOORE, R. F., AND SMITH, P. W.: COMMERCIAL HATCHERY
CHICK PRODUCTION. U. S. D. A. Sta. Bul. 81. 1945.
MENDUM, S. W.: USEFUL RECORDS FOR FAMILY FARMS. U. S. D. A. Farmers'
Bul. 1962. 1944.
MISNER, E. G.: COSTS AND RETURN FOR THE TURKEY ENTERPRISE. Cornell
Sta. Bul. 827. 1946.
NEIL, L. G.: COSTS HIGHER. SO IS GROWER'S PROFIT. U. S. Egg and Poultry
Mag., 53: No. 8, pp. 19–22, 34. 1947.
PERRY, ALVAH L., AND DOW, GEO. F.: COSTS AND RETURNS IN BROILER PRO-
DUCTION. Maine Sta. Bul. 441. 1945.
PERRY, ENOL C.: CHORE PRACTICES ON NEW HAMPSHIRE COMMERCIAL
POULTRY FARMS. II, PULLET REPLACEMENTS. N. H. Sta. Circ. 79. 1949.
ROBINSON, J. L.: PAYING FOR A FARM. U. S. D. A. Farm Credit Admin. Circ.
E–30. 1946.
WILCOX, R. H., AND CARD, L. E.: POULTRY COSTS AND PROFITS. Ill. Sta. Bul.
486. 1942.
WINTER, E. P.: MARKETING MARGINS AND COSTS FOR POULTRY AND EGGS.
U. S. D. A. Tech. Bul. 969. 1948.
WOODWARD, E. D.: SOME FACTORS THAT INFLUENCE POULTRY FARM IN-
COMES. Dept. Agr. Ec., Univ. Brit. Columbia, Vancouver, Canad. 1946.
WRIGHT, K. T.: DOLLARS AND SENSE IN FARMING. Mich. Sta. Sp. Bul. 324.
1943.

CHAPTER 15 ||||||||||||||||||||||||||||||||||||||||||||||||||||||

Turkey Varieties and Breeding Problems

▼

Turkeys are native to America, and before 1492 they were unknown to European or Asiatic civilizations. The Aztec Indians of Mexico had domesticated the wild turkey (Fig. 212), and as early as 1498 the Spanish imported turkeys to Spain. The birds proved very popular and apparently readily adjusted themselves to their new environment. As early as 1573 it is reported that they were plentiful in England. Domesticated turkeys were brought to New England by the early colonists from Europe and served as a nucleus from which the turkey industry of the United States developed.

Varieties

The six Standard varieties, Bronze, White Holland, Bourbon Red, Narragansett, Black, and Slate, were developed from the wild stock or from varieties descended from the wild stock. The weights for these varieties as given in the 1945 edition of the American Standard of Perfection are as follows:

Variety	Adult Tom	Yearling Tom	Young Tom	Adult Hen	Yearling Hen	Young Hen
Bronze.........	36	33	25	20	18	16
White Holland, Bourbon Red, Narragansett, Black, and Slate........	33	30	23	18	16	14

Popularity of the respective varieties. The Bronze turkey, which more nearly resembles the wild turkey, has remained the most popular variety raised. A nation-wide survey made by *Turkey World* of the 1938 turkey crop showed that the following proportions of the different varieties were raised that year: Bronze, 63.9%; White Holland, 13.5%; Narragansett, 9.7%; Bourbon Red, 9.1%; and Black, 3.8%. Apparently very few Slate turkeys are raised.

Bronze. The Bronze turkey has color markings similar to the wild turkey native to the Mississippi Valley and the eastern part of the United States (Fig. 213). The white markings in the tail, however, probably trace their

COURTESY U. S. FOREST SERVICE

Fig. 212. The native wild turkey as now found in New Mexico.

origin to the Mexican wild stock. The New England wild turkey has brown instead of white in the color pattern of the tail. During the nineteenth century the domesticated Bronze turkey was crossed with the wild New England stock.

The popularity of Bronze turkeys can be partly attributed to their resemblance to the beautiful wild stock, their vitality, their size, and the fact that they have been in the hands of progressive breeders. It is necessary to see these birds in their fully mature plumage to appreciate their beauty. The development of this color pattern may have been at the neglect of vitality and market qualities in some cases, but this variety has remained a popular turkey with the growers.

White Holland. The White Holland turkey takes its name from its solid white color and the fact that it was supposedly brought to America by the early Dutch colonists from Holland. A white variety originated in Europe probably as a "sport" from the Mexican stock imported by the Spaniards. However, the White Hollands which were developed in America very likely came from white "sports" from the Bronze variety. With the recent tendency toward smaller turkeys, White Hollands have been gaining in favor (Fig. 213).

Bourbon Red. This variety was developed by Mr. J. F. Barbee of Bourbon County, Kentucky, from crosses made about 1890. Mr. Barbee crossed Bronze, White Holland, and Buff varieties and selected from these crosses the birds which were red with white primaries, secondaries, and main tail feathers. This is a beautiful variety with good market qualities. The modern type and color pattern are illustrated in Figure 213.

Fig. 213. Breeds of turkeys. Top left, Narragansett. (Courtesy Hawkeye Turkey Farm and "Turkey World.") Top right, Black. (Courtesy "Turkey World.") Center left, Bourbon Red. (Courtesy Pleasant Valley Turkey Farm.) Center right, Bronze. (Courtesy Wallace Neel.) Bottom left, White Holland. (Courtesy U. S. D. A.) Bottom right, Slate. (Courtesy Wingert Turkey Farm.)

Narragansett. This variety takes its name from Narragansett Bay, the region in which it originated. It probably arose as the result of crossing the Norfolk Black, which the English colonists brought with them, with the New England wild stock and by later introducing some Mexican wild stock. This variety is somewhat similar in appearance to the Bronze. However, the birds are lighter in color and lack the copperish bronze markings which characterize the Bronze turkey. Figure 213 shows the Narragansett color pattern.

Black. The Blacks probably originated as "sports" from the turkeys introduced into Europe by the Spaniards. They were called the Black Norfolks and were later brought to America by the colonists. Black turkeys sometimes occur in flocks of Bronze turkeys. The importance of this variety in the past appears to have been its value as one of the parents for developing new varieties. Its relatively smaller size and its well-developed breast may make this variety more popular as a market turkey. A very good Black specimen is shown in Figure 213.

Slate. This variety is supposed to have originated in America from the crossing of Black Norfolks and White Hollands. The birds have slate or ash-blue plumage. Slate turkeys have never been popular in the United States and at present relatively few birds of this variety are raised in this country. They have the same standard weight as the Black variety.

Non-Standard varieties. From time to time new varieties arise, some to become popular and be admitted to the Standard and others soon to become extinct. The Royal Palm, a white turkey with black markings; the Nittany, named for Mt. Nittany near Pennsylvania State College where this variety was developed from the native wild turkeys; and certain small type turkeys, notably the Beltsville Small Whites, are making their bids for the favor of the turkey-buying public.

The future of the turkey industry depends quite largely on the success which may be achieved in breeding for market qualities and for birds which are efficient producers of human food.

Breeding Objectives

Color patterns. Turkey breeders should select for the color pattern desired in their respective varieties. Most of these color patterns are very well fixed, so that little attention need be paid to such characters. To neglect important market qualities and focus attention on fine distinctions in color designs is a mistake. The most successful breeders in the future will emphasize market qualities but retain also the color pattern of their varieties. Unless the color pattern becomes a secondary breeding objective, there may appear a division of turkey breeders as there has of breeders raising chickens; those who emphasize color pattern will comprise one group and those who are interested in utility values will constitute another.

Market qualities. Since the turkey is a meat animal, it should be bred for the most desirable market type and size. Already some breeders have made considerable progress in this direction. As in other animals, size and type are

COURTESY WALLACE NEEL

Fig. 214. Bronze toms of good market type. The bird on the left shows the proper body carriage. The other tom was "off balance" for this photograph.

inheritable characters which may be influenced by selection. Birds with compact bodies are being used quite extensively in turkey matings and attention is being centered on market quality. No doubt there are many market qualities other than size and shape which should be emphasized. Early maturity is receiving attention and it should be emphasized because the efficiency of the turkey as a producer of human food is dependent somewhat upon early maturity. The ability of the bird to grow mature plumage at an early age, fattening or finishing while yet young and probably immature, the texture of meat, and the distribution of fat are all market qualities which should receive the attention of the breeder. Figure 214 shows Bronze toms of good market type.

Size of turkey to raise. The producer should strive to satisfy the demands of the markets for turkeys as long as it is profitable to do so. Those who are emphasizing small size in turkeys should bear in mind that the overhead cost per pound for small turkeys is greater than for large turkeys. It is also true that the hotels and restaurants prefer the larger birds because they can get more servings per pound of large turkey. Hen turkeys, because of their smaller size and excellent quality, are in demand for family use. Table 117 shows the results obtained from a rather extensive survey made in 1936 by the National Association of Food Chains for the purpose of determining from their customers the demand for turkeys of different sizes. It will be observed that 50 per cent of the consumers patronizing the chain food stores preferred turkeys under twelve pounds. The Delaware station gathered some data (Table 118) on this problem in the city of Wilmington which showed that restaurants and wealthy customers have a very definite preference for turkeys weighing over thirteen pounds. It is evident that various sizes are in demand.

Egg production. Economical poult production requires high egg pro-

Table 117

CONSUMER DEMAND FOR TURKEYS BY SIZE OF BIRD [1]

Size of Turkey	Proportion of Total Demand *
Group 1 (8 and 9 pounds)........	25%
Group 2 (10 and 11 pounds)........	25%
Group 3 (12 and 13 pounds)........	23%
Group 4 (14 and 15 pounds)........	14%
Group 5 (16 and 17 pounds)........	8%
Group 6 (18 pounds and over)......	5%

* Represents weighted average of all returns to make allowances for the varying sizes of reporting companies.

Table 118

NUMBER OF CONSUMERS AND RESTAURANTS PREFERRING VARIOUS SIZES OF TURKEYS [2]

SIZES OF TURKEYS	ALL CONSUMERS		WEALTHY CONSUMERS		RESTAURANTS	
	Number	Per Cent	Number	Per Cent	Number	Per Cent
6 pounds..............	1	.5	...	...	...	...
8 pounds..............	5	.5	...	...	...	...
9 to 10 pounds........	49	27.1	4	21.0	...	...
11 to 12 pounds........	50	27.6	4	21.0	1	4.8
13 to 15 pounds........	42	23.2	5	26.3	8	38.1
Over 15 pounds........	38	21.0	6	31.7	12	57.1

duction in the breeding stock. Egg production in turkeys as in chickens can be increased by proper breeding. The basis of selection must be trap-nest records and progeny test records. The use of trap nests for obtaining egg-production records on turkeys is a recent development. The Oklahoma Agricultural Experiment Station has reported the trap-nest record of a turkey hen which laid 205 eggs in one year (1932). A number of turkey breeders and investigators are now using trap nests for obtaining egg-production records.

Unless the consumption of turkeys becomes less seasonal so that there is a greater demand for turkeys throughout the year, poult production will remain highly seasonal and there will be little demand for turkey eggs out of the regular hatching season. Under the present conditions early egg production and intensive production are most desirable. As in chickens, early sexual maturity and intensity of production are inherited characters which can be modified by breeding as well as by feeding and management.

Factors related to annual egg production in turkeys have been investigated by Asmundson at the California Agricultural Experiment Station, Davis,

[1] Survey made by the National Association of Food Chains, 1936.
[2] Del. Agr. Expt. Sta. Bul. 218, 1939.

U. S. D. A.

Fig. 215. Pendulous crop, an inherited condition.

California. For the years 1934, 1935, and 1936 the average annual egg production was 77.2, 76.1, and 79.4 eggs. He found that annual production was influenced most by (1) date of last egg, or the bird's persistency; (2) length of pause, or time out of production; (3) date of first egg, or starting early in the season; and (4) net spring rate of production. From these results it would appear that to increase annual egg production in turkeys, they must be bred for persistency and intensity of production without rest periods, and they must be bred and so managed that they start laying early in the season.

Young hens lay more eggs than do older birds. Records of egg production kept at the California station showed the following production per hen: first year, 77 eggs; second year, 50 eggs; third year, 44 eggs; fourth year, 45 eggs; and fifth year, 28 eggs. Egg production is reduced when turkey hens are permitted to remain broody and hatch their eggs. Date of hatching is also a factor influencing time of egg production. Early-hatched birds often lay during the winter months while late-hatched birds may not lay until late spring.

The elimination of inherited defects. The California station has shown that pendulous crops in turkeys are inherited. In matings which they made the percentage of offspring developing pendulous crops varied from none to

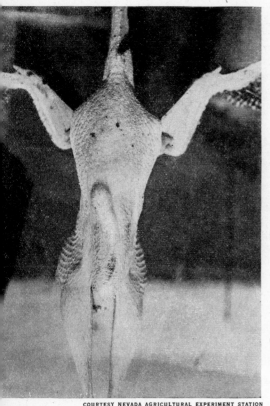

COURTESY NEVADA AGRICULTURAL EXPERIMENT STATION

Fig. 216. Crooked breast bone, a serious market defect.

100 per cent. They were also able to show that the occurrence of pendulous crops was greatly increased when turkeys were raised where the temperature was high, the humidity low, and where there was much sunshine. They concluded that the tendency for turkeys to develop pendulous crops was determined by one pair of recessive autosomal genes. If pendulous crops are inherited in the manner these investigators believe them to be, the breeder could eliminate this defect only by progeny testing his birds, and discarding any which produced off-pring developing this condition. This condition cannot be eliminated by merely culling turkeys that develop pendulous crops (Fig. 215).

The Kansas Agricultural Experiment Station has shown that in chickens the tendency to develop crooked breastbones is inherited. It appears logical to assume that in turkeys crooked breastbones also may be inherited. Birds showing evidence of crooked breastbones should be marketed and thereby kept out of the breeding pens (Fig. 216).

The progressive turkey breeder will not only select breeding stock free from market defects but he will study the inheritance of these defects and by scientific breeding eliminate them from his strain of turkeys.

Selection of Breeding Stock

The success of any breeding program depends upon the stock used in the breeding pens. Young birds which are intended for breeding purposes should be selected in the fall before any birds are marketed. Otherwise, some of the best birds may be sold and therefore lost for breeding.

The basis of selection should be, of course, those qualities which the breeder hopes to establish in his strain of birds. Since turkeys are produced primarily for meat, selection for desirable market characteristics should be considered fundamental in any turkey-breeding program. The market prefers a turkey which has a long, wide, and deep breast, and a compact body which is well-fleshed and covered with fat. The market also prefers turkeys which have well-matured plumage and few pinfeathers when dressed.

The Oklahoma Agricultural Experiment Station has reported results which show that such measurements as keel length, body depth in front, and shank length may be used as a basis for selecting turkeys at market age. Advancement can be made along these lines by breeding.

The specialty breeder who uses trap nests will make selection also on the basis of pedigrees and progeny records.

S. J. Marsden, Poultry Husbandman in charge of turkey investigations for the United States Department of Agriculture, has prepared the following outline for selecting turkey breeders:

I. **Head**
   A. Bright, round, outstanding eyes of proper variety color. Reject if off-colored, elongated, dull, sunken, injured, blind, or missing.
   B. Short, curved beak. Reject for ostrich beak, cross beak, and elongated beak but not for proper debeaking.
   C. Rugged but refined appearance, free from excess flesh. Reject for coarseness or weak appearance.
   D. Good depth and breadth, not elongated. Reject for crowhead.
II. **Back.**
   A. Wide and flat including part over ribs (heart girth). Reject for reach (arched) back, crooked back, narrow heart girth, or torn skin.
III. **Breast**
   A. Wide but not excessively so. Reject if too narrow or too wide and flat.
   B. Parallel to back. Reject if rear end of keel appears pushed in or dropped down away from the parallel position.
   C. Smooth-fleshed, width carried well back to rear of keel but not so much as to interfere with locomotion. Reject for heart-shaped breast (very wide in front and very narrow at rear).
   D. Breastbone (keel); straight, moderately long, free from knobbiness. Remove birds with crooked keels, noticeably curved, too short, decidedly rocker-shaped, decidedly dented, or possessing a knob which is the result of failure of flesh to cover the front point of the keel. Breastbone should be about the same length as the shank.
   E. Check crop region and reject for signs of pendulous crop.
IV. **Legs and feet**
   A. Drumsticks: plump, well-meated, and of a size sufficient to balance the rest of the body. Reject if undersized or straight-sided.
   B. Shanks of moderate length, strong, sturdy, not too short or too long, not coarse. Reject for legginess or abnormally short shanks.
   C. Reject for off-color, crooked toes, twisted shank, or any tendency toward bowlegs, knock-knees, slipped tendons, swollen hocks, or malformed hocks. One or two slightly crooked toes permitted in females but not in males.
V. **Wings and tail**
   A. Reject for split wing, slipped wing, twisted or off-colored wing and tail feathers. Clipped wing(s) permitted on females but not on males.

VI. **Balance**
Depends primarily upon leg placement; birds poorly balanced have legs placed too far back. Balance is indicated by:
A. Keel-leg relationship when bird is suspended by the legs, the body vertical and relaxed. Well-balanced birds show no decided gap between drumsticks and rear end of keel, the profile appearing smooth. Reject poorly balanced birds with a conspicuous gap showing a broken or notched profile. Keel should extend well back between the legs.

VII. **Skeletal proportions**
A. Moderate depth; keel nearly equal in length to the shank in market-age birds; slightly longer than shank in birds 32 weeks and older. Body depth should be about one-fifth greater than length of the keel in all except Beltsville Small Whites in which it should be about one-fourth greater. Measure by calipers or by spread of hand. Reject for shallow body or short keel.

VIII. **Color**
A. Conforming reasonably well to standard requirements. Reject for all standard disqualifications relating to color of plumage, legs, and feet and also for solidly "off-colored" beak or eyes. Reject males of Bronze, Bourbon Red, Narragansett, and other parti-colored varieties that do not have male-colored plumage and females that do not have female-colored plumage such as those lacking the normal white edgings on breast and body feathers. Reject Bronze turkeys for completely black backs and complete or almost complete lack of body bronzing and tail penciling.

IX. **Size**
A. Check for weight according to variety and age as shown in Table I, Regulation 22, Miscellaneous Publication 555, The National Turkey Improvement Plan. Weigh representative specimens. Reject for decided underweight or overweight.

X. **Quick market maturity** (Quick maturing turkeys are more efficient in the use of feed.)
The state of maturity can be checked accurately and effectively only where age is known and then only at 22 to 26 weeks for small-type and 24 to 30 for medium- and large-type turkeys. Quick maturing specimens will have the most market finish at the ages indicated.
A. Good market finish is indicated by:
1. Fat in skin. Have an assistant hold the bird so that breast skin is relaxed, then pluck a few feathers from the sparsely feathered area between the two feather tracts of the breast at a point just to rear of a line drawn from shoulder to front point of keel. Take a fold of skin between thumbs and forefingers of both hands. Grade A turkeys will have a creamy skin, a fold of which (containing a double thickness of skin) is about .07 to .14 inch thick; U. S. Grade B, .04 inch; and U. S. Grade C, .03 inch or less. This test is effective only at the point described. Ignore fat in skin at other places on the body.
2. *Pinfeathers long enough to be plucked cleanly.* U. S. Grade A dressed turkeys are permitted to have a few short pinfeathers, but only a very small number on the breast. In the live bird, check for pinfeathers too short to be picked on drumsticks, shoulders, and one

of the two narrow feather tracts that run parallel to the keel and just above it on either side.

Reject birds not showing proper degree of maturity (U. S. Grade A finish for small-type at 24–26 weeks, or large- and medium-type at 28–30 weeks). In the absence of a thorough check as above eliminate all obviously late-maturing specimens.

XI. **Carriage and action** (especially important in the selection of males).

A. Carriage (the bird standing or walking but not strutting): Birds with good balance stand high at the shoulders, the back sloping from front to rear at a 35–40° angle. Reject for front-heaviness.

B. Action: Gait free, active, and easy. Reject for waddling, limping, paddling (swinging feet outwards), or crippled condition.

Matings

Age of stock. Birds one year old are usually used for breeding purposes. For the production of market turkeys this appears to be the most practical method to follow because the females produce more eggs during their first laying season, hatchability is generally higher when young stock is mated, and the cost of keeping breeding stock from one season to another is eliminated. The progressive breeder who pedigrees his stock and uses progeny records must keep breeding stock for several seasons. From the data given in Table 119 it is evident that young turkey breeding females will produce more eggs during the breeding season and these eggs will be produced earlier in the season than if older birds are used.

Table 119

EFFECT OF AGE OF TURKEY BREEDING STOCK ON EGG PRODUCTION [3]

Age of Stock (Years)	Average Egg Production	First Egg After January 1 (Days)
1	76.6	67.3
2	49.5	78.8
3	44.2	80.3
4	44.6	87.6
5	27.6	96.2

Single male matings. Many turkeys are produced on farms where one male is mated with a few females. Many commercial turkey raisers also mate single males with from ten to fifteen females. Single male matings are necessary where pedigreed breeding methods are being followed, so that ancestry may be traced and progeny tests made. Where males are placed in adjoining breeding pens it is advisable to place some material such as burlap on the fence so that the males cannot see each other. Otherwise they exhaust their energy by parading before each other, "gobbling," and attempting to fight.

[3] Asmundson and Lloyd. University of California.

Flock matings. Large-scale turkey production has resulted in mass or flock matings where several males are used. In flock matings one tom is used for each fifteen to twenty females. A very simple method for preventing the males from fighting and the fertility from thereby being reduced is to confine the males in individual pens with openings only large enough for the females to pass through. These pens should be so arranged that the hens have to pass through to get feed or water. Solid partitions between the pens three or four feet high will prevent the toms from fighting through the fence.

Pedigree breeding of turkeys. The realization that the market qualities of turkeys are inherited has led to the pedigree breeding of turkeys. The trap nest has been found to be a practical device for determining the egg production of individual turkey hens and also for identifying the eggs laid by different birds. A record of all matings should be kept which shows the male and females used in each pen. An incubator record should also be kept which shows for each hen the number of eggs set, the number of infertile eggs, the number of dead embryos, and the poults hatched. Each poult should be wing-banded and suitable records kept so that the pedigree of any pedigreed bird can be determined at any time.

By keeping progeny records, valuable male and female breeding stock can be identified and better families can be kept and the inferior ones discarded. It is only by such methods that the breeder can hope to make much progress in breeding turkeys.

Breeding systems. Three systems of breeding are used in breeding turkeys: inbreeding, outbreeding, and crossbreeding. Close inbreeding (brother and sister, etc.) results in low hatchability, low fertility, high mortality, slow growth, and late maturity. Mating distantly related birds is a desirable method for the breeder who is doing pedigreed breeding to use in establishing desirable characters in his strain of turkeys.

Most turkey growers who are not interested in doing pedigree breeding find that outbreeding is the best system for them to follow. They can purchase breeding males from some breeder who is breeding the type they want. These males are mated with females selected from their own flock. They can purchase stock from the same breeder year after year with little danger of ill effects from inbreeding. Those who wish to do so may produce their own toms, if they have several individual mating pens, by following the plan shown in Figure 217. With four pens (A, B, C, D) the best male produced each year from the mating in pen A would be placed in B the following year; but the best females raised from the A mating would remain in pen A for the following breeding season, to be mated with the best male produced by the mating in pen D. The management of the other pens would be similar in that males produced in B would go to C and those produced in C to D.

Crossbreeding is sometimes used, but the crossing of the different varieties of turkeys has not, as yet, proved enough superior to outcrossing to justify its use. Turkey breeders and growers prefer to raise purebred stock.

Artificial insemination. The National Agricultural Research Center (1938) reported the successful use of artificial insemination in turkey breed-

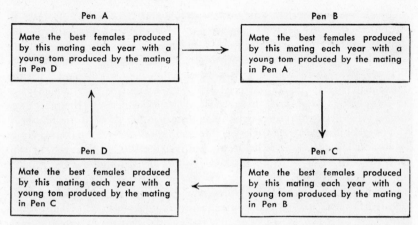

Pen A

Mate the best females produced by this mating each year with a young tom produced by the mating in Pen D

Pen B

Mate the best females produced by this mating each year with a young tom produced by the mating in Pen A

Pen D

Mate the best females produced by this mating each year with a young tom produced by the mating in Pen C

Pen C

Mate the best females produced by this mating each year with a young tom produced by the mating in Pen B

Fig. 217. A systematic breeding plan for the breeder who desires to produce his own breeding stock and avoid close inbreeding.

ing. They were able to increase fertility from an old tom by using artificial insemination instead of natural mating. While this method is not likely to gain widespread use, it does provide the breeder with a technique which may be quite helpful in introducing valuable blood into his flock.

Management of Breeding Stock

The failure of a turkey-breeding program can be traced frequently to the mismanagement of the breeding stock. While turkeys given their freedom on the farm may produce more fertile eggs than when kept under artificial conditions, they do respond to good management and produce maximum results when they have proper care and management.

Range or yards. During recent years there has been a change from range to yards for turkey-breeding stock. In those regions where blackhead is a serious turkey disease this change has been necessary in order to prevent all range from becoming contaminated with the organisms which cause this disease. The most practical yarding system is one where green feed can be grown in the yards. Wire fences from three to six feet high will confine turkeys if the yards are level and they cannot perch or roost on the fence. For single male matings yards 40′ x 120′ provide sufficient green feed. Gravel, crushed stone, or cinders placed around the house or roosting quarters help to maintain more sanitary conditions in the yards. Very small yards fifteen or twenty feet square covered by three or four inches of gravel, crushed stone, or cinders, as shown in Figure 218, may be used for single male matings. Results reported by the Pennsylvania Agricultural Experiment Station showed that breeding stock could be closely confined in such pens without interfering with breeding results. When confined in yards where there is no growing green feed, both cod liver oil and a high-grade alfalfa meal should be fed. The use of some fresh green feed was reported by the Pennsylvania station to increase

Fig. 218. A pen of turkey breeding stock confined to a small yard, covered with crushed stone. (Note saddles on females.)

hatching results even though 5 per cent of alfalfa meal was used in the mash.

Complete confinement. The New Hampshire Agricultural Experiment Station reported in 1938 that turkey-breeding stock kept in complete confinement in houses and artificially lighted so that they had a maximum of fourteen hours of light laid eggs which hatched as well as eggs laid by similar breeding stock on range, though the fertility was 7.7 per cent lower. The average production per bird for the breeding season was thirty-six eggs for the confined birds and thirty eggs for the birds on range.

Housing. The need for protection of turkeys against cold and rainy weather depends upon the climatic conditions which prevail where they are kept. They are generally considered to be less susceptible to the effects of weather than are chickens, and therefore require less protection. In most sections of the United States all that is required is roosting quarters protected by a roof and three walls. Adult turkeys may be confined in houses with satisfactory results, but the most economical provision for the southern part of the United States appears to be outside roosts only. For the northern part of the United States and Canada roosting sheds should be protected on the north, east, and west sides against winds, rain, and snow. Results reported by Scott and Payne in 1938 showed that housing was not necessary for turkey-breeding stock in Kansas.

Roosts (2″ x 4″) laid flat or four-inch poles provide satisfactory roosts for turkeys. Each bird should have about eighteen inches of space on the roosts. Open top boxes 2′ x 2′ and 10 to 12 inches deep supplied with some nesting material such as straw, excelsior, or cane pulp make very satisfactory nests. They may be located in the house or in some secluded spot in the yard. Where special breeding work is done, trap nests protected from rain and snow are

Fig. 219. Turkey hen entering trap nest. Note the doors on top for removing the birds from the nests and the hen's number painted on the saddle for identification.

used (Fig. 219). The house should provide about 8 to 10 square feet of floor space per bird so that plenty of room for feeders, waterers, and the birds will be available.

Artificial lighting. That turkeys may be brought into production as much as two months before they would otherwise lay, by using artificial lights, has been demonstrated by several investigators. The use of lights will usually bring mature turkeys into production within thirty days after the lights are started. The lights may be turned on early in the morning or all-night lights may be used. Figure 220 shows the results obtained at the Missouri Agricultural Experiment Station when all-night lights were used on Bronze turkey hens during their first laying season.

The Pennsylvania Station has reported that it is necessary to expose toms to lights at least one week or longer before the hens are placed under lights to insure satisfactory early fertility. Work at the Oklahoma Station indicates that for Oklahoma conditions both toms and hens respond to lights within the same length of time. These differences between the Pennsylvania and Oklahoma results are likely due to climate.

The Oklahoma Station has also shown that the source of light used is important. Electric, gasoline, and natural-gas lights were equally effective in stimulating egg production in turkeys, but kerosene lanterns did not have any effect on egg production.

Feeding. Suitable rations are necessary for high egg production and good hatchability. These rations may be similar to those used for feeding chicken breeding stock. Farmers who raise chickens and turkeys may use the same mash for both kinds of breeding stock, if extra vitamins A, D, and riboflavin

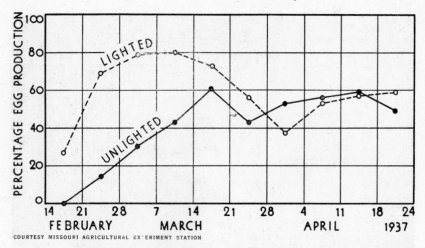

Fig. 220. Effect of all-night lights on egg production in turkeys.

are added to the turkey ration (Table 51). Breeding turkey toms will consume about six pounds of feed per week and for the same period the females
will consume about three pounds of feed. The cost of feed is the principal
item of expense in keeping breeding stock.

Rations for turkey breeding stock. Rations which are satisfactory for
feeding chicken breeding stock can be used for feeding turkey-breeding stock,
if properly fortified by minerals and vitamins (Table 51 and p. 552).

Protection of females against injury in mating. Turkey hens are frequently injured seriously by large toms tearing their backs while mating.
To prevent these injuries the sharp toenails and spurs of the toms may be
clipped, or "saddles" may be placed on the females. Many producers are
protecting the females by placing canvas "saddles" on them, as shown in
Figure 218. This should be done before the breeding season begins.

Cost of keeping breeding stock. The breeder who is following a scientific
breeding program must keep breeding stock throughout the year. The cost
of keeping this stock is a considerable item and includes labor, returns on
investment in stock, equipment, and land, losses from mortality, depreciation,
and feed costs. The feed consumption of turkey-breeding stock is shown in
Table 120.

Hatchery supply flocks. The development of specialized poult production by hatcheries has created a demand for turkey-hatching eggs. Many turkey eggs are shipped to hatcheries in the North Central states from California,
Texas, and other southern states. Egg production in turkeys is influenced by
light, and therefore turkeys located where the days become longer earlier in
the season than in other sections produce more early eggs. This factor will
always remain in favor of those southern states and most of the early-hatching
eggs will likely be produced in those areas. Hatcheries specializing in poult

Table 120

FEED CONSUMPTION OF BRONZE BREEDING STOCK. U. S. RANGE LIVESTOCK
STATION, MILES CITY, MONTANA, 1929–1935

SEASON	POUNDS OF MASH AND SCRATCH FEED CONSUMED PER WEEK	
	Males	Females
Winter period—Dec. 15 to Feb. 8. (Unlighted)	5.85	3.23
Winter-Spring period—Feb. 9 to May 31. (Morning lights Feb. 9–April 15)	5.13	2.73
Summer-Early Fall maintenance period—June 1 to October 18	3.50	1.40
Fall fattening period—Oct. 19 to Nov. 15	7.00	3.50
Total for 52-week period	240.88	117.12

production which are located in the northern states may continue to find it profitable to purchase turkey eggs from producers located in more favorable climates.

Turkey Improvement Associations

Variety associations. There are organized clubs for each of the varieties, except for the Slate turkeys. These associations promote their respective varieties, suggest standards for them, hold club meets, and encourage the exhibition of their varieties. They have done much to standardize color patterns and develop the type of the present-day turkey.

The National Turkey Improvement Plan. The primary objectives of this plan are to improve the production and market quality of turkeys and to reduce losses from disease. The plan (revised in 1950) provides for four breeding stages and three pullorum classes as follows:

BREEDING STAGES

1. U. S. APPROVED BREEDING STAGE

U. S. Approved flocks.—The flocks shall meet the following requirements: Toms and hens shall be carefully selected once each year for constitutional vigor and Standard bred qualities to a reasonably high degree. The following specifications should be emphasized:

(*a*) Conformation: Body should be deep and relatively rectangular in shape, flesh of breast well developed, giving this region a rounded fullness, in contrast to sharp-keeled birds lacking in muscular development. The front point of the keel should be well-fleshed and free from coarseness. The back should be flat and wide over its entire length. Leg bones should be sturdy, of medium length, and without coarseness. Normal turkey carriage, or posture (body carried at an angle of 35° to 45° from the horizontal) is important as are sturdy, strong legs placed squarely under the body.

(*b*) Shape of breastbone: Breastbone should be straight, relatively long, and parallel with the back. It should extend well up between the lower thighs (drumsticks) as the bird is suspended by the legs.

(*c*) Rate of maturity: Birds showing definite indications of late maturity should not be approved.

The method of selecting turkey breeding stock for Standard-bred and meat-production qualities prescribed by the State college of agriculture or other properly constituted State agency shall serve as a basis for the selection of toms and hens. Recommendations of special committees of the National Turkey Federation and the American Poultry Association on turkey type, weight, and other variety characteristics may properly be used as guides in developing and improving standards of selection. Emphasis at all times should be placed upon uniformity as regards conformation, size, color, carriage, and appearance of the birds remaining in the breeding flock after selection is completed. All birds to be used in U. S. Approved breeding flocks shall be selected by a State inspector or by a flock-selecting agent.

All birds selected for U. S. Approved breeding flocks shall be banded at the time of selection, with sealed and numbered leg or wing bands obtained from the official State agency. Birds rejected by the State inspector or the flock-selecting agent shall have leg and wing bands removed, and shall be kept separate from the breeding flocks. The selection of birds for U. S. Approved flocks shall be completed prior to March 1, and at least 10 days before any eggs are saved for hatching purposes, except that this 10-day interval shall not be required if all the toms found in the breeding flock are approved. No birds shall be selected and approved earlier than at 22 weeks of age.

Before any flock other than one affiliated with a participating hatchery may be recognized as a U. S. Approved flock, it must be inspected and approved by a State inspector. Each year at least one-third of the hatchery flocks supplying eggs to a U. S. Approved hatchery and at least one-third of the flocks selected by each flock-selecting agent shall be inspected and approved by a State inspector. The inspection of a flock by a State inspector shall consist in the physical examination, by handling, of a sufficient number of toms and hens to satisfy him that the flock-selection work performed meets the requirements of the U. S. Approved breeding stage.

No birds except those with official sealed and numbered leg or wing bands shall be allowed in the breeding flocks, and no toms shall be allowed with any other hens of breeding age on the same premises except in U. S. R. O. P., U. S. R. O. M., or candidate matings.

2. U. S. CERTIFIED BREEDING STAGE

U. S. Certified flocks.—These flocks shall fulfill all the requirements of U. S. Approved flocks and shall be free from disqualifications. The hens shall be mated to U. S. R. O. P. toms or to sons of U. S. R. O. M. matings. The toms shall be selected by a State inspector and the hens by a State inspector or a specially authorized flock-selecting agent. All flocks shall be inspected and approved by a

State inspector at least once during the breeding season. After the second year of U. S. Certified breeding work on any farm, hens to be used as breeders shall be from U. S. Certified flocks or from U. S. R. O. P. or U. S. R. O. M. matings.

3. U. S. RECORD OF PERFORMANCE BREEDING STAGE

U. S. Record of Performance embraces records of egg production, hatchability, and body weight made on the breeder's premises under official supervision and similar records made at State colleges of agriculture, and State and Federal experiment stations, when such records are passed on by the official State agency and when the individual birds meet other U. S. R. O. P. requirements. The birds produced by State colleges of agriculture and State and Federal experiment stations may be recognized as U. S. R. O. P. only for the use of U. S. R. O. P. breeders in their breeding work. The primary objective of this and the U. S. R. O. M. breeding stage is to produce young toms to head U. S. Certified flocks. When any disastrous event occurs that affects the pedigree breeding and progeny-testing work of any advanced turkey breeder, and when such event is immediately brought to the attention of his official State agency, this agency may, with the consent of the Bureau of Animal Industry, make an equitable revision of the qualifying requirements.

The trap nest used in U. S. R. O. P. work shall be of an approved type and shall be kept in perfect working order at all times. The breeding farm and all egg-production records shall be subject at all times to unannounced inspections by a State inspector. At the time of each inspection, the inspector shall have sole charge of the trap nests and of eggs laid. Each U. S. R. O. P. candidate shall be banded with a sealed and numbered official leg band. No hens other than those entered in U. S. R. O. P. shall be allowed in the pens where U. S. R. O. P. candidates are being trap-nested, except with the approval of the official State agency.

U. S. R. O. P. eggs and poults may be produced only on a U. S. R. O. P. breeder's premises except that with the approval of the official State agency (*a*) a U. S. R. O. P. breeder may have eggs hatched by any hatchery operating under the turkey plan provided the U. S. R. O. P. breeder does the pedigreeing of the poults; and (*b*) a U. S. Approved or U. S. Certified hatchery owner may produce U. S. R. O. P. poults from purchased U. S. R. O. P. eggs for the use of his hatchery-flock owners only, provided proper records of purchases are sent to the official State agency and a State inspector does the wing-banding of these poults.

When U. S. R. O. P. hatching eggs are transferred from one U. S. R. O. P. breeder to another U. S. R. O. P. breeder or hatcheryman for the purpose of hatching U. S. R. O. P. poults, the conditions that shall govern such a transaction include the following: (*a*) The U. S. R. O. P. breeder who sells the U. S. R. O. P. hatching eggs must send a report in triplicate at the time the eggs are shipped consisting of a list of the eggs sold, the pen or sire number and dam number of each egg, and the egg production, hatchability, and body weight of each dam, to his R. O. P. supervisor. If the eggs are shipped outside the State, these records shall be attested to by the R. O. P. supervisor, who shall retain one copy and mail one copy to the purchaser and one to the official State agency of the State to which the eggs are shipped. (*b*) Within 5 days after incubation has begun, the purchasing U. S. R. O. P. breeder or hatcheryman must submit to his official State agency a list of the U. S. R. O. P. eggs bought. (*c*) Within 5 days after hatching time the U. S. R. O. P. breeder or hatcheryman who purchased the eggs must send to his official State agency a list of the poults hatched from each dam and their respective wing-band numbers.

When U. S. R. O. P. poults, young toms, or mature birds are sold or transferred by members of the industry participating in the turkey plan, the individual making the sale must send a report in triplicate to his R. O. P. supervisor at the time these products are shipped giving the number of birds sold; the leg- or wing-band number, egg production, hatchability, and body weight of each dam, and the pen or leg-band number of the sire of each poult, young tom, or mature bird. If the poults, young toms, or mature birds are shipped outside the State, these records shall be attested to by the R. O. P. supervisor, who shall retain one copy and mail one copy to the purchaser and one to the official State agency of the State to which these products are shipped.

To be eligible for U. S. R. O. P. entry, all hens shall have been raised from U. S. R. O. M. matings, U. S. R. O. P. matings, or U. S. Certified flocks or other flocks of breeding satisfactory to the official State agency and the individual birds must meet the body type requirements prescribed by the official State agency. Eligibility shall be confined to any standard variety or other variety recognized by the official State agency.

All hens trap-nested on the premises of a U. S. R. O. P. breeder shall be considered as entered under U. S. R. O. P. supervision with the following exceptions: (*a*) All qualified U. S. R. O. P. hens may be trap-nested. (*b*) He may, with the approval of the official State agency, trap-nest any other variety which he is developing as a basis for future U. S. R. O. P. work. (*c*) With the approval of the official State agency, hens in their second or subsequent production years may be privately trapped to complete records that were begun before U. S. R. O. P. work was undertaken.

All matings shall be inspected at least two times each year. One or more consecutive days of inspection by the R. O. P. inspector shall represent a single inspection. In the event of an outbreak of contagious disease on a turkey farm where U. S. R. O. P. work is carried on, inspection may be temporarily suspended.

4. U. S. REGISTER OF MERIT BREEDING STAGE

This breeding stage incorporates all the requirements of the U. S. R. O. P. breeding stage and in addition includes progeny test records of viability and market quality of the progeny of qualified U. S. R. O. P. toms and hens. When any disastrous event occurs that affects the pedigree breeding and progeny testing work of any advanced turkey breeder, and when such event is immediately brought to the attention of his official State agency, this agency may, with the consent of the Bureau of Animal Industry, make an equitable revision of the qualifying requirements.

The U. S. R. O. P. breeder who desires to qualify for U. S. R. O. M. shall rear on his remises or have reared under his supervision poults hatched as set forth in paragraphs 4 or 5 of this section in order that viability and market quality requirements may be determined.

U. S. R. O. M. toms.—U. S. R. O. P. toms shall qualify for U. S. R. O. M. when the following requirements are met:

(*a*) All hatching eggs produced from the mating during the 8-week period for measuring hatchability and a minimum average of 20 eggs per hen and 200 eggs per mating shall be set.

(*b*) The average hatchability of all eggs set shall be 65 per cent or more. At altitudes of 3,000 to 3,499 feet, the minimum qualifying hatchability percentage shall be 60, and at altitudes of 3,500 feet or more the minimum qualifying hatchability percentage shall be 55.

(*c*) The minimum number of poults raised to 8 weeks of age shall be 75 per cent of all poults started, provided that at least 100 poults from each pen shall be started.

(*d*) Each young turkey reared, of those referred to in (*c*) above, shall be carefully examined not earlier than at 22 weeks of age by a State inspector or authorized agent of the official State agency. At the time of this examination, at least 60 per cent of all young toms and at least 80 per cent of all young hens shall be of U. S. Grade A market quality, due consideration being given to the age of the progeny and the climatic environment as related to their fattening and pinfeather condition, provided a minimum of 70 turkeys from each mating meet these requirements.

(*e*) Having met these requirements the tom may be banded by the R. O. P. supervisor or inspector with a sealed official leg band lettered "U. S. R. O. M."

U. S. R. O. M. hens.—U. S. R. O. P. hens shall qualify for U. S. R. O. M. when the following requirements are met:

(*a*) A minimum of 20 poults shall be started of those hatched during the 8-week period for measuring hatchability referred to in paragraph 14, section 3, of this article.

(*b*) Eighty per cent of all poults started shall be alive at 8 weeks of age.

(*c*) Each young turkey reared of those referred to in (*a*) above shall be carefully examined not earlier than at 22 weeks of age by a State inspector or authorized agent of the official State agency. At the time of this examination, at least 60 per cent of all young toms and at least 80 per cent of all young hens shall be of U. S. Grade A market quality, due consideration being given to the age of the progeny and the climatic environment as related to their fattening and pinfeather condition, provided a minimum of 12 turkeys meet these requirements.

(*d*) Having met these requirements the hen may be banded by the R. O. P. supervisor or inspector with a sealed official leg band lettered "U. S. R. O. M."

U. S. R. O. M. matings.—These matings may consist of:

(*a*) U. S. R. O. M. tom remated to the same hens with which he qualified; or

(*b*) U. S. R. O. M. hen remated to the same tom with which she qualified; or

(*c*) U. S. R. O. M. tom remated to the same U. S. R. O. M. hens with which he qualified.

Poults from U. S. R. O. M. matings.—These poults shall be banded with U. S. R. O. M. wing bands.

Sons of U. S. R. O. M. matings.—In order to qualify to head U. S. Certified flocks, a son of a U. S. R. O. M. mating shall have passed the final individual inspection of a State inspector not earlier than at 22 weeks of age and shall be banded at the time of inspection with an official sealed and numbered leg band. These leg bands shall be stamped with the letters "U. S. R. O. P."

At the time of inspection the son of a U. S. R. O. M. mating shall indicate strong vigor, shall show, upon handling, excellent body conformation and fleshing, and shall be an excellent representative of the variety in the judgment of the State inspector. The inspector shall make a complete record of the body weight, wing- and leg-band numbers of each tom banded.

The young toms from U. S. R. O. M. candidate matings are eligible for quali-
fication as sons of U. S. R. O. M. matings after their parent mating qualifies as a
U. S. R. O. M. mating.

PULLORUM CLASSES

The aim or goal in an official pullorum disease testing program for turkeys
shall be eradication rather than mere control of the disease. To that end every possible step should be taken not only to eradicate infected birds from the breeding
flocks, but also to eliminate all possible or probable avenues of infection for adult
breeding stock, poults, and growing turkeys. Complete segregation of turkeys from
chickens on the farm and in hatcheries at all stages of development, and during all
seasons of the year, is urgently recommended.

1. U. S. PULLORUM-CONTROLLED CLASS

This is a tolerance class. No breeder or hatchery should be content with having
qualified for this class. Control and eradication measures should be practiced continuously with a view to reducing the percentage of reactors each year and qualifying for the U. S. Pullorum-Passed class and then the U. S. Pullorum-Clean class
as soon as possible.

U. S. Pullorum-Controlled flocks.—These flocks shall meet the following requirements:

(*a*) All turkeys to be used as breeders shall be tested for pullorum disease
when more than 4 months of age under the supervision of an official State agency,
and shall contain fewer than 2 per cent reactors, the last test being made within 6
months immediately preceding the date of first sale of hatching eggs, poults, or
breeding stock from such flocks.

(*b*) All indicated carriers of pullorum disease shall be removed from the
premises on completion of the test and disposed of in a manner satisfactory to the
official State agency.

(*c*) All birds remaining in the breeding flock shall be properly leg- or wing-
banded.

(*d*) Individual birds introduced into U. S. Pullorum-Controlled flocks shall
have passed, within 6 months, a negative official test for pullorum disease.

A flock containing 2 per cent or more of reactors on the first test, on being
retested at intervals of not less than 21 days, and all reactors disposed of after each
test until the percentage of reactors is fewer than 2 per cent, may qualify as a
U. S. Pullorum-Controlled flock.

2. U. S. PULLORUM-PASSED CLASS

This class, which embodies the recognition of infected premises, permits no
tolerance in the official recognition of the flock. It emphasizes the advisability of
retesting at frequent intervals until no reactors are found and, therefore, is a more
effective step toward eradication than the tolerance class. No breeder should be
content with having qualified his flock for this class. Control measures should be
practiced continuously with a view to eliminating all infection and qualifying for
the U. S. Pullorum-Clean class as soon as possible.

U. S. Pullorum-Passed flocks.—These flocks shall meet the following requirements:

(*a*) All turkeys to be used as breeders shall be tested for pullorum disease when more than 4 months of age under the supervision of an official State agency, and shall contain no reactors, the last test being made within 6 months immediately preceding the date of first sale of hatching eggs, poults, or breeding stock from such flock. When reactors are found the flock may qualify as U. S. Pullorum-Passed, provided it is retested at intervals of not less than 21 days, until one negative test is obtained.

(*b*) All birds remaining in the breeding flock shall be properly leg- or wing-banded.

(*c*) Individual birds introduced into U. S. Pullorum-Passed flocks shall come from U. S. Pullorum-Passed or U. S. Pullorum-Clean flocks only, except that individual birds from other sources may be introduced provided they are quarantined for 15 days, then officially tested for pullorum disease and found to be negative.

·3. U. S. PULLORUM-CLEAN CLASS

U. S. Pullorum-Clean flocks.—These flocks shall meet the following requirements:

(*a*) All turkeys to be used as breeders shall be tested for pullorum disease when more than 4 months of age under the supervision of an official State agency and shall contain no reactors on the first or any subsequent test made within 6 months immediately preceding the date of first sale of hatching eggs, poults, or breeding stock from such flock.

(*b*) A Pullorum-Passed flock may qualify for the Pullorum-Clean class provided it has two consecutive negative tests for pullorum disease at least 21 days apart, the last test being made within 6 months immediately preceding the date of sale of hatching eggs or poults from such flock.

(*c*) All birds remaining in the breeding flock shall be properly leg- or wing-banded.

Individual turkeys introduced into U. S. Pullorum-Clean flocks shall come from U. S. Pullorum-Clean flocks only, except that individual turkeys from other sources may be introduced provided they are quarantined for 15 days, then officially tested for pullorum disease and found to be negative.

Flocks of this classification shall be designated as having been U. S. Pullorum-Clean for 1, 2, 3, etc., years.

Judging Turkeys for Exhibition, Live Market, or Dressed Quality

Until recent years the only shows for turkeys were the exhibition poultry shows. The realization that the winners in these exhibition shows were not necessarily the best market birds led to the establishment of shows where the live birds were judged for their market quality and also shows where dressed birds were exhibited. Renewed interest in turkey raising has also aroused an interest in the quality of poults and led to the day-old poult shows which are now held in some states.

Exhibition judging. While turkeys, like other species of poultry, are judged in the exhibition shows by comparison, the score card gives the evalu-

Fig. 221. Judging live turkeys. (Courtesy Turkey World, Mount Morris, Ill.)

ation for the different sections which should be considered by the judge (Fig. 221). The tendency toward utility in turkeys was recognized when the new score card was adopted at the annual convention of the American Poultry Association in St. Paul, Minnesota, July 16, 1938. This score card gives greater value to condition, vigor, and shape of breast but less to color than did the previous Standard of Perfection.

SCORE CARD FOR JUDGING TURKEYS

Symmetry		5
Condition and vigor		10
Weight		12
Head	Shape	3
	Color	1
Eyes	Shape	2
	Color	1
Throat-wattle—shape		1
Neck	Shape	2
	Color	3
Wings	Shape	4
	Color	6
Back	Shape	6
	Color	5
Tail	Shape	4
	Color	6
Breast	Shape	10
	Color	4
Body and fluff	Shape	6
	Color	4
Legs and Toes	Shape	3
	Color	2

Live market classes. In many turkey shows the judges are emphasizing market quality instead of color pattern. Some shows have live market classes in which turkeys are judged almost exclusively for market quality. Marsden and Martin have suggested the score card on page 552 for judging live market turkeys.

Dressed turkey exhibits. Since the turkey is primarily a market bird sold to the ultimate consumer in the dressed condition and since the dressed market appearance of the bird cannot be judged always by looking at the live specimen, there have arisen the dressed classes for turkeys (Fig. 222). They have served a very useful purpose in that they have educated producers to market demands and stimulated consumer demand for quality turkeys.

Poult shows. The poult show tends to focus attention on the production of quality poults. The quality of turkey poults is improving, but many inferior poults are being started by turkey raisers. The poult show serves as an educational medium for those interested in producing better poults. The Iowa State Turkey Poult Show, the first of its kind in the United States, for their fifth show May 11–13, 1939, used the following score card.

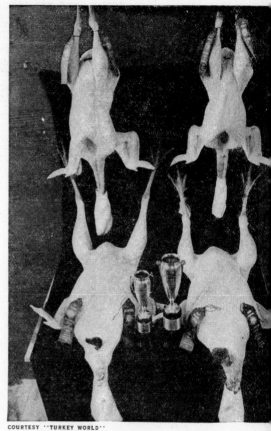

COURTESY "TURKEY WORLD"

Fig. 222. Champions at the Washington Turkey Show, December, 1939.

Sturdiness and activity	20
Perfection and development	20
Weight before feeding	10
Uniformity of size	14
Apparent breed type	10
Trueness to color	14
Uniformity of color	12

The production and sale of turkey poults by turkey breeders and hatcheries is a relatively new but very rapidly expanding business. The attention focused on quality by the poult shows should do much to improve the quality of the poults produced and sold. The primary consideration of the producer as well as the turkey hatcheryman is a healthy and vigorous poult. This poult score could well afford to assign more value to these points.

SCORE CARD FOR JUDGING LIVE MARKET TURKEYS [4]

SHOW_____DATE_____BAND No._____

VARIETY_____CLASS_____WEIGHT_____

Section Number and Name	Point value in scoring	Explanation

I. Standard quality	Vigor and condition 10
	Variety color...... 5
	Symmetry and
	  breed type...... 5
	Standard weight... 5
	  —
	Total............. 25
		This much weight is given to the general appearance of the bird.
		If crossbred turkeys are scored, the color is not considered.
		When exhibited in market classes as purebreds, specimens should creditably represent the variety and be free from serious disqualifications. Standard disqualifications, unless so serious as to impair the appearance or actions of the bird are not to disqualify.

II. Finish (fat)	20	A specimen should grade fully U. S. Special to rate 20.
III. Feathering	20	A specimen should be completely free of pinfeathers to rate 20. Short pinfeathers are especially undesirable.
IV. Fleshing, especially breast	20	A specimen should have a broad, fully fleshed breast, the width carrying out well towards the rear, and be fully fleshed in all other sections of the body. Drumsticks should be plump and moderately short.
V. Relationship of keel to shank and of keel to depth	10	As measured by sliding-jaw calipers, the length of the keel bone should equal, or exceed, the length of the shank. The depth depends upon size. The shank is measured by flexing it at a right angle to the tibia, bending back the center toe, and measuring the distance from back of hock to surface of the pad on the bottom of the foot, pressing calipers firmly but not strongly against the parts. The keel is measured by holding the calipers against the rear end of the bone and the sliding jaw against the front end. The depth is measured from middle of keel to middle of back.
VI. Shape of keel and relation of keel to back	5	The keel should be parallel or nearly so to the back and should be free from curves, dents, and knobs.
Total	100	

[4] From *Turkey Management*, by Marsden and Martin, 1939. By permission of The Interstate Printers and Publishers.

REVIEW QUESTIONS

1. Where did the early New England colonists obtain their turkey breeding stock?
2. What variety of turkeys is most popular in America? Why?
3. Name in order of importance the objectives of a turkey-breeding program.
4. What characters must be established in turkeys to insure high egg production?
5. What factors contribute to the occurrence of pendulous crops in turkeys?
6. Can turkey-breeding stock be confined to houses or small yards without reducing hatchability?
7. What is the purpose of turkey "saddles"?
8. What breeding stages are suggested for turkeys in the National Turkey Improvement Plan?

REFERENCES

AMERICAN STANDARD OF PERFECTION. American Poultry Association. Davenport, Iowa. 1945.

ASMUNDSON, V. S., AND JUKES, T. H.: TURKEY PRODUCTION IN CALIFORNIA. Calif. Ext. Circ. 110. Revised, 1944.

ASMUNDSON, V. S.: INHERITED DIFFERENCES IN WEIGHT AND CONFORMATION OF BRONZE TURKEYS. Poultry Sci., 27: 695–708. 1948.

BERRYMAN, CARL N., AND BUCHANAN, MARK T.: AN ECONOMIC STUDY OF WASHINGTON'S TURKEY INDUSTRY IN 1942. PART 1: BREEDING FLOCKS. Wash. Sta. Bul. 440. 1944.

BILLINGS, W. A.: TALKING TURKEY. Minn. Ext. Bul. 124. Revised, 1947.

BIRD, S.: MEASURING ROUNDNESS OF BREAST IN LINE TURKEYS. U. S. Egg and Poultry Mag., 51: 206–209, 235. 1945.

DARROW, M. D.: AND MORGAN, C. L.: LARGE VERSUS SMALL TYPE TURKEYS. S. C. Sta. Bul. 350. 1944.

HARSHAW, H. M., KELLOGG, W. L., RECTOR, R. R., AND MARSDEN, S. J.: THE COMPOSITION OF TURKEYS OF DIFFERENT VARIETIES AND STRAINS. Poultry Sci., 22: 126–136. 1943.

JULL, M. A.: Raising Turkeys, Ducks, Geese, Game Birds. McGraw-Hill Book Co., New York. 1947.

KLEIN, G. T.: Starting Right with Turkeys. The Macmillan Co., New York. 1946.

MARSDEN, S. J., AND LEE, ALFRED R.: TURKEY RAISING. U. S. D. A. Farmers' Bul. 1409. Revised, 1939.

MARSDEN, S. J., AND MARTIN, J. H.: Turkey Management, 4th ed. The Interstate, Danville, Ill. 1946.

THE NATIONAL TURKEY IMPROVEMENT PLAN. U. S. D. A. Misc. Pub. 555. 1948.

NEWLON, W. E., AND ASMUNDSON, V. S.: SELECTING TURKEYS FOR BREEDING IMPROVEMENT. Calif. Ext. Circ. 143. 1948.

PODALSKY, S.: GIFTS OF THE AMERICAS: THE TURKEY. Agr. in America, 4: 219. 1944.

Profitable Turkey Management, 6th ed. The Beacon Milling Co., Cayuga, N. Y. 1946.

TURKEY WORLD: Directory and Annual Review Issue. 25: No. 1. 1950.

VOORHIES, EDWIN C.: CALIFORNIA TURKEYS, SITUATION, AND OUTLOOK. Calif. Sta. Bul. 380. 1948.

CHAPTER 16 ‖‖‖‖‖‖‖‖‖‖‖‖‖‖‖‖‖‖‖‖‖‖‖‖‖‖‖‖‖‖‖‖‖‖‖‖‖

Turkey Production and Management

▼

Profits from turkey raising are determined largely by the efficiency attained in production, in the control of diseases and parasites, and in marketing.

Incubation

Artificial incubation has, quite generally, replaced natural methods because (1) the time of setting can be controlled; (2) a larger number of poults can be hatched at the same time; (3) egg production of the breeding stock is higher, because the hens do not take time out to set; (4) there is less danger of transmitting disease to the poults; and (5) artificial incubation is less expensive than the natural incubation of turkey eggs, if all items of cost are considered.

Selection of hatching eggs. The reasons for making a selection of turkey hatching eggs are to improve hatching results, and to improve the quality of the poults produced. The only egg characteristic thus far found to be associated with hatchability is egg size. (Table 121.) As in chicken eggs, it has been found that the very small eggs and the extremely large eggs do not hatch well. Extremely small eggs should be discarded because they produce undersized poults; but large eggs need not be discarded, because even though they may not hatch well, they are worth more for producing poults than any other use which can be made of them. The Kentucky Agricultural Experiment Station has reported that poults hatched from these small and large eggs lack vitality, and the mortality among them is higher than among poults hatched from eggs of a more normal size. The average weight of eggs laid by Bronze hens during their first season's production is about eighty-five grams or three ounces.

Small hens tend to produce smaller eggs than do larger hens. Eggs having abnormal shape and those with thin shells or cracked shells should not be used for hatching purposes.

Care of hatching eggs. The hatchability of the best hatching eggs can be destroyed by improper care while the eggs are being held before setting. The three factors most likely to reduce hatchability during this period are (1) abnormal holding temperatures, (2) holding the eggs too long, and (3) rough handling. Since the embryo undergoes development at temperatures above

Table 121

WEIGHT OF TURKEY EGGS

Hens Laying	Number Hens	Per Cent of Total	Average Grams	Average Ounces
Very small eggs—below 70 grams	4	1	67.00	2.36
Small eggs 70–79 grams	127	24	76.17	2.69
Medium-sized eggs—80–89 grams	298	56	84.01	2.96
Large eggs—90–99 grams	98	18	92.36	3.25
Very large eggs—100 grams and over	4	1	101.50	3.58
All hens	531	100	83.68	2.95

82° F., hatching eggs should be held at lower temperatures. Work at the Kansas Agricultural Experiment Station (Table 122) showed that excellent hatching results were obtained when turkey eggs were held between 55° F. and 60° F. for as long as four weeks. Eggs held at high temperatures undergo some embryonic development and are thereby weakened so that the percentage of hatch is reduced. When eggs are held at low temperatures hatchability is reduced, though turkey eggs apparently resist cold better than do chicken eggs. Temperatures near freezing for a few days will completely destroy hatchability. The length of time turkey eggs can be held without reducing hatching results is very largely dependent upon the temperature at which they are held. It has been shown that rough handling, which causes the air cells to become tremulous, reduces the hatchability of chicken eggs. No

Table 122

EFFECT OF HOLDING TEMPERATURE AND AGE OF EGG ON HATCHABILITY OF TURKEY EGGS [1]

Days Held	Hatchability Temp. 36°F. (1931)	Temp. 54°F. (1931)	Temp. 55–60°F. (1930)	Temp. 60–75°F. (1929)
1–6	66	71	89	72
7–13	52	65	90	73
14–20	27	75	85	45
21–27	6	67	84	14
28–34	0	61	86	6

[1] Kan. Agr. Expt. Sta. Bul. 276.

doubt turkey eggs are affected in a similar manner. Turkey eggs while being held before setting should be kept where the temperature is between 50° F. and 60° F. They should be held with the small end down in regular egg cases equipped with duck-egg fillers. Under the usual operating conditions they should not be held longer than two weeks. Turning by tilting the case is recommended if the eggs are held longer than one week.

Management of the Incubator

Poor hatches of turkey eggs are relatively more common than of chicken eggs. However, the cause is often found in the breeding stock or its management instead of in the incubation. There are, of course, incubation problems and the correct principles of incubation must be applied if satisfactory hatches of turkey eggs are to be obtained. Many turkey growers are purchasing poults or having eggs custom hatched, thus eliminating their problem of incubation. With good hatchable eggs the modern incubator when properly operated will give equally as satisfactory results when hatching turkey eggs as when used for hatching chicken eggs. The principles involved are the same but the requirements are slightly different.

Temperature. There are certain definite limits between which the temperature of the incubator must be kept if satisfactory hatching results are to be obtained with turkey eggs. Eggs incubated in forced-draft incubators hatch well when kept at from 99° F. to 100° F., if the other requirements for incubation are satisfied. Results obtained at the Kentucky Agricultural Experiment Station in 1935 showed that a satisfactory weekly schedule of operating temperatures to follow when incubating turkey eggs in sectional incubators was, for the respective four weeks, 100.5° F., 101.5° F., 102.5° F., and 103.5° F., when the bulb of the thermometer was level with the top of the eggs. The thermometer used in the incubators should be compared with a thermometer of known accuracy, preferably a physician's thermometer, so that no mistakes will be made when the temperatures are read.

Humidity. For best results the relative humidity for incubating turkey eggs is near 60 per cent for the first twenty-four days and 70 per cent for the last four days. Such humidity conditions produce about the correct evaporation from the egg and provide satisfactory hatching conditions. To obtain the above relative humidities in forced-draft incubators the wet bulb reading in such incubators should record for the first twenty-four days of incubation a temperature of 12° F. below the dry bulb temperature reading, and for the last four days of incubation the difference should be 9° F. When sectional machines are used, the most satisfactory methods for judging moisture conditions in the incubator are (1) observing the size of the air cell at intervals and estimating the rate of evaporation, (2) weighing a tray or sample of eggs at regular intervals and comparing the percentage loss in weight with experimental data which is available, and (3) using in "still-air" incubators a hygrometer which can be purchased from poultry supply houses. Work at the Kansas Agricultural Experiment Station indicates that the optimum loss of moisture from turkey eggs while being incubated is about 3.0 per cent or less per week or from 11 to 13 per cent for the first twenty-four days of incubation.

Ventilation. Proper ventilation of the incubator and the incubator room are essential for successful hatches from turkey eggs. The developing embryos require air containing about 21 per cent oxygen and not more than 1.5 per cent carbon dioxide. Since the oxygen requirements of the embryos increase as they develop, it is evident that ventilation must be increased as the hatch progresses. Any increase in ventilation tends to reduce the relative humidity of the incubator. For best results at hatching time the incubator must be well ventilated and the humidity kept high.

Turning. For satisfactory hatches turkey eggs must be properly turned while being incubated. They should be turned at least twice daily up to the twenty-fourth day of incubation. With machines equipped with turning devices which require but little labor, the eggs should be turned at least five times daily. If the turning is done by hand, turning twice daily will give satisfactory results, although the hatch could be increased somewhat by turning more often. Developing embryos are sensitive organisms and therefore the turning of eggs or shifting of their position should be done with a minimum of jarring.

Handling newly hatched poults. The newly hatched poults should not be exposed to temperatures lower than their hatching compartment until they have dried off. After they are "fluffed out," they may be allowed to drop into the nursery tray or be placed in boxes where the temperature is lower so that they may "harden." The bottom of the box or tray should be covered with material which will prevent slipping and therefore the spraddling of the legs. Poults may be held or shipped in regular chick boxes, placing from fifteen to eighteen poults in the compartments designed for twenty-five chicks (Fig. 223).

The production and sale of day-old poults. The production and sale of day-old poults has during the past few years made rapid progress. Turkey producers appear to be following the lead of poultry raisers who have quite largely turned to the purchase of day-old chicks instead of doing their own hatching. Many large turkey producers maintain breeding flocks which they use for producing poults for their own use and hatching eggs or poults for sale. The development of hatcheries which specialize in poult production has created a demand for turkey-hatching eggs which has stimulated the growth of hatchery supply flocks. If properly managed, the commercial production of day-old poults may be expected to increase, and such producers become the source of supply of most poults.

Brooding and Rearing

Success or failure in raising turkeys is usually determined during the brooding period. Young turkeys are quite sensitive at this age and they must receive proper care and attention while being brooded.

Fig. 223. Hatching turkeys. Above, traying turkey eggs. (Courtesy Lifer Turkey Farm.) Below, pedigreeing turkey poults. (Missouri Experiment Station.)

Fig. 224. Natural brooding of turkeys. Brooding costs are low. These turkeys will recover much waste grain.

Natural Brooding

Artificial brooding has quite generally replaced natural methods of brooding as turkey raising has become more commercialized. The turkey grower who raises several thousand turkeys each year cannot very well do so with hens. The producer who raises only a few turkeys often uses turkey hens for brooding and raising them. Hens may be used for brooding late-hatched poults, since the weather is then more favorable and the hens have completed the production of eggs suitable for hatching purposes. From twelve to fifteen poults can be brooded with a chicken hen and about twenty poults with a turkey hen. Figure 224 shows a flock of young turkeys being cared for by turkey hens.

Hens, either chicken or turkey, used for brooding poults should be free from disease and parasites. There is danger of spreading lice and blackhead as well as other diseases from the hens to the poults. The spread of lice to the poults can be prevented by dusting the hens with sodium fluoride at ten-day intervals twice before they are placed with the poults.

Artificial Brooding

Within the last fifteen or twenty years turkey raising has become highly commercialized and many growers now raise several thousand birds annually. Such large-scale operations are possible now because practical methods of artificial incubation and brooding have been developed (Fig. 225).

Brooding Requirements for Turkeys

Successful brooding of poults depends upon satisfying all of the essential requirements of the poults at this stage of their development. The environmental conditions necessary for satisfactory growth during the brooding period are proper temperature, adequate ventilation, sanitary quarters, and sufficient room.

COURTESY "TURKEY WORLD"

Fig. 225. Starting poults with an electric brooder. Note feed placed on egg-case filler flats to encourage eating the first few days. Small feeders and waterers for young poults are in place.

Temperature. The environmental temperature for poults must be controlled so that they are kept comfortable during the brooding period. For the first few days they should be confined by means of a guard near the source of heat so that they may learn where to go later to become warm, after the guard has been removed. Before the poults are placed under the hover, the temperature should be adjusted to about 95° F. two inches above the floor at the edge of the hover of a fuel-burning brooder or under the hover of an electric brooder. The temperature should be reduced about 5° F. each week until heat is no longer needed. After heat is no longer needed during the day, it will be needed at night to prevent chilling and piling.

Ventilation and humidity. Fresh air is necessary for normal growth and development. Ordinarily, a brooder house with an open front which has a muslin curtain for use in cold or windy weather will provide sufficient ventilation. Faulty brooder stoves when operated in tightly closed brooder houses sometimes cause carbon monoxide poisoning of poults. The condition of the air in a brooder house can be judged best when one first enters it. Foul air generally can be detected by odors.

Proper ventilation will help prevent dampness in the brooder house. One indication of poor ventilation in the brooder house is dampness. The brooder house should be kept reasonably dry at all times. However, an excessively dry brooder room causes poor feather growth and should therefore be avoided.

Sanitation. The prevention of disease in turkeys depends quite largely on the sanitation program followed. The brooder and all equipment used should be cleaned often and kept in a sanitary condition at all times.

Floor space. It is false economy to overcrowd poults in the brooder house. A good rule to follow is to allow for the first eight weeks at least one square foot of floor space for each poult. Each poult should also be provided with from 10 to 14 square inches of space beneath the canopy of the brooder stove. A brooder stove with a 52-inch canopy will provide room for 150 poults.

Brooding Equipment

The equipment needed for brooding poults is quite similar to, and in many instances the same, as that used for brooding chicks.

Houses. Movable colony brooder houses and permanent brooder houses are both used for brooding poults. A 10′ x 12′ colony brooder house will provide room for starting and brooding to eight weeks of age 125 poults. Permanent brooder houses are generally used by commercial turkey growers. When equipped with sun porches, they provide excellent brooder house facilities for the poults as long as they need heat.

Brooder stoves. Any brooder suitable for chicks can be used for starting poults. Colony brooder stoves are used in the small movable brooder houses and also in the individual pens of the long, permanent houses. Hot water brooding systems are very desirable for the long houses with many pens. Battery brooders are being used successfully by some producers for brooding poults as long as they need heat (Fig. 226).

Feeders and waterers. Poults should always have an opportunity to eat or drink when they so desire. The feeders and waterers used for chicks are satisfactory for poults. For the first eight weeks each poult should be provided with two inches of feeding space at such feeders, as shown in Figure 227. One fountain (one gallon size or larger) should be provided for each fifty poults. Both the feeding and watering space should be increased as the poults grow into larger birds.

Roosts. Roosts should be placed in the brooder house by the time the poults are three or four weeks old. These roosts should be 1″ x 2″, 1″ x 3″, or 1″ x 4″ laid flat and built on frames about one foot high, with poultry netting beneath them to prevent the poults from falling from the roosts and to keep them away from their droppings.

Brooder Management

Success in brooding turkeys depends quite largely upon the good judgment of the operator. The management practices followed are most important.

Providing brooding requirements. The requirements listed above must be provided. The poults must be kept comfortable regardless of outside

Fig. 226. Starting poults in a battery brooder reduces labor to a minimum and prevents early brooding troubles, such as piling.

weather conditions; the brooder room must be adequately ventilated; sanitary quarters must be maintained; the birds must be provided with plenty of room; and they must be properly fed.

Litter for poults. Litter is essential for maintaining a sanitary brooder house floor, unless batteries are used. For the first two weeks, coarse sand, gravel, peat moss, or other suitable litter is recommended. It is well to cover the litter with paper while teaching the poults to eat, so that they do not consume too much litter before they learn to find their feed, Later, coarser litters such as straw, shavings, or ground corncobs may be used. Wire floors are used by some producers. One-inch mesh wire floors covered with one-half-inch mesh hardware cloth for the first two or three weeks provides a very sanitary floor. Such floors are expensive and often inconvenient to move.

Educating the poults. One problem which taxes the beginner's ingenuity is that of teaching poults to eat. Some use rolled oats, others milk or clabber, and others finely chopped boiled eggs or green feed. Some producers place a few older poults or some day-old chicks with the poults to teach them to eat.

When placed under a canopy brooder, the poults should be confined by a guard such as shown in Figure 225. This will teach the poults where to go to become warm. All corners should be rounded off to prevent piling. Poults should be taught to roost early as this will prevent piling at night.

COURTESY MISSOURI AGRICULTURAL EXPERIMENT STATION

Fig. 227. Poults about ready for range. A reel feeder, water fountain, 2" x 4" roosts, and an electric hover are in use.

Rearing Turkeys

Raising or growing turkeys after they no longer need heat and the protection of a brooder house is a necessary part of any turkey production program.

Confinement or range. The producer must choose between raising turkeys in confinement or on range. Figure 228 shows turkeys being raised in complete confinement. Either system gives satisfactory results when properly managed. Confinement is necessary if all available range is contaminated with disease or parasites. Range can be made to supply green feed and thereby supplement the ration and reduce the feed costs. Confinement brooding requires more expensive equipment and is recommended only when suitable conditions are not available for growing turkeys on range. Limited range is preferred to free range for turkeys so that the range may be rotated. Turkeys which are well fed, however, remain near the feed and water.

Range shelters and roosts. Some growers use range shelters as roosting quarters for turkeys. In some cases roosts are provided on the roof of the range shelter as well as under the roof, as is shown in Figure 229. Poults can be moved to range earlier if range shelters are used than if they have to roost in the open without any protection against the weather.

Roosts are generally used but are not absolutely necessary for turkeys.

Fig. 228. Sun porch for raising turkeys in complete confinement. Note arrangement of feeders and waterers.

Some growers roost their turkeys on the ground. Recent investigations reported by the Wyoming Agricultural Experiment Station showed that four-inch poles were the most satisfactory roosts for growing turkeys. Two-by-fours laid flat and slightly tilted are also very good roosts. Narrow roosts increase the number of dented breastbones. Some producers build roosts on wheels so that they can be moved easily. Roosts placed on saw horses are satisfactory and can be moved easily. The roosting quarters, if permanent for the season, should be so arranged that the turkeys cannot get to the droppings.

Yards for growing turkeys. Where a small number of turkeys are raised, it is advisable to confine them to limited range by using temporary yards. One acre of land on which there is good growing green feed will provide enough range for 125 turkeys to market age. Movable fences, such as are generally used as snow fences along highways, make very good temporary fences for yarding turkeys. They should be moved about every two weeks and so arranged that about one-fourth of the acre is in the yard.

Shade. In most sections of the United States turkeys need shade during the summer months. Trees and growing crops such as corn, grain sorghums, and sunflowers provide the best shade for turkeys. But if such shade is not available, artificial shade should be provided.

Protection against predators and thieves. In some sections the greatest obstacles to turkey raising are predatory animals, including *Homo sapiens*. Well-constructed wire fences will protect turkeys against dogs, wolves, and coyotes. Flares arranged near the roosts will scare most animals away, as well as thieves. Some growers are curbing thieving by tattooing their birds. The

Fig. 229. A range shelter equipped with roosts beneath the roof and also on top of the roof.

tattoo marks are placed on the web of the wing and they are valuable in identifying stolen birds.

Requirements for Growth

Growth of turkeys. The growth rate of turkeys is higher than that of chickens, and as in chickens, growth is influenced by a number of factors. The producer of turkeys is interested in a relatively high rate of growth throughout the growing period so that economical gains may be obtained up to the age when the birds are marketable. A comparison of the sizes of turkeys of different strains at various ages as presented in Tables 123 and 124 shows wide differences. At twenty-four weeks of age the wild males averaged 11.03 pounds as compared to 21.20 pounds for the extra-large Bronze males; the wild birds were only about one-half the size of the domesticated strains which had been bred for large size. Heredity, therefore, is an important factor influencing growth.

The ration used influences the rate of growth; however, the mature body weight is not materially different if the rations used maintain the health of the turkey. High protein rations produce more rapid early gains, but the adult turkeys at twenty-eight weeks of age are about the same size as those grown on a lower protein level.

The weather is also a factor influencing growth. Turkeys grow slowly during hot weather, but later compensate for such retarded growth so that the mature body weight is about the same as if they had not been exposed to high temperatures.

Nutritive requirements of the turkey. The nutritive requirements of the turkey are similar to those of the chicken but vary in some respects. The turkey is quite sensitive to nutritive deficiencies and the wise producer

Table 123

GROWTH STANDARDS FOR MALE TURKEYS [2]

Age	Extra-Large Bronze [e]	Standard-Bred Bronze [a]	Medium-Sized Bronze [b]	White Holland [c]	Black [a]	Small Type—All Varieties [d]	Wild [a]
1 day	.12	.13	.13	.12	.11	.11	.11
2 weeks	.30	.33	.30	.34	.35	.33	.28
4 weeks	.80	.86	.80	.78	.87	.86	.62
8 weeks	3.20	3.13	2.79	2.33	2.92	2.99	2.06
12 weeks	6.80	6.54	5.40	5.38	5.66	5.45	3.62
16 weeks	11.80	10.35	8.58	9.39	8.53	8.35	5.90
20 weeks	17.00	14.47	12.10	13.15	12.27	11.11	8.94
24 weeks	21.20	18.23	15.17	16.42	15.54	14.21	11.03
26 weeks	23.00	20.18	16.91	...	17.79	16.03	12.06
28 weeks	24.20	21.35	18.51	...	19.54	17.79	12.58
30 weeks	25.00	23.35	20.30	...	21.36	...	...
32 weeks	25.60	23.95	...	...	...	...	...

[a] U. S. D. A.   [b] Okla. Expt. Sta.   [c] Pa. State College.   [d] The authors.   [e] Larro Research Farm, Detroit, Mich.

Table 124

GROWTH STANDARDS FOR FEMALE TURKEYS [3]

Age	Extra-Large Bronze [e]	Standard-Bred Bronze [a]	Medium-Sized Bronze [b]	White Holland [c]	Black [a]	Small Type—All Varieties [d]	Wild [a]
1 day	.12	.13	.12	.12	.12	.11	.11
2 weeks	.30	.30	.28	.32	.33	.29	.28
4 weeks	.70	.75	.72	.69	.80	.72	.60
8 weeks	2.50	2.68	2.42	1.97	2.58	2.23	1.84
12 weeks	5.60	5.28	4.51	4.31	4.69	3.86	3.16
16 weeks	9.00	7.67	6.80	6.95	6.62	5.80	4.85
20 weeks	11.90	9.67	8.67	8.88	8.75	7.38	6.82
24 weeks	14.20	11.15	9.95	10.74	9.96	8.71	7.52
26 weeks	15.00	12.04	10.58	...	10.94	9.44	7.92
28 weeks	15.70	12.48	11.11	...	11.81	10.02	8.34
30 weeks	16.20	13.28	11.57	...	12.53	...	...
32 weeks	16.60	13.37	...	...	...	...	...

[a] U. S. D. A.   [b] Okla. Expt. Sta.   [c] Pa. State College.   [d] The authors.   [e] Larro Research Farm, Detroit, Mich.

will use reliable rations and leave experimentation to the agricultural experiment stations established for that purpose.

Protein requirements. The turkey requires a high protein ration for the first few weeks when the rate of growth is high. But as the rate of growth diminishes and the birds approach maturity, the protein content of the ration

---

[2] Data from *Turkey Management,* by Marsden and Martin, 1939. By permission of The Interstate Printers and Publishers.

[3] Data from *Turkey Management,* by Marsden and Martin, 1939. By permission of The Interstate Printers and Publishers.

may be reduced. Work done at different stations on this subject indicates that a ration containing 24 per cent protein for the first six weeks, 20 per cent for next six weeks, and thereafter reduced to 15 or 16 per cent, by allowing the birds to choose mash or grain, provides the growing turkey with sufficient protein if that protein is of suitable quality. Meat scrap, fish meal, dried buttermilk, dried skim milk, and soybean oil meal are all suitable protein concentrates for turkey rations.

Vitamin requirements. Turkeys have higher vitamin requirements than chickens (Table 51) and therefore their rations must be well fortified with vitamins. Table 125 on Vitamin Requirements for Turkeys, prepared by Dr. Kratzer of the University of California, presents a resume of the requirements as established up to 1950. The whole field of vitamin research is so active that each year brings much new knowledge.

Mineral requirements. Though it is apparent that turkeys must receive in their rations all of the mineral elements necessary to sustain life and stimulate normal development, it is equally apparent that these elements are present in sufficient quantities in otherwise well-balanced rations if the birds have access to range so that no special mineral supplements are needed. For proof of this, witness the turkeys raised by a turkey hen on range. The principal mineral elements needed by turkeys are calcium, phosphorus, sodium, chlorine, manganese, iron, iodine, potassium, and magnesium. But even under the conditions of commercial production, only the first five of these need be fed as special supplements. Bone meal supplies calcium and phosphorus, salt supplies sodium and chlorine, and manganese sulphate may be used as a source of manganese. These should be incorporated in the mash as indicated by mash mixtures suggested in Table 128. (For a more detailed discussion of minerals see Chapters Nine and Ten.)

Energy requirements. Normal body activity and functions require energy for maintenance, growth, and egg production. Fats, proteins, and carbohydrates may serve as sources of energy. Such carbonaceous feeds as the grains are the principal sources of heat and energy in the ration.

Water requirement. Water is one of the most important nutrients for animal life. It constitutes by weight more than 50 per cent of the young growing turkey, makes digestion and absorption possible, is an important constituent of the blood and lymph and thereby serves as a carrier of the nutrients and waste products of the body, and it aids the body in temperature regulation by providing a means of evaporation.

Feed consumption of turkeys. The feed consumption of growing turkeys increases from about one and one-half pounds per bird during the first month (four weeks) to approximately twenty pounds during the seventh month. The total consumption of mash and grain per bird per month for turkeys completely confined is shown by Figure 230. The proportion of mash and grain which turkeys will consume, if they have their choice, varies with the protein content of the mash (Table 126). Evidently turkeys as well as chickens have the ability to choose feeds which satisfy their requirements at a particular stage of development.

Table 125

VITAMIN REQUIREMENTS OF TURKEYS [4]

Vitamin	Symptoms of Deficiency	Amount Recommended Per Pound of Feed	Best Sources
A *	Poor growth, unsteady gait, watery eyes, nasal discharge, white exudate from eyes and sinuses, pustules in mouth and esophagus, white flaky exudate in bursa of Fabricius, high mortality	Poults, 4,000 I.U. Breeders, 4,000 I.U.	Fresh greens, dehydrated alfalfa, fish oils, commercial concentrates
D *	Poults—rickets, characterized by poor growth, leg weakness, enlarged hocks, crooked keels, beaded ribs, soft bones and beak, high mortality. Breeders—low egg production, low hatchability, soft-shelled eggs	Poults, 800 AOAC units. Breeders, 800 AOAC units	Biologically tested fish oils (Activated animal sterol is more active than Vitamin D from fish oils when phosphorus of the ration is in organic combination. Vitamin D from cod liver oil should be supplied at 900 AOAC units per pound when inorganic phosphorus of ration is low). Direct sunlight can replace dietary vitamin D
E	Not studied in turkeys (may be produced experimental'y in chickens in which it results in paralysis and uncoordinated movements in chicks and poor hatchability in breeding hens)	Practical rations contain adequate amounts	Fresh greens, grain, dehydrated alfalfa
K	Blood fails to clot normally. Small injuries cause excessive bleeding	Practical rations contain adequate amounts	Fresh greens, dehydrated alfalfa
Thiamin (B1)	Not studied extensively in turkeys. (In chicks it results in poor growth, nervous symptoms including head retraction and convulsions, high mortality)	Practical rations contain adequate amounts	Grains, grain by-products, oil cake meals
Riboflavin * (B2G)	Poor growth, leg weakness, low hatchability in breeders	Poults, 2 milligrams. Breeders, 1.6 milligrams	Milk products, liver meal, fresh greens, dehydrated alfalfa, yeast fermentation products, synthetic riboflavin
Pantothenic acid *	Poor growth, high mortality dermatitis at corners of mouth	Poults, 6 milligrams	Yeast, molasses, liver meal, milk products, dehydrated alfalfa, wheat bran fermentation products, synthetic pantothenic acid
Pyridoxine (B6)	Poor growth, uncoordinated movements, convulsions high mortality	Poults, 2 milligrams	Grain, grain by-products, soybean oil meal, milk products, yeast, dehydrated alfalfa, animal products
Niacin	Poor growth, inflammation of the mouth, poor feathering, perosis	Poults, 25 milligrams	Wheat and wheat by-products, yeast, liver meal, fish meal, meat scrap, synthetic niacin
Biotin	Poor growth, dermatitis, perosis, high mortality	Exact requirements unknown	Fresh greens, dehydrated alfalfa, soybean oil meal, cane molasses, grain, grain by-products
Pteroyl-glutamic acid (Bc Folic acid)	Poor growth, cervical paralysis, mild anemia, high mortality	Poults, 0.5 milligram	Green feed, dehydrated alfalfa, yeast, liver meal, wheat bran, soybean oil meal, synthetic pteroyl-glutamic acid
Choline *	Poor growth, perosis	Poults 900 milligram	Yeast, oil cake meals, fish meal, liver meal, synthetic choline

[4] Kratzer. Turkey World. Jan. 1950, p. 48.

Table 125 *(continued)*

Vitamin	Symptoms of Deficiency	Amount Recommended Per Pound of Feed	Best Sources
Inositol	Poor growth, mild anemia	Practical rations contain adequate amounts	Wheat and wheat by-products, dehydrated alfalfa, soybean oil meal, liver meal, yeast
Animal protein factor complex * (Including B₁₂ and other components)	Poor growth in poults	Unknown	Fish meal, condensed fish solubles, liver meal, milk products, meat scrap, fermentation products
Ascorbic acid C	Dietary source not required by turkeys		
Unknown factors	There is experimental evidence for the existence of other growth promoting and growth inhibiting factors in natural feedstuffs. Further research is required to determine their importance in turkey feeding practice		

* These vitamins must be given special consideration in formulating practical turkey rations.

Efficiency of gains made by turkeys. Turkeys are efficient meat-producing animals. During the first twelve weeks of their lives, turkeys will increase their body weight by one pound for each three pounds or less of feed consumed (Fig. 231). After the third month, the feed required to produce a pound of gain increases rapidly, rising to above seven pounds during the seventh month and as much as ten pounds for the eighth month. The turkey producer is interested in the amount of feed required to produce a

Table 126

RATIO OF MASH CONSUMPTION TO GRAIN CONSUMED BY GROWING TURKEYS [5]

APPROXIMATE PERCENTAGE OF CRUDE PROTEIN IN THE DIET	PROPORTION OF MASH TO SCRATCH CONSUMED DURING THE BROODING AND REARING PERIOD											
	1–4 Weeks	5–8 Weeks	9–12 Weeks	13–16 Weeks	17–20 Weeks	21–24 Weeks	25–28 Weeks	29–32 Weeks	1–24 Weeks	1–28 Weeks	1–32 Weeks	9–28 Weeks
18	96:4	97:3	90:10	97:3	90:10	67:33	39:61	...	85:15	74:26	...	77:23
20	94:6	97:3	87:13	87:13	71:29	46:54	30:70	...	72:28	61:39	...	64:36
22	92:8	94:6	85:15	89:11	67:33	47:53	30:70	24:76	72:28	62:38	54:46	64:36
24	84:16	88:12	74:26	77:23	65:35	48:52	30:70	20:80	67:33	58:42	54:46	59:41
26	91:9	86:14	79:21	77:23	61:39	39:61	27:73	...	63:37	54:46	...	57:43
28	87:13	82:18	72:28	70:30	54:46	33:67	25:75	...	57:43	49:51	...	51:49
30	84:16	81:19	70:30	63:37	48:52	28:72	26:74	...	53:47	46:54	...	47:53

[5] Data from *Turkey Management,* by Marsden and Martin, 1939. By permission of The Interstate Printers and Publishers.

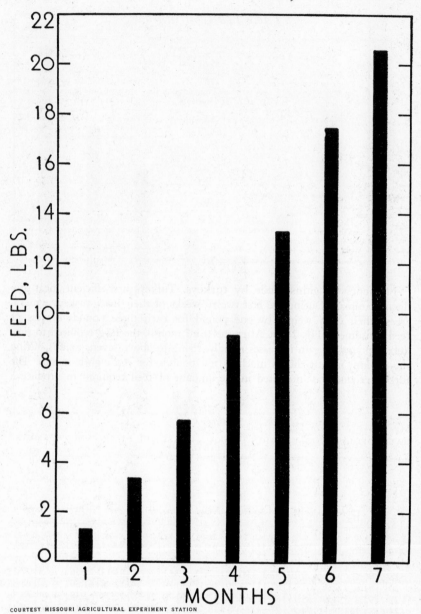

Fig. 230. The amount of feed consumed per month by growing Bronze turkeys.

pound of marketable turkey. Since most turkeys are in market condition by the twenty-fourth to twenty-eighth week of age, feed requirements calculated to that age give the information desired by the producer. Table 127

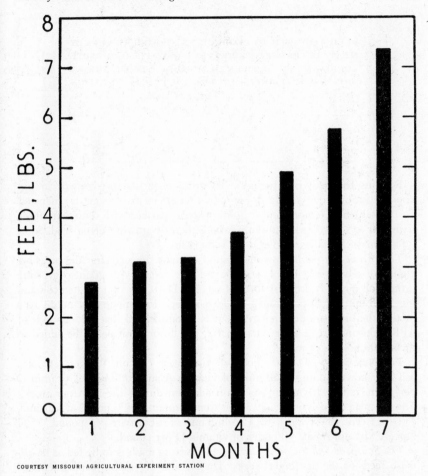

Fig. 231. The pounds of feed required to produce one pound of gain by Bronze turkeys.

shows the feed (mash and grain) required to produce one pound of gain with Bronze turkeys raised in complete confinement to twenty-eight weeks of age. Turkeys raised on range where there is growing green feed would consume less mash and grain per pound of gain because they would consume considerable quantities of green feed and insects. Results reported by the Indiana and the Oregon Agricultural Experiment Stations show that male turkeys utilize feed more efficiently than female turkeys from the eighteenth to twenty-eighth weeks (Indiana) and twenty to thirty-two weeks (Oregon).

In studies which have been made at the Missouri Station, it has been found that males make more efficient gains than females after the 16th week of age and that from 17 to 30 weeks of age the males require both less protein and carbonaceous nutrients per pound of gain than are required by females during the same period. These data are of course limited to the periods covered.

Table 127

FEED REQUIRED TO PRODUCE ONE POUND OF TURKEY
MEAT IN BRONZE TURKEYS RAISED IN COMPLETE
CONFINEMENT TO TWENTY-EIGHT WEEKS OF AGE AT
THE MISSOURI AGRICULTURAL EXPERIMENT STATION

Lots	1936	1937
1	4.7	4.9
2	4.8	5.2
3	4.7	5.3

Rations for growing turkeys. To promote satisfactory growth in turkeys the rations must satisfy the nutritive requirements previously discussed.
Fortunately these requirements can normally be satisfied with simple mixtures,
if the turkeys have access to range where there is growing green feed. Some
typical mash formulas are listed in Table 128.

The Minnesota poult growing mash is intended for use after the birds are
eight to twelve weeks old. It is to be fed free choice with grain to growing
turkeys on range. A little dry form of vitamin D (0.5 lb. of a product containing 2000 units of D per gram) is added to each 1000 pounds of mash, even
though the birds are on range. Also, it is recommended that 0.25 pounds of
APF supplement (12.5 mg. vitamin B_{12} per lb. or equivalent) be added to
each 1000 pounds of mash.

The New York (Cornell) poult starting mash contains 0.5 per cent of a
fish liver oil containing 2000 units of vitamin A and 400 units of vitamin D
per gram. It is fed without any grain addition during the first four weeks.
The calculated analysis is: 29.3 per cent protein, 1.73 per cent calcium,
1.06 per cent phosphorus, 3.14 milligrams of riboflavin per pound, 7500
units of vitamin A, and 900 units of vitamin D per pound.

The Southern States Co-operative poult starting mash is to be fed as an all-
mash feed for the first eight weeks. The amount of vitamin supplements to
be added will vary with the products used. A sufficient quantity is used to
meet the requirements recommended by the National Research Council
(Table 51). It is recommended that most of the vitamins A and D used in the
mash be derived from fish sources. The calculated protein content of the mash
is 24 per cent.

The turkey-breeding growing mash is to be fed free choice with grain after
the birds are ten to twelve weeks old.

The turkey-breeding mash is to be kept before the birds at all times. A limited amount of grain, about equal to the mash consumption, is fed. Oyster
shell should be available at all times.

The Washington turkey breeding mash is to be fed with a limited amount
of grain (60 parts mash to 40 parts whole grains) and free access to oyster
shell. The riboflavin and vitamins A and D added will vary with the potency
of the products used. Sufficient quantities are added to meet the recommendations of the National Research Council (Table 51).

Table 128

TURKEY MASH FORMULAS

Ingredients	Starting		Growing		Breeding	
	Southern States (1)	New York (2)	Minne-sota (3)	Southern States (1)	Washing-ton (4)	Southern States (1)
Ground yellow corn	27.9	18.0	27.5	31.8	11.0	21.5
Wheat bran	3.5		10.0	10.0		10.0
Wheat middlings	10.0	15.0	15.0	5.0	15.0	10.0
Ground oats	10.0	10.0	15.0	10.0	10.0	12.5
Ground barley					10.0	
Meat scraps	5.0	5.0	10.0	3.7		5.0
Fish meal	6.2	5.0			8.0	7.5
Dried milk		5.0				
Cane molasses				3.0		
Soybean oil meal	25.0	30.0	15.0	25.0	15.0	12.5
Corn gluten meal						5.0
Bone meal or low fluorine rock phosphate		1.0		1.5	3.5	2.5
Ground limestone or oyster shell	2 0	1.0	2.0	1.0	3.5	1.0
Salt—iodized and manganized *	0.5	0.5	0.5	0.5	0.8	
Dried brewers' yeast or distillers' solubles	1.2	5.0				
Dried whey	3.7	2.0		1.0	3.2	2.5
Alfalfa meal (17% protein, De-hydrated)	5.0	2.5	5.0	7.5	20.0	10.0
Riboflavin supplement †	+		+	+ ·	+	+
Vitamin A and D feeding oil †	+	+			+	+
D—activated animal sterol (Dry vitamin DL)	+		+	+		+
APF supplement †			+			
Total	100.0	100.0	100.0	100.0	100.0	100.0

(1) Southern States Cooperative. Baltimore, Md. 1949–1950 Rations.
(2) Cornell Univ. Poultry Dept. Ext. Stencil 192. 1948.
(3) University of Minnesota. Poultry Mashes. 1950.
(4) Wash. Ext. Bul. 388. 1949.
 * A mixture of 9 parts of iodized salt and 1 part of feeding grade manganese sulphate.
 † The amount of vitamin supplement added will vary with the potencies of the products used. See table 51.

Marketing Turkeys

Since turkey production is highly seasonal and the producing areas are located far from the largest cities, the marketing of turkeys constitutes a major problem and sometimes taxes the facilities of the existing marketing agencies.

Seasonal production. The turkey remains primarily a holiday bird; and fortunately, conditions in the major producing areas are such that the bulk of the turkey crop can be matured and finished most economically for the Thanksgiving and Christmas markets. While turkeys can be grown for marketing during any month of the year, climatic conditions in the United States are most favorable for producing a turkey crop for marketing late in the fall and during the winter. Most of the turkeys consumed out of this natural marketing season are dressed birds which have been held under refrigeration. The quality of these birds is usually superior to the freshly killed turkeys at that time. The proportion of the turkey crop marketed by months varies somewhat from year to year. If turkey prices advance from Thanksgiving to Christmas, the following fall there is a tendency for the producers to hold turkeys for the Christmas market. If warm weather prevails during the fall months in the large producing areas, the birds will be slow in finishing, and therefore a larger proportion of the crop will be marketed late.

Table 129 shows the proportion of turkeys marketed by months in 1947. There is a growing tendency to market turkeys throughout the year, but the bulk of the crop continues to be marketed in November and December.

Table 129

PROPORTION OF TURKEY CROP MARKETED IN DIFFERENT MONTHS

Geographic Divisions	1947			
	Oct. or Earlier	Nov.	Dec.	Jan. or Later
	Per Cent			
North Atlantic	11.6	43.2	34.7	10.5
E. N. Central	9.2	44.2	41.5	5.1
W. N. Central	34.2	38.9	23.1	3.8
South Atlantic	22.6	34.3	32.7	10.4
South Central	11.0	40.9	38.1	10.0
Western	15.5	41.3	33.1	10.1
United States	19.8	40.5	32.1	7.6

Turkey production and consumption in the United States. Table 130 shows that from 1931 to 1947 the number of turkeys raised was about doubled and that the consumption of turkey meat in 1946 was 265 per cent of that consumed in 1929.

Turkey size increasing. The type and size of turkey raised and marketed has changed within a very few years. The introduction of the broad-breasted type turkey has within the past 10 years almost completely changed the type of turkey marketed and has also increased the size (Table 131).

Selecting birds for market. Many turkey growers sell their entire crop at one time and sometimes before all the birds are ready for marketing. Birds lacking finish or having immature plumage should be held until they will dress into good market specimens. Only fat turkeys free from pinfeathers command the best prices. Immature turkeys lacking finish are frequently sent to market, where they sell for less than the cost of producing them. If these birds had been kept by the producer until they were mature and finished they would have commanded higher prices and returned a profit to the grower. While it is more difficult to grade live turkeys than the dressed birds, an experienced turkey raiser can select those birds which are finished. The birds which are ready for market have mature plumage; they are well-fleshed, as

Table 130

Year	Number of Turkeys Produced	Average Weight Per Bird	Total Pounds Produced	Pounds Per Capita (Dressed Wt.)	
				Production	Consumption
	Thousands	*Pounds*	*Thous. Pounds*	*Pounds*	
1929..........	18,136	13.2	239,133	1.7	1.7
1930..........	17,052	13.4	228,146	1.7	1.8
1931..........	17,923	13.6	243,982	1.7	1.7
1932..........	21,964	13.8	302,940	2.1	2.1
1933..........	22,813	14.0	319,231	2.4	2.4
1934..........	21,310	14.1	299,597	2.2	2.2
1935..........	20,487	14.5	297,960	2.1	2.1
1936..........	27,642	14.7	405,418	2.8	2.7
1937..........	25,391	14.8	375,828	2.7	2.7
1938..........	26,547	14.9	395,017	2.7	2.7
1939..........	33,201	14.9	494,019	3.0	3.0
1940..........	33,572	15.1	505,527	3.6	3.5
1941..........	32,497	15.9	516,527	3.5	3.5
1942..........	32,359	16.3	525,899	3.6	3.7
1943..........	31,854	16.2	516,673	3.3	3.3
1944..........	35,170	16.8	591,342	3.9	3.3
1945..........	43,791	17.4	762,487	4.8	4.3
1946..........	40,291	17.9	720,177	4.8	4.5
1947 *	34,795	18.1	629,162	4.2	4.5

* Preliminary.

Table 131

Year	Hens	Toms	All
1937................	11.9	17.6	14.8
1938................	11.9	17.9	14.9
1939................	11.9	17.9	14.9
1940................	12.0	18.2	15.1
1941................	12.7	19.1	15.9
1942................	13.0	19.6	16.3
1943................	12.9	19.5	16.4
1944................	13.1	20.3	16.7
1945................	13.4	21.3	17.4
1946................	13.8	21.9	17.9
1947................	13.8	22.4	18.1

shown by a well-covered breast, pinbones, and back; and they are well covered with fat, as shown by a light cream-colored skin on the breast. Some turkeys, such as those with extremely crooked breastbones and deformed

[6] U. S. D. A. Bureau of Agricultural Economics.
[7] U. S. D. A. Bureau of Agricultural Economics.

Fig. 232. Turkey production is an important industry in many states. Nine thousand turkeys on the Rahns Turkey Farm, Mountain Lake, Minnesota.

backs, should be used at home instead of being sent to market. By selecting for market only those birds which are finished, the grower can increase his net returns from turkey raising.

Catching market turkeys. The producers of turkeys lose thousands of dollars annually because of bruised carcasses resulting from improper handling while the birds are being caught and cooped. Much of this damage can be avoided by the use of some simple equipment and by handling the birds carefully. For small flocks the best procedure seems to be to drive a few birds at a time into a small pen and pick the birds up by grasping them by the wings near the body, instead of grabbing them by the legs and throwing the birds on the floor or ground and thereby bruising the breast.

Where large flocks are raised (Fig. 232), a catching chute is indispensable. Figure 233 shows a movable catching chute. The birds can be driven into such a chute and rapidly caught without bruising or otherwise damaging the turkeys. Producers who have changed to the use of the catching chute from less efficient methods report a marked improvement in the quality of the birds they market, because bruises have been practically eliminated.

Methods Used in Marketing Turkeys

Turkeys are sold by producers direct to consumers, to local buyers, and to commission merchants, in co-operative pools and through packers on a custom dressing basis.

Direct marketing. Since most turkeys are raised far from the large centers of population, only a very small percentage of the turkey crop is sold by the

COURTESY CALIFORNIA AGRICULTURAL EXPERIMENT STATION

Fig. 233. Catching, grading, and loading chute.

producer to the consumer. However, in some cases very profitable outlets have been developed by producers who sell dressed turkeys direct to the consumers. Such direct sales necessitate the dressing of the birds by the producer or custom dressing at a local killing plant. Some producers have developed a mail-order business and ship the dressed turkeys by parcel post or express.

Local buyers. In the Middle West, most of the turkeys are sold alive to the local buyers, either private or co-operative, who represent the central packing plants. The birds are trucked to these central plants where they are killed and otherwise prepared for market. Storekeepers who were once important purchasers of both dressed and live turkeys are no longer important marketing agencies. Local poultry buyers who purchase both poultry and eggs purchase turkeys from the nearby producers and send them to the concentration packing plants.

Commission merchants. Both live and dressed turkeys are consigned to commission men in the large city markets by small producers located where there are few or no local buyers. With the development of better highways which increase the scope of the local buyers' activities, this method of selling turkeys continues to decrease. Commission men and wholesale receivers continue to receive large quantities of turkeys both live and dressed in car-lot shipments which come from large producers and country buyers.

Co-operative pools. Co-operative marketing of turkeys has developed most in the northwestern states of Colorado, Wyoming, Utah, Nevada, Montana, Idaho, Washington, and Oregon. Co-operative efforts were first directed to local pools where the producers assembled their turkeys and sold to the highest bidder. While these pools still exist, most of them in the Northwest have been organized into a regional association, known as the Northwest Turkey Growers Association. This regional association serves as the co-operative sales agency for the turkey growers of the Northwest who desire to market their turkeys co-operatively. The association sells annually more than 10,000,000 pounds of dressed turkeys. Their volume and territory served are both increasing.

Custom dressing by packers. In some areas, notably the Northwest, the poultry packers in conjunction with the producers have developed a plan of marketing turkeys in which the packer acts as a selling agent for the producer, rendering the necessary marketing services at a fixed service charge. The producer may be given part payment for the turkeys when they are delivered and the balance when final returns are received. Such a plan appears to give the producer some of the advantages of co-operative membership without his joining a co-operative.

Killing and dressing turkeys. Turkeys are killed by sticking and bleeding. Removal of the feathers may be accomplished by dry picking, semi-scalding, or hard scalding. Dry picking is the method most generally used by the producer. Wax picking, once quite generally used in commercial packing plants, has been replaced largely by picking machines. A description of these different methods is given in Chapter Thirteen.

Home or packing plant dressing. Whether turkeys shall be dressed on the producer's place or in the packing plant depends upon the section of the country where the turkeys are raised. If suitable packing plant facilities are available, as in most sections of the Middle West, the most efficient procedure is to have the turkeys dressed in these plants. They not only have adequate facilities and trained men for killing and dressing but they also have suitable refrigeration. Home dressing can be used where the weather is cool or markets are nearby. It has the advantage of teaching the producer the relationship between the condition of the live turkey and the dressed market bird. Unless he sees his low-grade birds after they are dressed it is difficult to show the producer that his birds are really inferior. This method of dressing is used quite generally in the Northwest.

Loss in dressing. The loss in weight from (1) fasting, (2) slaughtering, dry picking, and overnight chilling, and (3) full drawing of Bronze turkeys was reported by Marsden in 1937. A summary of these results is given in Table 132. Marsden's results also showed that large turkeys lose slightly less (in percentage loss) than do small turkeys.

Table 132

PERCENTAGE LOSS IN WEIGHT OF YOUNG BRONZE TURKEYS AS REPORTED
BY MARSDEN, U. S. D. A., 1937

	Overnight Fasting		Slaughtering, Dry Picking, and Chilling		Full Drawing	Total Loss Due to Killing, Dressing, and Full Drawing
	No. Birds	Loss	No. Birds	Loss		
Young males....	155	3.33	32	10.00	14.65	23.18
Young females..	85	3.32	33	9.54	15.39	23.47

Fig. 234. A dressed turkey attractively displayed.

For estimating prices for blood- and feather-dressed turkeys and for full-drawn birds, the producer may assume that for each 100 pounds of live turkey there would be 90 pounds after blood and feather dressing and only about 75 pounds after the birds were full drawn. This loss in weight plus the cost of dressing and drawing would have to be charged to the dressed and drawn birds.

Cooling. Failure to properly cool dressed turkeys results in lower quality, and sometimes the birds become unfit for food. The internal body temperature of the birds should be lowered to at least 36° F. before they are packed in boxes. This will require from twelve to twenty-four hours in the cooler after dressing. Turkeys killed for immediate consumption may be cooled in ice water, but birds prepared for distant markets must be air-chilled. Government graders are not permitted to grade turkeys unless the birds have been pre-cooled to 36° F. or unless the grader supervises the cooling after grading.

Grades and grading. The federal grades for both live and dressed turkeys are described in Chapter 13. Turkeys are more generally graded and sold according to the federal grades than are chickens.

Packing. Until recently, barrels were used quite generally for packing turkeys, but boxes are now replacing barrels. The lightweight, wire-bound veneer wood box, made to hold six to eight birds in a single layer packed breast up or side pack is a popular package. Boxes of suitable sizes are prepared by specialized manufacturers and should be purchased from them. Boxes should be

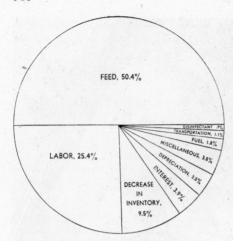

FEED, 50.4%

LABOR, 25.4%

DISINFECTANT .9%
TRANSPORTATION, 1.1%
FUEL 1.8%
MISCELLANEOUS, 2.5%
DEPRECIATION, 3.5%
INTEREST, 3.9%
DECREASE IN INVENTORY, 9.5%

Fig. 235. Percentage distribution of costs of producing and marketing turkeys. (Maryland Agricultural Experiment Station Bulletin 355, 1933.)

lined with parchment or waxed paper and the birds should be arranged and decorated to display them to best advantage. Special wrappers made out of parchment paper and cellophane are being used to wrap full-drawn birds (Fig. 234).

Shipping turkeys. Both live and dressed turkeys are shipped to the central markets. Live turkeys, usually coming on the large eastern markets, are from nearby producing areas; but some live birds are shipped to New York City from the Middle West and Southwest. Most of the nearby turkeys are moved by truck, but those from more distant sections are shipped in live-poultry cars. Dressed turkeys as packed in boxes or barrels are shipped in refrigerated cars holding from 20,000 to 30,000 pounds. These cars should be iced with ice mixed with 10 or 15 per cent of salt so that the temperature of the car will be near or below freezing. The car should be carefully braced to prevent shifting of boxes.

Cost of Producing Turkeys

The cost of producing turkeys influences greatly the profits derived from this business. Since feed cost is the most important item in the cost of producing turkeys, the turkey grower should reduce this cost item to a minimum by using the most economical rations consistent with satisfactory growth and development. The distribution of costs in producing and marketing turkeys as reported by the Maryland Agricultural Experiment Station for 147 turkey farms, 1931–32, is shown in Figure 235.

Diseases and Parasites

The prevention and control of diseases and parasites is necessary if turkey raising is to be profitable. Major shifts of the industry have occurred because of the ravages of disease. Turkey raising, once an important industry in the East and Middle West, was almost completely abandoned in many areas because of losses from blackhead. The industry shifted to the West and Southwest where climatic conditions were more favorable for the control of blackhead. New discoveries made in recent years on the prevention and control of blackhead have made turkey raising again profitable in the East and Middle West, and the industry appears to be shifting to those areas which are nearer the principal markets.

The control of turkey diseases and parasites depends primarily on sanitation. The essentials of a sanitation program for raising turkeys may be briefly summarized as follows: Grow clean poults in clean houses with clean feed and water, and maintain clean range where the poults are raised. Such a program implies much but it will insure healthy turkeys.

If an outbreak of disease occurs, someone properly trained and familiar with the diseases of turkeys should be consulted at once. The veterinary departments of the state colleges of agriculture and state departments of agriculture are generally equipped to diagnose turkey diseases and advise as to the control measures which should be applied.

Mortality in Young and Old Turkeys

Though the death loss in both young turkeys and among breeding stock has been declining in recent years losses are still too high, especially in young stock grown to market age. Those who can keep these losses below the average figures shown in Table 133 will find turkey raising more profitable than those who experience heavier losses. The control of losses from diseases and parasites is essential to success in growing turkeys.

Table 133

DEATH LOSS OF TURKEYS

Geographic Division	Young turkeys lost as a per cent of total numbers bought and home hatched						Breeding stock lost as a per cent of breeders on hand January [8]					
	1942	1943	1944	1945	1946	1947	1942	1943	1944	1945	1946	1947
	Per Cent						*Per Cent*					
North Atlantic.....	19	23	23	18	18	19	8	8	9	8	7	8
East North Central.	23	23	23	20	20	18	11	11	10	9	8	8
West North Central	28	29	23	18	18	18	11	12	10	8	7	6
South Atlantic.....	31	38	30	24	23	21	11	12	10	13	9	8
South Central.....	43	44	38	32	39	35	16	14	15	15	13	12
Western..........	21	21	22	22	16	14	7	8	7	6	6	6
United States......	28.8	29.7	25.9	22.3	21.7	20.2	11.1	11.4	10.4	9.3	8.3	7.6

Sanitation and disease prevention. The prevention of disease in turkeys depends on the program of sanitation followed by the grower. The New Hampshire Agricultural Experiment Station has outlined the following program for the growing of healthy turkeys:

NEW HAMPSHIRE GROW HEALTHY POULT PROGRAM

To reduce the mortality in rearing poults, to grow turkeys that are healthy, thrifty and free from disease, and that will make a good profit for the owner, the following practices are recommended.

---

[8] U. S. D. A. Bureau of Agricultural Economics.

Clean Poults

1. Healthy, disease-free poults.
2. From stock which has demonstrated ability to produce thrifty, healthy, vigorous birds.
3. Hatched from clean eggs and in clean incubators.
4. Purchased from a reliable breeder.

Clean Brooder Houses

1. Clean, scrape and scrub. (If desired, hot water and lye, one 13-ounce can to 5 gallons of water, may be used.)
2. Use reliable disinfectants.
3. Clean thoroughly all equipment used for brooding.
4. Do all cleaning of brooder houses before moving to clean range.
5. The use of wire sun porches is recommended.

Clean Ground

1. Land not contaminated by drainage water or poultry manure.
2. Land not used by poultry for three years or more.
3. Land as far from previous range as possible.
4. A sodded range is desirable.

Clean Litter

1. Change litter at least once each week as long as poults are confined to brooder house. (Exception—highly absorbent commercial litters usually are not changed during brooding period.)
2. Keep litter as dry and clean as possible at all times.
3. Use a dry, clean, inexpensive litter.
4. If a wire platform is used inside or outside of house, it must be thoroughly cleaned as regularly as the brooder house itself.

Clean Feed and Water

1. Use platform and keep area dry beneath water fountains.
2. Place all feed and water dishes on wire platforms inside house.
3. On range, move all hoppers to clean spot each week.
4. Use a good standard feed mixture.
5. Start poults on mash at least by the time they are 48 hours old.
6. Place feed on egg cup flat for first two days and feed often.
7. Feed in hoppers from the third day on, having feed continuously before poults.
8. Clean scratch feed in hoppers after 16 weeks.
9. Hard grain should be hopper-fed.

Clean Management

1. Maintain a quarantine between old and young stock, also from other poultry.
2. Avoid crowding, chilling and overheating.
3. Teach poults to range by moving feed containers regularly.
4. Encourage early roosting.
5. Move to clean range when disease threatens.
6. Allow one square foot of floor space per poult. Not over 150 to be started under one hover.

7. Number of poults should be reduced when their growth or limited floor space causes crowding and dirty house.
8. Confine poults to house for four weeks. Allow range on wire platforms in front of the brooder house after this time.
9. Avoid wet area around the water fountains.
10. Provide sufficient shade on range. A corn or sunflower field is ideal if natural shade is not available. Avoid a dense shade. If no other shade is available, construct a frame and place some boards or burlap sacks on it. This frame should be moved at regular intervals.

Blackhead. This disease probably causes greater losses in turkeys than all other diseases (Fig. 236). It is caused by a protozoan organism which may be carried by either chickens or turkeys. The blackhead organism will live only a few hours outside the fowl's body unless contained within cecal worm eggs, in which case it may survive and remain infectious for turkeys for several months. Young turkeys less than three months old are most susceptible to attacks of this disease. The disease affects the liver and the most noticeable symptom, found when turkeys having blackhead are killed and examined, is an enlarged liver covered with sunken ulcerlike areas, as shown in Figure 237. No satisfactory medical treatment has as yet been found for this disease. Poults raised by artificial methods, away from chickens and old turkeys on ground where neither turkeys nor chickens have ranged or their droppings have been spread during the past two years, seldom suffer from blackhead. If an outbreak of blackhead occurs, the best program to follow appears to be as follows: (1) Remove all sick birds from the flock, and either kill or confine these birds away from the healthy birds; (2) Clean the houses, thoroughly scrubbing them with hot lye water; (3) If convenient, confine the flocks to houses and wire-floored sun porches for several days, cleaning the house daily; and (4) Move the healthy birds to clean range. If the birds are too large to be confined in brooder houses, they may be moved directly to clean range.

Pullorum disease. Turkeys have probably been infected with pullorum disease by their association with chickens. Many flocks of turkeys are, as yet, free of the disease and until recent years very few reactors were found in turkeys. It has been shown that poults hatched in incubators with chickens which have pullorum disease also suffer outbreaks of this disease.

Turkeys which have pullorum disease may be detected by the tube agglutination test. A rapid antigen test has also been developed for satisfactorily determining turkey reactors having pullorum disease.

This disease in turkeys can be controlled by testing the breeding stock and removing all reactors to the disease, then incubating the eggs either away from chicken eggs or only in incubators where chicken eggs from flocks tested for pullorum disease are hatched.

Lice. Lice seldom cause trouble when turkeys are hatched and brooded artificially, but when hens are used severe losses may occur. Hens used for hatching or brooding turkeys should be carefully deloused so that when they come in contact with the poults they will be free of all lice. The control of lice requires only a small amount of effort on the part of the caretaker and losses

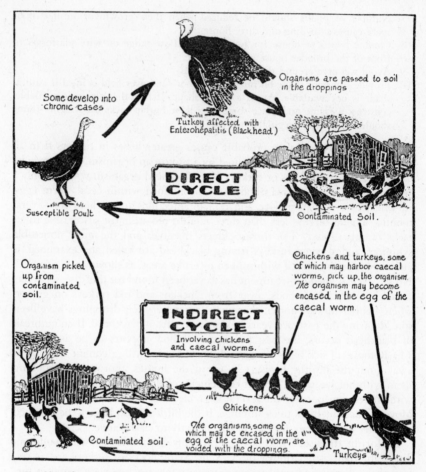

Fig. 236. Life cycle of Histomonas meleagridis, the parasite causing blackhead in turkeys.

from lice are a reflection on the care the turkeys have received. By dusting the hens twice at ten-day intervals with sodium fluoride, all lice can be destroyed.

Coccidiosis. Though turkeys do develop coccidiosis, they are not so susceptible to this disease as are chickens. Methods of control and the symptoms of the disease are quite similar to those described for chickens. (See Chapter Eleven.) The organism causing coccidiosis in chickens does not cause coccidiosis in turkeys, and vice versa. The most effective method of control appears to be daily cleaning for several days after an outbreak of coccidiosis so that the organisms cannot undergo the twenty-four-hour incubation period outside of the body of the turkey which is necessary for them to become infectious.

Trichomoniasis. This disease, because the symptoms are somewhat similar, may be confused with coccidiosis. It is only within recent years that trichomoniasis has been recognized as a distinct disease of turkeys and the causative

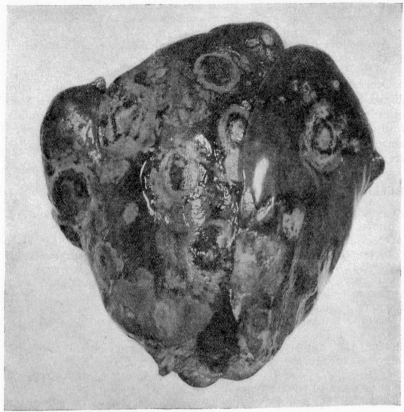

COURTESY MISSOURI AGRICULTURAL EXPERIMENT STATION

Fig. 237. The liver of a turkey which died of blackhead.

organism identified. This disease usually affects poults from six to ten weeks of age. The most common symptoms are listlessness and yellow, foamy, and semi-liquid droppings. The California Agricultural Experiment Station in 1937 made the following recommendations for the prevention and control of this disease.

1. Avoid all contact of poults with chickens and adult turkeys.
2. Brood by artificial means on new ground or with brooder equipment having cement floor or wire platforms in both the houses and yards. Purchase, if possible, the entire brood at one time and early in the season.
3. Use a sane, sound management program. The brand of feed is of little importance. If the feeding method used in previous years was successful, stick to it.
4. Keep visitors out of the brooding pens.
5. Do not visit the turkey yards of any other grower. Discuss your problems with him on the street corner or at his home, not in his turkey yard.

6. If disease breaks out, get an accurate diagnosis. Send or take some of the sick specimens to a diagnostic laboratory, and do not accept a field diagnosis until it has been confirmed by the laboratory.
7. Avoid all drastic treatment until the laboratory diagnostic report is received. The treatment should then be based on the laboratory findings.

Other diseases and parasites. Turkeys are afflicted with many of the other diseases and parasites of chickens, which are described in Chapter Eleven. Some of the more common of the other diseases which affect turkeys are botulism, fowl cholera, fowl pox, colds, roup, fowl typhoid, and tuberculosis. Turkeys are infested by cecum worms, gapeworms, roundworms, and tapeworms. They are attacked not only by lice but also by mites and ticks.

REFERENCES

ACKERSON, C. W., AND MUSSEHL, F. E.: THE UTILIZATION OF FOOD ELEMENTS BY GROWING POULTS. Neb. Sta. Res. Bul. 151. 1947.

ALEXANDER, LUCY M., SCHOPMEYER, GRACE E., AND MARSDEN, S. J.: YIELD OF COOKED EDIBLE PORTION OF YOUNG ROASTED TURKEY. Poultry Sci., 27: 579–587. 1948.

ASMUNDSON, V. S., AND MACILRAITH, J. J.: PRE-INCUBATION TESTS WITH TURKEY EGGS. Poultry Sci., 27: 394–401. 1948.

BARRETT, F. N., CARD, C. G., AND BERRIDGE, ASHLEY: FEEDING AND CONFINEMENT REARING EXPERIMENT WITH TURKEYS DURING 1944. Mich. Sta. Quart. Bul. 29: 88–101. 1946.

BESLEY, A. K., AND MARSDEN, S. J.: A STUDY OF TURKEY CURING AND SMOKING. Poultry Sci., 20: 496–506. 1941.

BIRD, H. R., MARSDEN, S. J., AND KELLOGG, W. L.: SUPPLEMENTS FOR SOYBEAN MEAL IN TURKEY DIETS. Poultry Sci., 28: 53–59. 1949.

BLAKELY, R. M., AND ANDERSON, R. W.: THE INFLUENCE OF THIOURACIL ON GROWTH, FATTENING, FEED CONSUMPTION, AND THYROID WEIGHT OF TURKEY BROILERS. Poultry Sci., 28: 185–188. 1949.

BOUCHER, ROBERT V.: EFFICACY OF VITAMIN D FROM DIFFERENT SOURCES FOR TURKEYS. Jour. Nutrition, 27: 403–413. 1944.

BRANT, A. WADE, DRAPER, C. I., AND EVANS, R. J.: GROWING TURKEYS ON RATIONS LOW IN ANIMAL PROTEIN. Wash. Sta. Bul. 441. 1944.

BROADBENT, DEE A., THOMAS, W. PRESTON, AND BLANCK, GEO. T.: AN ECONOMIC ANALYSIS OF TURKEY PRODUCTION IN UTAH. Utah Sta. Bul. 318. 1945.

BUSHNELL, L. D.: PULLORUM TESTING OF TURKEYS. Poultry Sci., 24: 208–211. 1945.

DAVIS, GEO. T., AND THAYER, ROLLIN H.: FINISHING MARKET TURKEYS WITH ESTROGEN. Poultry Sci., 27: 79–83. 1948.

DAWSON, L. E., AND WOOD, G. B.: FROZEN TURKEY QUARTERS. Purdue Exp. Sta. Bul. 537. 1949.

DEVOLT, H. M., AND HOLST, A. P.: COMPARATIVE VALUE OF CHLOROHYDROXY-GUINALINE AND VIOFORM AS PREVENTIVES OF BLACKHEAD (INFECTIOUS ENTEROHEPATITIS) OF TURKEYS. Poultry Sci., 28: 641–643. 1949.

FISCHER, C. M., AND DELOACH, D. B.: CONSUMER RESPONSE TO THE MARKETING OF CUT-UP TURKEY. Ore. Sta. Bul. 457. 1948.

FUNK, E. M.: PROTEIN CONTENT OF CONCENTRATES FOR TURKEYS. Mo. Sta. Bul. 471. 1943.

FUNK, E. M.: THE RELATIVE EFFICIENCY OF GAINS IN WEIGHT MADE BY MALE AND FEMALE BRONZE TURKEYS. Poultry Sci., 22: 3–10. 1943.

GARLAND, F. W., JR., WINTER, A. R., AND AMIET, E. R.: A COMPARISON OF METHODS OF TESTING TURKEYS FOR SALMONELLA PULLORUM INFECTION. Poultry Sci., 28: 63–68. 1949.

GOODEARL, G. P., AND MOORE, F. E.: TURKEY CAPONS. N. D. Sta. Bul. 307. 1941.

GOODEARL, G. P.: FEEDING TURKEYS FOR MARKET FINISH. N. D. Sta. Bul. 328. 1943.

GOODEARL, G. P.: SELECTION OF FEEDS BY GROWING TURKEYS. N. D. Sta. Bul. 335. 1945.

HAMMOND, J. C.: LACK OF WATER A CAUSE OF LOOSE, SLIMY GIZZARD LININGS ACCOMPANYING EARLY MORTALITY IN POULTS. Poultry Sci., 23: 477–480. 1944.

HARPER, J. A., AND GRIEBELER, W. L.: TURKEY RANGE EQUIPMENT. Ore. Sta. Circ. 176. 1948.

HINSHAW, W. R.: DISEASES OF TURKEYS. Calif. Sta. Bul. 613. 1943.

INSKO, W. M., MACLAURY, D. W., AND BAUTE, E. A.: WEIGHT OF TURKEY EGGS IN RELATION TO HATCHABILITY. Ky. Sta. Bul. 449. 1943.

INSKO, W. M., MACLAURY, D. W., AND RINGROSE, ARTHUR T.: EFFECT OF RELATIVE HUMIDITY AND AMOUNT OF TURNING ON HATCHABILITY OF TURKEY EGGS AND LIVABILITY OF POULTS. Ky. Sta. Bul. 438. 1942.

JAAP, R. G.: ACTIVITY OF SYNTHETIC ESTROGENS ON ORAL ADMINISTRATION IN THE DOMESTIC FOWL AND TURKEY. Endocrinology, 37: 369–376. 1945.

KNIGHT, D. R., MCDOUGLE, H. C., AND DURANT, A. J.: TRICHOMONIASIS OF TURKEYS. Mo. Sta. Bul. 456. 1942.

KRATZER, F. H., AND WILLIAMS, DELBERT: THE PANTOTHENIC ACID RE-QUIREMENT OF POULTS FOR EARLY GROWTH. Poultry Sci., 27: 518–523. 1948.

LLOYD, MALCOLM D., REED, CLEMENT A., AND FRITZ, JAMES C.: EXPERI-ENCES WITH HIGH PROTEIN DIETS FOR CHICKS AND POULTS. Poultry Sci., 28: 69–74. 1949.

MARGOLF, P. H., HARPER, J. A., AND CALLENBACH, E. W.: RESPONSE OF TUR-KEYS TO ARTIFICIAL ILLUMINATION. Pa. Sta. Bul. 486. 1947.

MARSDEN, STANLEY J., CARPENTER, ROWENA S., AND SWICKARD, MARY T.: TURKEY ON THE TABLE THE YEAR ROUND. U. S. D. A. Farmers' Bul. 2011. 1949.

MCGINNIS, J., AND CARVER, J. S.: THE EFFECT OF RIBOFLAVIN AND BIOTIN IN THE PREVENTION OF DERMATITIS AND PEROSIS IN TURKEYS. Poultry Sci., 26: 364–371. 1947.

MISNER, E. G.: COST AND RETURNS FOR THE TURKEY ENTERPRISE. Cornell Sta. Bul. 827. 1946.

MOTZOK, I., AND SLINGER, S. J.: STUDIES ON THE CALCIUM AND PHOSPHORUS REQUIREMENTS OF BROAD-BREASTED BRONZE TURKEYS. Poultry Sci., 27: 486–491. 1948.

NORTH, MACK O.: THE INFLUENCE OF PROTEIN CONCENTRATES UPON THE QUALITY OF MEAT IN TURKEYS. Wyo. Sta. Bul. 264. 1943.

PAARLBERG, DON, AND WATSON, D. J.: FACTORS AFFECTING THE PRICE OF TURKEYS. Ind. Sta. Bul. 536. 1949.

PHILLIPS, R. E., AND WILLIAMS, C. S.: RELATIONSHIP OF SPECIFIC GRAVITY AND SHELL APPEARANCE TO THE HATCHABILITY OF FERTILE TURKEY EGGS. Poultry Sci., 23: 110–113. 1944.

POULTRY COUNCIL OF STATE OF WASHINGTON: FEEDING TURKEYS. Wash. Ext. Bul. 327. 1947.

POULTRY COUNCIL OF THE STATE OF WASHINGTON: TURKEY BROODING AND REARING EQUIPMENT. Wash. Ext. Bul. 325. 1948.

POULTRY COUNCIL OF THE STATE COLLEGE OF WASHINGTON: FEEDING AND MANAGING OF TURKEY BREEDERS. Wash. Ext. Bul. 388. 1949.

POULTRY COUNCIL OF THE STATE COLLEGE OF WASHINGTON: TURKEY BREEDER HOUSES AND EQUIPMENT. Wash. Ext. Bul. 371. 1948.

POULTRY BRANCH, PRODUCTION, AND MARKETING ADMIN., U. S. D. A.: GRADING DRESSED TURKEYS. Farmers' Bul. 1815. 1949.

ROBERTS, J. B.: MARKETING TURKEYS IN KENTUCKY. Ky. Sta. Bul. 458. 1944.

ROBERTS, ROY E.: STARTING AND GROWING RATIONS FOR TURKEYS. Ind. Sta. Bul. 517. 1946.

SAMPSON, F. R., AND WILSON, W. O.: TURKEY EGG HATCHABILITY IN SOUTH DAKOTA. S. D. Sta. Bul. 375. 1944.

SCOTT, M. L., HEUSER, G. F., AND NORRIS, L. C.: ENERGY, PROTEIN AND UNIDENTIFIED VITAMINS IN POULT NUTRITION. Poultry Sci., 27: 773–780. 1948.

SHERWOOD, D. H., AND LARSON, CARL A.: FIFTEEN YEARS OF TURKEY INVESTIGATIONS AT THE UMATILLA BRANCH EXP. STA. Ore. Sta. Circ. 429. 1948.

SLINGER, S. J., GARTLEY, K. M., AND EVANS, E. V.: PELLETED AND UNPELLETED DIETS HIGH IN DEHYDRATED GREEN FEEDS FOR TURKEYS GROWN IN CONFINEMENT. Poultry Sci., 28: 556–561. 1949.

SLINGER, S. J., HILL, D. C., GARTLEY, K. M., AND BRANION, H. D.: SOYBEAN OIL MEAL AND SUNFLOWER SEED OIL IN RATIONS FOR BROAD-BREASTED BRONZE TURKEYS. Poultry Sci., 28: 534–540. 1949.

THAYER, R. H., AND DAVIS, GEO. T.: USE OF ESTROGENS IN TURKEY BROILER PRODUCTION. Poultry Sci., 27: 176–181. 1948.

WILLIAMS, I. L., AND WIEGERS, H. L.: TURKEY STEAKS. Neb. Sta. Circ. 84. 1947.

CHAPTER 17 ||||||||||||||||||||||||||||||||||||||||||||||||||||||||

Ducks, Geese, and Miscellaneous Poultry

▼

When speaking of the poultry industry, one generally has chickens in mind. In the preceding two chapters, the increasing importance of the turkey industry was pointed out. There are other species of birds classed as poultry that are of considerable economic importance. The chief ones among them are ducks and geese. Pigeons and guineas are also of some importance.

Ducks

The duck industry. According to the 1940 census, there were 12,138,820 ducks raised in the United States in 1939. The industry has just about held its own during the last thirty years.

The greatest numbers of ducks are raised in the following states, listed in order of production: New York, Pennsylvania, Ohio, California, Illinois, Massachusetts, New Jersey, Minnesota, Wisconsin, Iowa, Michigan, and South Dakota. Commercial duck raising has been developed most extensively in New York. The number of ducks kept, in proportion to the total population, is much lower in the United States than in most other countries. The relative number in Great Britain, Ireland, and New Zealand is several times larger than in this country.

Intensive duck farming on a large scale has been more successful than intensive chicken raising (Fig. 238). Ducks stand confinement well, are more easily brooded, and are less subject to disease than are chickens.

Ducks are raised primarily for meat purposes. They are especially adapted for this on account of the rapidity of growth, hardiness, and ease of handling. Duck raising, as a business, is limited, for the demand for duck meat is not so steady nor its popularity so great as for chicken. Summer resorts and large cities with a foreign population make the best markets.

The demand for duck eggs is very limited. They are larger than chicken eggs, but bring about the same price or less. They find some use in the baking industry.

Breeds of ducks. There are eleven standard breeds of ducks which have been admitted to the American Standard of Perfection. Most of them have descended from the mallard, or wild duck, which is widely distributed, ranging from eastern Asia to North America. The duck was first domesticated in

569

U. S. D. A.

Fig. 238. Large duck farm on Long Island.

Asia. The ancestors of most of our present breeds were imported from there. The breeds of ducks may be divided into meat, egg, and ornamental classes.

The meat class includes the Pekin, Aylesbury, Muscovy, Rouen, Cayuga, Buff, and Swedish breeds.

The Pekin is by far the most popular. It was introduced from China about 1873. This breed is kept almost exclusively by commercial duck farmers throughout the United States, and is a great favorite on general farms. The Pekin (Fig. 239) is distinguished by a creamy white plumage, a long, broad, deep body, and a full breast. The skin is yellow and the shanks, toes, and bill are reddish-orange color. The standard weight of the mature drake and duck are nine and eight pounds, respectively. The Pekins are hardy, are fair layers, practically nonsetters, and are especially adapted for the production of meat. They are timid and easily frightened, very docile, and easily confined by low fences.

Other meat breeds are not so well adapted to commercial or general farming. The Aylesbury is not so hardy as the Pekin. The Muscovy ducks vary in size. They are not easily confined by ordinary fences. The Rouen matures slowly and has dark pinfeathers.

The egg class includes only one breed, the Runner, commonly called the Indian Runner. It was probably developed in Belgium and Holland. There are three standard varieties of Runner ducks: the Fawn and White, the White, and the Penciled.

All the varieties have the same shape, but differ in plumage color. The breast is full, the body is long and narrow, sloping gradually into the neck and carried erect, with no indication of a keel, the body resembling somewhat that

Fig. 239. Some breeds of ducks. Upper left, Pekin. Upper right, Rouen. Lower left, Runner. Lower right, Muscovy.

of a penguin in shape. The Runner duck is much smaller than breeds of the meat type, the adult drake having a standard weight of four and one-half pounds and the duck four pounds. They are among the best layers of all the American standard breeds of ducks and hold the same relative position in the duck family that the Leghorn does among the breeds of chickens. This breed lays a good-sized white egg, considerably larger than a chicken egg. Runner ducks are active, are good foragers, nonsitters, and hardy. Their skin is yellow and they make fair broilers, weighing from two and one-half to three pounds at about six weeks of age. They are not adapted for the production of large green ducks, but may be kept to produce ducklings of broiler size.

The ornamental class includes the Call, Crested White, and Black East India breeds of ducks.

The Call is small and may be considered the bantam of the duck family. The ornamental breeds are kept for exhibition and are used as decoys in wild duck shooting. The other ornamental breeds are also small.

Characteristics of ducks. Ducks have certain characteristics which class them as waterfowls and differentiate them from land fowls, such as the chicken and turkey.

The duck is provided with short legs and webbed feet. These are assets in swimming. The bill is covered by a soft, sensitive membrane and edged with horny plates. Solid food material obtained from the water may be held and the water forced out through the plates. The feathers are concave toward the body and have a thick, soft covering on the under surface. They are well greased, and this helps to keep water from reaching the skin. The duck is further protected from the cold by having a thick layer of fat beneath the skin. This acts as a body insulator.

The duck does not have so large a percentage of edible muscle meat as the chicken. The meat is dark. The keel is flat and boatlike.

Duck breeding. Duck breeding for useful purposes in this country has been confined largely to breeding Pekin ducks for meat production.

Selection of breeders is usually made each year from the young ducks before the flock is marketed. The males can be identified by the middle tail feathers, which are curled up. Breeding ducks are selected for good length, width, and depth of body, and for early maturity. Stock showing signs of coarseness is discarded. Heavy birds with very deep keels have a tendency to take on too much fat and are likely to show low egg production, poor fertility, and lack of vigor. Most ducks are kept only through their first laying season, as young ducks are better producers and lay earlier than older ones.

Mating of breeders is usually done in flocks (Fig. 240). One male is used for every six or seven females. Inbreeding is generally practiced. This may account for the poor hatchability that is often encountered.

Before much progress can be made in duck breeding, it will be necessary to trap-nest ducks; make pen matings; keep the breeders more than one year; and use the birds that have the best production, hatchability, and livability records.

Incubation of duck eggs. The incubation period for duck eggs from most of the breeds is twenty-eight days. Muscovy duck eggs require a thirty-three- to thirty-five-day incubation period.

Duck eggs are generally hatched in incubators and under the same conditions used for hatching chicken eggs (Fig. 241). More moisture is required

U. S. D. A.

Fig. 240. Flock of breeding ducks and breeding house.

at hatching time than is generally used for chicken eggs. Directions of the incubator manufacturer should be followed until experience has shown that improvements can be made.

Brooding ducks. Ducks are easier to brood than chicks or turkeys. They do not require so much heat or heat for so long a time. The ducks are removed from the incubator as soon as the hatch is completed. They are taken to the brooder house as soon as possible, placed under the brooder, and given feed and water.

About 100 to 150 ducks are placed in each pen and under each brooder. The temperature under the hover should be about 90° F. the first week, 85° F. the second week, 75° F. the third week, and about 65° F. the fourth and fifth weeks. When the birds are about six weeks old, they are transferred to the fattening shed where no artificial heat is used.

Straw or shavings make a very good litter for the brooder house. A guard should be placed around the brooder, one or two feet away from it, to keep the ducks from wandering away from the heat until they become accustomed to the brooder.

The pen should be cleaned every week or ten days.

Housing ducks. The house should be located on well-drained soil. A chicken house is satisfactory for ducks. Shed-type houses are often used (Fig. 240). It is desirable to allow from four to six square feet of floor space for each breeding duck. Breeders are kept in flocks of from about 75 to 250.

Straw or shavings make satisfactory litter. The house should be cleaned as

Fig. 241. Hatching ducks. Top, a duck hatchery. (Courtesy Ridgeway Duck Farm.) Center, traying duck eggs. (U. S. D. A.) Bottom, a good hatch. (Courtesy Myers Poultry Farm.)

often as necessary to keep it clean and dry. Proper ventilation in the duck house, as in the chicken house, will help keep the place comfortable.

No perches are provided for ducks or other waterfowl because it is not their nature to roost. They rest on the floor.

Nests are generally provided which are made like stalls. They are about 12 inches wide, and 18 inches deep, and separated by boards about 12 inches high. The partition boards are nailed to a strip about 5 inches high, which forms the front of a row of nests placed against the back or side of the building. Some breeders provide no nests, but allow the birds to lay on the floor.

Troughs are generally used for water and mash boxes for feed.

Breeding ducks are generally provided with outside range (Fig. 242). When the range is limited or the farm large, the yards are limited to about one hundred feet in length and the width of the pen. If they extend into a stream, it will aid in keeping the place more sanitary. Fences about two feet high will hold ducks in their respective yards.

Feeding ducks. The quantitative nutritive requirements of ducks have not been carefully studied. Rations suitable for chickens appear to give satisfactory results when fed to ducks. The optimum protein level for efficient growth appears to be about 18 per cent. Ducks may be grown on dry mash feed or a combination of dry and wet mash. However, many duck feeders still prefer to feed all of the ration as a wet mash. The following rations and feeding directions are based upon the recommendations of the United States Department of Agriculture (*Farmers' Bulletin* 697, 1933):

Starting duck rations are used for the first two or three weeks. One such all-mash ration consists of yellow corn, 35; bran, 31; flour middlings, 10; alfalfa leaf meal, 5; dried milk, 5; meat scraps, 5; rolled oats, 5; sand, 3; salt, 1; and cod liver oil, 1. The ducks are fed all they will clean up four times daily. The ducks are fed as soon as placed in the brooder house. The mash is fed in the form of a wet crumbly mixture. Shallow water troughs should be placed near the feeders. Some investigators advocate the use of 5 to 10 per cent more meat scraps in the ration than listed in the above formula.

Growing duck rations are fed from the time the ducks are about two or three weeks old until they are around six weeks old. One of the rations advocated consists of corn, 45; bran, 24; flour middlings, 10; meat scraps, 10; ground oat groats, 5; limestone, 3; dried milk, 2; and salt, 1. Green feed to the amount of 10 per cent of the mash, by bulk, should be added to the ration. The birds are fed as much of the wet crumbly mash as they will clean up three times daily.

Finishing duck rations are fed from the time the birds are about six weeks old until they are marketed. One of the finishing or fattening rations listed consists of corn, 50; bran, 18; flour middlings, 13; meat meal, 12; ground oats, 5; dried milk, 2, with 10 per cent of the bulk of the mash in green feed added. The ducks are fed as much of the wet mash as they will clean up, three times daily.

If ducks are raised in confinement, 5 per cent alfalfa meal may be used to replace the green feed. About 1 per cent cod liver oil should be included in the

Fig. 242. Growing ducks. Top, brooding in a multiple-unit house. The brooder hovers are under the track and walk. Note the low pen partitions. (U. S. D. A.) Center, feeding ducks on range. Note the track and car for hauling feed. Bottom, outside runs in connection with a multiple-unit brooder house. (Courtesy C. M. Ferguson.)

ration, also, for ducks raised in confinement. It should be eliminated from the ration about a month before the birds go to market in order to eliminate any fishy odor or taste from the meat.

Breeding duck rations vary in protein content with the egg production desired. From the time the young ducks are separated to be used as breeders (about July) until a short while before eggs are wanted from them for hatching (about November), the birds are fed a bulky ration of low protein content. One such ration consists of bran, 40; yellow corn, 30; flour middlings, 25; and meat scraps or fish meal, 5. The mash is mixed with about one-third its bulk of green feed.

Shortly before eggs are desired for hatching, the protein content of the ration is increased. One mash feed used for the production of hatching eggs, when the birds have outside yards, consists of corn, 45; bran, 20; flour middlings, 20; meat scraps, 10; and ground oats, 5. This mash is mixed with green feed and fed as a wet mash. The breeders are often fed a little whole corn in addition to the mash feed.

Oyster shells or limestone grit are kept before the layers at all times.

Lights may be used to stimulate egg production, as in the case of chickens.

Duck diseases. Ducks are not so susceptible to diseases as are chickens. Possibly this may be accounted for on the basis of selection. The breeders are picked out on the basis of vigor during the growing period. Another possible explanation is the fact that ducks have been accustomed to living in large numbers under rather unsanitary conditions. This unfavorable environment through the years may have resulted in the establishment of a natural immunity against disease.

Some farmers who have been unable to produce chickens and chicken eggs profitably, because of disease, have changed to the production of ducks and duck eggs. They are usually successful in raising the ducks, but often find themselves handicapped because of a lack of a good market.

One should not get the impression that ducks are entirely immune from disease. They are troubled by keel disease, pneumonia, and some other troubles.

Keel disease is indicated by lack of activity, loss of appetite, diarrhea, and heavy losses within a few hours. The trouble generally occurs in hot weather. It results from eating moldy or decayed feed or litter. To eliminate the trouble, renew the litter in the house, fill up the filthy puddles in the yards with sand, and feed fresh mash that is free from mold.

Pneumonia, colds, or bronchitis may be indicated by a sticky coat, watery eyes, wheezing, and sniffling sounds when breathing. This respiratory trouble results from overcrowding, poor ventilation, exposure, and overheating.

Marketing ducks. Since ducks are raised primarily for meat production, duck meat is the chief duck product marketed.

Ducks are generally marketed when about eleven weeks old, but the age may vary from nine to thirteen weeks, according to the condition of the birds, their weight, and the season of the year. The New York market prefers a duck that weighs about five and one-half pounds (Fig. 243).

The ducks should not be held after the long tail feathers have reached their full length. If held longer, the birds go through a kind of molt, the gains are poor, and the quality of the meat is of lower value.

A V-shaped trap made of panels of fence, into which the ducks are driven,

Fig. 243. Growth and marketing of ducks. Upper left, a 24-day-old duckling. Upper right, carcass of a 5½-pound duck produced in 9½ weeks. Lower left, slightly more than half grown. Lower right, at 9½ weeks. Ready for market.

saves much handling of the ducks. The birds are handled by the neck. There is considerable loss in weight when ducks are marketed alive. Most of them are sent to market dressed.

Ducks being dressed are hung up by the feet, the jugular vein severed in the throat below the base of the skull, the bird scalded or steamed, and the feathers plucked. Long pinfeathers are usually removed with a dull knife, and the down is rubbed off with the moistened hand or shaved off with a very sharp knife. Each duck yields about two and one-half ounces of marketable feathers which help pay for the picking.

After the ducks are picked, they are usually washed and put in ice-cold water to cool and plump. They are then graded and packed for shipment. Prices are highest from December to April. Large cities provide the best markets. Duck raisers count on marketing fifty to sixty-five green ducks for each breeder kept on the farm.

Duck eggs are not in much demand. It is claimed that they have a strong taste. They are used in bakeries and are popular around Easter. Pure white duck eggs are more popular than the colored ones. They should be marketed more frequently than chicken eggs because they deteriorate in quality more rapidly in hot weather.

Geese

Geese, like ducks, are raised primarily for meat production. They are hardy and easily and cheaply raised on general farms, since they will get almost all the feed they need from a good pasture. Geese are raised in all sections of the United States, but most of them are produced in the North Central states. Geese make up only about .5 per cent of the poultry raised in the United States.

Breeds of geese. All breeds of geese in the United States are descended from the wild gray goose and have been domesticated for many centuries. Six breeds are recognized as standard in this country, namely, Toulouse, Emden, African, Chinese, Canada, and Egyptian. The breeds found on most farms are crossed or mixed breeds and several pounds lighter than the standard breeds.

The Toulouse (Fig. 244) is the largest and most popular breed of geese. The adult gander weighs twenty-six pounds and the adult goose twenty pounds. This breed has a broad, deep body, and is loose feathered. The color of the plumage is dark gray on the back, gradually shading to light gray edged with white on the breast, and to white on the abdomen. The Toulouse will lay from fifteen to thirty-five eggs a year.

The Emden is a pure white, closely feathered breed of geese (Fig. 244). The adult gander weighs twenty pounds and the goose eighteen pounds. The Emden does not lay quite so many eggs as the Toulouse, but is a better sitter.

The other breeds of geese are of much less economic importance.

Breeding and management of geese. Geese are generally raised in small numbers on general farms. They are very hardy and not subject to many diseases. They thrive well on pasture. Geese need a shed or some other means of protection from the snow and cold, and shade for protection from the hot sun.

Geese, like other kinds of poultry, should be selected for size, production, and vigor. Medium-sized birds are the most desirable. They should be mated several months before the breeding season. Birds should be mated in the fall

COURTESY "POULTRY TRIBUNE"

Fig. 244. Breeds of geese. Left, Emden; right, Toulouse.

when hatching eggs are wanted in the spring. Geese matings are not changed from year to year unless the birds will not mate.

It is difficult to determine sex in geese, especially the young stock. The gander is usually somewhat larger and coarser than the goose and has a shrill, high voice, while the female has a harsh, coarse cry. The gander has a longer neck and a larger head.

A gander may be mated with from one to four geese, but pair or trio matings usually give the best results. A young gander is usually mated with only one or two geese. Flock or pen matings may be used. Four to twenty-five geese may be ranged on an acre of ground. Fences two or three feet high will keep geese confined to a given range.

Toulouse and Emden geese breed and produce some stock in the second year, but do not mature or give best results before the third year. Females may be kept until eight to ten years old and ganders until six or seven years old.

Geese are allowed to make nests on the floor of the house or in large boxes or barrels, or shelters scattered on the range for that purpose. Goose eggs should be gathered daily, kept in a cool place, and hatched under a hen, goose, or in an incubator. From three to seven eggs may be set under a hen, or ten to fifteen under a goose. Eggs set under a hen should be turned by hand as they are too large for the hen to turn. The period of incubation of goose eggs varies from twenty-eight days in the small breeds to thirty-four or thirty-five days in the large breeds.

Goslings may be brooded with a hen, a goose, or with an artificial brooder. If brooded in the spring, when pasture is good, they will need only heat for a week or so. Goslings should be kept dry and out of water until they are two to four weeks old.

Artificial incubation. Studies made at Ohio State University indicate that the following practices will result in good hatchability.

1. Turn eggs completely over at least once daily and preferably four times.
2. Incubate the eggs at 99 to 99.5° F. in a forced-draft incubator.
3. Maintain a high humidity, especially during the hatch. A wet bulb reading of 94° F. should be maintained during the hatch.
4. Dip the eggs in lukewarm water for about a minute twice weekly.

Feeding geese. Geese are generally raised where they have a good grass range or pasture, and, except during the winter months, usually pick up most of their living. The pasture may be supplemented with light feeds of home-grown grains or wet mash daily, depending upon the condition of the pasture.

Breeding stock should be fed grain and roughage during the winter, when pasture is not available. Oats make a desirable grain feed. A limited amount of corn, wheat, or barley may be used. Silage may also be used. In the early spring, the geese should be fed a mash feed in addition to the roughage and grains, in order to stimulate egg production. Any satisfactory chicken laying mash may be fed as a wet mash two or three times daily. Oyster shells or limestone grit should be kept available for eggshell formation.

Goslings may be fed a chick mash when raised in confinement. When raised on green grass range, they may be fed a mixture of grains mixed with liquid skim milk or buttermilk to make a crumbly mash. When goslings are raised in small numbers on good pasture, they will need little or no grain or mash feed after they are about three or four weeks old. Whole grains should not be fed until the goslings are well-feathered.

Finishing geese for market involves fattening them. They may be range or pen fattened for about a month before going to market. The birds are given all the corn they will clean up and are fed a wet mash three times daily. The wet mash consists of two parts corn meal and one part middlings mixed with liquid milk to make a batter. The pens should be kept partly darkened and the birds disturbed as little as possible. An increase in weight of from four to six pounds can be obtained by this method of feeding.

Noodling geese is a better means of fattening but involves more labor. The birds are fed six to seven noodles five times daily at four-hour intervals.

Marketing geese. There is some demand for young geese from June to January, but most of them are sold at Thanksgiving and Christmas. Ten-weeks-old goslings may weigh as much as ten to twelve pounds and are marketed as green geese. If not sold at this age, they should not be sold until about five months old. Large cities containing a considerable foreign population are usually the best markets for geese.

Geese are usually killed and picked in the same manner as other kinds of poultry, but are much more difficult to pick than chickens. Care should be taken in handling geese at market time as the flesh bruises easily. After killing and bleeding, the feathers are generally removed following scalding or steaming. After geese have been picked, they are generally washed and put in ice water to cool.

Feathers have been plucked from live geese for centuries. They are usually

Fig. 245. A pair of White King breeders entered in the New Jersey pigeon-breeding contest, with a pair of squabs. The record of this pair was 19 squabs in a year, weighing 383 ounces.

picked in the spring or fall, or both times. The feathers are removed only when the quills are dry and do not contain blood. Just before the molt is a good time to pluck the feathers. About a pound of feathers may be obtained from a goose during a year. The demand for goose feathers has been declining in recent years.

Goose livers are mixed with pork, flour, butter, and spices and sold under the name of "Patty" and other trade names. Austria exported about 700,000 pounds at $1.25 per pound during 1937 and 1938. Other European countries also export goose-liver materials.

Pigeons

Pigeons are kept in all parts of the United States for squab production, messengers, and exhibition (Figs. 245 and 246).

There is a demand for squabs, especially in large cities, to take the place of game. The chief difficulties in squab production are in finding suitable markets

Fig. 246. A section of the signal corps (U. S. Army) carrier pigeon exhibit at the Seventh World's Poultry Congress.

for the small amount of squab meat produced by individuals and in finding suitable stock for producing big squabs.

Breeding pigeons. There are many breeds of pigeons, but only a few of economic value for squab production. The Homer is probably the most popular breed of pigeons. It is prolific, hardy, active, and quiet in temperament.

It is difficult to determine by casual observation the age and sex of pigeons, and this makes it difficult for the buyer to determine the value of the stock. The medium-sized breeds of pigeons which do not raise at least six pairs of squabs annually to market age should be either culled or remated. Good pigeons for breeders have a white or pinkish-white skin and light-colored legs. Pigeons are most valuable as squab producers when two to five years old.

Pigeons mate in pairs and usually remain with their mates throughout life, although the mating may be changed if desired. To bring about the mating desired, place the male and female in a coop and leave them there for six to fourteen days, or until they become settled.

The pigeon hen lays an egg, generally skips a day, and then lays again. The male generally sits on the eggs during the middle of the day, and the female the remainder of the time. The incubation period for pigeon eggs is about seventeen days.

Feeding and management of pigeons. Squabs are reared and fed by both of the parent birds on a thick, creamy mixture called pigeon milk, produced in the crops of the pigeons. Pigeons usually feed their squabs shortly after they themselves are fed.

Pigeons are not fed any mash or green feed. They are fed a ration of whole grains and supplied with water and grit. A grain mixture advocated by the

Fig. 247. A pigeon house.

New Jersey Agricultural Experiment Station (New Jersey Station Bulletin 634, 1937) is as follows:

Whole yellow corn	40 lbs.
Kaffir corn	20
Durham wheat	15
Canada peas	15
Hemp seed	2.5
Millet	2.5
Hulled oats	2.5
Buckwheat	2.5
Total	100.0 lbs.

The grain should be fed twice daily, the birds being given all they will eat. Pigeons should not be disturbed more than is absolutely necessary.

Pigeons may be kept in most any available building when kept in small groups. The quarters should be dry, well ventilated, and provided with plenty of daylight. Pigeons are allowed two and one-half to three and one-half square feet of floor space per bird. Not more than forty pairs should be kept in a single pen.

Nearly all pigeons kept for squab production are confined by the use of an outside fly or yard covered with wire which is built on the south side of the house (Fig. 247).

The interior fittings should consist of a double nest for each pair of breeders, nest, bowls, and feed hoppers. Nest compartments should be 12 inches high, 16 inches deep, and 24 inches wide, divided into two parts. A box of straw may be kept in the pen so that the pigeons may build their own nests. The feed hoppers and drinking vessels should be covered with wire in such a way that the birds cannot get in them. Shallow bath pans should be kept in the yards and the birds allowed to use them, except in cold weather.

Marketing squabs. The production of squabs from each pair of breeders varies from one or two to as high as ten or eleven pairs a year. Homer squabs generally weigh eight to eleven pounds per dozen. They gain two-thirds of their mature weight in four weeks. Squabs are fed by their parents until mar-

keted. They are sold when three or
four weeks old, before they can
leave their nests. Squabs are in
good condition when fully feathered under the wings.

Squabs are killed and dressed
much like other poultry.

Guineas

The guinea fowl is often used
as a substitute for game birds,
such as grouse, partridge, quail,
and pheasant.

Most of the guineas are raised

U. S. D. A.

Fig. 248. A Pearl guinea fowl.

in small numbers on general farms of the Middle West and southern states.

Guineas might be more popular were it not for their harsh and seemingly
never-ending cry, and their bad disposition. There were 948,755 guineas
raised in the United States in 1939.

Guineas are found in the wild state in Africa. They have been domesticated
and scattered throughout the world. Of the three domesticated varieties, the
Pearl is by far the most popular. It has a purplish-gray plumage, dotted or
"pearled" with white (Fig. 248).

Like quail and most other wild birds, guinea fowls have a tendency to mate
in pairs. However, one male may be mated with three or four hens. If given
the freedom of the farm, the birds generally hide their nests. They may lay
twenty or thirty eggs in the spring of the year before going broody. The incubation period for guinea eggs is twenty-eight days. They may be hatched
in incubators and brooded under brooders, using the same procedures as used
for chickens.

Guineas are fed in much the same manner as chickens. If given a chance,
they forage well and can be depended upon to secure much of their food from
weed seeds, grass, insects, and worms, when kept in small numbers.

The marketing season for guinea fowl is during the late summer and fall.
The demand is for young birds weighing from one and one-half to two
pounds each. They are killed and dressed in much the same manner as
chickens.

Peafowls

Peafowls once had some importance as food for man, but now they are
kept almost entirely for ornament (Fig. 249).

The native home of the peafowl is in India. The birds like range and
shrubbery or trees for a home. When confined to yards with sheds for shelters,
they should be some distance from the house because the birds are noisy,
especially at night.

Fig. 249. The peafowl.

Four or five hens may be mated with one cock bird. The birds start to lay the second year and may lay five to nine eggs per year. The eggs may be incubated artificially or under hens. The incubation period is twenty-eight to thirty days. The young birds may be brooded artificially or with hens.

Peafowls are generally fed a ration consisting largely of grains and green feeds. When given freedom of a range, the birds will secure most of their food from weed seeds, grass, insects, worms, etc.

Swans

Swans are kept largely for ornamental purposes and probably should not be classed as poultry. They are more common in European countries than in the United States.

Swans are very hardy and need no protection except in extremely cold weather. They live in pairs and remain faithful to each other until death. Swans make nests of sticks and rubbish and lay from six to eight large greenish-white eggs each year. The incubation period of swan eggs is about six weeks.

Swans live on water plants, soft roots, and insects, under natural conditions. They may be fed the same kind of food fed to other poultry. It should be supplemented with green succulent feed.

Swans live to be very old. The females will breed for thirty years, and the males have been known to live for more than sixty years.

REFERENCES

General and Miscellaneous

HURD, L. M.: Modern Poultry Farming. The Macmillan Co., New York. 1944.

JULL, M. A.: FOWLS OF FOREST AND STREAM TAMED BY MAN. Nat. Geog. Mag., Vol. 57, No. 3, pp. 327–371. 1930.

JULL, M. A.: Raising Turkeys, Ducks, Geese, Game Birds. McGraw-Hill Book Co., New York. 1948.

LAMON, H. M., AND SLOCUM, R. R.: Ducks and Geese. 1922.

LEE, R. R.: THE GUINEA FOWL. U. S. D. A. Farmers' Bul. 1391. 1931.

LIPSCOMB, J. K., AND HOMES, H.: DUCKS AND GEESE. (Gt. Brit.) Min. Agr. and Fisheries Bul. 70, 3rd ed. 1941.

MCATEE, W. L.: PEAFOWL AND THEIR CARE. U. S. D. A. Misc. Pub. 127. 1931.

MILBY, T. T., AND HENDERSON, E. W.: THE COMPARATIVE GROWTH RATES OF TURKEYS, DUCKS, GEESE, AND PHEASANTS. Poultry Sci., 16: 155–165. 1937.

OLLSON, N.: INVESTIGATION ON THE VITAMIN D REQUIREMENTS OF CHICKS, POULTS, DUCKLINGS, AND GOSLINGS: Annals Royal Agr. Col. Sweden 16: 1–38. 1948.

SHOEMAKER, ANNA: HOW TO RAISE GUINEAS. Pennsylvania Farmer. April 9, 1949.

WRIGHT, WALDO: HE RAISES GUINEAS FOR PROFIT. Amer. Poultry Jour. 80: No. 5, pp. 8, 14–15. 1949.

Ducks

BLACK, J. D. G.: THE VITAMIN D REQUIREMENTS OF INTENSIVELY KEPT DUCKLINGS. Proc. Eighth World's Poultry Cong., pp. 96–102. 1948.

DUCKS. THE STANDARD AND MOST AUTHORITATIVE WORK UPON ALL WATER-FOWL YET PUBLISHED. The Feathered World. 1927.

FRITZ, J. C., ARCHER, W., AND BARKER, D.: RIBOFLAVIN REQUIREMENTS OF DUCKLINGS. Poultry Sci., 18: 449–454. 1939.

GARSIDE, J. S.: SALMONELLA INFECTIONS IN DUCKS. Jour. Compar. Pathol. and Ther., 54: 61–76. 1944.

GORDON, R. F., AND GARSIDE, J. S.: SALMONELLA INFECTIONS IN DUCKS: OBSERVATIONS ON THE VALUE OF THE AGGLUTINATION TEST IN THE ERADICATION OF INFECTION AND INVESTIGATIONS ON THE CYCLE OF INFECTION VIA THE EGG. Jour. Compar. Pathol. and Ther., 54: 61–76. 1944.

GRAHAM, R., BRANDLY, C. A., AND DUNLAP, G. L.: STUDIES ON DUCK SEPTICEMIA. Cornell Vet., 28: 1. 1938.

HAMLYN, W. L., BRANION, H. D., AND CAVERS, J. R.: THE INFLUENCE OF PROTEIN ON THE GROWTH OF DUCKS. Poultry Sci., 13: 333–337. 1934.

HEGSTED, D. M., AND PERRY, R. L.: NUTRITIONAL STUDIES WITH THE DUCK. V. RIBOFLAVIN AND PANTOTHENIC ACID REQUIREMENTS. Jour. Nutrition, 35: 411. 1948.

HILBERT, K. F.: DISEASE PROBLEMS OF LONG ISLAND DUCK RAISERS. Proc. Seventh World's Poultry Cong., pp. 231–233. 1939.

HORTON, D. H.: A COMPARISON OF FEEDING A TWELVE PER CENT AND A NINETEEN PER CENT PROTEIN RATION TO WHITE PEKIN DUCKLINGS. Poultry Sci., 11: 107–109. 1932.

HORTON, D. H.: THE LOSS IN DUCK EGGS DURING INCUBATION. Poultry Sci., 11: 23–27. 1932.

HORTON, D. H.: THE VALUE OF DRIED SKIM MILK IN FEEDING DUCKLINGS. Poultry Item, Vol. 36, No. 8, p. 5. 1934.

HUNTER, J. M.: Profitable Duck Management. The Beacon Milling Co., Cayuga, N. Y. 1940.

HURD, L. M., AND HILBERT, K. F.: DUCK GROWING. Cornell Ext. Bul. 345. 1936. Reprinted, 1945.

LEE, A. R.: DUCK BREEDING. U. S. D. A. Yearbook, pp. 1367–1378. 1937.

LEE, A. R.: DUCK RAISING. U. S. D. A. Farmers' Bul. 697. 1933.

LIPSCOMB, J. K., AND HOWES, H.: DUCKS AND GEESE. Gt. Brit. Min. Agr. and Fish. Bul. 70. 3rd ed. 1941.

MANESS, HUBERT: PEKING DUCK—A CHINESE SPECIALTY AND ONE OF THE WORLD'S GREAT GOODS. U. S. Egg and Poultry Mag., 53: 22–23, 37–39. 1947.

MANWELL, R. D., AND HATHEWAY, A. E.: THE DUCK AS A HOST FOR THE AVIAN MALARIA. Amer. Jour. Hyg., 37: 153–155. 1943.

MARSHALL, E. K., LITCHFIELD, J. T., AND WHITE, H. J.: SULFONAMIDE THERAPY OF MALARIA IN DUCKS. Jour. Pharmacol. and Expt. Ther., 75: 89–109. 1942.

MORTHLAND, J. F.: DUCK PRODUCTION. Poultry Supply Dealer. Nov. 1948.

PETERSON, E. H., MORRILL, C. C., AND GRAHAM, R.: EMBRYO MORTALITY ACCOMPANIED BY PASTY EYES AND SEVERE LOSSES IN DUCKLINGS ASSOCIATED WITH AVITAMINOSIS. Amer. Jour. Vet. Res., 6: 96–102. 1945.

PRITSKER, I. Y.: RESEARCHES ON THE HATCHING QUALITIES OF EGGS. I. FATTY DEPOSITS ON THE SHELLS OF DUCK EGGS AS AFFECTING THEIR HATCHABILITY. Poultry Sci., 20: 99–101. 1941.

ROBERTS, R. E.: LEVELS OF MEAT SCRAPS AND DRIED MILK IN RATIONS FOR YOUNG DUCKS. Poultry Sci., 15: 136–140. 1936.

ROBERTS, R. E.: METHODS OF FEEDING DUCKS. Poultry Sci., 13: 338–342. 1934.

ROMANOFF, A. L.: A STUDY OF ARTIFICIAL INCUBATION OF RUNNER DUCK EGGS: REQUIREMENTS. Poultry Sci., 22: 148–154. 1943.

SERFONTEIN, P. J.: FEEDING EXPERIMENTS WITH DUCKS. Farming in So. Africa, 18: 807–818. 1943.

SERFONTEIN, P. J.: DUCK FARMING IN SOUTH AFRICA. World Poultry Sci., J. 3: 227–231. 1947.

SERFONTEIN, P. J.: SEX DIFFERENTIATION IN DAY-OLD DUCKLINGS. Farming in So. Africa, Vol. 10, No. 113. p. 349. 1935.

STEAD, E. F.: FURTHER OBSERVATIONS ON MOULT IN THE DUCK FAMILY. Roy. Soc. New Zeal. Trans, and Proc., 68: 105. 1938.

Geese

BUREL, E. E.: THE GOOSE LIVER INDUSTRY. Egg and Poultry Mag., Vol. 45, No. 7, p. 394. 1939.

COLES, J. D.: AEGYPTIANELLOSIS AND LEG-WEAKNESS OF THE GOOSE. Jour. So. African Vet. Med. Assoc., 8: 98–100. 1937.

IVES, P. P.: Domestic Geese and Ducks. Orange Judd Publishing Co., New York. 1947.

LEE, A. R.: GOOSE RAISING, U. S. D. A. Farmers' Bul. 767. 1933.

MORTHLAND, J. F.: COMMERCIAL GOSLINGS A REALITY WITH MODERN HATCHING METHODS. Poultry Supply Dealer 26: No. 5, pp. 12–13, 38. 1949.

PHILLIPS, R. W., JOHNSON, R. G., AND MOYER, R. T.: CHINA'S GOOSE INDUSTRY. World Poultry Sci., J. 4: 34–35. 1948.

RANDLES, C. A.: Hatchability of Goose Eggs. M. S. Thesis Ohio State University. 1948.

SNYDER, CLARA: GEESE FOR CHRISTMAS. Egg and Poultry Mag., Vol. 38, No. 12, p. 24. 1932.

SNYDER, CLARA: THE GOOSE HANGS HIGH. Egg and Poultry Mag., Vol. 39, No. 12, p. 16. 1933.

TANGL, HARALD: GOOSE FATTENING PROBLEMS IN HUNGARY. Proc. Eighth World's Poultry Cong., pp. 254–261. 1948.

Pigeons

COLE, L. J.: THE ORIGIN OF THE DOMESTIC PIGEON. Proc. Seventh World's Poultry Cong., pp. 462–466. 1939.

GAUGER, H. C., GREAVES, R. E., AND COOK, F. W.: PARATYPHOID OF PIGEONS. N. C. Sta. Tech. Bul. 62. 1940.

HAYNES, S. K.: PRACTICAL PIGEON PRODUCTION. Orange Judd Co., New York. 1944.

HOGAN, A. G., RICHARDSON, L. R., JOHNSON, P. E., AND NISBET, R. N.: PIGEON ANEMIA AS A DEFICIENCY DISEASE. Jour. Nutrition, 20: 203–214. 1940.

HOLLANDER, W. F.: AUTO-SEXING IN THE DOMESTIC PIGEON. Jour. Heredity, 33: 135–140. 1942.

HOLLANDER, W. F., AND RIDDLE, O.: GOITER IN DOMESTIC PIGEONS. Poultry Sci., 25: 20–27. 1946.

LEE, A. R., AND HAYNES, S. K.: SQUAB RAISING. U. S. D. A. Farmers' Bul. 684. Rev. 1942.

LEE, J. G., AND HOGAN, A. G.: VITAMINS REQUIRED BY PIGEONS. Mo. Sta. Tech. Bul. 342. 1942.

LEVI, W. M.: MAKING PIGEONS PAY. Orange Judd Co., New York. 1946.

PLATT, C. S.: EFFECT OF RESTRICTING THE CEREAL DIET OF PIGEONS TO CORN AND WHEAT. Proc. Seventh World's Poultry Cong., pp. 466–468. 1939.

PLATT, C. S.: PROGENY-TESTING IN THE BREEDING OF PIGEONS. Poultry Sci., 20: 232–233. 1941.

PLATT, C. S.: RECORDS OF SQUAB PRODUCTION IN NEW JERSEY, 1931–1944. N. J. Sta. Bul. 729. 1946.

PLATT, C. S., AND DARE, R. S.: SQUAB PRODUCTION. N. J. Sta. Bul. 634. 1937.

PLATT, C. S.: THE CARE OF HOMING PIGEONS. N. J. Sta. Hints to Poultrymen 31: No. 3, 1944.

RICE, E. E.: THE NATIONAL STANDARD SQUAB BOOK, 58TH ED. Squab Pub. Co., Melrose, Mass. 1944.

CHAPTER 18 ‖‖‖

Game Bird Production

▼

In the origin of wildlife, Nature furnished a place for different species of birds and animals. In their respective habitat they thrived and were abundant. Nature has not changed, but still many species have been reduced in numbers and several have vanished. The last heath hen disappeared May 9, 1931, on Martha's Vineyard Island in Massachusetts. Such has been the history of the passenger pigeon, formerly perhaps the most numerous of all birds, inhabiting practically the whole forested area of eastern North America. The species seems to have disappeared during the nineteenth century, leaving no trace.

What are the causes of bird destruction? Wild predatory animals, prowling dogs and house cats, and winged vermin such as the Cooper's hawk are found to do much damage to some of the species. Scarcity of food supply, absence of natural cover, and long droughts are important factors. An increasing number of hunters, long hunting seasons and excessive kills, pot hunting, and bootlegging sales in violation of reasonable conservation regulations have taxed the normal existence of the game birds to an extent with which nature has been unable to cope.

As a result of increased interest and effort in game restoration, the propagation of game birds has developed into an industry of considerable magnitude in the United States. Many states operate game farms for the production of game birds to be used to restock depleted areas. Conservation commissions have been organized in a number of states to encourage and promote the natural propagation of game birds.

Bobwhite and Quail

The true quail and partridge are Old World birds, and their American representatives are the bobwhite and quail (Fig. 250). There are about seventy species in the western hemisphere, but only seven are found north of the southern border of the United States. These birds are rather small in size with heads completely feathered and sometimes crested; the nostrils are covered with a naked scale; the legs are stout and moderately long; the front toes are webbed at the base, the hind toe raised and rather small; the wings are short, rounded, arched, and strong, the tail varying from less than one-

590

Fig. 250. The bobwhite, or quail.

half to about four-fifths the length of the wing; and the body is heavy. A great variation in plumage color is shown among the members of this family.

In general, quail welcome the extension of agriculture, and the added food supply in farmed areas results in an increase of their number. Because of their cheerful disposition and their value as destroyers of insects, quail are welcomed by farmers. As shown by investigations of the Biological Survey, these birds with rare exceptions are not only harmless, but usually are very useful to agriculture. The bobwhite constantly feeds on injurious weed seeds and insects, and thus renders valuable service to the farmer. Many sportsmen consider the bobwhite the finest game bird in the world.

The true bobwhite's distribution is eastern North America from South Dakota, southern Minnesota, southern Ontario, and southeastern Maine south to eastern and northern Texas, the Gulf coast, and northern Florida west to eastern Colorado. They were introduced into central Colorado, New Mexico, Utah, Idaho, California, Oregon, and Washington. This bird was once far more plentiful than it is today.

Other species of quail are mountain quail, found in the humid district of the Pacific coast; masked bobwhite, found in southern Arizona; scaled quail, found in the southwestern part of the United States; California quail; Mearn's quail in Texas and Arizona; and the Gambel's quail, distributed in the desert region of southern California, southern Nevada, Arizona, and southwestern Utah east to Colorado and western Texas.

Natural Propagation

The quail's daily habits are quite similar everywhere. These habits—such as feeding, roosting, dusting, avoiding their natural enemies and hunters, and mating procedures—should be considered in the bird's protection and restoration.

In discussing the natural propagation of the bobwhite it is best to begin with the covey in midwinter, when the birds of several broods are together. Stoddard found that in a small car, with curtains drawn, he could follow the coveys and could observe them to an excellent advantage.

Cocks were observed to become very pugnacious toward one another as the warm days of spring came, puffing themselves up and bluffing with lowered heads as they met when feeding. All the birds in the covey began to increase their conversation or chatter at this period. The cocks began to strut and to pay considerable attention to the females, but the females appeared in no way excited over the males' actions.

Such scenes as the above become more numerous as spring progresses. The actual time of pairing depends largely upon the weather, and Stoddard found that it begins with the first bobwhite call notes. These calls have been observed to appear as early as February, but generally they begin during March and April, depending on the climatic conditions.

Pairing. It was observed that mated cocks fight with more spirit and with better results in defense of a mate than when in quest of one. The cocks are not particularly quarrelsome after being mated a few days, and contrary to the common belief, several nests may be incubated simultaneously in close proximity. As many as five in a single acre hatching off successfully were reported by Stoddard. Observations tend to indicate that the pairs may remain mated from season to season if both survive, though evidence on the point is not conclusive.

Season of nesting. The most important nesting months are May, June, July, and August, but nests have been found as early as April and as late as October. The actual season depends again on the climatic region and the environment.

Selection of nesting site. A wide variety of nesting sites is utilized by bobwhites. The nests may be built in open woodland, in or around a clearing or in fields, or in any type of environment normally used by the birds at any season.

Construction of bobwhite nests. Nests are constructed of the grasses, mosses, or other suitable building material of the preceding season's growth available near the spot selected for the nest.

Concealment of nests. The quail is very adept in concealing its nest. Usually the nest is hidden by a mixture of green vegetation and dead growth of the preceding year, but seldom by the former alone, because dead growth is required for nest construction.

Egg laying. Normally an egg is deposited each day until the set is complete, or progressively at a later hour each day until laying time comes late in the evening, when the day is missed and laying is resumed at an earlier hour the next morning. The female may fly to the nest to lay or she may walk to the nest with her mate accompanying her within a short distance of the nest. The female is normally on the nest only ten to fifteen minutes while laying her egg. The normal size of a setting is fourteen to fifteen eggs; but the early sets of the season contain more eggs than those deposited later.

Incubation. Some days, in extreme cases, a week may elapse between the time of laying the last egg and the beginning of incubation. In one case, however, where the laying of the last egg was observed by Stoddard, incubation started at once. Incubation may be performed either by the cock or by the hen, more frequently by the latter.

Hatching. The eggs are pipped around the twenty-first day of incubation or about forty-eight hours before hatching. This proves to be a critical time at the nest, for the plainly audible cheeping of the confined chicks may attract the attention of a prowling enemy, and result in the destruction of the brood. Worse yet, the "thief ants" may enter the eggs and consume the chick alive as soon as the inner membrane is punctured. If all is well, the chicks will emerge on the twenty-third day and all the eggs will probably hatch within one or two hours.

Hatching percentages in the wild. Stoddard found that from nests observed containing 2,874 eggs, over 86 per cent of the eggs hatched, about 5 per cent being infertile and 5 per cent dead embryos; the remaining eggs were not classified. Seasons of droughts may cause wholesale losses, for there must be sufficient moisture present to keep the eggs in proper condition for hatching.

Brooding. The chicks are brooded a large part of the time for the first two weeks by either one or both parents. When less than a week old, they are brooded fully three-fourths of the time or even more, short periods of feeding and exercising being taken between longer periods of brooding. Protection is required at first from heat as well as from cold and wet. During the hot summer days the young are brooded in the shade of trees, bushes, or smaller ground vegetation most of the time. The chicks search in all directions from the parents when in search of insects, berries, and other food material. They immediately start picking up grit for grinding material. Early in the morning their moisture requirements are satisfied by dewdrops. The dewdrops are taken from the grass tips by both young and old. Later in the day, berries and tender succulent vegetation growing near the ground provide moisture, and the brood is seldom far from such a supply. Thus, with a large portion of their food of high water content, the broods are entirely independent of a supply of surface water and they have been found to thrive in abundance far from such a supply.

Feeding. The parents make no attempt actually to feed the young, which search for food themselves from the beginning. Grasshoppers and other insects caught by the cock are most frequently eaten by the hen. The wings, which develop rapidly, are a great aid in capturing insects. The young may take flights of a few feet within one week after hatching. The young scratch exactly as do the old birds from the first. The parents' duty seems to be in watching for danger. The brood scatters to hide at the first alarm, though none is given unless the danger is one that cannot be dealt with by battle. The coloring of the chicks enables them to conceal themselves so that they are very difficult to find.

Covey formation. As the birds grow older, their range may encroach upon the range of other broods. Thus several broods may come together to form a larger covey. These broods are of different parents and are not, as many believe, several broods of one pair of adults.

Roosting. As the broods grow and the temperature drops, the young coveys take up the more perfect roosting formation characteristic of bobwhite, sides close together with heads out, forming a circle. This method gives maximum warmth, yet allows opportunity for free use of the wings for a sudden flush in case of disturbance at night. At fifteen weeks of age the young are scarcely distinguishable from their parents.

Artificial Propagation of the Bobwhite

Due to the efforts of game breeders, there have been developed effective methods of hand rearing the bobwhite. Thousands of quail have been artificially reared in recent years. Artificial propagation of the bobwhite has been used for restocking in depleted areas. This method, combined with improvement of the environment, may bring about the restoration of the quail in many areas. Other species of quail probably can be bred successfully under the same system as the bobwhite.

Selection of breeding stock. Though birds trapped in the wild can be used as breeders, much better results are obtained with birds raised in captivity. If selection of breeders can be made from large numbers, it is best to select the strongest or largest birds of the flock. If possible, birds which have not been near any disease should be selected.

Management of breeding stock. Most game bird farms find that a great deal of trouble can be avoided by keeping quail on wire. A pen 5 feet by 10 feet will winter about twenty quail. A small shed should be built at one end of the pen to protect the feed hoppers and water containers. Straw may be placed on the wire under the shed. This affords a place of protection from cold. Three-fourths-inch mesh poultry netting is very suitable for quail after they are half grown. The United States Department of Agriculture recommends outside pens for keeping breeders until they are placed in the breeding pens in the spring, for wintering the birds, and for holding surplus birds at other seasons. These pens are about 12 feet by 70 feet in dimensions.

Breeding or laying pens. There are many types of breeding pens (Figs. 251 and 252). While good results may be secured in bottomless pens resting on the ground, these have not been found so satisfactory as pens with wire bottoms. The wire-bottom pen may be constructed in a variety of ways. Certain essentials must be recognized in building the pens. The floor space

Fig. 251. Breeding and laying pens are shown here and on the following page. Above, breeding coops, with grit and clabber containers on top, at White Oak Quail Farm, near Richmond, Virginia. (Courtesy Fish and Wildlife Service, U. S. Department of the Interior.) Right, a plan for a movable game bird pen for breeding stock or growing birds. (Courtesy More Game Birds in America Foundation.)

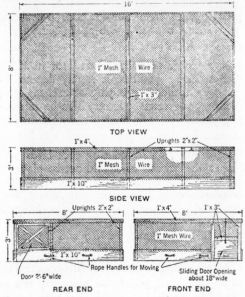

should be adequate; and a minimum of eighteen square feet per pair is recommended. There should be an enclosed space with a minimum area of six square feet, which includes a nest approximately twelve inches square. The pen should be elevated to a position where vegetation will not touch the

COURTESY FISH AND WILDLIFE SERVICE, U. S. DEPARTMENT OF THE INTERIOR

Fig. 252. Male and female bobwhites in laying pen. Nest, feeders, and waterer shown. (Overton Quail Farm, Petersburg, Virginia.)

bottom and, at the same time, provide practical means of caring for the birds. There should be adequate facilities for water, feed, and grit. Breeding pens should be located in an area that is not accessible to dogs, cats, or vermin. It is also better to keep people away from the breeders because quail are easily excited.

Feeding. The number of eggs that a quail hen lays is largely dependent upon the food she eats during the laying period. To obtain good hatchability it is necessary that the nutrients required for the development of the chick be in the ration. A quail breeder who has only a few birds may find commercially prepared game bird laying mash, of which there are a number on the market, more economical than preparing his own. The mash should be placed in feeders and kept before the breeders at all times. Grain, if fed to the breeders, should be fed sparingly. Water should be furnished in small clean dishes or galvanized cups. An abrupt change from maintenance to the laying ration should never be made, especially where the latter differs radically from the former. Green feed should be fed daily and fine grit should be available at all times.

Mating. Best results are usually obtained by placing one hen and one cock in an individual pen. Some pairs will not mate, and because of this they should be watched until the pairs have become mated. If they do not mate, the matings can be changed until the birds are properly paired. Unpublished data obtained at the Missouri Agricultural Experiment Station show that quail will tolerate a degree of polygamy. From 224 eggs obtained from five pens, each containing one male and two females, 204 eggs (91.07 per cent) were fertile. This was a higher degree of fertility than was obtained with paired matings.

Egg production. Bobwhites start laying about the first of April in the South and a few weeks later in the northern states, but the exact time will vary with the weather and treatment of the birds. By the use of artificial lights quail can be brought into egg production before the natural time of laying. Results of experiments at the Missouri Agricultural Experiment Station show that when quail are exposed to artificial lights at night, they come into early egg production and total annual egg production is increased. The number of eggs laid depends upon the birds, as well as upon feeding and management. Quail under the same treatment have been found to vary greatly in egg production. Wild trapped birds will not produce so many eggs as pen-raised birds. Twenty may be considered as a fair average for the first season, with an increase as the birds become tamer during the successive seasons. Pen-raised birds will produce upward of sixty eggs per hen per season. The Game Conservation Institute obtained an average of eighty eggs per hen. One quail, under artificial lights at night from January to May, at the Missouri station, laid 159 eggs from February to September.

Incubation

Methods of incubating eggs of the domestic fowl apply to the bobwhite's eggs. The two methods are natural and artificial. For a small number of eggs, it may be more profitable to use the hen, but there is greater danger of disease and parasites. The treatment of the eggs from the time they are laid to the time the young are hatched is a very important part of successful game bird propagation.

Selection and care of the hatching eggs. Most gamekeepers advise gathering eggs once each week to reduce the number of times the birds are excited. If the birds have access to an outside pen and cannot see the gamekeeper when gathering the eggs, it is advisable to gather daily. Eggs allowed to remain in the nests during hot summer days are likely to start germination, and this results in lower hatchability.

Care in gathering. Quail eggs must be handled carefully. Their shells are very brittle and are easily broken. The caretaker should let the birds know when he is approaching. If he whistles before nearing the pens, the birds will become accustomed to him and may actually become friendly.

Holding. The eggs that are being held for setting should be stored in a cool place (a temperature of 50° F. to 60° F. is desirable), and should not be subjected to widely varying temperatures. A basement or cellar usually proves adequate. The eggs should be stored with the small end down. Eggs should not be held longer than two weeks before being set.

Operation of the incubator. Proper temperature, proper amount of moisture in the incubator, sufficient ventilation, and position of the egg are the important factors to consider in operating the incubator.

Temperature. Quail eggs can be incubated very successfully at a temperature slightly lower than that required for the incubation of chicken eggs. The best information on proper temperature can be obtained from the manufacturer of the particular incubator in use. Romanoff found that the most efficient temperatures for the incubation of quail eggs in a natural-draft machine was 101° F. throughout incubation.

Humidity. The proper amount of moisture in the incubator is very important for the incubation of quail eggs. Too much moisture may prevent adequate evaporation necessary to allow space for the chicks to turn in the eggs and break the shell. Humidity is dependent upon moisture in the machine, ventilation, and condition of the room in which the machine is operated. Romanoff found that when the incubator is operated at a constant temperature and air circulation, a relative humidity rising from 65 per cent at the beginning of incubation to 75 per cent toward the end of the incubation period gave most satisfactory results.

Ventilation. Ventilation is necessary for the control of humidity and in removing gases. It also furnishes oxygen. Most manufacturing companies give directions as to the amount the ventilators should be opened during the various stages in incubation.

Turning the eggs. Quail eggs should be turned from two to five times daily for the first twenty days. Most incubators are equipped with devices which enable one to turn the eggs easily.

Hatching the eggs. The eggs should be moved to the hatching tray where a high humidity is maintained. The hatching tray should be covered or enclosed to prevent the active chicks from getting out of the tray. Pedigree baskets made of one-fourth-inch mesh wire prove good containers for the chicks. The chicks should be removed to brooders immediately after they are dry.

Brooding

For many years bantams or medium-sized hens were used as foster mothers in brooding quail chicks (Fig. 253). Due to disease and improvement in electric and other nonhen brooders, this practice is decreasing.

For large-scale production, the colony brooder house has proved most successful (Fig. 254). A two-compartment colony quail brooder, each compartment capable of accommodating one hundred birds, which was devised at the Game Conservation Institute in 1932, has been used successfully. The Missouri State Quail and Pheasant Farm built brooder houses of tile as protection against extremely hot and cold weather.

Most heating units in use are electric hovers of which there are many types. Some game farms use hot water heated colony brooders successfully. The heater should be dependable and supply a fairly constant temperature.

A layer of sand and oat hulls one and one-half inches deep may be on the brooder floor. The sand should cover the area under the hover and the oat hulls the remainder of the floor. The temperature beneath the hover should be

Fig. 253. Natural brooding of game birds with chicken hens. The hen is confined to the coop and the young are confined to a small run, for the first few days, by the boards in front of the coop.

started at 95° F. and reduced about 5 degrees each week. The best indication of a proper temperature is the action of the chicks. Adjust the temperature to where the chicks show that they are comfortable. The chicks should be confined to the hover for two days, during which time the house should be well ventilated. Then after two days the chicks can be given the run of the entire compartment in the day, but at night they should be confined to the hover. The chicks may be allowed access to the outside run after the fifth day, providing the weather is mild.

Feeding. There are many tested commercial quail rations which may be used. For a beginner it is usually more profitable to use commercial feeds and follow the manufacturer's directions. Some brands of feed are in pellets and some in meal form. It is important to obtain starting feed for young chicks and growing feed for older chicks. Feeding hard boiled eggs with mash to the very young chicks at the start may be of some benefit. Young chicks tend to eat the boiled eggs sooner than they will mash. Feed the boiled eggs from two to three times daily by pulverizing and sprinkling over the mash. The mash and fresh clean drinking water should be before the birds at all times. The most important thing to maintain is sanitation in feeding and watering at all times. Finely cut succulent green feed should be fed daily. Many game breeders feed a wet mash, daily, for the first month along with the dry mash. Grit should be kept before the chicks at all times. The birds may be changed to growing mash after one month of age. Special utensils are necessary in feeding quail chicks because of their small size. Very flat feeders are necessary for the younger chicks. Several companies manufacturing game equipment offer adequate utensils for feeding and watering of quail.

Fig. 254. Above, brooders at White Oak Quail Farm, near Richmond, Virginia. (Courtesy Fish and Wildlife Service, U. S. Department of the Interior.) Below, colony brooder houses equipped with electric brooders and wire-floored sun porches for game bird propagation. (Courtesy E. W. Callenbach, Pennsylvania State College.)

Sanitation. The success of propagation of quail depends to a very large extent on sanitation. The droppings from the sand beneath the hover should be removed every morning, and all litter should be removed weekly. Confine the birds to the run when cleaning the house. Care should be taken to keep all flies from finding a way into the pens. The water should be changed daily. All utensils should be washed in lye water to keep them clean.

Foster parent method of propagation. The Missouri Quail Hunters, Inc. and the Missouri Conservation Commission have developed a program of quail propagation in which breeding stock is maintained for producing eggs to be hatched in incubators. The chicks are brooded until one to two weeks old when they are placed with two foster parents (a male and female) and soon thereafter released where conditions are considered favorable. Wild foster parents are being compared with pen-raised parents. It is believed this plan will overcome some of the difficulties encountered in releasing pen-reared quail.

COURTESY FSH AND WILDLIFE SERVICE, U. S. DEPARTMENT OF THE INTERIOR

Fig. 255. Ring-neck pheasant. (Drawing by Sim.)

Pheasants

Within recent years the rearing of pheasants has begun to attract attention in the United States, and propagating enterprises, ranging from a few birds to farms raising many thousands of birds, are found throughout the country.

The original home of the pheasant was in Asia. Today, with the exception of the cold northern regions, it is represented in all civilized countries of the world. The ring-necked pheasant imported from China, its natural home, has a broad white ring about the neck (Fig. 255). It is called by various names, among them being Chinese pheasant, China pheasant, Chinese ringneck,

Mongolian pheasant, Denny pheasant, and Oregon pheasant. The English pheasant has no ring about the neck. It is imported from Europe and is commonly called the English pheasant, dark-necked pheasant, and Hungarian pheasant. There is also an English ring-neck pheasant in America, a hybrid between the English and ring-necked pheasants. The Mongolian pheasant resembles the English pheasant except for a white ring about the neck. This species is the rarest of the four kinds in America. It is a native of Asia. Many other imported species are found occasionally in American parks and aviaries.

History of the American Pheasant

Five million pheasants are bagged annually in the United States. The leading states are South Dakota, Minnesota, Nebraska, North Dakota, Iowa, Wisconsin, Illinois, Pennsylvania, New York, New Jersey, Connecticut, and Massachusetts.

Probably the first ring-necked pheasants brought to the United States were bought by Judge Owen N. Denny in a Shanghai public market in 1882. He bought four pairs of Chinese pheasants, costing thirty-five cents a pair.

Judge Denny shipped pheasants to the state of Washington with great success. By 1892 fifty thousand pheasants were killed on the opening day of hunting. After this successful introduction an increased interest in pheasants developed in the eastern and central states. English pheasants were successfully introduced into America early in the nineteenth century.

Rearing pheasants for stocking purposes in America was given a great boost when in 1912 the American Game Association established demonstration game farms and published a special bulletin on pheasant rearing.

Natural Propagation of Pheasants

In general the pheasants are birds which inhabit open or brushy country and not woodlands. They prefer swampy regions, brushy areas, or old meadows, where they can hide from their numerous enemies.

Winter flocks. In the fall months the pheasants begin to congregate into flocks. The size of the flocks may vary greatly, depending on the number of birds in the vicinity. During the winter the flocks roam through the fields, usually in search of feed. They often come to barnyards and associate with the domestic fowls.

Courtship. As spring approaches, the large flocks break up into several smaller ones, and the males become less friendly toward one another. The males generally begin their crowing call in March, depending on the climatic conditions and the latitude. Soon after crowing commences, the cocks begin beating their wings. The call is a challenge to other males and an invitation to the females.

Territories. The exact amount of territory which one male will defend is not known. It depends largely upon the environment and the number of birds in a given area. The male usually selects an elevated spot to do his crowing, which warns other males to keep away. Beebe believes that where there is a surplus of females the birds may be polygamous, but that often an individual male may care for only one mate and brood. Some writers believe pheasants are naturally polygamous in the wild, but some males may have monogamous tendencies. Generally, in the spring, one male will be seen with several females.

Nesting. The pheasant will usually begin to lay in April or May, depending on the latitude and the climatic conditions. Birds may nest as late as September. Nests are generally found to be placed on the ground, usually in a small natural or scooped out depression. The nests are lined with grass, moss, or whatever materials are near the spot. Pheasants often build their nests under natural cover. Randall reported that studies made in Pennsylvania show a large mortality among pheasant nests. Only 20.3 per cent of 310 nests under observation were successful. Less than one nest in four produced young. Only 23.1 per cent of 445 nests examined in Iowa by Hammerstrom were successful. English reported that 34.8 per cent of nests studied in Michigan hatched. Randall reported that causes of nest failures were mowing, 49.8 per cent; harvesting, 3.6 per cent; and cutting weeds, 2.0 per cent. Approximately 30 per cent of the losses were due to predators.

Egg laying. The number of eggs in a clutch varies considerably. Randall reported clutch size varying from 4 to 23, the average being 10.8 eggs. Hammerstrom's studies showed a range in clutch size from 4 to 26 eggs, averaging 11.2 eggs. The clutch size declines as the season advances.

Incubation. As a rule the female incubates the eggs with no assistance from the male. The setting hen is well protected on her nest, both by her coloration and by her lack of scent. Hammerstrom found that fertility varied but little between three seasons of study, and averaged 93.1 per cent. Randall reported 94.1 per cent fertility, with 90 per cent of all eggs hatching. The eggs develop and hatch on the twenty-third or twenty-fourth day of incubation (Fig. 256).

Care of the young. Soon after the young are hatched, usually within twelve to twenty-four hours, they are moved from the nest. As soon as the chicks grow strong enough to travel, the hen leads them in search of food. After the young are six to seven weeks old, the cock bird occasionally wanders with the flock. By thirty to forty days of age the young birds are fully feathered. Pheasants do not increase greatly in weight until they have obtained most of their feathers.

Roosting. Generally pheasants roost on the ground, although it is not uncommon to find them roosting in trees. They do not form the roosting circle which is characteristic of the quail.

Feeding. From studies made in Michigan, Dalke reported the following: Adult pheasants do not feed as soon as they leave the roost, but wander about, taking little food until about an hour after sunrise. They seldom feed during the middle of the day, summer, or winter. The pheasant is an omnivorous feeder. Corn, wheat, and barley comprise 83 per cent of all the grain eaten.

COURTESY E. W. CALLENBACH, PENNSYLVANIA STATE COLLEGE

Fig. 256. A hatch of ring-necked pheasant chicks. They may be shipped in chick boxes the same as chicks.

Adult pheasants are not large consumers of insects and other invertebrates, in comparison with other food eaten.

Artificial Propagation

More pheasants than any other kind of game bird are raised by man, and probably nine-tenths or more of the total number of pheasants reared in this country are ringnecks. In the East the English ringnecks predominate and in the West the Chinese ringnecks are most common. The hybrid ring-neck has a variety of qualifications which make it an outstanding bird to propagate artificially. It is prolific and also polygamous and sufficiently con-trollable to be a success on a game farm. It retains its wild instinct so that it can well protect itself when released. The bird seems to thrive better in the colder northern states. The same methods of propagation may be applied with equal success in the rearing of all pheasants.

Selection of breeding stock. Care should be used in selecting breeding stock. The birds should be carefully selected for health, vigor, egg production, purity of strain, and size. If possible, a nearby source should be chosen and the stock inspected. The breeders are generally selected in the fall and held in a comfortable pen until the matings are made in the spring.

Management of breeding stock. The success of a pheasant enterprise depends largely upon the care and management of the breeding birds. To obtain the most profitable results from artificial propagation of pheasants, the birds must be comfortable at all times.

Pens. The small game breeder can do away with some expense by using one enclosure for both holding and laying pen. These pens are usually large enough to accommodate one cock and five females and are portable to permit their being moved to fresh ground. These pens may vary in size. Many breeders use pens having dimensions 8 feet by 16 feet, 3 feet high. The main problem is to have sufficient room for the breeding birds, and pens which can be moved. A shelter should be built in one end of the pen for protection from the weather and to furnish a place for feeding and laying.

Community pens are most economical for the large-scale breeder who prefers to rear birds under natural conditions. Most pens of this make are of the open type, and the wings of the birds are clipped to prevent escape. The size of these pens depends upon the number of birds which are to be used. For one hundred hens and twenty cocks a pen 150 feet by 150 feet proves suitable. These pens should be constructed of inch mesh poultry netting to prevent vermin from entering them. The pen should be six or seven feet high and extend from six to twelve inches below the surface of the ground. The ground should be well drained and covered with a good growth of vegetation.

Mating. Pheasants should be taken from the winter holding pen and placed in laying pens about four weeks prior to the start of the mating season. This is usually done during March. Only the best birds should be used in matings, placing one cock bird with five females.

Feeding. The breeders should be started on their laying ration when placed in laying pens. A gradual change should be made from wintering feed to the laying ration by adding a small portion of the laying ration to the scratch grain until nothing but laying ration is being fed. Many pheasant producers prefer feeding good commercial laying mash. The mash should be kept in hoppers and before the birds at all times. Oyster shell, grit, and charcoal as well as fresh drinking water should be kept before the birds also. Green feed should be provided. To avoid disturbing the birds, they should be fed and watered from the outside of the pen. The waterers should be washed daily and the feed should be kept free of contamination.

Egg production. Pheasants start laying in April in most parts of the United States, but the exact time depends upon the weather and their management. The number of eggs laid by the females also depends upon the treatment as well as the bird's capacity for high egg production. The number of eggs laid can usually be increased by the use of improved feeding and other management practices. Pheasants will lay up to fifty or more eggs in a season, but a conservative estimate for the season is an average of about thirty-five good eggs per hen.

Incubation

Artificial incubation has gone through an experimental stage, but it is now used by many breeders. It is especially desirable for large-scale production. Hens are still being used by some breeders (Fig. 258).

Selection and care of the hatching eggs. It is necessary to collect eggs once a day. Gathering eggs twice a day is recommended for open pens to

Fig. 257. Pheasants at winter feeding hopper.

prevent thefts by crows and formation of egg-eating habits by the pheasants. The eggs should be graded for size, shape, and condition. Thin-shelled, cracked, undersized, or poorly shaped eggs should not be stored for setting. The eggs should be stored in a well-ventilated room ranging in temperature from 50° F. to 60° F. A cellar or basement is a satisfactory place to hold pheasant eggs. Pheasant eggs should not be held in storage longer than two weeks before they are set.

Operation of the incubator. Factors affecting the incubation of the eggs of the domestic fowl and bobwhite also affect pheasant eggs. The care of the incubator in hatching quail and pheasant eggs, however, differs slightly.

Temperature. Romanoff in 1934 found that the temperature requirements for pheasant and quail eggs are different, and that it would not be advisable to incubate them together in the same incubator, particularly at the end of the hatching period. He reported best results when a natural-draft machine was operated at 102° F. the first period, 101° F. at the second period, and 100° F. at the third or concluding period.

Humidity. The proper amount of moisture depends upon the ventilation and conditions under which the incubator is operated. It is also dependent upon the make of the machine, which makes it advisable to follow the manufacturer's instructions. Romanoff found that at constant temperature and air circulation, pheasant eggs require higher humidity at the beginning and lower at the end of incubation—that is, falling from about 75 per cent relative humidity to 65 per cent. Three ways of determining the moisture condition of the eggs are by the rate of evaporation, measured by the size of the air cell; the loss of weight due to evaporation; and the wet bulb thermometer readings. Fifteen per cent loss for the twenty-one days is recommended.

Fig. 258. Setting hen on pheasant eggs, showing feeding pen in foreground.

Ventilation. The amount of ventilation varies with the type of machine. Ventilation provides oxygen, eliminates carbon dioxide and other gases, and is a factor in the regulation of the evaporation. As a general rule, the ventilators are gradually opened to a maximum on the fifteenth day, but ventilation is reduced to a minimum when the eggs start to pip around the twenty-first day.

Turning. Eggs should be turned three to five times daily. The Pennsylvania Agricultural Experiment Station obtained best results when eggs were incubated for eighteen days at a relatively high humidity in an agitated-air or forced-draft incubator; and the eggs were hatched in a sectional, "still-air" incubator.

Brooding

There is a yearly increase in the number of game breeders using artificial methods of brooding. Artificial brooding eliminates danger from the hen spreading diseases and parasites to the young, and economizes on land and labor.

Equipment. Colony brooder houses prove satisfactory for pheasant raising. The Pennsylvania Agricultural Experiment Station brooded pheasant chicks satisfactorily in colony houses (Fig. 254) with attached wire-floored sun porches. California breeders use a colony brooder house in connection with concrete runs covered with sand until the birds no longer need heat. The house should be located in the center of a desirable range for the birds. The land should be well drained, fresh, and contain a good growth of vegetation.

Cleanliness, adequate floor space, dryness, sunlight, and ventilation are important factors to be considered in the brooder house. These conditions are important in practicing a sanitation program.

Coal brooders, oil-burning stoves, electric hovers, or a hot water heating system may be used. The temperature at the outer edge of the hover should be regulated at 95° F. for the first week. The floor of the brooder house should be covered with a dry litter of fine sand, oat hulls, or fine hay. It is necessary to keep the chicks near the heat until they are capable of finding their way to and from the stove. The feed and water should be placed near the stove for several days. After ring-necked pheasant chicks are six weeks to eight weeks of age, they should not be confined to a colony house and a small sun porch.

Feeding. The successful propagation of pheasants depends in a large measure upon the use of a proper ration. For the first three to four days, young pheasants should have feed placed on paper or cloth spread over the litter. By sprinkling feed in front of the birds, they may be taught to eat more quickly. The following feeding results were obtained at the Pennsylvania Agricultural Experiment Station in 1934:

1. Better early growth of ring-necked pheasant chicks was obtained on rations of higher protein content than those used for chicks of the domestic fowl.
2. The best growth and feathering and the greatest feed consumption per 100 chicks were secured through the use of a ration analyzing approximately 28 per cent protein.
3. A free choice (cafeteria) ration did not give satisfactory results as measured by growth, feather development, or livability.
4. The use of ordinary commercial (55 per cent protein) meat scraps and fish meal in the preparation of a high protein mash caused the development of an appreciable percentage of slipped tendons.

Many pheasant breeders are using commercial rations, especially in brooder operations. These feeds are generally fed in the form of mashes or pellets or in combination with grain mixture.

Skoglund in 1940 obtained excellent results, as measured by growth, feed consumption efficiency, mortality, cannibalism, and occurrence of perosis, from the following ration:

Ground yellow corn meal	224 lbs.
Wheat bran	300
Flour wheat middlings	250
Ground oats	200
Dried skim milk	250
Alfalfa leaf meal	100
50 per cent protein meat scraps	221
White fish meal	55
Soybean oil meal	390
Salt	10
Cod liver oil (400 A.O.A.C. chick units of vitamin D)	5

Fig. 259. Wild turkey gobbler, Wichita Mountains, Wildlife Refuge, Oklahoma.

Sanitation. A sanitation program should be practiced at all times, which will prevent the outbreak and spread of disease.

The Wild Turkey

At one time wild turkeys were abundant. (Fig. 259.) Early writers have told of wild turkeys gathering in flocks of hundreds and migrating to new feeding areas. Wild turkeys are wide-ranging birds, requiring a larger area on which to roam than do most resident species. Some gobblers have been known to travel fifteen miles from their roosts. The wild turkeys in this country to-day chiefly inhabit deep woods and the borders of swamplands. One may also find them in the neighborhood of streams or in oak groves. When sub-marginal lands and wooded areas were taken over for farms, the turkey was driven off its best nesting and feeding ground. On many of its original ranges in the United States, the turkey is already gone. Various factors have caused the depletion in numbers of this wild species, but the chief factor was the influence of man.

Realizing the importance of the wild turkey as food in certain areas, as an object of sport, and as an insectivorous bird, and taking a lesson from the past when other species were permitted to die out, federal agencies, state governments, private organizations, and individuals are taking steps to save this species.

Natural Propagation of Wild Turkeys

Wild turkeys inhabit the forest but wander into fields in search of food. They may be successfully introduced in farming regions, where the woodlands are not large, provided that the area is large. They are polygamous, usually one gobbler caring for several hens.

Winter flocks. During the winter months the wild turkeys are in large mixed flocks, feeding and roosting together. During extremely bad weather and when food is scarce, they may wander near the farms and mix with domestic birds.

Mating. As the spring days approach, the large mixed flocks begin to separate into small groups. Each small group usually is made up of about five birds, three or four females and one or possibly two males. The first sign of the mating or nesting season is the shifting of the range of the birds from the dense cover of the uplands to more open country and the breaking up into smaller groups.

Nesting. Usually each hen will withdraw from her group to locate her nest, but occasionally more than one hen has been found laying in the same nest. Two hens are frequently found setting on the same nest. The turkey hen may select her nesting site in any one of many environments. She usually selects a site with good visibility overhead and on at least two sides. She also prefers a place which offers facilities for an escape by flight. The hen will depend upon her coloration and sense of sight and hearing to escape from danger. The sides of logs, heavier limbs or treefalls, and jutting rocks offer choice nesting sites. The turkey nest is seldom far from water. The turkey hen makes regular trips to water and usually all watering is done at the same place. When the eggs begin to hatch, the hen apparently does without water until her brood can follow her. The nest is usually only a slight depression in the ground which may have resulted from the bird wallowing, or it may have been a natural depression. The hen pulls leaves and twigs around her while she is on the nest. Apparently most hens cover their eggs when leaving their nests.

Egg laying. The laying season may extend from the latter part of March to June, depending upon the climatic condition and the environment. Blakey in 1937 reported that in Missouri the peak of the laying season may be placed in the last two weeks of April, and that of incubation during the last two weeks in May. The wild turkey hen usually lays one egg daily, each successive egg being laid a little later in the day. The hen may skip a day and begin over again, laying early in the morning. The hen generally runs with the family group after laying her egg. The average clutches in the wild range from eight to sixteen eggs, with fourteen- to sixteen-egg clutches being most common. Artificially propagated wild hens will exceed this number, some birds laying twenty or more eggs. Blakey reported that measurements and weights of five hundred eggs showed an average length of 59.75 mm. and width of 45.69 mm. with a weight of 66.55 grams.

Incubation. The wild turkey egg requires twenty-eight days to hatch. After the last egg is laid, the hen may not set on the eggs regularly until the second or third day has passed. The hen does all the incubating, never being assisted by the gobbler, but the gobbler remains in the vicinity of the family group. The hen leaves the nest more frequently at first. Toward the last of incubation she leaves only for water, except during the last two or three days, when she doesn't leave at all. As long as the hen feels that she is not seen, she will remain on her nest, relying on her coloration for concealment. Should the nest be located, the hen immediately leaves to seek cover elsewhere or acts crippled, a deception that is common to many birds trying to lead intruders from their nests or broods.

Hatching. The actual hatching period appears to cover one to two days, depending upon the treatment the eggs receive. Blakey reported that from 991 eggs incubated by restocked wild turkey hens, 87.6 per cent hatched, with a loss from all causes of 12.3 per cent of all eggs set. Of this 12.3 per cent, 3.8 per cent were infertile; 1.1 per cent died in the shell; and 7.3 per cent were lost to predators and unknown causes.

Brooding. Soon after the poults are hatched, the hen leads her brood away in search of food. The poults are in great danger during this period. If the grass is too wet, the poults will suffer from exposure. The losses during the first and second weeks may be great in bad weather because the young birds cannot stand wetting and chilling. The hen does her best to shelter the young poults during bad weather and at nights. The favorite range for the brood is generally borders of open fields near heavy cover. As the poults grow older, they may range farther into open fields in search of food. The brood feeds almost continuously, except when the birds rest during the extremely hot part of the day. Dusting is important in combating fleas, lice, ticks, and chiggers. The poults require water daily. The water is generally obtained from dew which is on the ground cover, by green feed, or from small surface pools. If the poults survive, by fall they will be almost fully developed.

Artificial Propagation of Wild Turkeys

The methods of artificially propagating domestic turkeys can be used in propagating wild turkeys. If the birds are to be released, a method should be used which will insure the birds of retaining their wild instinct, which is necessary for the birds' survival. Wildness results partly from parental education and partly from reaction experience obtained from the environment and from flocking with other turkeys. Characteristics which the wild turkey should possess are (1) reaction to man and predators, which makes the bird a desirable hunting resource and capable of protecting itself, and (2) a reaction to the environment, which keeps the bird in good physical condition. It is important to breed only the native wild species for liberation. For more fully described methods of propagating turkeys see Chapter Sixteen.

Selection of breeding stock. The greatest difficulty in propagating wild turkeys to be released in the wild has been to obtain turkeys that were true native wild turkeys. Only the true wild species should be selected for breeders. Even though one has native wild turkeys, there is great danger of the young birds becoming so domesticated that they cannot survive in the wild. In many localities no confined gobblers are utilized, but breeding pens are scattered throughout territories of the native wild turkey range where native gobblers are available. Poles are leaned against the fence to enable the wild gobblers to get into the enclosed pens.

Pens. Some pens are made with five-foot field fencing, or rabbit wire. Other breeders prefer a seven- to nine-foot fence. The pen contains a pole roost which may or may not be protected by wire netting or a shed. Laying facilities are furnished by scattering brush heaps over the breeding field.

Feeding. Breeding birds may be fed on rations recommended in Chapter Sixteen for the domestic birds. The feed should be placed in feeders, scattered about the breeding area.

Egg production. Turkey hens under confinement do not generally nest in the usual manner. Several may lay in the same nest. They may produce an average of fifty or more eggs during the breeding season. The eggs should be collected daily and should be held in a cool, moist, well-ventilated room. They may be held from one to two weeks before they are placed in the hatchery. To obtain the greatest number of eggs from the hens, artificial incubation should be practiced.

Incubation. Factors affecting the hatching of domestic turkey eggs also affect the hatching of wild turkey eggs. The operation of the incubator should be the same as that recommended in Chapter Sixteen.

Brooding. Wild turkey poults may be brooded in the same manner as domestic poults. Proper brooding facilities include the brooder house, which offers adequate ventilation without drafts, maximum degree of light, a wire-bottom sun porch, a properly regulated brooder stove which supplies sufficient heat, and other facilities for feeding and watering. The poults are raised in the brooder house until six to eight weeks of age and then moved to range pens. Feeding recommendations for the poults are the same as recommendations for domestic poults. The poults are held in the smaller range pens until fourteen to eighteen weeks of age, at which time they are released in the wild. One method of propagating poults is to allow the hen to hatch and brood the poults until they are six to eight weeks of age, at which time the hen and brood are released.

Other Upland Game Birds

Chukar partridge. One of the newest game birds in this country is the chukar partridge. (Fig. 260.) This species has been liberated in many states and with success in some states. The species is one of many originally found in Asia and southern Europe. This introduced species' home was along the southern slope of the Himalaya mountains. The chukar can apparently stand any climate other than regions excessively damp. In its native home, it is found at altitudes ranging from sea level to more than 15,000 feet. The adult bird weighs from one to two pounds, which makes the bird about four times larger than our native bobwhite. In general the bird's color is buff to gray, with a black necklace around the throat and vertical bars of black and brown on the sides. Red feet and beak are characteristics of the adult birds. The males can be distinguished from the females by their larger heads and body, coarser features, and by their more pronounced spur buds after the first year. The chukar has a very powerful flight, usually flying down hill, if possible, when flushed.

Natural propagation. In the wild the birds are monogamous. The chukar builds its nest in a hollow scratched in the ground, usually lined with grass or leaves. Sometimes they are built in the open or they may be located in the pro-

COURTESY WISCONSIN CONSERVATION DEPARTMENT

Fig. 260. Chukar partridge at winter feeding hopper.

tecting shelter of shrubs or large rocks. The nest is generally difficult to find. A normal clutch in the wild is about twelve to fourteen eggs, which are yellowish-white speckled with brown. The young are brooded in a manner similar to the brooding of quail chicks by the adults. The pairs gather into coveys during the fall, and remain in coveys until the following spring, at which time they break up into pairs. The food of the wild chukar consists of berries, insects, grain, and green shoots.

Artificial propagation of Chukar partridge. The chukar can be artificially propagated as easily as any other game bird. Methods used for propagating quail and pheasants can be used in propagating chukars. The birds are generally paired, but the Missouri Agricultural Experiment Station obtained better results, as measured by fertility and hatchability, from a pen having one male mated to four females than from single pair matings. The average egg production for chukars in confinement is practically the same as for quail. One female, under artificial lights at night from January to May, laid 145 eggs from February to September at the Missouri Agricultural Experiment

Fig. 261. The ruffed grouse or partridge.
(U. S. D. A. Farmers' Bulletin 497.)

Station. The chukar generally starts laying in April and continues into August or September. The chukar partridges can be brooded and reared the same as quail. Bade in 1935 reported that no other game bird was as easily brooded as the baby chukar.

Ruffed grouse. There are four recognized races of this grouse (Fig. 261), the ruffed grouse, the Canada ruffed grouse, the Oregon ruffed grouse, and the gray ruffed grouse. This species is distributed over a large part of the wooded region of the United States and Canada. The ruffed grouse is a hardy dweller in forests, deep thickets, and on rocky mountain slopes. It will disappear from regions depleted of trees. Its drumming is a pleasant and common sound of the woods where the species is found. The drumming usually is a call to the female or a challenge to combat. Often the male will drum apparently for no purpose other than for exercise. The bird's startling noise when rising and its powerful flight make it a very good game bird.

Natural propagation of ruffed grouse. The ruffed grouse is a polygamist. The grouse nests on the ground, but the nest is protected from prowlers by the female's coloration and lack of scent. The nest is generally in thickets, woods, or dense undergrowth, sheltered under a log, stump, or tree. The nest is constructed of old grass, twigs, leaves, roots, and a few feathers. The average clutch size is usually ten to fifteen eggs, the eggs varying from whitish to brownish in color. The brood leaves the nest as soon as the natal down is dry, but does not range far from the neighborhood of the nest. The young generally feed themselves, the mother spending her time watching for enemies. The chicks can use their wings in about a week after they leave the nest and can fly a good distance within three weeks. As the birds grow older, they learn to roost by themselves in shrubs or trees. By October the birds begin to lay on fat and to grow downy covering for body and legs to protect them during winter. The birds may move from the higher regions to swamps and valleys for food and shelter during winter and there they remain until the spring days bring forth the mating instinct.

Artificial propagation of ruffed grouse. The system used in rearing quail can be applied to grouse. Grouse eggs are easy to hatch in an incubator and by using a good sanitation program and by proper feeding the birds can be grown to maturity successfully.

Prairie chicken. This species is distributed from Michigan and Indiana southward to Texas and westward to the Great Plains (Fig. 262). They have been greatly reduced in numbers because of predators and the destruction of their food and cover. The food of prairie chickens consists of many insects and green feed in the summer, and fruit, seeds, and grains during the winter. The bird nests on the ground in open prairie country, the nest usually being sheltered by grass or bushes. It is placed in a slight depression in the ground and lined with grass and a few feathers. Eight to twelve eggs make a clutch. Very few prairie chickens have been artificially propagated.

Fig. 262. Prairie Chicken. (U. S. D. A. Farmers' Bulletin 497.)

Sage hen. The sage hen is the largest of the upland game birds, excepting only the wild turkey. It inhabits the sage brush plains from Canada south to California and New Mexico. This species has rapidly decreased in numbers. The bird nests on the ground, usually under a sage brush and near a spring or stream. The birds are polygamous and have special mating grounds. In winter they assemble in groups and usually find protection and food in the valleys or in the timber. Their food consists of insects and sage leaves.

Hungarian partridge. These birds are descendants of birds that have been imported and released in the United States. They are generally monogamous and are usually penned in pairs in artificial propagation. These birds have multiplied quite rapidly in Canada and several states in the United States, especially Oregon and Washington. This species has also thrived in Wisconsin, Ohio, North and South Dakota, Montana, Illinois, and Iowa. Some birds are found in other states. Hungarian partridges have very little use for timber and brush. They seem to dislike swamps and prefer grass fields rather than fence rows and woods in which to build their nests. Winter food can be furnished by planting corn, kaffir, or sorghums. Rearing equipment and methods are similar to those for quail. Feeding may follow the recommendations given for quail and pheasants. In the wild, the birds are rapid flyers and, therefore, good targets for sportsmen.

Releasing Artificially Propagated Game Birds

To obtain the maximum results, all birds should be released in an area that best meets their requirements. For the upland game birds, the first recommendation for an ideal area is suitable cover. Before releasing game birds, everything possible should be done to improve the food conditions and increase the protection of the birds by improving the cover and by freeing the area from the more destructive enemies. Having obtained an area with adequate cover for protection, and sufficient food and nesting facilities, certain directions can be followed in liberating the birds. The best season of the year for releasing birds is in the spring after the leaves and grasses are beginning to turn green. The birds should be fed before releasing, preferably on green succulent feed. The birds should be taken to the selected covert late in the evening to prevent them from wandering too far before becoming localized. The coop should be placed so that the opening faces the cover. It is advisable to scatter some grain around the box before opening the door for release. The birds should never be forced from the coop; allow them to walk out of their own accord. The birds may be enticed to remain in the area if some feed is scattered near the cover occasionally. The number of birds to release in an area depends upon the species and upon the environmental factors such as food supply, cover, and number of wild birds already present in the area. Two to six pairs of quail are usually released to a cover. With pheasants best results are secured where cocks and hens are released in the ratio of one cock to three hens. For wild turkeys, it is recommended that a flock of about fifteen birds be released together. It is best to release the younger turkeys, fourteen to eighteen weeks appearing to be the best age for liberation. It is best to release the artificially propagated turkeys near wild turkey ranges.

Waterfowl

The North American continent has always possessed a great variety and, at one time, an abundance of waterfowl. Most species were abundant as late as forty years ago, but the beginning of the twentieth century marked a perceptible decrease of waterfowl. In many instances the decrease has been alarming. This decrease has been attributed to several factors, including (1) destruction of water and marsh lands once used for feeding, nesting, and breeding grounds; (2) a large number of hunters taking a heavy yearly toll; (3) pollution of waters; (4) disease and parasites; and (5) natural enemies. Agriculture has claimed vast areas of land once inhabited by wild fowl. The great breeding grounds of the North and West once possessed all requisites for waterfowl existence. Prairie grasses afforded good nesting cover. The many lakes, streams, and potholes offered unlimited food and protection. Most of the breeding and nesting grounds within the United States have been destroyed by man or drought.

Realizing the possibility of waterfowl vanishing completely, federal agencies, state governments, and many private organizations are studying means of increasing the number of waterfowl.

Three species of waterfowl—ducks, geese, and swans—make up the greater part of the artificially propagated aquatic game birds. Several thousand waterfowl are propagated annually in the United States, ducks being propagated in greatest numbers. The mallard is the most common and most important species of the duck family. This species is found in most of North America and is plentiful except in regions where it has been destroyed. Wild mallards have furnished sport for man for many years and tame mallards have been used for food for centuries. The mallard is the chief waterfowl of most game preserves. This species is a hardy one, staying in the cold regions as long as food and fresh water are plentiful. When water freezes in the North, they migrate southward. There are numerous other species of ducks in North America.

The Canada goose is familiar to nearly everyone. It nests in the northern regions of North America and migrates to the southern states during the fall. The Canada geese feed largely on vegetable matter as do most waterfowl. They often enter the grain fields during the fall migration. The Canada goose is rather easily reared from pairs held in captivity. The birds are allowed to hatch their eggs and rear their young.

The swans are distributed over North America. At one time they were abundant, but large numbers were killed by man and today they are scarce.

Aiding Game Birds in Their Natural Environment

Very few farms are entirely free from waste areas where food and cover can be provided for game birds. Allowing these waste areas to grow natural vegetation may provide sufficient food and cover. Cover is probably the most important factor in game production. It protects the birds against their predator enemies and also extreme climatic conditions such as heat, cold, snow, and storms. Game birds also need cover in which to nest and rear their young. The quail, pheasant, and partridge will nest in the edges of fields of grain or grass, roadside thickets, and along the margin of woodlands.

Many birds seem to prefer nesting in grain and hayfields. The farmer who is interested in saving his game bird crop should use means to avoid destroying the nests or the young birds while harvesting. A simple homemade device can be fastened to the harvesting machinery to flush the birds ahead of the cutterbar, enabling the driver to avoid destroying the nest or the young birds.

A good water supply should be available if game birds are expected to survive and increase on the farm. Ponds well distributed offer good watering facilities for the upland game birds and may be used by waterfowls. Vegetation should be allowed to grow in and near the pond to furnish food for waterfowl as well as protection for the land birds while drinking or bathing.

Winter feeding. In many areas under normal conditions there is sufficient

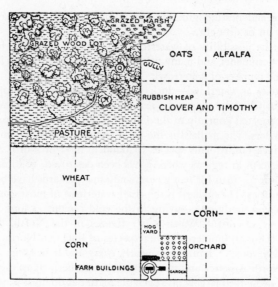

Fig. 263. Map of a 160-acre corn-belt farm before it was improved for wild life. (See also Figure 260.) Hogs use orchard in foreground; no trees on lawn about farm buildings; only one covey of quail (Q in circle) on farm.

food and cover during the spring, summer, and fall for most game birds. Winter is a critical period for all species of birds because during this period the birds meet numerous hardships. Food supplies diminish in quantity and quality, coverts become bare of foliage and therefore the birds become exposed to excessive cold, deep snows, and blizzards. If birds obtain sufficient food, they can stand considerable cold and with man's aid by feeding, they can survive many hardships. The feeding should be carried on over an extended period because short intermittent feeding, although helpful, is not completely satisfactory. The feeding, to be of most value, should be planned and continued throughout the critical period, which is the entire winter.

Upland game birds. The natural winter foods of upland game birds are chiefly weed seeds, buds, dried fruits, and dried berries. Acorns are also relished as well as other nuts. These natural foods seldom supply the birds' needs, unless large patches of weeds are allowed to grow. But farmers consider weeds undesirable and, therefore, destroy them before they bear fruit.

On some farms there may be a shortage of food only, but many farms may be scarce of both food and cover. There are many types of shelters that can be built which will protect the birds from adverse weather as well as providing a place for feeding. A shelter may be constructed of either brush or fodder. The best results are generally obtained from the simpler and more natural feeding stations which require little attention. (Figs. 263 and 264.) Winter feeding of birds can be accomplished by leaving corn standing or shocked in the field. If it is possible, a small patch of barley, rye, or wheat should be left

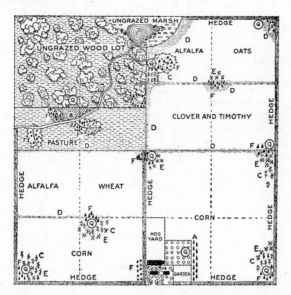

Fig. 264. Map of farm shown in Figure 259 after it had been improved for wild life. Woods and marsh fenced and ungrazed; pond constructed in marsh; rubbish heap surrounded by trees; gullies planted; orchard protected from hogs; trees planted on lawn; wheat acreage decreased and alfalfa acreage increased to offset woods formerly grazed; A, windbreak round buildings; B, millet patch; C, standing corn feed patch; D, hay strip left standing; E, shocks of corn left in field; F, cover patches—low spruces, large thorny roses, grapevines, sumac, hay. Numerous quail covies now on farm. (U. S. D. A. Farmers' Bulletin 1719.)

close to cover. Other grains such as milo, sorghums, buckwheat, and kaffir are relished by most upland game birds during the winter.

Waterfowl. Although waterfowl are migratory, they are often in need of feed. Severe winters may reach far into the South to freeze the waters and cut off the natural food supply. At this time the birds are much in need of food. They welcome feed such as corn, wheat, rice, barley, or other grains. The feed should be scattered near the water where they normally feed.

Waterfowl are benefited immensely by the construction of artificial ponds and lakes. Lakes and ponds are built by constructing dams across water courses. The dam should be located at a site which will prevent its being washed out by storms and where enough water will be caught to keep the pond or lake full and fresh. Earthen dams are generally the most simple and practicable type, but rock-filled and concrete dams are usually more durable. Food and cover are essential requirements for a good pond or lake. The waterfowl's food consists largely of tubers, stems, leaves of water plants, shoots and seeds of grains and grasses, and fruits of trees and shrubs. Water plants are affected by several factors, including (1) quality of the soil, (2) climatic condition, and (3) condition of water. The turbidity and level of water should be controlled as much as possible by terracing, proper rotation of crops, and by construction of spillways.

REFERENCES

BADE, AUGUST: THE CHUKAR PARTRIDGE IN CALIFORNIA. Calif. Fish and Game, pp. 233–236. July, 1937.

BEAL, F. E. L.: SOME COMMON BIRDS USEFUL TO THE FARMER. U. S. D. A. Farmers' Bul. 630. 1926.

BEEBE, WILLIAM: PHEASANTS. THEIR LIVES AND HOMES. Doubleday, Doran and Co., Garden City, New York. 1936.

BLAKEY, H. L.: THE WILD TURKEY ON THE MISSOURI OZARK RANGE. Wildlife Res. and Management Leaflet BS–77, Washington, D. C. 1937.

CALLENBACH, E. W., AND HILLER, C. A.: THE ARTIFICIAL PROPAGATION OF RING-NECKED PHEASANTS. Pa. Agr. Expt. Sta. Bul. 299. 1933.

CHUKAR PARTRIDGE NOW SUCCESS IN STATE. Calif. Conservationist. November, 1936.

COTTOM, C.: FOOD HABITS OF NORTH AMERICAN DIVING DUCKS. U. S. D. A. Tech. Bul. 643. 1939.

CUNNINGHAM, C. H.: PARATYPHOID INFECTION IN QUAIL. Amer. Jour. Vet. Res., 4: 190–193. 1943.

DALKE, P. L.: FOOD HABITS OF ADULT PHEASANTS IN MICHIGAN BASED ON CROP ANALYSIS METHOD. Ecology, Vol. 18, No. 2. 1937.

DAMBACH, C. A.: THE RELATIVE IMPORTANCE OF HUNTING RESTRICTIONS AND LAND USE IN MAINTAINING WILDLIFE POPULATIONS IN OHIO. Ohio J. Sci., 48: 209–229. 1948.

DARLING, J. N., SHELDON, H. P., AND GABRIELSON, IRA N.: GAME MANAGEMENT ON THE FARM. U. S. D. A. Farmers' Bul. 1759. 1936.

DAVIDSON, V. E.: SHRUBS FOR WILDLIFE ON FARMS IN THE SOUTHEAST. U. S. D. A. Leaflet 200. 1940.

DURANT, A. J., AND DOLL, E. R.: ULCERATIVE ENTERITIS IN QUAIL. Mo. Sta. Res. Bul. 325. 1941.

FISHER, L. W.: STUDIES OF THE EASTERN RUFFED GROUSE IN MICHIGAN. Mich. Sta. Col. Agr. Expt. Sta. Tech. Bul. 166. 1939.

GAME BIRDS—HOW TO MAKE THEM PAY ON YOUR FARM. More Game Birds in America, 500 Fifth Ave., New York. 1939.

GOOD, E. E., AND DAMBACH, C. A.: EFFECT OF LAND USE PRACTICES ON BREEDING BIRD POPULATIONS IN OHIO. J. Wildlife Mgt. 7: 291–297. 1943.

GRANGE, W. B.: FEEDING WILDLIFE IN WINTER. U. S. D. A. Farmers' Bul. 1783. 1937.

HAMMERSTROM, F. N.: A STUDY OF THE NESTING HABITS OF THE RING-NECKED PHEASANTS IN NORTHWEST IOWA. Iowa State Col. Jour. Sci., Vol. 10, No. 2. 1936.

HERMAN, C. M., AND CHATTIN, J. E.: EPIDEMIOLOGICAL STUDIES ON COCCIDIOSIS OF CALIFORNIA QUAIL. I. OCCURRENCE OF EIMERIA IN WILD QUAIL. Calif. Fish and Game, 29: 168–179. 1943.

HERMAN, C. M., CHATTIN, J. E., AND SAARNI, R. W.: FOOD HABITS AND INTENSITY OF COCCIDIAN INFECTON IN NATIVE VALLEY QUAIL IN CALIFORNIA. Jour. Parasit., 29: 206–208. 1943.

HINSHAW, W. R., AND EMLEN, J. T.: PASTEURELLOSIS IN CALIFORNIA VALLEY QUAIL. Cornell Vet., 33: 351–354. 1943.

HINSHAW, W. R., AND McNEIL, E.: HEXAMITA SP. FROM THE RING-NECKED PHEASANT. Jour. Amer. Vet. Med. Assoc., 101: 503. 1942.

HUDSON, C. B.: FOWL CHOLERA IN RING-NECKED PHEASANTS. Jour. Amer. Vet. Med. Assoc., 104: 211–212. 1944.

JULL, M. A.: Raising Turkeys, Ducks, Geese, Game Birds. McGraw-Hill Book Co., New York. 1947.

LEEDY, D. L.: SOME WILDLIFE LAND USE RELATIONSHIPS IN OHIO. Ohio J. Sci. 48: 151–160. 1948.

MARTIN, A. C., AND UHLER, F. M.: FOOD OF GAME DUCKS IN THE UNITED STATES AND CANADA. U. S. D. A. Tech. Bul. 634. 1939.

MCATEE, W. L.: THE RING-NECK PHEASANT AND ITS MANAGEMENT IN NORTH AMERICA. American Wildlife Institute, Washington, D. C. 1945.

MCATEE, W. L.: GROUPS OF PLANTS VALUABLE FOR WILDLIFE UTILIZATION AND EROSION CONTROL. U. S. D. A. Circ. 412. 1936.

MCATEE, W. L.: PROPAGATION OF AQUATIC GAME BIRDS. U. S. D. A. Farmers' Bul. 1612. 1930.

MCATEE, W. L.: PROPAGATION OF UPLAND GAME BIRDS. U. S. D. A. Farmers' Bul. 1613. 1930.

MORE GAME BIRDS BY CONTROLLING THEIR NATURAL ENEMIES. More Game Birds in America. 500 Fifth Ave., New York. 1939.

More Game Birds in America, A Foundation: MORE UPLAND GAME BIRDS. 500 Fifth Ave., New York. 1938.

More Game Birds in America, A Foundation: PHEASANT BREEDING MANUAL. 500 Fifth Ave., New York. 1938.

NAGEL, W. O., AND BENNIT, RUDOLF: FEEDING STATIONS AND SHELTERS FOR QUAIL ON MISSOURI FARMS. Univ. of Mo. Agr. Expt. Sta. Circ. 356. 1937.

NESTER, R. B., AND LLEWELLYN, L. M.: ABNORMAL FEATHERING OF PEN-REARED BOBWHITES. Poultry Sci., 23: 72–75. 1944.

OLSEN, ANNA A.: SMALL GAME FOR DINNER. Iowa Sta. Bul. P96. 1948.

PEARSON, T. G.: Birds of America. Garden City Publishing Co., Garden City, N. Y. 1936.

PEARSON, A. M., AND STURKIE, D. G.: FOOD CROPS FOR GAME BIRDS ON FARM LANDS. Ala. Sta. Circ. 90. 1944.

QUAIL BREEDING MANUAL. More Game Birds in America, 500 Fifth Ave., New York. 1939.

QUORTRUP, E. R., AND HOLT, A. L.: DETECTION OF POTENTIAL BOTULINUS-TOXIN-PRODUCING AREAS IN WESTERN DUCK MARSHES, WITH SUGGESTIONS FOR CONTROL. Jour. Bact., 41: 363–372. 1941.

RANDALL, P. E.: NESTING HABITS AND CAUSES OF NEST MORTALITY OF THE RING-NECKED PHEASANT. Pa. Game News, Vol. 10, No. 9.

RAE, T.: Profitable Game Bird Management, 4th ed. The Beacon Milling Co., Cayuga, N. Y. 1947.

RAE, THOMAS: Profitable Game Bird Management, 6th ed. The Beacon Milling Co., Cayuga, N. Y. 1947.

ROMANOFF, ALEXIS L.: STUDY OF ARTIFICIAL INCUBATION OF GAME BIRDS. TEMPERATURE AND HUMIDITY REQUIREMENTS FOR PHEASANT AND QUAIL EGGS. Cornell Univ. Agri. Expt. Sta. Bul. 616. 1934.

SHILLINGER, J. E., AND MORLEY, L. C.: DISEASES OF UPLAND GAME BIRDS. U. S. D. A. Farmers' Bul. 1781. 1937.

SIMON, F.: THE PARASITES OF THE SAGE GROUSE. Wyo. Univ. Pubs. 7: 77–100. 1940.

SKOGLAND, W. C.: AN IMPROVED RATION FOR STARTING RING-NECKED PHEAS-ANTS. Pa. Agr. Expt. Sta. Bul. 389. 1940.

622   *Poultry: Science and Practice*

SMALL REFUGES FOR WATERFOWL. More Game Birds in America, 500 Fifth
Ave., New York. 1939.

STADELMAN, W. J., CALLENBACH, E. W., MURPHY, R. R., AND BOUCHER,
R. V.: RATIONS FOR BOBWHITE QUAIL. Pa. Game News 11: No. 11: Feb.,
1945.

STODDARD, H. L.: The Bobwhite Quail, Its Habits, Preservation and Increase.
Charles Scribner's Sons, New York. 1931.

STOVER, D. E.: HEXAMITA SP. FROM THE RINGED-NECK PHEASANT TRANSMIS-
SIBLE TO TURKEYS. Jour. Amer. Vet. Med. Assoc., 103: 37. 1943.

SYVERTON, J. T., AND COWAN, I. M.: BIRD POX IN THE SOOTY GROUSE (DEN-
DRAGAPUS FULIGINOSUS FULIGINOSUS), WITH RECOVERY OF THE VIRUS.
Amer. Jour. Vet. Res., 5: 215–222. 1944.

TREPPENSEE, R. E.: Wildlife Management: Upland Game and General Principles. McGraw-Hill Book Co., New York. 1948.

WEHR, E. E., AND OLIVER, L.: THE EFFICACY OF BARIUM ANTIMONYL TAR-
TRATE FOR THE REMOVAL OF GAPEWORMS FROM PHEASANTS. Helminthol.
Soc. Wash. Proc., 10: 87–89. 1943.

Western Cartridge Company: UPLAND GAME PROPAGATION. Western Cartridge
Co., East Alton, Ill. 1940.

Appendix

AGRICULTURAL COLLEGES AND EXPERIMENT STATIONS IN THE
UNITED STATES AND CANADA

Agricultural colleges and experiment stations offer publications covering many agricultural subjects, including poultry. A list of the available bulletins, circulars, leaflets, etc., and information regarding them may be obtained from the institutions. Except where otherwise noted, the state experiment stations in the United States are at the colleges of agriculture.

UNITED STATES

Alabama	Auburn	Missouri	Columbia
Alaska	College	Montana	Bozeman
Arizona	Tucson	Nebraska	Lincoln
Arkansas	Fayetteville	Nevada	Reno
California	Berkeley	New Hampshire	Durham
Colorado	Fort Collins	New Jersey	New Brunswick
Connecticut		New Mexico	State College
College and		New York	
station	Storrs	College and	
Station	New Haven	station	Ithaca
Delaware	Newark	Station	Geneva
Florida	Gainesville	North Carolina	Raleigh
Georgia	Athens	North Dakota	Fargo
Hawaii	Honolulu	Ohio	
Idaho	Moscow	College	Columbus
Illinois	Urbana	Station	Wooster
Indiana	Lafayette	Oklahoma	Stillwater
Iowa	Ames	Oregon	Corvallis
Kansas	Manhattan	Pennsylvania	State College
Kentucky	Lexington	Puerto Rico	Rio Piedras
Louisiana	University	Rhode Island	Kingston
Maine	Orono	South Carolina	Clemson
Maryland	College Park	South Dakota	Brookings
Massachusetts	Amherst	Tennessee	Knoxville
Michigan	East Lansing	Texas	College Station
Minnesota	St. Paul	Utah	Logan
Mississippi	State College	Vermont	Burlington

Virginia	Blacksburg	Wisconsin	Madison
Washington		Wyoming	Laramie
College and		United States	
station	Pullman	Department of	Washington,
Station	Puyallup	Agriculture	D. C.
West Virginia	Morgantown		

CANADA

Alberta	Edmonton	Quebec	Macdonald Col-
British Columbia	Vancouver		lege
Manitoba	Winnipeg	Dominion De-	
Nova Scotia	Truro	partment of	
Ontario	Guelph	Agriculture	Ottawa
Saskatchewan	Saskatoon		

ABSTRACT JOURNALS

Hundreds of scientific publications which contain agricultural information, including poultry, are published annually. The data from the bulletins and articles are summarized in brief abstracts and published in special abstract journals. Some of these are as follows:

Biological Abstracts. Philadelphia, Pa.
Chemical Abstracts. Columbus, O.
International Review of Poultry Science. Rotterdam, Holland.
Poultry Digest. Hanover, Pa.

SCIENTIFIC JOURNALS

Many scientific journals regularly or frequently contain articles including poultry data. Some of these journals are as follows:

American Journal of Anatomy. Philadelphia, Pa.
American Journal of Cancer. Baltimore, Md.
American Journal of Hygiene. Baltimore, Md.
American Naturalist, New York City.
Anatomical Record. Philadelphia, Pa.
Biochemical Journal. London, England.
Biological Bulletin. Woods Hole, Mass.
Canadian Journal of Research. Ottawa, Canada.
Cornell Veterinarian. Ithaca, N. Y.
Endocrinology. Los Angeles, Cal.
Genetics, Brooklyn, N. Y.
Hilgardia. Berkeley, Cal.
Journal of Agricultural Research. Washington, D. C.
Journal of Agricultural Science. London, England.
Journal of the American Veterinary Medical Association, Chicago, Ill.
Journal of Bacteriology. Baltimore, Md.
Journal of Biological Chemistry. Baltimore, Md.
Journal of Comparative Pathology and Therapeutics. London, England.
Journal of Economic Entomology. Geneva, N. Y.

Journal of Experimental Biology. London, England.
Journal of Experimental Medicine. Baltimore, Md.
Journal of Experimental Zoology. Philadelphia, Pa.
Journal of General Physiology. Baltimore, Md.
Journal of Helminthology. London, England.
Journal of Heredity. Washington, D. C.
Journal of Infectious Diseases. Chicago, Ill.
Journal of Morphology and Physiology. Boston, Mass.
Journal of Nutrition. Philadelphia, Pa.
Journal of Parasitology. Urbana, Ill.
Physiological Reviews. Baltimore, Md.
Poultry Science. Quelph, Ontario.
Science. New York City.
Scientific Agriculture. Ottawa, Canada.
United States Egg and Poultry Magazine. Chicago, Ill.
Veterinary Medicine. Chicago, Ill.

POPULAR POULTRY JOURNALS

Many popular poultry journals and farm papers contain practical poultry information. Some of the poultry journals are as follows:

American Poultry Journal. Chicago, Ill.
Canadian Poultry Review, Toronto, Ontario.
Eggsaminer. Portland, Ore.
Everybody's Poultry Magazine. Hanover, Pa.
Hatchery and Feed. Mt. Morris, Ill.
Hatchery Tribune. Mount Morris, Ill.
Modern Poultry Keeping, London, Eng.
Nulaid News. San Francisco, Cal.
Pacific Poultryman. Palo Alto, Col.
Poultry Industry. Boston, Mass.
Poultry Item. Sellersville, Pa.
Poultry Supply Dealer. Chicago, Ill.
Poultry Tribune. Mount Morris, Ill.
Turkey World. Mount Morris, Ill.

CHART FOR DETERMINING IMPORTANT CHARACTERISTICS OF STANDARD VARIETIES IN THE AMERICAN, ASIATIC, ENGLISH AND MEDITERRANEAN CLASSES

Class	Characters	Comb	Breed	Variety	Ck	Ckl	Hen	Pullet
							Standard Weight	
American Class	Varieties in this class have yellow skin, non-feathered shanks, red earlobes and all except the Lamonas lay brown-shelled eggs.	Single	Plymouth Rocks	Barred, White, Buff, Silver-Penciled, Partridge, Columbian and Blue	9½	8	7½	6
			Javas	Mottled and Black	9½	8	7½	6½
			Jersey Giants	Black	13	11	10	8
			Rhode Island Reds	Single-Comb	8½	7½	6½	5½
			New Hampshires	*Chestnut	8½	7½	6½	5½
			Lamonas	*White	8	7	6½	5½
		Rose	Wyandottes	Silver-Laced, Golden-Laced, White, Black, Buff, Partridge, Silver-Penciled and Columbian	8½	7½	6½	5½
			Dominiques	*Barred	7	6	5	4
			Rhode Island Reds	Rose-Comb	8½	7½	6½	5½
			Rhode Island Whites	*Rose-Comb	8½	7½	6½	5½
		Cushion	Chanteclers	White	8½	7½	6½	5½
				Partridge	10	8½	7½	6½
Asiatic Class	Varieties in this class have feathered shanks, red earlobes, lay brown-shelled eggs. The Langshans have white skin and the other breeds have yellow skin.	Pea	Brahmas	Light	12	10	9½	8
				Dark and Buff	11	9	8½	7
		Single	Cochins	Buff, Partridge, White, and Black	11	9	8½	7
			Langshans	Black, and White	9½	8	7½	6½

English Class

Varieties in this class have non-feathered shanks, red earlobes. All except the Dorkings and Redcaps lay brown-shelled eggs. The Cornish have yellow skin but the other breeds have white skin.

Comb	Breed	Variety				
Single	Dorkings	White	7½	6½	6	5
		Silver-Gray and Colored	9	8	7	6
	Orpingtons	Buff, Black, White, and Blue	10	8½	8	7
	Sussex	Speckled, Red, and Light	9	7½	7	6
	Australorps	*Black	8½	7½	6½	5½
Rose	Redcaps		7½	6	6	5
Pea	Cornish	Dark, White, White-Laced Red and Buff	10½	8½	8	6½

Mediterranean Class

Varieties in this class have non-feathered shanks and white earlobes. They are noted for their white-shelled eggs. The Leghorns and Anconas have yellow skin but the other breeds have white skin.

Comb	Breed	Variety				
Single	Leghorns	Dark Brown, Light Brown, White, Buff, Black, Silver, Red, Black Tailed, Red and Columbian	6	5	4½	4
	Minorcas	Black	9	7½	7½	6½
		White and Buff	8	6½	6½	5½
	Spanish	White-Faced Black	8	6½	6½	5½
	Blue Andalusian	Single-Comb	7	6	5½	4½
	Anconas	Single-Comb	6	5	4½	4
Rose	Leghorns	Dark Brown, Light Brown, and White	6	5	4½	4
	Minorcas	Black and White	8	6½	6½	5½
	Anconas	Rose-Comb	6	5	4½	4
Buttercup	Buttercups		6½	5½	5	4

*Non-standard variety names.

Table 1

COMPOSITION OF POULTRY PRODUCTS AND FEEDSTUFFS [1]

FEEDSTUFFS	WATER (MOISTURE)	ASH (MINERALS)	CRUDE PROTEIN	CARBOHYDRATES Crude Fiber	CARBOHYDRATES Nitrogen-Free Extract	FAT, OR ETHER EXTRACT
	Per Cent	Per Cent	Per Cent	Per Cent	Per Cent	Per Cent
Poultry Products						
New-laid egg, entire............	65.9	10.0	12.8	...	...	10.6
Chick, at hatching time.........	78.8	1.9	15.3	...	...	4.1
Broiler, entire bird.............	65.8	3.9	23.2	...	...	5.6
Leghorn hen, entire fowl........	55.8	10.0	12.8	...	...	10.6
Grains and Seeds						
Barley......................	10.4	2.9	11.8	5.9	66.9	2.1
Barley (Pacific Coast States)....	10.1	2.6	8.7	5.7	71.0	1.9
Beans, navy..................	13.4	3.6	22.7	5.8	53.0	1.5
Beans, pinto..................	9.1	4.5	22.7	4.5	58.0	1.2
Bread.......................	33.8	1.5	7.9	.7	55.4	.7
Brewers' grains, dried...........	7.0	3.7	26.2	14.7	41.8	6.6
Broomcorn...................	11.6	3.1	10.5	8.3	63.0	3.5
Buckwheat...................	11.9	1.8	10.1	10.4	63.5	2.3
Buckwheat middlings...........	11.4	4.7	28.6	6.0	42.2	7.1
Coconut meal (old process)......	9.3	6.1	20.5	11.1	44.7	8.3
Corn........................	11.9	1.3	9.3	2.1	71.2	4.2
Corn, Argentine...............	11.0	1.7	11.0	1.8	68.8	5.7
Corn, bran...................	9.9	2.3	9.9	9.6	61.6	6.7
Corn meal....................	11.2	.9	8.8	1.1	75.5	2.5
Corn-gluten feed..............	9.7	6.1	25.9	7.2	48.5	2.6
Corn-gluten meal..............	8.9	1.5	43.0	2.6	42.1	1.9
Cottonseed meal (41% protein)..	7.5	5.8	41.8	11.4	27.1	6.4
Cowpeas.....................	11.1	3.5	23.5	4.1	56.3	1.5
Distillers' grains (corn)........	7.0	2.3	31.2	11.5	37.5	10.5
Durra.......................	10.0	2.0	10.2	1.7	72.6	3.5
Feterita.....................	10.2	1.6	13.2	1.8	70.2	3.0
Field peas....................	9.3	3.3	23.3	5.9	57.0	1.2
Flaxseed.....................	10.3	4.4	22.3	7.1	23.1	32.8
Garden peas..................	11.8	3.0	25.6	4.4	53.6	1.6
Hempseed....................	7.6	5.9	22.9	18.6	18.4	26.6
Hempseed meal................	7.3	7.8	31.7	23.9	25.3	4.0
Hominy (pearled).............	11.8	.7	7.4	.6	77.6	1.9
Hominy feed..................	8.8	2.9	11.0	5.1	65.5	6.7
Kafir........................	11.7	1.6	11.5	2.0	70.1	3.1
Linseed meal (old process)......	9.4	5.8	35.3	8.5	35.0	6.0
Malt sprouts..................	7.9	5.9	26.0	13.0	45.7	1.5
Millet (proso).................	9.6	3.4	11.6	8.7	63.1	3.6
Milo........................	11.0	2.0	11.0	2.2	70.9	2.9
Oats........................	10.1	3.4	11.2	11.3	59.5	4.5
Oatmeal, or rolled oats..........	8.6	2.2	16.2	2.1	64.2	6.7
Peanuts (hulls on).............	6.0	2.8	24.8	17.8	14.0	34.6
Peanut kernels................	5.4	2.3	30.4	2.7	11.6	47.6
Peanut meal (no hulls) (old process).....................	6.9	5.6	45.7	9.2	24.0	8.6
Rice (whole).................	10.3	4.7	7.9	8.8	66.3	2.0

[1] Mostly from U. S. D. A. Yearbook of Agriculture, 1939.

628

COMPOSITION OF POULTRY PRODUCTS AND FEEDSTUFFS (cont'd.)

| FEEDSTUFFS | WATER (MOISTURE) | ASH (MINERALS) | CRUDE PROTEIN | CARBOHYDRATES | | FAT, OR ETHER EXTRACT |
				Crude Fiber	Nitrogen-Free Extract	
	Per Cent	Per Cent	Per Cent	Per Cent	Per Cent	Per Cent
Rice (polished)................	11.8	.5	7.5	.4	79.4	.4
Rice bran....................	8.8	10.9	13.0	12.5	41.1	13.7
Rye.........................	10.7	2.0	11.5	2.1	72.0	1.7
Soybeans....................	8.8	4.8	37.9	5.0	26.6	16.9
Soybean meal................	9.1	5.6	43.9	5.9	30.0	5.5
Shallu......................	10.0	1.8	12.9	1.8	70.0	3.5
Sunflower seed...............	7.4	3.4	16.0	28.6	21.4	23.2
Sunflower seeds (hulled).......	5.0	3.8	28.0	6.0	16.2	41.0
Velvetbeans.................	10.0	3.0	24.8	6.2	50.8	5.2
Wheat......................	11.0	1.8	12.4	2.4	70.5	1.9
Wheat bran.................	10.2	5.9	15.6	9.0	55.1	4.2
Wheat flour.................	12.9	.4	10.7	.4	74.2	1.4
Wheat-flour middlings.........	10.5	3.5	17.0	5.1	59.3	4.6
Wheat-germ meal.............	8.7	4.6	28.9	2.7	44.7	10.4
Wheat middlings (standard)....	11.1	4.1	16.9	6.6	56.6	4.7
Wheat red-dog flour...........	10.2	2.7	16.9	3.2	62.6	4.4
Wheat shorts (gray)..........	10.3	4.1	17.6	5.5	58.0	4.5
Feeds of Animal Origin						
Beef scrap...................	6.5	21.5	58.0	2.2	.7	11.1
Bone meal, steamed...........	3.1	73.8	13.0	.8	2.8	6.5
Bone meal, special steamed.....	3.1	85.1	6.5	2.6	2.1	.6
Buttermilk..................	90.8	.8	3.2	.0	4.6	.6
Buttermilk, condensed.........	71.6	3.5	10.6	.0	12.2	2.1
Buttermilk, dried.............	7.1	10.1	33.4	.4	44.0	5.0
Crab meal...................	8.1	40.1	34.7	8.5	6.5	2.1
Fish meal (average of unidentified fish meals).............	8.0	19.7	60.4	.7	3.5	7.7
Fish meal, herring.............	9.1	12.1	66.0	.6	3.0	9.2
Fish meal, menhaden..........	8.0	20.4	57.5	.8	4.1	9.2
Fish meal, whitefish (high ash)...	7.8	26.0	61.6	.4	1.2	3.0
Fish meal, whitefish (low ash)...	12.1	17.6	60.9	.6	.1	8.7
Fish meal, sardine.............	8.0	15.0	67.0	.4	3.6	6.0
Fish meal, tuna...............	5.0	20.2	60.7	.4	5.1	8.6
Liver meal, Argentine..........	5.0	5.0	65.4	.8	9.8	14.0
Meat scrap (55% protein).......	6.7	24.2	55.2	2.2	1.0	10.7
Meat-and-bone scrap (50% protein)....................	6.0	29.2	50.0	2.1	1.8	10.9
Pork liver, dried..............	4.8	5.3	63.7	.4	15.0	10.8
Pork cracklings...............	5.0	2.3	56.4	.0	4.1	32.2
Shrimp meal (or bran).........	11.0	33.9	42.0	9.5	1.4	2.2
Skim milk...................	90.5	.7	3.5	.0	5.1	.2
Skim milk, dried..............	6.0	7.9	35.0	.0	50.0	1.1
Tankage (60% protein).........	8.0	19.5	59.8	2.7	1.8	8.2
Whey.......................	93.7	.6	.8	.0	4.9	.0
Whey, dried.................	6.3	8.5	12.5	.3	71.7	.7
Green Feeds, etc.						
Alfalfa, fresh.................	73.8	2.5	4.6	7.5	10.7	.9
Alfalfa-leaf meal..............	7.8	12.0	20.4	17.1	40.1	2.6

| FEEDSTUFFS | WATER (MOIS- TURE) | ASH (MIN- ERALS) | CRUDE PROTEIN | CARBOHYDRATES | | FAT, OR ETHER EXTRACT |
				Crude Fiber	Nitrogen- Free Extract	
	Per Cent	*Per Cent*	*Per Cent*	*Per Cent*	*Per Cent*	*Per Cent*
Alfalfa meal..................	8.3	8.7	16.0	27.3	37.2	2.5
Beet pulp, dried..............	9.0	3.3	9.3	19.1	58.5	.8
Cabbage.....................	90.8	.8	1.8	1.1	5.2	.3
Cane molasses................	24.8	8.2	3.0	.0	64.0	.0
Carrots......................	88.4	1.1	1.1	1.2	7.9	.3
Grapefruit refuse, dried........	9.3	4.3	4.8	11.6	68.7	1.3
Kale.........................	88.4	1.9	2.4	1.5	5.3	.5
Mangels.....................	90.1	1.1	1.5	.8	6.4	.1
Orange peel, dried............	14.0	4.1	5.8	10.6	64.8	.7
Orange-pulp meal.............	10.8	3.4	7.5	8.9	67.9	1.5
Potatoes.....................	78.8	.9	2.0	.5	17.7	.1
Rape........................	84.6	2.2	2.6	2.4	7.6	.6
Red clover hay...............	12.3	6.7	12.7	25.7	39.6	3.0
Rutabagas...................	88.8	1.0	1.2	1.5	7.3	.2
Turnips......................	90.6	.8	1.3	1.1	6.0	.2
Yeast, brewers', dried..........	7.0	7.3	46.5	1.1	35.3	2.8

Table 2

MINERAL ELEMENTS IN POULTRY FEEDSTUFFS AND POULTRY PRODUCTS [2]

Feedstuff	Calcium (Ca)	Phosphorus (P)	Manganese (Mn)	Potassium (K)	Sodium (Na)	Chlorine (Cl)	Sulphur (S)	Iron (Fe)	Magnesium (Mg)
	Per Cent	Per Cent	Parts per Million	Per Cent	Per Cent	Per Cent	Per Cent	Parts per Thousand	Per Cent
Grains and Seeds									
Barley	.05	.36	16	.52	.05	.11	.02	.04	.12
Beans, navy	.16	.45	13	1.16	*	...	...	...	...
Bread	.03	.10	4	.10	.38	.63	.13	T	T
Buckwheat	.06	.43	80	.27	.07	.02	.01	...	.15
Coconut meal	.29	.64	85	1.90	...	...	...	...	...
Corn	.01	.29	5	.31	.03	.06	.15	.04	.10
Corn-gluten meal	.06	.40	4	.02	...	...	...	...	...
Cottonseed meal (41% protein)	.23	1.18	18	1.48	.05	.03	.46	.60	.65
Cowpeas	.10	.46	30	1.45	.16	.04	.24	.01	.21
Distillers' grains (corn, dried)	.04	.30	20	.13	.42	.09	.59	...	.22
Field peas	.08	.40	30	...	...	...	...	...	...
Hominy	.01	.08	2	.14	T	.05	.16	.01	.03
Kafir	.03	.35	16	.34	.06	.10	.16	...	.13
Linseed meal	.33	.74	40	1.27	...	...	...	...	...
Millet	.01	.33	35	.43	.04	.02	...	...	...
Milo	.04	.32	15	.36	...	...	...	...	...
Oats	.10	.36	34	.40	.17	.07	.20	.10	.12
Oatmeal (rolled oats)	.08	.44	20	.37	.03	.09	.20	.05	.13
Peanut meal	.18	.56	...	1.16	...	...	...	...	...
Rice, polished	.01	.09	12	.04	.03	.04	.10	T	.03
Rye	.05	.36	40	.54	.06	.01	T	.03	.20
Soybean oil meal (41% protein)	.28	.66	...	2.20	.51	.04	.45	.20	.25
Sunflower seed	.41	.99	...	.66	...	...	...	...	...
Wheat	.04	.39	39	.44	.03	.08	.20	.05	.13
Wheat bran	.11	1.21	119	1.24	.20	.09	.27	.08	.53
Wheat-flour middlings	.07	.69	113	.89	...	...	...	...	...
Wheat middlings, standard	.08	.93	119	1.04	.17	.03	.23	.10	.38
Feeds of Animal Origin									
Beef scrap	7.23	3.73	5	...	...	...	...	...	...
Buttermilk, liquid	.18	.10	...	.15	...	...	...	...	...
Buttermilk, condensed	.56	.33	.2	.39	...	...	...	...	...
Buttermilk, dried	1.56	1.05	.4	.71	.95	.36	.08	...	.81
Crab meal	13.25	.50	...	1.90	...	...	...	...	...
Fish meal	6.50	3.60	45	...	...	...	...	...	...
Fish meal, herring	3.83	2.5	...	...	...	...	...	...	...

* Data not given
T Less than .01

[2] Mostly from U. S. D. A. Yearbook of Agriculture, 1939, and Ohio Agr. Expt. Sta. Bul. 255.

Feedstuff	Calcium (Ca)	Phosphorus (P)	Manganese (Mn)	Potassium (K)	Sodium (Na)	Chlorine (Cl)	Sulphur (S)	Iron (Fe)	Magnesium (Mg)
	Per Cent	Per Cent	Parts per Million	Per Cent	Per Cent	Per Cent	Per Cent	Parts per Thousand	Per Cent
Fish meal, whitefish..	5.84	3.04	...	.32	1.58	1.65	...	...	.22
Fish meal, sardine....	4.73	2.63	40	.65	.42	...	...	...	.28
Fish meal, tuna......	6.25	3.46	...	...	...	...	...	...	...
Liver meal..........	.11	.90	4	...	...	...	...	...	...
Meat scraps (50% protein)...........	10.2	4.91	10	...	...	...	...	...	...
Pork liver, dried.....	.06	1.12	4	...	...	...	...	...	...
Skim milk, dried.....	1.27	.96	.6	1.46	...	...	...	...	...
Skim milk, liquid....	.13	.11	.12	.12	.05	.09	.03	T	.01
Tankage (60% protein)...........	7.16	3.53	14	.55	1.66	2.44	.60	...	.15
Whey, liquid........	.05	.04	1	.17	.03	.12	.01	...	.01
Whey, dried........	.83	.70	14	2.76	.46	1.95	.14	...	.14
Poultry Products									
Eggs...............	.07	.23	...	.06	.10	.17	.20	.03	.02
Green Feeds, etc.									
Alfalfa, green........	.42	.07	7	.57	...	...	...	...	...
Alfalfa-leaf meal.....	1.90	.22	30	2.42	...	...	...	...	...
Alfalfa meal.........	1.44	.21	26	1.91	...	...	...	...	...
Cabbage............	.07	.04	21	.24	T	.02	.06	.01	.02
Cane molasses.......	.56	.06	...	2.62	...	1.11	...	...	.33
Carrots.............	.06	.07	...	.40	.10	.04	.02	.01	.02
Grapefruit refuse, dried.............	.74	.10	...	...	...	...	...	...	...
Kale...............	.18	.07	...	...	...	...	...	.03	...
Orange peel, dried....	.73	.11	...	...	...	...	...	...	...
Potatoes............	.02	.06	3	.43	.02	.04	.02	.01	.03
Rape...............	.34	.07	50	.67	.06	.01	.03	...	.05
Red clover hay......	1.17	.18	40	1.58	...	...	...	...	...
Rutabagas..........	.06	.04	...	.41	.08	.06	.08	T	.02
Turnips.............	.05	.05	...	.37	.11	.12	.02	.01	.05
Yeast, dried........	1.26	1.21	...	...	...	...	...	...	...
Mineral Feedstuffs									
Bone, fresh..........	22.95	10.42	12	...	...	...	...	...	...
Bone meal..........	27.00	13.00	13	...	...	...	...	...	...
Bone meal, steamed..	28.80	13.34	5	...	...	...	...	...	...
Bone meal, special steamed..........	31.30	14.49	2	.18	.56	.06	.31	...	.75
Crab shell...........	23.74	2.55	300	...	...	...	...	...	...
Gypsum............	25.00	...	...	...	...	...	...	...	...
Limestone, high calcium...........	39.20	...	200	...	...	...	...	...	...
Oyster shell, washed..	38.00	...	100	...	...	...	...	...	...
Manganous sulphate, anhydrous........	...	...	36.3%	...	...	...	...	...	...
Manganous sulphate, tetrahydrate.......	...	...	24.3%	...	...	...	...	...	...

Table 3

VITAMIN CONTENT OF POULTRY FEEDSTUFFS (PER POUND) *

Feedstuff	Vitamin A I. U.	Riboflavin Mg.	Pantothenic Acid Mg.	Choline Mg.	Niacin Mg.	Thiamine Mg.	Vitamin B₁₂ Mg.
Alfalfa, fresh green	56,000	2.20	5.00	?	8.20	.70	
Alfalfa meal, dehyd., 20%	122,000	8.40	17.00	?	24.00	3.00	
Alfalfa meal, dehyd., 17%	89,000	6.70	16.00	500	22.00	2.00	
Alfalfa meal, dehyd., 13%	48,000	6.00	?	?	18.00	?	
Alfalfa meal, sun cured, 13%	15,000	4.20	?	?	17.00	?	
Barley	320	.59	3.00	500	31.10	2.50	
Buckwheat		.25	.65	?	20.00	2.30	
Buttermilk, dried	200	13.00	19.50	?	7.80	1.30	
Cane molasses, liquid		1.00	15.00	290	21.00	.45	
Corn, white	Trace	.55	3.00	200	7.30	2.30	
Corn, yellow, average	2,270	.52	2.70	200	7.50	2.10	
Corn-gluten meal (yellow)	12,000	1.00	6.00	750	13.60	?	
Cottonseed meal	150	1.50	5.00	1,180	20.00	5.80	
Distillers' d. grains (corn)	1,100	3.45	5.00	1,800	38.00	2.00	
Distillers' solubles corn, dried		7.50	10.40	2,750	70.00	4.00	
Fish meal, menhaden		2.20	?	1,500	?	?	.11
Fish meal, sardine		3.00	3.50	1,720	?	.45	
Fish solubles, cond.	1,800	9.00	16.30	1,200	145.00	2.00	.36
Kafir	280	.50	2.80	?	18.00	2.30	
Linseed meal	200	1.15	3.60	750	22.00	5.90	
Liver meal (pork)	45,000	40.00	80.00	4,760	450.00	7.00	.23
Meat scrap, 50%		2.45	2.00	1,000	25.00	.50	.04
Milo	370	.50	3.90	?	33.00	?	
Oats	250	.59	4.65	420	6.60	3.45	
Peanut meal	150	2.20	24.00	850	75.00	3.00	
Rice, rough		.60	?	?	13.00	1.20	
Rye	70	.68	4.60	?	6.80	2.00	
Skim milk, dried	130	8.50	15.00	490	7.00	1.55	
Soybean meal, 43%		1.55	?	?	18.50	4.00	
Soybean meal, 41%	170	1.25	6.20	1,300	18.00	?	
Wheat, average	125	.55	5.00	330	27.50	2.30	
Wheat, bran	075	1.35	11.40	460	139.00	3.50	
Wheat-flour middlings	160	.85	4.60	?	44.00	4.00	
Wheat standard middlings	225	1.15	7.20	500	56.50	5.00	
Whey, dried		10.90	21.00	700	8.50	1.00	
Yeast, brewers', dried		16.00	50.00	1,500	200.00	25.00	

* Mostly from the Scientific Feeding of Chickens. By H. W. Titus. Published by the Interstate Printers and Publishers, Inc. Danville, Illinois.

Table 4

Feedstuff	Organic Matter	Crude Protein	Crude Fiber	Nitrogen-Free Extract	Fat, or Ether Extract	Total Digestible Nutrients
	Per Cent	Per Cent	Per Cent	Per Cent	Per Cent	Per Cent
Grains and Seeds						
Barley....................	76	75	7	83	62	68
Buckwheat................	72	59	8	85	87	65
Corn, whole or cracked.......	87	76	12	90	86	80
Corn, ground..............	88	79	6	92	88	81
Corn meal.................	87	74	7	90	89	80
Corn, Argentine, whole or cracked..................	88	84	16	91	81	83
Corn, Argentine, ground......	88	83	13	91	91	84
Cottonseed meal...........	72	76	12	86	86	69
Cowpeas..................	75	55	12	87	89	65
Feterita..................	89	88	33	91	81	82
Field peas.................	74	76	12	80	80	66
Garden peas...............	83	88	10	86	86	72
Kafir.....................	90	84	19	93	80	81
Millet....................	78	76	17	87	78	72
Milo.....................	89	83	31	92	78	80
Mixed feed, laying mash......	85	85	44	88	92	83
Oats.....................	66	74	12	74	84	62
Oatmeal, or rolled oats.......	87	79	14	91	92	85
Rice, whole...............	74	75	5	84	72	65
Rice bran.................	52	60	3	52	87	41
Rye......................	79	68	8	84	27	60
Soybeans..................	79	74	20	93	86	86
Soybean meal..............	77	83	2	82	82	71
Shallu....................	90	78	39	94	85	83
Wheat....................	82	75	8	87	50	73
Wheat bran................	46	66	9	47	42	41
Wheat middlings...........	54	65	8	55	54	48
Wheat shorts..............	68	69	13	71	85	63
Feeds of Animal Origin						
Beef scrap................	90	92	...	...	94	77
Buttermilk, dried...........	81	82	...	81	78	72
Fish meal.................	90	91	...	...	94	71
Meat scrap and meat-and-bone meal.....................	87	90	...	...	93	70
Skim milk, dried...........	87	90	...	85	95	76
Tankage..................	85	85	...	...	96	69
Green Feeds, etc.						
Alfalfa-leaf meal............	30	99	4	..	...	...
Alfalfa meal...............	29	64	2	34	22	25
Beet pulp, dried............	17	37	0	19	0	15
Potatoes..................	75	47	6	84	...	16
Clover hay................	23	71	10	14	36	20

[4] U. S. D. A. Yearbook of Agriculture, p. 842. 1939.

Table 5

APPROXIMATE CONVERSION EQUIVALENTS FOR EGGS AND EGG PRODUCTS [5]

1 pound of —	is equivalent to —
Frozen or liquid egg	10.2 United States eggs in shell
Dried whole egg	3.6 lbs. liquid whole egg
Dried yolk	2.25 lbs. liquid yolk
Dried albumen	7.3 lbs. liquid albumen
Liquid whole egg	.55 lbs. liquid white and .45 lbs. liquid yolk
Dried whole egg	.25 lbs. dried white and .75 lbs. dried yolk

[5] Tariff Information Surveys, G11, U. S. Tariff Commission and *Egg and Poultry Magazine,* 46: 301. 1940.

Table 6

POULTRY: EDIBLE WEIGHT IN TERMS OF PERCENTAGE LIVE WEIGHT AND DRESSED WEIGHT FOR SPECIFIED KINDS AND CLASSES [6]

Kind of Class	Dressed Weight in Terms of Live Weight	Edible Weight in Terms of Dressed Weight	Edible Weight in Terms of Live Weight
Unfattened broilers	88.3%	54.27%	47.92%
Fattened broilers	90.81	60.73	55.15
Unfattened roasters	88.9	56.86	50.55
Fattened roasters	91.7	63.07	57.84
Fattened capons	91.97	67.46	62.05
Fattened hens	92.03	64.22	59.09
Squab guineas	82.52	60.25	49.72
Squab pigeons	82.08	73.94	60.66
Ducks	...	60.17	...
Geese	...	65.07	...
Turkeys	90.4	66.53	61.00

[6] *Egg and Poultry Magazine,* 46: 301. 1940.

Table 7

AVERAGE WEIGHTS OF PARTS OF CARCASS OF WHITE PLYMOUTH ROCK
COCKERELS AND PULLETS KILLED AT DIFFERENT WEIGHTS,
EXPRESSED IN PERCENTAGE OF THE EMPTY WEIGHT [7]

	Males	Females	Males	Females	Males	Females
Approximate slaughter weight.................	2	2	4	4	6	5
Age in days...............	103	73	169	189	250	219
Percentage "fill"...........	2.6	4.8	3.4	2.6	2.9	3.7
Empty weight in grams.....	967	915	1725	1787	2509	2245
Offal						
Feathers................	4.8%	7.2%	7.8%	8.5%	8.1%	7.5%
Blood..................	4.8	3.7	4.2	3.3	4.2	3.5
Head...................	3.4	3.1	3.1	2.7	2.8	2.4
Shanks and feet.........	5.8	5.0	5.5	3.7	4.5	3.6
Total offal..............	18.7	19.0	20.6	18.2	19.7	16.9
Viscera						
Heart..................	.48	.49	.42	.48	.45	.45
Liver..................	2.3	2.5	2.1	1.7	2.0	1.9
Kidneys................	.64	.68	.5	.55	.52	.62
Pancreas...............	.3	.31	.21	.24	.18	.22
Spleen.................	.2	.26	.17	.18	.16	.21
Lungs..................	.43	.46	.53	.45	.45	.40
Testicles...............	.03	...	.09	...	.26	...
Digestive tract...........	11.9	11.4	8.6	9.4	7.9	8.6
Total viscera............	16.2	16.1	12.6	12.9	12.0	12.4
Dressed carcass						
Skin...................	7.3	8.0	7.4	9.2	7.6	10.0
Neck...................	3.9	3.8	3.7	2.9	3.4	2.7
Legs above hock.........	20.2	18.3	22.1	19.3	22.2	19.0
Wings..................	6.4	6.2	6.6	5.4	5.9	5.4
Torso..................	22.0	24.0	24.6	29.3	26.4	30.2
Total dressed carcass.....	59.9	60.3	64.3	66.1	65.6	67.3
Total bone in dressed carcass	19.1	17.6	19.1	15.0	16.7	14.7
Total flesh and fat in dressed carcass.................	33.4	34.0	36.0	41.0	40.2	41.8
Total flesh, fat, and edible viscera.................	40.7	41.9	42.0	47.0	45.9	47.6

[7] Ill. Agr. Expt. Sta. Bul. 278, 1926, and *Egg and Poultry Magazine*, 46: 303. 1940.

Table 8

POULTRY PRODUCT	BASIS OF ANALYSIS	REFUSE	COMPOSITION OF EDIBLE PORTION			
			Water	Protein	Fat	Ash
		Per Cent	Per Cent	Per Cent	Per Cent	Per Cent
Chicken eggs						
Total edible..............................			74.0	12.8	11.5	1.0
	as purchased	11	65.9	11.4	10.2	.9
White only.................................			87.8	10.8	0.0	.6
Yolks only.................................			49.4	16.3	31.9	1.7
Duck eggs						
Total edible..............................			70.8	13.1	14.3	1.0
	as purchased	11	63.0	11.7	12.7	.9
Goose eggs						
Total edible..............................			70.4	13.9	13.3	1.1
	as purchased	13	61.2	12.1	11.6	1.0
Turkey eggs						
Total edible..............................			72.6	13.1	11.8	.8
	as purchased	12	63.9	11.5	10.4	.7
Small broilers (¾–1½ lbs.)						
Total edible..............................			74.9	21.6	2.7	1.4
	as purchased (live)	58	31.5	9.1	1.1	.6
	as purchased (dressed)	52	36.0	10.4	1.3	.7
	as purchased (drawn)	32	50.9	14.7	1.8	1.0
Broilers (1½–2½ lbs.)						
Total edible..............................			71.2	20.2	7.2	1.1
	as purchased (live)	51	34.9	9.9	3.5	.5
	as purchased (dressed)	45	39.2	11.1	4.0	.6
	as purchased (drawn)	25	53.4	15.2	5.4	.8
Flesh only.................................			74.0	20.6	4.4	1.1
Giblets....................................			73.7	19.2	4.5	1.3
Fryers (2½–3½ lbs.)						
Total edible..............................			67.6	20.0	11.0	1.0
	as purchased (live)	47	35.8	10.6	5.8	.5
	as purchased (dressed)	40	40.6	12.0	6.6	.6
	as purchased (drawn)	22	52.7	15.6	8.6	.8

[8] *Proximate Composition of American Food Materials,* U. S. D. A. Circ. 549, 1940, and *Egg and Poultry Magazine,* 47: 38–40. 1941.

Poultry Product	Basis of Analysis	Refuse	Composition of Edible Portion			
			Water	Protein	Fat	Ash
		Per Cent	Per Cent	Per Cent	Per Cent	Per Cent
Flesh only..............................			73.4	20.6	4.8	1.1
Giblets................................			74.0	19.7	3.5	1.3
Roasters (over 3½ lbs.)						
Total edible........................			66.0	20.2	12.6	1.0
	as purchased (live)	46	35.6	10.9	6.8	.5
	as purchased (dressed)	39	40.3	12.3	7.7	.6
	as purchased (drawn)	23	50.8	15.6	9.7	.8
Flesh only..............................			72.8	21.1	4.5	1.1
Giblets................................			72.4	19.8	4.8	1.3
Hens and cocks						
Total edible........................			55.9	18.0	25.0	1.1
	as purchased (live)	42	32.4	10.4	14.5	.6
	as purchased (dressed)	36	35.8	11.5	16.0	.7
	as purchased (drawn)	20	44.7	14.4	20.0	.9
Flesh, skin and giblets..................			59.7	18.1	21.1	1.0
Flesh only..............................			70.3	21.3	7.1	1.1
Giblets................................			66.8	18.6	11.6	1.2
Capons (over 4 lbs.)						
Total edible........................			56.6	21.4	21.2	1.2
	as purchased (live)	40	34.0	12.8	12.7	.7
	as purchased (dressed)	34	37.4	14.1	14.0	.8
	as purchased (drawn)	17	47.0	17.8	17.6	1.0
All classes						
Light meat only..........................			72.5	23.3	3.2	1.2
Dark meat only..........................			73.0	21.0	4.7	1.1
Canned						
Meat only...............................			61.9	29.8	8.0	2.4
Meat and broth..........................			70.2	23.2	3.4	1.6
Duck (domesticated)						
Total edible........................			54.3	16.0	28.6	1.0
	as purchased (dressed)	36	34.8	10.2	18.3	.6
	as purchased (drawn)	16	45.6	13.4	24.0	.8

Poultry Product	Basis of Analysis	Refuse	Composition of Edible Portion			
			Water	Protein	Fat	Ash
		Per Cent	Per Cent	Per Cent	Per Cent	Per Cent
Flesh only............................			68.8	21.4	8.2	1.2
Goose (domesticated)						
Total edible..............................			51.1	16.4	31.5	.9
	as purchased (dressed)	41	30.1	9.7	18.6	.5
	as purchased (drawn)	10	46.0	14.8	28.4	.8
Flesh and skin..............................			49.7	15.9	33.6	.9
Flesh only................................			68.3	22.3	7.1	1.1
Turkeys (medium fat)						
Total edible...............................			58.3	20.1	20.2	1.0
	as purchased (live)	39	35.6	12.3	12.3	.6
	as purchased (dressed)	33	39.1	13.5	13.5	.7
	as purchased (drawn)	19	47.2	16.3	16.4	.8
Flesh and skin..............................			63.0	22.8	13.0	1.1
Flesh only................................			68.6	24.0	6.7	1.1
Light meat only............................			69.2	24.5	4.6	1.2
Dark meat only............................			68.0	23.2	9.4	1.1
Turkeys (fat birds)						
Total edible...............................			50.7	18.4	29.3	.9
Turkeys (thin, young birds)						
Total edible...............................			69.9	20.6	7.8	1.1
Gizzard						
Chicken.................................			71.1	23.1	3.8	1.1
Ducks...................................			73.3	21.3	3.7	1.1
Goose...................................			73.0	21.4	5.3	1.0
Turkey..................................			66.6	20.5	10.6	1.0
Heart						
Chicken.................................			69.6	20.5	7.0	1.3
Turkey..................................			69.8	16.2	12.7	1.1
Liver						
Chicken.................................			69.6	22.1	4.0	1.7
Goose...................................			66.9	16.5	10.0	1.2
Turkey..................................			70.9	22.0	4.8	1.6

Index